MATHEMATICS OF STATISTICS

PART TWO

BY

J. F. KENNEY
University of Wisconsin

AND

E. S. KEEPING
University of Alberta

SECOND EDITION SECOND PRINTING

NEW YORK
D. VAN NOSTRAND COMPANY, INC.
NEW YORK

TORONTO LONDON

NEW YORK
D. Van Nostrand Company, Inc., 250 Fourth Avenue, New York 3
TORONTO
D. Van Nostrand Company (Canada), Ltd., 25 Hollinger Road, Toronto
LONDON
Macmillan & Company, Ltd., St. Martin's Street, London, W.C. 2

Copyright, 1939, 1951, by

D. VAN NOSTRAND COMPANY, Inc.

Published simultaneously in Canada by
D. Van Nostrand Company (Canada), Ltd.

All rights in this book are reserved. Without written authorization from D. Van Nostrand Company, Inc., 250 Fourth Avenue, New York 3, New York, it may not be reproduced in any form in whole or in part (except for quotation in critical articles or reviews), nor may it be used for dramatic, motion-, talking-picture, radio, television or any other similar purpose.

First Edition, June, 1939

Seven Reprintings

Second Edition, June, 1951

Reprinted August, 1953

PRINTED IN THE UNITED STATES OF AMERICA

To

Harold Hotelling

PREFACE

The first edition of this book occupied for several years the considerable gap between the multitudinous textbooks of elementary descriptive statistics requiring little mathematical background and the ever-growing technical and often highly mathematical literature of statistics scattered throughout many journals.

Since 1939, however, numerous books have appeared dealing at different levels with the mathematical side of statistics. For the serious graduate student with adequate preparation there are such works as S. S. Wilks' *Mathematical Statistics*, H. Cramér's *Mathematical Methods of Statistics*, and the encyclopedic two-volume treatise by M. G. Kendall, *The Advanced Theory of Statistics*. The increasing interest in the teaching of statistics in universities and colleges has brought forth also several books at the undergraduate level. These presuppose some mathematical competence on the part of the reader but not the degree of maturity required by the specialist treatises mentioned above.

This new second edition is an enlargement and revision of the first and is intended to provide as much of the mathematical foundation for the customary procedures of experimental statistics as an undergraduate student can reasonably be expected to assimilate. It presupposes the equivalent of a second course in Calculus (usually called Advanced Calculus), and preferably a course in elementary statistics corresponding approximately to Part I of Kenney's *Mathematics of Statistics* (1954, Van Nostrand). Special functions such as the Gamma and Beta functions, and special methods, such as the use of the Jacobian in multivariate problems involving change of variable, are explained in the text. The elements of matrix algebra are included in Chapter X because of the great elegance and conciseness of matrix notation in many problems of least squares and multivariate analysis.

Although the book is thus definitely mathematical, and not for those who merely want a set of cook-book recipes for the practical problems of statistics, an attempt has been made to balance the experimental and mathematical sides of the subject. Numerous worked examples illustrate the application of the theory to concrete problems, while the theory serves to emphasize the practical limitations of the mathematical models on which many of the commonly used statistical techniques are based.

In a field as extensive as that of statistics it is inevitable that a single volume, even a fairly bulky one, cannot adequately cover the whole range. Some topics, undoubtedly of importance, must be omitted or passed over lightly, and the choice of topics to be presented is largely a matter of personal taste, for which there is no accounting. In this book the main concern is with those problems of estimation and inference that are common to all branches of science using experimental or observational data, and in particular with the attempt to estimate the characteristics of a population from those of a sample and to assess the reliability of such estimates. Throughout the book, emphasis is placed on the *fallibility* of statistics, on the sampling variance and standard error of a statistic, and on the idea of a confidence interval within which, with a specified degree of confidence, one may claim that the true value of some estimated quantity will lie.

Since the concept of *probability* is fundamental to statistical inference, the first chapter is concerned mainly with the elements of the calculus of probability. No attempt is made to give a rigorous foundation, which would require the mathematical subtleties of set theory and measure theory, but the basic formulas are developed from the simple classical definition of probability, which is adequate for many problems.

The first five chapters, dealing mainly with theoretical distributions, are in a sense introductory to the remaining chapters which treat statistics proper, and in particular with the exact distributions of sample statistics calculated from small samples. In most cases the distributions are worked out in detail, but occasionally, as for example for the distribution of the correlation coefficient in a sample from a bivariate normal population with a non-zero correlation, the complete derivation is too long to be given in full and some steps are merely indicated. The techniques of analysis of variance and covariance are discussed, at least for the more commonly occurring experimental situations; experimental design, however, is dealt with only very briefly. Multivariate analysis has been for the most part omitted because of its mathematical difficulty, but some discussion is given of multiple regression and of multiple and partial correlation. Some of the more theoretical aspects of statistical inference, the method of maximum likelihood, and the testing of hypotheses are given in Chapter XII, although these ideas and methods have been used quite freely in earlier chapters.

In this book the older definition of sample variance, $\sum_{i=1}^{N} (X_i - \bar{X})^2/N$, has been used, instead of the definition $\sum_{i=1}^{N} (X_i - \bar{X})^2/(N-1)$ which is favored by many writers. This has been done deliberately, after due consideration, in the belief that the advantages outweigh the disadvantages. It is true that the sample variance is an unbiased estimate of the population variance with the second definition, but not with the first. However, the necessity of a factor $N/(N-1)$ is not important to the mathematical statistician, whatever it may be to the experimentalist, and similar, but different, factors to remove bias occur in other connections. There is a serious pedagogical objection to $N-1$. Since the notion of variance usually precedes the concept

Preface

of sampling, $N - 1$ seems quite unnatural to students and the reason for using it is difficult to explain. Moreover, when students come to calculating the variance for a theoretical distribution such as the binomial, they use N (or its equivalent) instead of $N - 1$. This is likely to seem arbitrary and puzzling to them if variance has previously been defined with $N - 1$. It seems to be true that most mathematical statisticians (including Cramér and Kendall, but not Wilks) prefer the definition with N, whereas most experimentalists, with the high authority of R. A. Fisher, prefer to use $N - 1$.

In the arrangement of the book we have, as a rule, preferred to deal with purely mathematical topics as they naturally arise, instead of segregating them all in a preliminary chapter at the beginning. However logical, this latter practice is likely to be discouraging to those students whose interest is mainly in the applications. For this reason, also, we have not collected together all the "non-central" distributions which are referred to in the book but have dealt with them as they occur.

The number of problems in the first edition has been considerably increased. Some of these are mathematical exercises and some are numerical problems illustrating the application of the theory to actual or fictitious experimental data. Where it has seemed advisable, hints for the solution are given, and answers are supplied to most of the numerical problems. The tables given in the Appendix suffice for the commoner statistical tests, but the student should, if possible, have access to more complete tables such as those of Fisher and Yates (*Statistical Tables for Biological, Agricultural and Medical Research*, 3rd edition, 1949, Oliver and Boyd) or Karl Pearson (*Tables for Statisticians and Biometricians*, Part I, 2nd edition, 1924, University College, London). These, and other special tables, are frequently referred to in the text. Practice in the use of a computing machine is advisable, particularly in the more elaborate calculations which occur in the analysis of variance, partial and multiple correlation, and the solution of sets of linear equations.

It is hardly possible for the authors to express their manifold indebtedness to all those writers from whose books, papers, and lectures they have derived help and inspiration. A list of references is given at the end of each chapter, but this is in no sense intended as a bibliography of the subject. It serves mainly to suggest a few books and papers for supplementary reading and to indicate the source of further details for many of the proofs and discussions given in the text.

In particular the authors are indebted to the publisher's readers who examined the book in manuscript and whose criticisms and suggestions helped greatly in giving it a final polishing.

February, 1951

E. S. K.
J. F. K.

CONTENTS

CHAPTER		PAGE
I	PROBABILITY	1

1.1 Importance. — 1.2 The Classical Definition of Probability. — 1.3 The Frequency Definition. — 1.4 Other Definitions of Probability. — 1.5 Some Theorems of Algebra. — 1.6 Some Fundamental Theorems of Probability. — 1.7 The Axiomatic Treatment of Probability. — 1.8 Some Examples of Probability. — 1.9 Continuous Probabilities. — 1.10 Bayes' Theorem. — 1.11 Bayes' Theorem for Future Events. — Problems. — References.

II	THE BINOMIAL DISTRIBUTION AND THE NORMAL AND POISSON APPROXIMATIONS	22

2.1 The Binomial or Bernoulli Distribution. — 2.2 Graphical Representation. — 2.3 Frequency Functions. Stieltjes Integrals. — 2.4 Distribution Functions. — 2.5 Mathematical Expectation. — 2.6 Moments. — 2.7 The Cauchy Distribution. — 2.8 Moments of the Bernoulli Distribution. — Problems. — 2.9 Approximating the Binomial with the Normal Curve. — 2.10 The DeMoivre-Laplace Theorem. — 2.11 Simple Sampling of Attributes. — 2.12 Bernoulli's Theorem. — 2.13 Tables of the Normal Law. — 2.14 The Poisson Exponential Approximation. — 2.15 Poisson and Lexis Schemes. — 2.16 The Hypergeometric Distribution. — Problems. — References.

III	SOME USEFUL INTEGRALS AND FUNCTIONS	55

3.1 Some Properties of Definite Integrals. — 3.2 The Gamma Function. — 3.3 Stirling's Approximation. — 3.4 The Beta Function. — 3.5 Reduction to Gamma and Beta Functions. — 3.6 Incomplete Beta and Gamma Functions. — Problems. — References.

IV	DISTRIBUTIONS OF TWO OR MORE VARIABLES; MOMENT-GENERATING FUNCTIONS; THE LAW OF LARGE NUMBERS	67

4.1 Joint Distribution of Two Variables. — 4.2 Moments. — 4.3 Discrete Variables. — 4.4 Joint Distribution of More than Two Variables. — 4.5 Some Theorems on Expectation. — 4.6 Moment-generating and Characteristic Functions. — 4.7 Some Examples of Moment-generating Functions. — 4.8 Change of Scale and Origin. — 4.9 Uniqueness Theorem for Characteristic Functions. — 4.10 Cumulants and the Cumulant-generating Function. — 4.11 Additive Property of Cumulants. — 4.12 Sheppard's Corrections. — 4.13 Orthogonal Linear Transformations. — 4.14 The Bienaymé-Tchebycheff Inequality. — 4.15 The Weak Law of Large Numbers. — 4.16 The Strong Law of Large Numbers. — 4.17 The Central Limit Theorem. — Problems. — References.

Contents

CHAPTER		PAGE
V	THE GAMMA, BETA, AND CHI-SQUARE DISTRIBUTIONS; THE PEARSON AND GRAM-CHARLIER SYSTEMS OF CURVES; CURVE FITTING	94

5.1 The Gamma Distribution. — 5.2 The Beta Distributions. — 5.3 The Chi-square Distribution. — 5.4 Distributions of Sums of Squares. — Problems. — 5.5 Pearson System. — 5.6 Some Pearson Types. — 5.7 Gram-Charlier and Edgeworth Series. — 5.8 Curve Fitting. — 5.9 An Example of Curve Fitting. — 5.10 Approximate Tests of Normality. — 5.11 The Multinomial Distribution. — 5.12 Chi-square as a Measure of Sample Deviation. — 5.13 The Chi-square Test of Hypotheses. — 5.14 The Chi-square Test Applied to Curve Fitting. — 5.15 The Lognormal Distribution. — Problems. — References.

| VI | FUNDAMENTALS OF SAMPLING THEORY WITH SPECIAL REFERENCE TO THE MEAN . . . . | 127 |

6.1 Introduction. — 6.2 Method of Attack. — 6.3 Point Estimation and Interval Estimation. — 6.4 Confidence Belts and Limits. — 6.5 Standard Error of the Mean. — 6.6 Confidence Limits for the Mean. — 6.7 Null Hypothesis and Significance Tests. — 6.8 The Distribution of the Mean. — 6.9 An Experiment. — Directions. — 6.10 Standard Errors of Moments. — 6.11 Sampling from a Finite Parent Population. — 6.12 Size of Sample to Have a Given Reliability. — 6.13 Standard Error of an Observed Proportion. — 6.14 Standard Error of a Difference of Proportions. — 6.15 Confidence Limits for the Parameter of a Binomial Distribution. — 6.16 Sampling from a Finite Binomial Population. — 6.17 Confidence Limits for the Difference of Parameters in Two Binomial Distributions. — 6.18 Confidence Limits for the Poisson Distribution. — 6.19 Picking a Random Sample. — 6.20 Tests for Randomness. — 6.21 Stratified Sampling. — 6.22 Systematic Sampling. — Problems. — References.

| VII | SMALL OR EXACT SAMPLING THEORY . . . . | 160 |

7.1 Introduction. — 7.2 Expected Value of s^2. — 7.3 Degrees of Freedom. — 7.4 Standard Error of the Variance. — 7.5 The Distribution of s^2 in Samples from a Normal Population. — 7.6 The Analytical Approach. — 7.7 The Geometrical Derivation of the Sampling Distribution of Variance. — 7.8 The Distribution of the Standard Deviation. — 7.9 The "Best" Estimate of the Population Standard Deviation. — 7.10 The $(\bar{x}, s)$-Frequency Surface. — 7.11 "Student's" Distribution. — 7.12 Student's t-Distribution. — 7.13 Difference Between Two Means. — 7.14 Fisher's z-Distribution. — 7.15 Significance of Difference Between Variances. — 7.16 The Distribution of F. — 7.17 Confidence Limits. — 7.18 Standard Errors of the k-Statistics and of g_1 and g_2. — 7.19 The Distribution of Extreme Values and of the Range. — 7.20 Confidence Limits for the Binomial and Poisson Distributions. — Problems. — References.

| VIII | LINEAR REGRESSION, SIMPLE CORRELATION, AND CONTINGENCY . . . . | 199 |

8.1 Linear Regression. — 8.2 The Standard Error of Estimate. — 8.3 The Normal Correlation Surface. — 8.4 Limiting Forms. — 8.5 Tetrachoric

Contents

CHAPTER		PAGE
	Correlation. — 8.6 Linear Regression as Estimated from a Sample. — 8.7 The Sample Standard Error of Estimate. — 8.8 Confidence Limits for the Constants of the Regression Line. — 8.9 Confidence Limits for the True Regression and for an Estimated y Corresponding to Any Given x. — 8.10 Confidence Limits for x, Given y, When the Regression Is Calculated for Fixed x. — 8.11 Linear Regression with the x's and y's Both Subject to Error. — 8.12 The Distribution of r When $\rho = 0$. — 8.13 Confidence Limits for the Variance Ratio of Two Correlated Variates. — 8.14 The Distribution of r When ρ Is Not Zero. — 8.15 Fisher's z'-Transformation. — 8.16 Rank Correlation. — 8.17 Kendall's Method of Rank Correlation. — 8.18 Ties in Rank Correlation. — 8.19 Contingency Tables. — 8.20 The $2 \times n$ and 2×2 Contingency Tables. — 8.21 The Exact Distributions for 2×2 Tables. — 8.22 The Combination of Probabilities from 2×2 Tables. — Problems. — References.	
IX	ANALYSIS OF VARIANCE AND COVARIANCE	238
	9.1 Analysis of Variance. One-way Classification. — 9.2 Two-way Classification, with One Individual in Each Sub-class. — 9.3 Interpretation of the Mean Square. — 9.4 Three-way Classification (One Member in Each Sub-class). — 9.5 Assumptions Made in Analysis of Variance. — 9.6 Transformations to Stabilize Variance. — 9.7 Tests of Homogeneity of Variance. — 9.8 The Behrens-Fisher Test. — 9.9 Estimation of Components of Variance. — 9.10 Confidence Limits for the Component of Variance Due to Treatment Effects. — 9.11 Effect of Unequal Numbers in the Sub-classes on the Estimation of Treatment Effects. — 9.12 Interaction with Unequal Sub-class Numbers. — 9.13 Proportional Sub-class Numbers. — 9.14 The Missing Plot Technique. — 9.15 Analysis of Covariance. — 9.16 Experimental Design. — 9.17 Split Plots. Confounding. — 9.18 Intra-class Correlation. — Problems. — References.	
X	MATRIX ALGEBRA AND THE METHOD OF LEAST SQUARES	289
	10.1 Introduction. — 10.2 Normal Equations. — 10.3 Matrix Algebra. — 10.4 Transposition. — 10.5 Matrices and Linear Transformations. — 10.6 The Determinant of a Matrix. — 10.7 The Inverse of a Matrix. — 10.8 Numerical Solution of Normal Equations. — 10.9 Calculation of the Inverse of a Matrix. — 10.10 Moving Decimal Points in Matrix Elements. — 10.11 Non-symmetric Matrix Equations. — 10.12 Improvement of an Approximation to the Inverse Matrix. — 10.13 Variance and Covariance of the Regression Coefficients in Linear Regression. — 10.14 Residuals. — 10.15 Distribution of Sum of Squares of Residuals. — 10.16 Confidence Limits for the True Regression Coefficients. — 10.17 Omission of Variates in Multiple Regression. — 10.18 Solution of a Set of Linear Equations with More Equations than Unknowns. — 10.19 Weighted Observations. — 10.20 Condition Equations or Equations of Constraint. — Problems. — References.	
XI	CURVILINEAR REGRESSION; MULTIPLE AND PARTIAL CORRELATION	323
	11.1 The Correlation Ratio. — 11.2 A Test for Linearity of Regression. — 11.3 Fitting a Polynomial of Second or Higher Order. — 11.4 Orthog-	

CHAPTER	PAGE

onal Polynomials. — 11.5 Seidel's Method of Successive Approximations. — 11.6 Exponential and Modified Exponential Regression. — 11.7 Fitting a Simple Harmonic Curve to a Series of Observations. — 11.8 Estimation of x for a Given y in Curvilinear Regression. — 11.9 Estimation of Maximum or Minimum in Curvilinear Regression. — 11.10 The Geometrical Picture of Multiple Regression and Correlation. — 11.11 Variance about the Regression Plane. — 11.12 Variance Due to Regression. — 11.13 The Multiple Correlation Coefficient. — 11.14 Some Limiting Cases of Multiple Correlation. — 11.15 The Distribution of the Multiple Correlation Coefficient for Samples from an Uncorrelated Parent Population. — 11.16 The Distribution of the Multiple Correlation Coefficient for a Correlated Parent Population. — 11.17 Partial Correlation. — 11.18 Partial Correlations with k Variables. — 11.19 The Distribution of the Partial Correlation Coefficient. — 11.20 Correlograms. — 11.21 Discriminant Functions. — 11.22 An Alternative Approach to Discriminant Functions. — Problems. — References.

XII FURTHER CONSIDERATIONS ON STATISTICAL INFERENCE   367

12.1 Introduction. — 12.2 The Best Unbiased Estimate of a Parameter. Fisher's Inequality. — 12.3 Consistent and Efficient Statistics. — 12.4 Sufficient Statistics. The Method of Maximum Likelihood. — 12.5 Curve-fitting by the Method of Maximum Likelihood. — 12.6 The Chi-square Test of Goodness of Fit. — 12.7 The Correction of an Inefficient Estimate. — 12.8 The Neyman-Pearson Theory of Confidence Intervals. — 12.9 A Geometrical Illustration of Confidence Intervals. — 12.10 The Determination of Confidence Intervals. — 12.11 Confidence Intervals and Fiducial Inference. — 12.12 Tests of Hypotheses. — 12.13 The Power of a Test. — 12.14 Uniformly Most Powerful Tests. — 12.15 Confidence Regions with More than One Parameter. — 12.16 Composite Hypotheses. — 12.17 The Power of the t-Test. — 12.18 The Power Function of Analysis of Variance Tests. — 12.19 Sequential Tests of Hypotheses. — 12.20 Expected Number of Observations in a Sequential Probability-Ratio Test. — 12.21 Test of a Hypothesis Against a One-sided Alternative. — 12.22 The Sequential Test for a Binomial Distribution. — 12.23 Tolerance Limits for a Parent Population. — Problems. References.

APPENDIX TABLES 407

INDEX 419

FOREWORD

The following sections are more difficult mathematically, or are less important in the general scheme of this book, and may be omitted on a first reading:

§§ 1.7, 2.15, 2.16, 4.12, 4.16, 4.17, 5.4, 5.12, 5.15, 6.20, 6.21, 6.22, 7.7, 7.8, 7.9, 7.18, 8.4, 8.5, 8.13, 8.14, 9.7, 9.8, 9.10, 9.12, 9.15, 9.17, 9.18, 10.11, 10.12, 10.16, 10.17, 11.1, 11.2, 11.7, 11.8, 11.9, 11.16, 11.18, 11.19, 11.21, 12.11, 12.15, 12.16, 12.23.

Chapters I to V (Probability and Distribution Theory) could be covered substantially in one quarter with three lecture periods a week; Chapters VI to IX (Sampling Statistics and Analysis of Variance) in a second quarter; and Chapters X to XII (Least Squares, Multivariate Problems, and Statistical Inference) in a third. For a two-semester course, the major part of Chapters I to VII would, in the first semester, give a grounding in the basic ideas of small-sample theory. The second semester might then deal with special techniques and methods in statistical theory, as covered in Chapters VIII to XII.

CHAPTER I

PROBABILITY

1.1 Importance. The theory of probability is one of the most interesting branches of modern mathematics and is becoming conspicuous for its applications in many fields of learning. This subject is of fundamental importance, not only in the theory of insurance and statistics, but also in various branches of the biological and physical sciences. The following quotations from contemporary writers indicate the importance of probability theory in the philosophy of modern science.

It was, I think, Huxley who said that six monkeys, set to strum unintelligently on typewriters for millions of millions of years, would be bound in time to write all the books in the British Museum. If we examined the last page which a particular monkey had typed, and found that it had chanced, in its blind strumming, to type a Shakespeare sonnet, we should rightly regard the occurrence as a remarkable accident, but if we looked through all the millions of pages the monkeys had turned off in untold millions of years, we might be sure of finding a Shakespeare sonnet somewhere amongst them, the product of the blind play of chance. . . .*

These and other considerations have led many physicists to suppose that there is no determinism in events in which atoms and electrons are involved singly, and that the apparent determinism in large-scale events is only of a statistical nature. When we are dealing with atoms and electrons in crowds, the mathematical law of averages imposes the determinism which physical laws fail to provide. . . . We can only speak in terms of probabilities.

— *The Mysterious Universe*, Sir James Jeans.

In order to understand the nature of knowledge about social and economic life, it is necessary to know something about the theory of probability; because knowledge in these fields, in general, is essentially indeterminate knowledge. There are two fundamental ideas which need to be grasped in order to understand the social sciences. The first idea is that all science is philosophical. . . . The time honored aim of philosophy has been to discover and interpret (to the extent possible to the human mind) the characteristics of nature. By nature is meant all things, material and psychic, external to man, and man himself. In many fields the minds of men have penetrated into the mysteries of nature and have produced knowledge concerning them. In the physical aspects (both external to man and in man) great progress has been made towards the attainment of apparently precise knowledge, within certain definite

---

* This illustration is picturesque, but it may be noted that the time the monkeys might be expected to take to produce one sonnet by chance would be vastly greater than the whole estimated time that our solar system has existed, or indeed than the time the earth is likely to remain a possible abode of life. (See Problem 21 at the end of the chapter.)

limits; while in the field of the psychic the progress has been towards increasing the probabilities of truth of a great variety of hypotheses. But it is characteristic of the psychic aspects of knowledge that the facts in those fields are indeterminate, not precise, and apparently dynamic. Even in the physical and chemical world, the discoveries of recent years have emphasized a great realm of indeterminacy, particularly when confronting great velocities and infinitely small particles within the atom. Thus the second idea to grasp is that in all fields of knowledge, even the physical, beyond the limited range of relatively precise knowledge accumulated by man, there is a vast frontier of speculation. It has been the function of scientific method — the new tool of philosophy — to penetrate ever deeper into this realm of speculative knowledge. Primarily this has been made possible by the development of the theory of probabilities.
— *Elementary Statistics*, James G. Smith.

There exist in nature systems of chance causes which operate in such a way that the effects of these causes can be predicted — by making use of customary probability theory in which objective probabilities in the limiting statistical sense are substituted for the mathematical probabilities.
— *Economic Control of Quality of Manufactured Product*, W. A. Shewhart.

It appears likely that the further development of the theory of probability in the next few decades may turn out to be a major chapter in the history of science.
— *Science*, January 18, 1929.

The great extension in the use of statistics in the last two decades has been associated with and largely made possible by mathematical developments based upon the theory of probability.
— Harold Hotelling, *Journal American Statistical Association*, March Supplement, 1931

1.2 The Classical Definition of Probability. The notion of probability plays a basic role in statistical theory, yet it is not easy to define in a satisfactory way. We shall consider briefly some of the attempts at definition.

The classical definition, as given by Laplace, is as follows: If an event can take place in n mutually exclusive ways, all equally likely, and if r of these correspond to what may be called "success," then the probability of success in a single trial is r/n. Thus, if a coin is equally likely to fall "head" or "tail," the probability of "head" is $\frac{1}{2}$.

This definition is applicable to many problems suggested by games of chance, provided that certain assumptions are made. We assume, for instance, that dice are homogeneous and unbiased, or that a deck of cards is perfectly shuffled. It was, in fact, in order to deal with such problems that mathematical probability was originally developed in the latter half of the seventeenth century.

The definition has, however, obvious deficiencies. It is not clear how one is to know whether the various ways are "equally likely," nor how one is to deal with problems where they are known *not* to be equally likely. There is, for example, a definite probability of throwing 6 with a given biased die, although it may not be $\frac{1}{6}$. Furthermore, there is a class of problems in which the number of ways cannot be enumerated because they are infinite. We may ask, for example, what is the probability that a point selected at random on a circular target should lie in the bull's-eye, and we can give a numerical answer, once an unambiguous procedure has been specified for making the random selection. For these various reasons many writers have preferred a different form of definition.

1.3 The Frequency Definition. The probability that a male United States citizen, aged 50, and able to pass an ordinary medical examination, will die within a year has undoubtedly a meaning, although not one that can be given in terms of the classical definition. Such a probability is assessed by an insurance company when it fixes the premium that the man must pay to buy $1000 of insurance. Bases for assessing this probability are various mortality tables prepared from the records of large companies. In other words, the probability is estimated statistically, and not *a priori*. Such procedures have suggested the following definition of probability:

If an event has occurred r times in the way described as "success," in a series of n independent random trials, all made under the same essential conditions, the ratio r/n is called the relative frequency of success. The limit of r/n, as n tends to infinity, is the probability of success in a single trial.

There are limitations to this definition also. How is one to know whether all the essential conditions have remained unchanged? In the illustration given above, from insurance, we know that conditions have *not* remained constant. Because of improvements in hygiene and advances in medical science, there has been for many years a steady increase in normal life expectancy. However, this difficulty is common to all branches of science in which it is customary to make replications of an experiment or observation; the scientist must rely on his judgment as to what factors may be expected to exert a perceptible influence on the result. Another difficulty is that, on this definition, we can never know an empirical probability precisely, because we can never make infinitely many trials. But when n is large a very good *estimate* of the probability can be made, and this is usually sufficient.

It must be noted that the word "limit" is used in a special sense here. Mathematically, r/n tends to a limit p if for any given positive number ϵ we can find a number N such that for all $n > N$ we can be sure that $|r/n - p| < \epsilon$. That is, for large enough n, the difference between r/n and p is, and remains as n increases, less than ϵ. But in a sequence of chance events this cannot be guaranteed. After throwing a coin 10,000 times, it is possible, although not likely, that the next 1000 tosses should all turn out to be heads.

We need, in fact, a new definition of limit appropriate to a sequence of random variables. It is a matter of experience that in a large number of tosses of a coin the relative frequency of "heads" fluctuates less and less violently as the number n increases, and shows a marked tendency to become practically constant when n is very great. Provided the conditions may be assumed to be uniform, the relative frequency of success in a series of random trials always shows this tendency to settle down to a comparatively stable value. We can, therefore, assert that to the random event E we may assign a number p ($0 \leq p \leq 1$) called the probability of E, such that in a long series n of repetitions it is practically certain that the relative frequency of occurrence of E, say r/n, will be approximately equal to p. This is expressed by saying that r/n *converges in probability* or *converges stochastically* to the limit p. This notion may be made more precise. We can assign a small positive number ϵ and say that r/n is approximately equal to p if $|r/n - p| < \epsilon$, and Bernoulli's theorem (§ 2.12) then gives a lower limit for n corresponding to an agreed interpretation of "practically certain."

The word "random" was used previously in defining probability. It is a familiar term in statistics, but one that is not easy to define. Roughly, a sequence of trials is random if the results follow no recognizable pattern. In the unending sequence of digits that represents $\frac{1}{7}$ as a decimal fraction, namely, .142857142857142857 $\cdots$, the relative frequency of the digit 1 approaches $\frac{1}{6}$ as a limit, but the sequence is obviously not random. A sequence of 0's and 1's, such as 011010111001010001 $\cdots$ may be described as random if when we pick out any subsequence by some pre-assigned rule, the limiting frequency of 0's in the subsequence is the same as it is in the original sequence. We may, for example, pick out every second term, or every term following a zero, or make any other rule we please, provided, of course, that the decision as to whether a particular term is picked does not depend on *that* term. We could not, obviously, decide to pick all the zeros.

This definition of randomness is due to von Mises.[1] There has been considerable discussion as to whether a truly random sequence, known as a *collective*, actually exists. It seems, however, that, given any distribution, it is possible to define a collective in which the relative frequencies tend to the limits prescribed by the distribution. The laws of probability relate to such a collective which, as von Mises points out, is an ideal thing like the points and lines of geometry. Actual pencil or chalk lines are only approximations to the ideal lines about which we reason, and in a similar way actually observed sequences of events are more or less crude approximations to ideal collectives. How far the laws of probability apply to events in the real world can be determined only by trial and observation.

1.4 Other Definitions of Probability. A fundamentally different approach to the subject is that of J. M. Keynes [2] and Harold Jeffreys [3] to whom probability is a measure of the degree of rational belief in a proposition. In this sense one can speak of the probability, for example, that Bacon wrote the plays commonly attributed to Shakespeare, although such a probability is meaningless on either the classical or the frequency definition and should rather, as

Hotelling suggests, be called "credibility." By making certain more or less arbitrary assumptions, it is possible to calculate the probabilities of compound events, but we shall not pursue this matter further.

A more sophisticated approach to the definition of probability than any of those discussed above is the *axiomatic* one. The method consists in laying down a number of axioms and proceeding to deduce the theorems required. The axioms, of course, are not completely arbitrary, since we wish to deduce theorems that are approximately verified by experience, but, once they are laid down, the rest of the theory follows with logical rigor. An example of such a treatment is to be found in Kolmogoroff's little book *Foundations of the Theory of Probability*.[4] This is also the method used by Cramér in his valuable work *Mathematical Methods of Statistics*,[5] where the treatment is based on the theory of sets of points and of the "measure" of a set. At the level of this book it will not be possible to enter into the details of a rigorous treatment, but in § 1.7 we give an indication of the axiomatic approach.[11]

1.5 Some Theorems of Algebra.

Theorem 1.1. *The number of permutations of n distinguishable things taken r at a time is denoted by the symbol $P(n, r)$ and given by*

$$(1.1) \qquad P(n, r) = n(n-1)(n-2) \cdots (n-r+1) = \frac{n!}{(n-r)!}$$

where the symbol $n!$ ("n factorial") is defined by

$$(1.2) \qquad n! = n(n-1)(n-2) \cdots 3 \cdot 2 \cdot 1, \quad n = 1, 2, 3 \cdots$$

and $0! = 1$.

Theorem 1.2. *If n things consist of n_1 all alike of type T_1, n_2 all alike of type T_2, $\cdots$, n_k all alike of type T_k, so that $\sum_1^k n_i = n$, the number of permutations of all n things is*

$$\frac{n!}{n_1! n_2! \cdots n_k!}$$

This follows since the $n_i!$ permutations of the n_i things among themselves are indistinguishable.

Theorem 1.3. *The number of combinations of n different things taken r at a time, is denoted by $C(n, r)$, or more commonly in recent times by $\binom{n}{r}$ which may be read "n above r," and is given by*

$$(1.3) \qquad C(n, r) = \binom{n}{r} = \frac{n!}{r!(n-r)!}$$

Since $0! = 1$, $\binom{n}{0} = \binom{n}{n} = 1$. We define $\binom{n}{r}$ as equal to 0 for all $r > n$.

Theorem 1.4. *The total number of combinations of n distinguishable things taken 1, or 2, $\cdots$ or n at a time is $2^n - 1$.*

Note that $\binom{n}{r}$ is the coefficient of the $(r+1)$th term in the binomial expansion of $(x+y)^n$, that is,

(1.4) $\quad (x+y)^n = x^n + \binom{n}{1} x^{n-1} y + \cdots + \binom{n}{r} x^{n-r} y^r + \cdots + y^n$

$$= \sum_{r=0}^{n} \binom{n}{r} x^{n-r} y^r$$

If we let $x = y = 1$, this becomes

(1.5) $\quad\quad\quad 2^n = 1 + \binom{n}{1} + \binom{n}{2} + \cdots + \binom{n}{n}$

Theorem 1.5. *The number of ways in which n distinguishable things can be divided into k classes, n_1 in the first class, n_2 in the second and so on, is*

$$\frac{n!}{n_1! n_2! \cdots n_k!}$$

where $\sum n_i = n$. This number is the coefficient of $x_1^{n_1} x_2^{n_2} \cdots x_k^{n_k}$ in the multinomial expansion of $(x_1 + x_2 + \cdots + x_k)^n$.

Theorem 1.6. *The number of ways of putting m distinguishable objects into n exactly similar compartments $(n \geq m)$, not more than one in each compartment, is $n!/(n-m)!$. This follows since $n-m$ of the compartments, being empty, are indistinguishable among themselves.*

If the objects are not distinguishable, the number is

$$\frac{n!}{(n-m)! m!} = \binom{n}{m}$$

since the m occupied compartments cannot now be distinguished among themselves. Rearrangements of the order of occupied and empty compartments count as different ways.

Theorem 1.7. *The number of ways of putting m distinguishable objects into n ordered compartments, when any number from 0 to m may go in each compartment, is n^m.*

This follows since each object may go into n different compartments, irrespective of where the others go.

Theorem 1.8. *The number of ways of putting m indistinguishable objects into n ordered compartments, any number in each compartment, is*

$$\binom{n+m-1}{m}$$

If the objects are indistinguishable the number of ways required is the number of ways of separating the m objects, supposed set out in a row, by $n-1$ partitions. These partitions in effect divide the objects among n compartments, labeled, say, from left to right. The number of ways is that of arranging $n + m - 1$ things, that is, m objects and $n - 1$ partitions, m all alike of one kind and $n - 1$ all alike of another kind, and hence is

$$\frac{(n + m - 1)!}{m!(n - 1)!} = \binom{n + m - 1}{m}$$

Theorem 1.9 (Binomial Theorem for a negative integral index). *If n is a positive integer*

(1.6) $\quad (1 + x)^{-n} = 1 - nx + n\frac{(n + 1)}{2}x^2 - \frac{n(n + 1)(n + 2)}{2 \cdot 3}x^3 + \cdots$

for values of $|x| < 1$. This may be written

(1.7) $\qquad\qquad (1 + x)^{-n} = \sum_{k=0}^{\infty}(-1)^k \binom{n + k - 1}{k} x^k$

1.6 Some Fundamental Theorems of Probability. In a set of random trials there may be various possible outcomes of a single trial. These will be called *events*. An event may be *simple* or *compound*.

A *simple event* can be represented by some value or values of a single random variable x, where x is a real number. In some cases, x can take only a set of discrete values; in other cases it may range over a finite or infinite interval of the real axis. Thus, the results of successive tosses of a coin may be represented by a sequence of 0's and 1's, so that x can take only these two values. If x is a measurement of height for a group of a hundred grown men, it may range anywhere from, say, 60 to 80 inches, but is quite unlikely to be outside this interval. An "event" may, for instance, be a measured height in the interval 70 to 71 inches.

A *compound event* requires two or more random variables for its representation. Thus, if two dice are thrown at the same time, the real number x (with discrete values 1, 2, $\cdots$ 6) corresponds to one die and the real number y (with the same set of discrete values) to the other die. The compound event consisting of the simultaneous observation of the two dice, which are supposed to be distinguishable, may be represented by a point of rectangular coördinates (x, y). These points form a square lattice of 36 points in the xy-plane. If x represents height and y weight for a group of men, both x and y may range over finite intervals, and the compound event consisting of a measurement of height and a measurement of weight for one particular individual is represented by a point of coördinates (x, y) lying in a certain region of the xy-plane. The extension to more than two variables is obvious.

We shall presently establish certain basic theorems of probability with the help of the classical definition (§ 1.2). It will be assumed that the phrase "equally likely" has a well-understood sense.

It will be convenient to use the notation on the next page:

$p(A)$ = probability that the simple event A happens,
$p(\tilde{A})$ = probability that A does not happen (often called the probability of not-A),
$p(AB)$ = probability that both A and B happen on the same trial (probability of the compound event A *and* B).
$p(A + B)$ = probability that either A or B happens or that both happen (probability of the compound event A *or* B).
$p(A \mid B)$ = probability that A happens when it is known that B happens (conditional probability of A, given B).

If A and B are *mutually exclusive*, they cannot both happen on the same trial, so that $p(AB) = 0$. Thus A might be the event of throwing 6 and B the event of throwing 1 with a single die. But if A is the event of throwing a number greater than 4 and B the event of throwing an even number, both events could happen in a single trial. Any event which cannot happen has probability 0, and any event which always happens has probability 1. It may be noted that on the frequency definition of probability the converses of these statements are not true. An event has probability 1 if the limiting relative frequency of its occurrence is 1, and this does not imply that it always happens. It might, for instance, fail once in the first ten trials and never fail again. Similarly an event has probability 0 if the limiting relative frequency of its occurrence is 0, which does not mean that it never happens.

Theorem 1.10. *If A and B are mutually exclusive,*

(1.8) $$p(A + B) = p(A) + p(B)$$

This is called the *addition theorem* for probabilities.

Suppose that, out of n mutually exclusive and equally likely cases, a correspond to the event A and b to the event B. If these n are all the possible cases, $p(A) = a/n$, and $p(B) = b/n$. Also, by definition, $p(A + B) = (a + b)/n$, since there are $a + b$ cases which correspond to either A or B. The theorem follows at once.

Theorem 1.11. *If $A_1, A_2, \cdots A_n$ are mutually exclusive events,*

(1.9) $$p(A_1 + A_2 + \cdots + A_n) = p(A_1) + p(A_2) + \cdots + p(A_n)$$

The proof is an obvious extension of that just given.

Theorem 1.12. $p(A) + p(\tilde{A}) = 1$. For by Theorem 1.10 the left-hand side is equal to $p(A + \tilde{A}) = 1$, since A must either happen or not happen.

Theorem 1.13.

(1.10) $$p(A + B) = p(A) + p(B) - p(AB)$$

Since A must occur in combination either with B or not-B, we have
$$p(A) = p(AB) + p(A\tilde{B})$$

Sec. 6   Some Fundamental Theorems of Probability

Similarly
$$p(B) = p(AB) + p(\tilde{A}B)$$
By the definition of $p(A + B)$, and Theorem 1.11,
$$p(A + B) = p(AB) + p(A\tilde{B}) + p(\tilde{A}B)$$
whence equation (1.10) follows at once, on substituting for $p(A\tilde{B})$ and $p(\tilde{A}B)$.

Theorem 1.14.

(1.11) $p(A_1 + A_2 + A_3) =$
$p(A_1) + p(A_2) + p(A_3) - p(A_1A_2) - p(A_1A_3) - p(A_2A_3) + p(A_1A_2A_3)$

If B stands for the event $A_2 + A_3$ (that is, the occurrence of at least one of the two events A_2 and A_3),
$$p(B) = p(A_2) + p(A_3) - p(A_2A_3)$$
and

(1.12) $\quad p(A_1 + A_2 + A_3) = p(A_1 + B) = p(A_1) + p(B) - p(A_1B)$

By definition and Theorem 1.13,
$$p(A_1B) = p(A_1A_2 + A_1A_3) = p(A_1A_2) + p(A_1A_3) - p(A_1A_2A_3)$$

Hence, by substituting for $p(B)$ and $p(A_1B)$ in equation (1.12), we arrive at (1.11). This theorem may be extended by induction to any finite number of events. The general statement is

(1.13) $\quad p(A_1 + A_2 + \cdots + A_n) = \sum_i p(A_i) - \sum_{ij}' p(A_iA_j)$
$$+ \sum_{ijk}'' p(A_iA_jA_k) - \cdots$$
$$+ (-1)^{n-1} p(A_1A_2 \cdots A_n)$$

where $\sum_{ij}'$ means the sum over all i and j, with $i \neq j$,

$\sum_{ijk}''$ means the sum over all i, j, k, with no two of them equal, and so on.

Theorem 1.15.

(1.14) $\qquad p(AB) = p(A)p(B \mid A) = p(B)p(A \mid B)$

For, out of the total of n possible and equally likely cases, let r be favorable to A and s to both A and B. Then, by definition, $p(A) = r/n, p(B \mid A) = s/r$, $p(AB) = s/n$. But $s/n = s/r \cdot r/n$, which proves the first part of the theorem. The second follows on interchanging A and B and noting that $p(AB) = p(BA)$.

This theorem may also be extended to compound events with more than two constituents. Thus,

(1.15) $\qquad p(ABC) = p(A)p(B \mid A)p(C \mid AB)$

The events A and B are said to be *independent* if the probability of each is unaffected by whether the other happens or not. That is, A and B are independent if $p(A \mid B) = p(A)$ and $p(B \mid A) = p(B)$. Actually, one of these conditions entails the other, since if $p(B \mid A) = p(B)$, we have from (1.14)

(1.16) $$p(AB) = p(A)p(B)$$

and it then follows from (1.14) and (1.16) that $p(A \mid B) = p(A)$. The result expressed by equation (1.16) is

Theorem 1.16. *If A and B are independent, the probability of the compound event AB is the product of the respective probabilities.* This is called the **multiplication theorem** *for probabilities.*

The theorem may be extended to three or more independent events. Thus

(1.17) $$p(ABC) = p(A)p(B)p(C)$$

It must be noted, however, that independence means what is sometimes called "complete mutual independence." Each event must be independent not only of each of the others but also of any combinations of the others. Even for only three events this requires four conditions, namely, $p(A \mid B) = p(A)$, $p(A \mid C) = p(A)$, $p(B \mid C) = p(B)$, and $p(C \mid AB) = p(C)$. There are five other conditions which may be deduced from these by means of (1.15) and the equivalent forms given by interchanging A, B, and C in all possible ways.

A simple example given by Uspensky [10] illustrates the fact that three events ABC may be "pairwise independent" without being independent in the foregoing sense. Four discs in a bowl are numbered respectively 112, 121, 211, 222, and one disc is drawn at random. Let A, B, C denote respectively the events "the first digit is 1," "the second digit is 1," and "the third digit is 1," in the number drawn. Then it is easily seen that $p(A) = p(B) = p(C) = \frac{1}{2}$, and $p(AB) = p(AC) = p(BC) = \frac{1}{4}$, so that $p(AB) = p(A)p(B)$, etc. Hence A and B, A and C, and B and C are separately independent. However, $p(ABC) = 0$ and hence is *not* equal to $p(A)p(B)p(C)$. In other words, A, B, C are not independent. We shall use the word "independent" in the future to mean this complete mutual independence, so that the multiplication theorem will always hold for independent events.

1.7. The Axiomatic Treatment of Probability. The theorems of § 1.6 have been established only for situations in which the classical definition applies. They may be established, with greater difficulty, on the frequency definition of probability, using the idea of "collectives." The axiomatic approach is somewhat as follows.

If the event A is represented by a certain set S of values of x, we assume that there exists a function $f(S)$, called the probability of A, such that $0 \leq f(S) \leq 1$ and such that $f(S_1 + S_2 + \cdots + S_n) = f(S_1) + f(S_2) + \cdots + f(S_n)$, where $S_1, S_2, \cdots S_n$ are sets of values of x, no two of which have any point in common. Clearly, $S_1, S_2, \cdots S_n$ correspond to mutually exclusive events, and the foregoing statement represents the addition theorem for probabilities. Extending this theorem to an infinite number of non-overlapping sets, we assume that $f(S)$ is a *completely additive* function of S. That is, if we write $f(S) = p(A)$,

(1.18) $$p(A_1 + A_2 + \cdots) = p(A_1) + p(A_2) + \cdots$$

If x and y are random variables, we further assume that the combination (x, y), which corresponds to a compound event, is also a random variable and so has a probability distribution. This means that, if T is a set of values of y corresponding to the event B, so that $p(B)$ is a function of T, say $g(T)$, the probability of the compound event AB is a function of S and T, say $h(S, T)$, which has the same general properties as $f(S)$. That is, it is non-negative, completely additive, and is equal to 1 when S and T cover the whole range of possible values of their respective variables.

We now *define* the conditional probabilities of B, given A, and of A, given B, by

(1.19) $$p(B \mid A) = h(S, T)/f(S), \qquad p(A \mid B) = h(S, T)/g(T),$$

which correspond to (1.14). It is understood, of course, that $f(S)$ and $g(T)$ are not zero.

For a *fixed set* S, the ratio $h(S, T)/f(S)$ is a completely additive function of T, and when T includes the whole range of y, $h(S, T) = f(S)$. The ratio has, therefore, the properties of a probability, and the same statement holds for the second ratio in (1.19).

Finally, we define the two events A and B as *independent* when

(1.20) $$h(S, T) = f(S) \cdot g(T)$$

for any sets S and T. By (1.19), this implies

$$p(B \mid A) = g(T) = p(B)$$

and

$$p(A \mid B) = f(S) = p(A)$$

corresponding to our previous definition of independence.

The theorems of § 1.6 have, therefore, a wider validity than appears from the proofs given, provided that we interpret "probability" in the above general sense. How far the assumptions made correspond to real-life situations is a matter to be considered in each individual problem.

1.8 Some Examples of Probability. In this section we give a few typical calculations in elementary probability. Although they are concerned with rather trivial problems of cards, dice, and betting, they provide excellent illustrations of the fundamental theorems and in such problems the assumption of equally likely cases is a fairly reasonable one.

Example 1. Find the probability that a hand of 13 cards contains 4 aces.

The fundamental assumption here is that any *specified* hand is as likely as any other, dealt from a well-shuffled deck. The total number of ways of dealing a hand is, by Theorem 1.3, $(52!)/(13!)(39!)$. If the hand contains 4 aces, the remaining 9 cards may be chosen from the 48 cards other than aces. The number of ways is $(48!)/(9!\,39!)$. The probability required is the ratio of this number to the total number of ways of dealing the hand. Hence

$$p = \frac{48!\,13!}{9!\,52!} = \frac{10 \cdot 11 \cdot 12 \cdot 13}{49 \cdot 50 \cdot 51 \cdot 52} = \frac{1}{379}$$

Example 2. There are 7 horses in a race. A man has 5 dollars to bet with, in multiples of 1 dollar. In how many ways can he bet on one or more horses to win?

By Theorem 1.8 the number is $\binom{11}{5} = 462$. We here think of the number of ways of putting 5 objects (dollars) into 7 distinguishable compartments, any number from 0 to 5 in one compartment.

Example 3. Calculate the probability of obtaining a total of s points in a throw of n dice.

The total number of ways, all assumed equally likely, in which n dice may appear is 6^n, assuming that the dice are distinguishable. The number of favorable ways (in which the total number of points is s) is equal to the number of ways in which n integers ranging from 1 to 6 can add up to s, $(n \leq s \leq 6n)$.

This number is the coefficient of x^s in $f(x) = (x + x^2 + x^3 + x^4 + x^5 + x^6)^n$, since every favorable arrangement contributes one term to x^s in the expansion of $f(x)$.

Now

$$f(x) = x^n(1 + x + \cdots + x^5)^n = x^n\left(\frac{1 - x^6}{1 - x}\right)^n$$

so that the coefficient of x^s in $f(x)$ is the coefficient of x^{s-n} in $(1 - x^6)^n(1 - x)^{-n}$, that is, in

$$\sum_{k=0}^{n}(-1)^k\binom{n}{k}x^{6k}\sum_{l=0}^{\infty}\binom{n+l-1}{l}x^l$$

Putting $6k + l = s - n$, we obtain for this coefficient

$$c_{s-n} = \sum_{k=0}^{\left[\frac{s-n}{6}\right]}(-1)^k\binom{n}{k}\binom{s - 6k - 1}{s - 6k - n}$$

where $\left[\dfrac{s-n}{6}\right]$ denotes the integer equal to or next below $\dfrac{s-n}{6}$.

The required probability is, therefore,

$$\frac{c_{s-n}}{6^n} = \frac{1}{6^n}\sum_{k=0}^{\left[\frac{s-n}{6}\right]}(-1)^k\binom{n}{k}\binom{s - 6k - 1}{n - 1}$$

since

$$\binom{n}{r} = \binom{n}{n - r}$$

Thus for $n = 3$ and $s = 12$, $\dfrac{s - n}{6} = 1.5$, so that k takes only the values 0 and 1. The probability is

$$\frac{1}{216}\left[\binom{3}{0}\binom{11}{2} - \binom{3}{1}\binom{5}{2}\right] = \frac{25}{216}$$

Example 4. We will calculate the probability of winning in the game of "craps." One player will win if (*a*) he throws 7 or 11 with two dice, (*b*) he throws 4, 5, 6, 8, 9, or 10 and if, on repeated throwing thereafter, the same number recurs before 7 shows up. We assume the dice to be perfect, so that every combination has an equal chance * of appearing. Of the 36 ways in which two dice may appear, six give a total of 7 and two give 11. Hence by the addition theorem the chance of 7 *or* 11 is $6/36 + 2/36 = 2/9$.

The chance of 4 is 3/36, and the chance that it will reappear before 7 is $3/(3+6) = 1/3$, since the probabilities of 4 and 7 are proportional to 3 and 6 respectively. Hence by the multiplication theorem, the probability that 4 is thrown *and* that 4 reappears before 7 is $3/36 \cdot 1/3 = 1/36$. This is the chance of winning on 4. It is also the chance of winning on 10, since the probabilities of throwing 4 and 10 are equal. The probability of 5 is 4/36, and the chance of winning on 5 is $4/36 \cdot 4/(4+6) = 2/45$. This is the same as for 9. The probability of 6 is 5/36, and the chance of winning on 6 is $5/36 \cdot 5/(5+6) = 25/396$, the same as for 8. Hence the total probability of winning is

$$\frac{2}{9} + \frac{2}{36} + \frac{4}{45} + \frac{50}{396} = \frac{244}{495} = 0.493$$

Example 5 (Chevalier de Méré's Problem). Why does it pay to bet consistently on seeing 6 at least once in 4 throws of a die, but not to bet on seeing double-6 at least once in 24 throws with 2 dice?

This is a famous problem in the history of our subject. Betting on dice was a common pastime at the French court in the middle of the seventeenth century, and the Chevalier was not only a confirmed gambler but also a very observant player and an amateur mathematician. It seemed to him obvious from common sense that the two events mentioned should have the same odds, but it did not seem to work out so in practice. At length he consulted Blaise Pascal (1623–1662), who calculated the probabilities. From a correspondence on this and similar matters between Fermat and Pascal, the whole subject of mathematical probability may be considered to take its rise.[6]

The probability of *not* seeing 6 in one throw is 5/6. Since successive throws are assumed independent, the probability of not seeing 6 in 4 throws is $(5/6)^4$. The probability of seeing 6 is $1 - (5/6)^4 = 0.516$. 0.518

Similarly the probability of seeing double-6 in 24 throws with 2 dice is

$$1 - \left(\frac{35}{36}\right)^{24} = 0.491$$

The first probability is, therefore, greater than $\frac{1}{2}$ and the second less. The difference is rather small, however, and the fact that it showed up in practice is a tribute to the perseverance of the Chevalier de Méré.

1.9 Continuous Probabilities. In some types of problem it is not possible to enumerate the favorable cases and the total cases, because both these are infinite in number. In these problems there is a probability $f(x)\,dx$ that a certain variable x will take values between x and $x + dx$; $f(x)$ is then called a *probability density*.

If x can take all values from $-\infty$ to ∞, and if the range from α to β is considered a success, the probability of success is defined as

$$\int_\alpha^\beta f(x)\,dx \Big/ \int_{-\infty}^\infty f(x)\,dx = \int_\alpha^\beta f(x)\,dx$$

since

$$\int_{-\infty}^\infty f(x)\,dx = 1$$

---

* Here, and elsewhere, "chance" is used as a synonym for "probability."

Sometimes, of course, x can, in the nature of things, take only values in a finite range. In such cases $f(x)$ is supposed identically zero for all values outside this range.

Example 6 (Bertrand's Problem). If a chord is drawn at random in a given circle, what is the probability that its length is at least equal to the radius?

There is no unique answer to this problem, since it depends upon our interpretation of drawing a chord "at random." We may, for example, choose one end A anywhere on the circumference and then choose the other end B similarly. The assumption here is that, A having been fixed, all angular positions of B with respect to A are equally likely. If θ is this angular position, the total range of θ is from 0 to 2π. The favorable range is from $\pi/3$ to $5\pi/3$, so that, $f(\theta)$ being assumed constant, the probability is 2/3.

But we might also choose any radius OA and select a point B on it at random, drawing our chord through B perpendicular to OA. If x is the distance OB and r the radius of the circle, the favorable range of x is from 0 to $\sqrt{3}r/2$ and the total range from 0 to r. Hence, if $f(x)$ is assumed constant, the probability is $\sqrt{3}/2$.

Other answers are also possible. Each answer is correct on its own interpretation and each corresponds to some possible experimental set-up. Thus, if a circle were drawn on a table-top and a piece of straight wire longer than the diameter were tossed on the table at random, the chord being measured whenever the wire crossed the circle twice, the relative frequency of success would probably tend to the value $\sqrt{3}/2$. On the other hand, if a radial line were drawn on a transparent roulette wheel, and if immediately beneath the wheel there were placed a fixed circle of diameter equal to the length of the radial line and such that the axis of the roulette wheel passed through a point on its circumference, the line would sometimes come to rest crossing this circle. If the chord were measured each time this happened, the experimental relative frequency would probably tend to 2/3.

Example 7 (Buffon's Problem). Parallel straight lines, a distance a apart, are drawn on a table, and a thin needle of length $l < a$ is tossed onto the table at random. What is the probability that the needle will cross a line?

Let θ be the angle that the needle makes with the lines. All values of θ from 0 to π may be assumed to be equally likely.

The needle will cross the nearest line if the distance y of its center from that line is less than $\frac{1}{2}l \sin \theta$. If all distances from 0 to $\frac{1}{2}a$ are equally likely, the required probability is

$$\int_0^\pi \int_0^{\frac{1}{2}l \sin \theta} dy\, d\theta \Big/ \int_0^\pi \int_0^{\frac{a}{2}} dy\, d\theta = \frac{2}{\pi a} \frac{l}{2} \int_0^\pi \sin \theta\, d\theta = \frac{2l}{\pi a}$$

This gives an experimental method of determining π. Lazzerini claimed to have found a value 3.1415929 from 3408 trials. The accuracy of this result, if genuine, is a remarkable coincidence.

1.10 Bayes' Theorem. Let there be n mutually exclusive and exhaustive events $A_1, A_2, \cdots A_n$, that is, at least one of them, and not more than one, must have happened, but it is not known which one. Suppose also that an event B may follow any one of the events A_k, with known probabilities, and that B is known to have happened. What is then the probability that it was preceded by the particular event A_k?

We suppose that the *a priori* probabilities $p(A_1)$, $p(A_2)$, $\cdots p(A_n)$ are known, and also the probabilities $p(B \mid A_1)$, $p(B \mid A_2)$, $\cdots p(B \mid A_n)$. We have to calculate $p(A_k \mid B)$, the *a posteriori* probability of A_k.

Now the probability that A_k happens and is followed by B is $p(A_k) \cdot p(B \mid A_k)$. The probability that B happens, no matter which of the A_k preceded it, is
$$\sum_{k=1}^{n} p(A_k) \cdot p(B \mid A_k)$$
Hence the probability that when B happens it is preceded by A_k is given by

(1.21) $$p(A_k \mid B) = \frac{p(A_k) \cdot p(B \mid A_k)}{\sum_{k=1}^{n} p(A_k) \cdot p(B \mid A_k)}$$

This is the famous rule stated by Bayes.[7]

The rule as it stands is undoubtedly correct but of very limited application, since the *a priori* probabilities are seldom known except in artificial examples. On the other hand, the assumption made by Bayes that, in the absence of any information to the contrary, the *a priori* probabilities may be taken as equal is a highly dubious one. The interested reader may refer to a paper by R. A. Fisher [8] on "Uncertain Inference" in which this assumption is criticized and an alternative approach suggested. A quotation follows.

Thomas Bayes' paper of 1763 was the first attempt known to us to rationalize the process of inductive reasoning. From time immemorial, of course, men had reasoned inductively; sometimes, no doubt, well, and sometimes badly, but the uncertainty of all such inferences from the particular to the general had seemed to cast a logical doubt on the whole process. By the middle of the eighteenth century, however, experimental science had taken its first strides, and all the learned world was conscious of the effort to enlarge knowledge by experiment, or by carefully planned observation. To such an age the limitations of a purely deductive logic were intolerable. Yet it seemed that mathematicians were willing to admit the cogency only of purely deductive reasoning. From an exact hypothesis, well defined in every detail, they were prepared to reason with precision as to its various particular consequences. But, faced with a finite, though representative, sample of observations, they could make no rigorous statements about the population from which the sample had been drawn.

Bayes perceived the fundamental importance of this problem and framed an axiom, which, if its truth were granted, would suffice to bring this large class of inductive inferences within the domain of the theory of probability; so that, after a sample had been observed, statements about the population could be made, uncertain inferences, indeed, but having the well-defined type of uncertainty characteristic of statements of probability. Bayes' technique in this feat is ingenious. His predecessors had supplied adequate methods, given a well-defined population, for stating the probability that any particular type of sample might result. His problem was: given a particular kind of sample, to state with what probability a particular type of population might have given rise to it. He imagines, in effect, that the possible types of population have themselves been drawn, as samples, from a super-population, and his axiom defines this super-population with exactitude. His problem thus becomes a purely deductive one to which familiar methods were applicable.

Example 8. A bag contains 10 balls, either black or white, but it is not known how many of each. A ball is drawn at random and is white. What is the probability that the bag contained at least 5 white balls originally?

To start with there are 11 possibilities (the number of white balls may be 0, 1, 2, $\cdots$ 10). Let the corresponding *a priori* probabilities be $p_0, p_1, \cdots p_{10}$.

The event B is the drawing of a white ball. If the bag contained k white balls,

$$p(B \mid A_k) = \frac{k}{10}$$

Therefore the probability of k white balls initially is

$$\frac{\frac{k}{10} p_k}{\sum_{k=0}^{10} \frac{k}{10} p_k}$$

and the probability required is

$$p = \frac{\sum_{k=5}^{10} \frac{k}{10} p_k}{\sum_{k=0}^{10} \frac{k}{10} p_k} = \frac{\sum_{5}^{10} k p_k}{\sum_{1}^{10} k p_k}$$

This cannot be evaluated unless the p_k are known.

(*a*) Assume that all values of k are equally likely, before the ball is drawn. Then $p_k = \frac{1}{11}$ for all k. Hence

$$p = \frac{\sum_{5}^{10} k}{\sum_{1}^{10} k} = \frac{9}{11} = 0.82$$

(*b*) Assume that the bag was filled originally by picking 10 balls at random from a mixture of a very large number of black and white balls in equal proportions. The probability of k white and $10 - k$ black is then proportional to $\binom{10}{k}$. Therefore

$$p = \frac{\sum_{5}^{10} k \binom{10}{k}}{\sum_{1}^{10} k \binom{10}{k}} = \frac{3770}{5070} = 0.74$$

Note that on assumption (*b*) the *a priori* probability of at least 5 white balls is

$$\frac{1}{2^{10}} \sum_{k=5}^{10} \binom{10}{k} = 0.62$$

This is increased by the additional knowledge given by the drawing of a single white ball to 0.74.

Since the values of p_k are unknown the problem does not have a unique solution. Moreover, if they were known we should be back in the domain of deductive probabilities again since all the probabilities in the right-hand member of (1.21) would then be known *a priori*. It is only when $p(A_k)$ are

Sec. 10   Bayes' Theorem

unknown that we are properly in the domain of *a posteriori* probability. In practical problems the $p(A_k)$ are scarcely ever known.

Bayes realized this and argued that the A_k's may be considered equally probable unless we have some reason to think they are not. Under this "doctrine of insufficient reason," the A_k's are assumed to have equal existence probabilities. In this case, $p(A_k)$ = constant and would cancel in (1.21), thus permitting a definite solution in Example 8. It appears that Bayes had serious doubts about this "doctrine" for he withheld his entire treatise from publication until his doubts should be resolved, and it was only after his death that his paper was published by friends. Laplace, however, was less cautious, and he incorporated the doubtful theorem into his *Théorie Analytique des Probabilités*. Robed in the authority of Laplace it went unquestioned for a long time. Boole was the first, in 1854, to criticize the assumption of "the equal distribution of our knowledge, or rather of our ignorance" and "the assigning to different states of things of which we know nothing, equal degrees of probability." Today, it is well known that the assumption of constant existence probabilities may lead to mathematical contradictions. This may clearly be seen in the following example, given by R. A. Fisher.[9]

For a continuous variable, Bayes' theorem (1.21) may be written

$$(1.22) \qquad p(x \mid B) = \frac{f(x)p(B \mid x)}{\int_{-\infty}^{\infty} f(x)p(B \mid x)\, dx}$$

where $f(x)$ is the *a priori* probability density of x and $p(B \mid x)$ is the probability of the event B when x has an assigned value.

Let θ be the probability that a random individual from an infinite population has a particular characteristic, which we call "success." The probability that in a sample of n the first r individuals selected are successes and the next $n - r$ failures will be $\theta^r(1 - \theta)^{n-r}$. Since the r successes and $n - r$ failures can be rearranged in $\binom{n}{r}$ ways, the probability of r successes and $n - r$ failures in any order, is

$$p(r \mid \theta) = \binom{n}{r} \theta^r (1 - \theta)^{n-r}$$

Hence the probability density of θ, given r, is

$$(1.23) \qquad p(\theta \mid r) = \frac{f(\theta)p(r \mid \theta)}{\int_0^1 f(\theta)p(r \mid \theta)\, d\theta}$$

If we assume that all values of θ from 0 to 1 are equally probable, *a priori*, we can put $f(\theta) = 1$, and then

$$(1.24) \qquad p(\theta \mid r) = C\theta^r(1 - \theta)^{n-r}$$

where C depends on the integral in (1.23).

If $\hat{\theta}$ is an estimate of θ, so chosen as to make this probability a maximum, we easily find by equating to zero the derivative of $\theta^r(1 - \theta)^{n-r}$ with respect to θ that $\hat{\theta} = r/n$.

But by the very nature of the doctrine of insufficient reason we have no more reason to assume all values of θ to be equally likely than we have to assume the same thing for some function of θ, say $\phi = \sin^{-1}(2\theta - 1)$. Since $d\phi/d\theta = [\theta(1-\theta)]^{-1/2}$, a constant probability density for ϕ means a probability density for θ proportional to $\theta^{-1/2}(1-\theta)^{-1/2}$. In fact $f(\theta)$ will be $\theta^{-1/2}(1-\theta)^{-1/2}\pi^{-1}$, in contradiction to the previous assumption.

Bayes' rule then gives

$$(1.25) \qquad p(\theta \mid r) = C_1 \theta^{r-1/2}(1-\theta)^{n-r-1/2}$$

and the estimate of θ found by maximizing this is $\hat{\theta} = (2r-1)/(2n-2)$. Clearly, any number of different estimates could be obtained by choosing different functions ϕ, and logically one is as good as another, on Bayes' argument. Unless, therefore, there is some cogent reason, depending on the physical circumstances of a problem, for regarding one variable rather than another as having a constant probability density, Bayes' rule, as commonly applied, is an unsafe basis for statistical inference. As we shall see later, statements can be made about population parameters (such as θ), subject to assigned risks of being wrong, without the necessity of making any assumptions regarding *a priori* probabilities.

1.11 Bayes' Theorem for Future Events. Bayes' theorem may be extended to the probability of future events, as follows. Let C be an event which occurs after B and which itself follows one and only one of the events $A_1, A_2, \cdots A_n$. It is required to calculate the probability of C when it is known that B has happened.

The probability that B happens is

$$\sum_{k=1}^{n} p(A_k) p(B \mid A_k)$$

The probability that B happens and is followed by C is

$$\sum_{k=1}^{n} p(A_k) p(B \mid A_k) p(C \mid A_k, B)$$

Hence the probability that C happens if B happens is

$$(1.26) \qquad p(C \mid B) = \frac{\sum_k p(A_k) p(B \mid A_k) p(C \mid A_k, B)}{\sum_k p(A_k) p(B \mid A_k)}$$

Example 9. With the conditions as stated in Example 8, what is the probability that if a second ball is drawn at random (without the first ball being returned to the bag) it also will be white?

Here events B and C both consist of the drawing of a white ball.

$$p(B \mid A_k) = \frac{k}{10}, \quad p(C \mid A_k, B) = \frac{k-1}{9}$$

$$p(C \mid B) = \frac{\sum_{k=1}^{10} \frac{k(k-1)}{90} p_k}{\sum_{k=1}^{10} \frac{k}{10} p_k} = \frac{1}{9} \frac{\sum_{1}^{10} (k^2 - k) p_k}{\sum_{1}^{10} k p_k}$$

If all compositions are assumed equally likely *a priori*, $p_k = \frac{1}{11}$, and

$$p(C \mid B) = \frac{1}{9} \frac{\sum_{1}^{10}(k^2 - k)}{\sum_{1}^{10} k} = \frac{2}{3}$$

In Example 9 we have used the algebraic formulas:

(1.27) $$\sum_{k=1}^{N} k = \tfrac{1}{2} N(N+1)$$

(1.28) $$\sum_{k=1}^{N} k^2 = \tfrac{1}{6} N(N+1)(2N+1)$$

For reference we may add the further results:

(1.29) $$\sum_{k=1}^{N} k^3 = \tfrac{1}{4} N^2(N+1)^2$$

(1.30) $$\sum_{k=1}^{N} k^4 = \tfrac{1}{30} N(N+1)(2N+1)(3N^2 + 3N - 1)$$

Problems

1. Prove both algebraically and verbally that
(a) $P(n, r) = C(n, r) P(r, r)$, (b) $\binom{n}{r} = \binom{n}{n-r}$.

2. From among nine men $A, B, C, D, E, F, G, H, I$, a committee of four men will be chosen. The nine names will be written on nine separate cards and four cards drawn at random one at a time from a box.
(a) In how many different ways may the four cards come out? *Ans.* 3024.
(b) How many different committees are possible not including the man A? *Ans.* 70.

3. Consider the word "introduce." (a) In how many of the possible arrangements of all its letters will there be a consonant in the first place? *Ans.* 201,600. (b) From its letters how many four letter permutations consisting of three vowels and one consonant can be formed? *Ans.* 480. (c) If five of its letters are selected at random what is the probability that two are vowels and three are consonants? *Ans.* 10/21.

4. On a table there are four different biographies with brown backs and seven different novels with red backs. (a) If all of the books are placed upright in a row on a shelf, in how many different ways may they be arranged so that the orders of the colors are different? *Ans.* 330. (b) In how many different ways may two of the biographies and three of the novels be selected and arranged on the shelf so that the orders of the books are different? *Ans.* 25,200.

5. In a box there are five red billiard balls with the numbers 1, 2, 3, 4, 5, painted on them (one on each ball), and three white billiard balls with the numbers 1, 2, 3, similarly painted on them. From the box a man draws two balls at random. (a) What is the probability that one of the balls drawn is white and the other is red? *Ans.* 15/28. (b) What is the probability that the two balls drawn have either the same color or the same number? *Ans.* 4/7.

6. A bag contains four white, five red, and six black balls. Three are drawn at random. Find the probability that (a) no ball drawn is black, (b) exactly two are black, (c) all are of the same color.

7. An urn contains four white and five black balls. Three balls are drawn at random and replaced by green balls. If then two balls are drawn at random, what is the probability that they are all of the same color? *Ans.* 29/108.

8. Write out the expressions for $\binom{n-1}{2}$; $\binom{n-1}{3}$; $\binom{s}{x}$.

9. Write in expanded form:

(a) $\sum_{x=0}^{s} \binom{s}{x}$,

(b) $\sum_{x=1}^{s} \binom{s-1}{x-1}$

10. Twelve cards have been dealt, six down, and the other six showing a jack, two kings, a seven, a five, and a four. What is the probability that the next card will be a four or less? (*National Mathematics Magazine*, **13**, p. 94.)

11. From an urn containing ten balls, numbered from one to ten, balls are drawn, one by one and placed in a row of holes, numbered from one to ten, each ball being placed in the proper hole. What is the probability that there will not be an empty hole between two filled ones at any time of the drawing? (*American Mathematical Monthly*, **45**, p. 635.) *Ans.* 2/14,175.

12. Use equation (1.4) and the identity $(x+y)^m(x+y)^n = (x+y)^{m+n}$ to prove that

$$\sum_{r=0}^{k} \binom{m}{r}\binom{n}{k-r} = \binom{m+n}{k}$$

where $k = 0, 1, 2, \cdots m+n$.

13. From the result of Problem 12 prove that

(a) $\sum_{r=0}^{k} \binom{k}{r}^2 = \binom{2k}{k}$,

(b) $\binom{m+1}{k} = \binom{m}{k} + \binom{m}{k-1}$.

14. Prove that the probability that some one of the hands of cards in a particular bridge deal contains all 13 cards of a suit is about 1 in 40 thousand millions.

The fact that more cases are reported of hands of this character than seems reasonable from the extremely small probability, appears to be due to the imperfect shuffling in actual play.

15. Work out Example 9, § 1.11, on the assumption (b) of Example 8.

16. A bag contains 10 balls, black or white, but it is not known how many of each. A ball is drawn at random, looked at and replaced, three times, and each time it is white. What is the probability that a fourth drawing will also give a white ball?

17. A bag contains six balls, identical except for color, and known to be either white or black. A ball is drawn, looked at, and replaced, and the balls are then shaken up. This is done four times, and three times the ball is white. What can be said about the contents of the bag, and about the chance that if a fifth ball is drawn similarly it will be white?

18. A card is drawn at random from a deck and replaced, then a second drawing is made, and so on. If the cards are well shuffled each time, how many drawings must be made in order that there may be at least an even chance of seeing the ace of spades? *Ans.* 36 or more.

19. Five cards are drawn at random from a deck 1000 times. How many times would you expect to get: (*a*) 5 of one suit; (*b*) 4 of one suit; (*c*) 3 of one suit, 2 of another; (*d*) 3 of one suit, 1 each of two others; (*e*) 2 of one suit, 2 of another, 1 of a third; (*f*) 2 of one suit, 3 of different suits. Note that the expected number for any combination is 1000 times the probability of that combination. *Ans.* (*a*) 2, (*b*) 43, (*c*) 103, (*d*) 223, (*e*) 365, (*f*) 264.

20. There are 30 students in a class. Evaluate the probability that at least two have the same birthday. (Assume that the year contains 365 days, all of them equally likely as birthdays.) *Ans.* 0.706.

21. Assume that (*a*) a Shakespeare sonnet contains about 600 letters (including punctuation marks and spaces); (*b*) a typewriter has 42 keys; (*c*) a monkey can strum on the typewriter at a speed of 300 letters a minute; show that the time that may be expected to elapse before one of the six monkeys mentioned in the quotation on page 1 produces any one of the approximately 150 Shakespearian sonnets is of the order 10^{965} years. (The estimated total life of the solar system, according to G. Gamow, is of the order 10^{10} years.)

Hint. The expected time in years is the reciprocal of the probability that the event occurs in any one year.

References

1. R. von Mises, *Probability, Statistics and Truth*, 1939 (First Lecture).
2. J. Maynard Keynes, *A Treatise on Probability*, 1921, Chapters I to IV.
3. H. Jeffreys, *Theory of Probability*, 2nd ed., 1948, Chapter I.
4. A. Kolmogoroff, *Grundbegriffe der Wahrscheinlichkeitsrechnung*, 1933. (Republished Chelsea Publishing Company, 1946. Translated as *Foundations of the Theory of Probability*, 1950.)
5. H. Cramér, *Mathematical Methods of Statistics*, 1946. The first part deals with the theory of sets and measure, and with other mathematical topics. The meaning of probability is discussed in Chapters 13 and 14.
6. I. Todhunter, *History of the Mathematical Theory of Probability*, 1865, pp. 11–12.
7. T. Bayes, "An Essay towards solving a Problem in the Doctrine of Chances," *Phil. Trans. Roy. Soc.*, **53**, 1763, p. 370.
8. R. A. Fisher, "Uncertain Inference," *Proc. Amer. Acad. Sci.*, **71**, 1936, p. 245.
9. R. A. Fisher, "On the Mathematical Foundations of Theoretical Statistics," *Phil. Trans. A.*, **222**, 1922, pp. 324–325. See also R. von Mises, "On the Correct Use of Bayes' Formula," *Ann. Math. Stat.*, **13**, 1942, pp. 156–165.
10. J. V. Uspensky, *Introduction to Mathematical Probability*, 1937, pp. 34–35.
11. For a discussion of the relative merits of the "collective" and "axiomatic" approaches to the definition of probability, two papers in volume 12 of the *Ann. Math. Stat.*, 1941, may be consulted: "On the Foundations of Probability and Statistics," R. von Mises, p. 191; "Probability as Measure," J. L. Doob, p. 206. The second of these papers is followed by a discussion in which both authors participate. See also W. Feller, *Probability Theory and Its Applications*, Vol. I (Wiley, 1950), pp. 1–7.

CHAPTER II

THE BINOMIAL DISTRIBUTION AND THE NORMAL AND POISSON APPROXIMATIONS

2.1 The Binomial or Bernoulli Distribution. Suppose that a sample of s individuals from a given population is divided into two groups according as the members have or have not a certain attribute. Such a division is called a *dichotomy*. For example, the division may be into "heads" and "tails" for a population of coin tosses, or "male" and "female" for a population of children, where for this purpose "tail" is regarded as synonymous with "not-head" and "female" with "not-male." The occurrence of the attribute is frequently, and conventionally, called a "success." If x individuals have the attribute in question, x is an integer which may take any value from 0 to s inclusive, and x/s is called the relative frequency of success. The process of selecting an individual is often called a "trial."

The proportion p of individuals having the attribute in the parent population may be taken as the probability that any one individual selected at random has this attribute and, if the parent population is very large compared with s, p will not change appreciably in the process of selecting the whole sample. Then the probability that the first x members have the attribute and the remaining $s - x$ do not is $p^x(1 - p)^{s-x}$. Since the number of ways of rearranging the sample without changing its composition is $\binom{s}{x}$, the probability of x successes in s trials is given by

$$(2.1) \qquad p(x, s) = \binom{s}{x} p^x q^{s-x}$$

where q is written for $1 - p$. This is the same as the term containing p^x in the expansion of the binomial $(q + p)^s$.

The probabilities that the attribute occurs 0, 1, 2, $\cdots$ s times in a sample of s are, therefore, given by the successive terms in $(q + p)^s$. This result was obtained by J. Bernoulli and was published posthumously in 1713 in a work called *Ars Conjectandi*. A discrete frequency distribution with frequencies proportional to these probabilities is, therefore, called a *Bernoulli* or *binomial* distribution. If we take N sets of s trials each, the theoretical absolute frequencies are $Np(x, s)$ and hence may be integers if p is a rational fraction and N is suitably chosen.

In evaluating $p(x, s)$, it is convenient to use tables of logarithms of factorials. From (2.1) we have

$$\log p(x, s) = \log s! - \log x! - \log (s - x)! + x \log p + (s - x) \log q$$

Sec. 3 Frequency Functions. Stieltjes Integrals

Seven-figure tables of log $n!$ for $n = 1$ to $n = 1000$ are given in Glover's *Tables of Applied Mathematics*, and in Pearson's *Tables for Statisticians and Biometricians*, Part I.

An alternative systematic procedure for calculating $p(x, s)$ is suggested in Example 1, § 2.10.

Extensive tables of the binomial distribution are now available, giving individual terms and the accumulated sums of terms. (See the footnote to § 6.15.)

2.2 Graphical Representation. A binomial distribution may be represented graphically by a histogram. This is accomplished by constructing rectangles centered at $x = 0, 1, 2, \cdots s$ with heights proportional to the terms of the binomial. Since the values of x constitute a discrete series it might seem more logical to represent the relative frequencies by ordinates instead of rectangles. However, since the base of each rectangle is unity the number representing its height is also its area, and the representation by areas will be useful in our work.

If we are thinking of relative frequencies or probabilities the sum of the areas of all the rectangles is unity, whereas if we are thinking of absolute frequencies the total area of the histogram is N. Thus if six coins are tossed 64 times the theoretical absolute frequencies are given by the terms of $64(\frac{1}{2} + \frac{1}{2})^6$. These are 1, 6, 15, 20, 15, 6, 1 and their sum is 64.

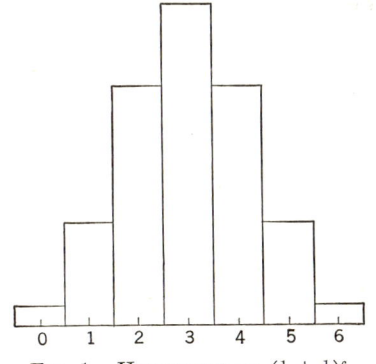

Fig. 1. Histogram of $(\frac{1}{2} + \frac{1}{2})^6$

It is often convenient to think of a frequency distribution as a distribution of *mass*. Here the masses (proportional to the frequencies) are concentrated at the points $x = 0, 1, \cdots s$ along the x-axis.

2.3 Frequency Functions. Stieltjes Integrals. The notion of frequency functions relates to theoretical universes. The concept is an idealization of observed distributions comparable to the idealization of the outlines of material objects into the straight lines and circles of geometry.

A continuous variable x is said to have the frequency function $f(x)$, which we take to be single-valued and non-negative, if the frequency of occurrence of x in the range $a < x < b$ is measured by

(2.2) $$\int_a^b f(x)\, dx$$

If x has the frequency function $f(x)$ with total frequency N, then

(2.3) $$\int_{-\infty}^{\infty} f(x)\, dx = N$$

and $y = f(x)$ is called a *theoretical frequency curve* or, more briefly, a *frequency curve*. If the actual occurrence of the variable is limited to a finite range, $f(x)$ is defined to be identically zero outside that range. If the total area under the curve is taken as unity, so that

$$(2.4) \qquad \int_{-\infty}^{\infty} f(x)\, dx = 1$$

then $y = f(x)$ is variously called the *probability density*, the *probability distribution*, or the *probability function* of x. Then, $f(x)\, dx$ gives, to within infinitesimals of order higher than that of dx, the probability that x lies in the interval $(x, x + dx)$. Under condition (2.4), the integral (2.2) denotes the *probability* that x lies in the interval (a, b). Under condition (2.3), (2.2) denotes the *frequency* of values in the interval (a, b). A suitable function can be regarded, therefore, either as a frequency function or as a probability function according as condition (2.3) or (2.4) is imposed. The distinction can be adjusted by determining appropriately a constant factor in $y = f(x)$. If the variable x has only discrete values and if $f(x)$ is the probability of occurrence of the value x, then

$$(2.5) \qquad \sum_{x} f(x) = 1$$

the sum being over all the admissible values of x.

The continuous and discrete cases may conveniently be included together by writing the left-hand side of (2.4) or (2.5) as a *Stieltjes integral*

$$(2.6) \qquad \int_{-\infty}^{\infty} dF(x) = 1$$

where this integral is interpreted as $\int_{-\infty}^{\infty} f(x)\, dx$ when x is continuous and as $\sum_{x} f(x)$ when x is discrete. It also covers cases where $f(x)$ is partly continuous and partly discrete, although we shall not encounter examples of this nature. The Stieltjes integral is not merely a convenient short-hand device. It plays an important role in the more advanced treatment of mathematical statistics. The reader may refer to an expository article by J. Shohat[1] for a further discussion of this integral.

2.4 Distribution Functions. The function $F(x)$ that appears in (2.6) is called the *distribution function*, or, when multiplied by N, the *cumulative frequency function*. It may be written

$$(2.7) \qquad F(x) = \int_{-\infty}^{x} dF(x)$$

and is interpreted as $\int_{-\infty}^{x} f(x)\, dx$ if the distribution possesses a frequency function or as $\sum_{r \leq x} f(r)$ if the distribution is discrete. Clearly $F(x)$ is a non-negative, non-decreasing function which is zero at $x = -\infty$ and 1 at $x = +\infty$. For a discrete distribution it increases in steps at the values of x for which the frequency function is not zero, and is continuous on the right. Thus for the binomial distribution of Figure 1, the distribution function is of the form shown in Figure 2. For a continuous distribution, $F(x)$ is usually more or less of the form indicated in Figure 3. A variable x for which a distribution function exists is often called a *variate*.

FIG. 2

FIG. 3

2.5 Mathematical Expectation. If there is a probability $f(x_i)$ that a variable x will have the value x_i, $i = 1, 2, \cdots n$, and if the set of values x_i includes all possible values of x, the *expected value* or *expectation* of x is

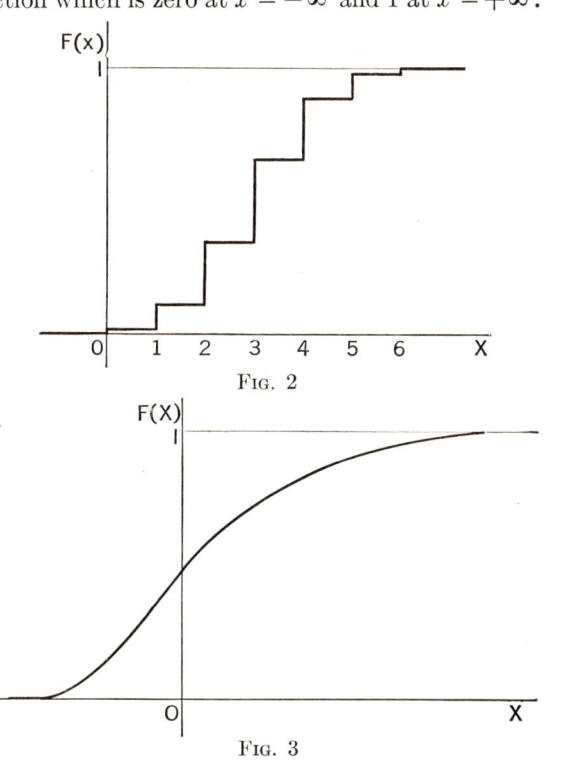

(2.8) $$E(x) = \sum_{i=1}^{n} x_i f(x_i)$$

where, of course,

$$\sum_{i=1}^{n} f(x_i) = 1$$

Thus, if I buy a ticket in a lottery in which there is a prize of $1000 and ten prizes of $50, and if 10,000 tickets are sold, my expectation, or the expected value of my ticket, is

$$\frac{1}{10,000} \times 1000 + \frac{10}{10,000} \times 50 + \frac{9989}{10,000} \times 0 = \$0.15$$

or 15 cents. If in a gambling game the expectation is equal to the stake, the game is said to be "fair." The fair price for the lottery ticket mentioned would be 15 cents. Actual gambling games and lotteries are usually not fair, in this sense, since a substantial percentage is taken by the organizers or the "bank."

If the variable x is continuous and if $f(x)\,dx$ is the probability of a value between x and $x + dx$, the expected value of x is

$$(2.9) \qquad E(x) = \int_{-\infty}^{\infty} x f(x)\,dx$$

where

$$\int_{-\infty}^{\infty} f(x)\,dx = 1$$

provided the integral on the right of (2.9) exists. (An example where it does not exist is given in § 2.7.)

If the variable x has the distribution function $F(x)$, whether continuous or not, its expectation is given by

$$(2.10) \qquad E(x) = \int_{-\infty}^{\infty} x\,dF(x)$$

which is equivalent to (2.8) and (2.9).

If in an actual sample of N individuals there are N_i with the value x_i ($i = 1, 2, \cdots n$), the arithmetic mean of the sample is

$$(2.11) \qquad \bar{x} = \frac{1}{N} \sum_{i=1}^{n} x_i N_i$$

As N increases, the ratio N_i/N approximates more and more closely in the stochastic * sense to the probability $f(x_i)$ that a randomly chosen individual of the parent population will have the value x_i. Hence as N increases, $\bar{x}$ tends to the value $E(x)$. In other words, the expected value may be regarded as the mean of the hypothetical parent population characterized by the theoretical frequencies $f(x_i)$.

2.6 Moments. The expected value of a function $g(x)$ is defined as

$$(2.12) \qquad E\{g(x)\} = \int_{-\infty}^{\infty} g(x)\,dF(x)$$

provided the integral exists.

If $g(x) = x^r$, where r is a positive integer, (2.12) defines the rth *moment about the origin*, ν_r. Clearly $\nu_1 = E(x)$, the population mean. If $g(x) = (x - \nu_1)^r$, the same equation defines the rth *moment about the mean*, μ_r. That is,

$$(2.13) \qquad \nu_r = \int_{-\infty}^{\infty} x^r\,dF(x)$$

$$(2.14) \qquad \mu_r = \int_{-\infty}^{\infty} (x - \nu_1)^r\,dF(x)$$

---

* That is, in the sense of the theory of probability rather than in the sense of the mathematical theory of limits (see § 1.3).

Obviously, $\mu_0 = 1$ and $\mu_1 = 0$, whatever the distribution, provided ν_1 exists. In particular, for $r = 2$, the *variance* is defined by

$$\mu_2 = \sigma^2 = \int_{-\infty}^{\infty} (x - \nu_1)^2 \, dF(x)$$

where σ is called the *standard deviation*. If the variable is changed from x to τ, where

(2.15) $$\tau = (x - \nu_1)/\sigma$$

the distribution, expressed as a function of τ, is in *standard form*, and τ is called a *standardized variable*. The variable τ is a pure number, since x and σ are in the same units. A distribution in standard form has mean 0 and standard deviation 1.

By expanding $(x - \nu_1)^r$ in powers of x, it is readily proved from (2.13) and (2.14) that

$$\mu_2 = \nu_2 - \nu_1^2$$
$$\mu_3 = \nu_3 - 3\nu_2\nu_1 + 2\nu_1^3$$
$$\mu_4 = \nu_4 - 4\nu_3\nu_1 + 6\nu_2\nu_1^2 - 3\nu_1^4, \quad \text{etc.}$$

and, in general,

(2.16) $$\mu_r = \nu_r - \binom{r}{1}\nu_{r-1}\nu_1 + \binom{r}{2}\nu_{r-2}\nu_1^2 - \cdots$$
$$+ (-1)^k \binom{r}{k}\nu_{r-k}\nu_1^k + \cdots + (-1)^{r-1}\left\{\binom{r}{r-1} - 1\right\}\nu_1^r$$

The moment-measure of *skewness* of a theoretical distribution is defined as

(2.17) $$\alpha_3 = \frac{\mu_3}{\sigma^3}$$

It is a pure number, 0 for a symmetrical distribution, positive for a distribution with a long tail to the right (because of the high contribution to $(x - \nu_1)^3$ for large positive values of x) and negative for a distribution with a long tail to the left. It is sometimes denoted by γ_1 or $\pm\sqrt{\beta_1}$, the former being Fisher's notation and the latter Karl Pearson's. We shall generally use Fisher's notation.

The moment-measure of *kurtosis* for a theoretical distribution is defined as

(2.18) $$\alpha_4 = \frac{\mu_4}{\sigma^4}$$

This is also a pure number. In Pearson's notation it is called β_2. It used to be regarded as a measure of "peakedness" but is now recognized to be greatly influenced by the behavior of the "tails" of the distribution.[2] Since for the normal (Gaussian) distribution, the value of α_4 is 3, the excess of α_4 over 3 is often taken as a natural measure of kurtosis. This quantity, $\gamma_2 = \alpha_4 - 3$, is sometimes called the *excess*.

On the hypothesis that a parent population has a certain theoretical distribution, the moments of a *sample* from that population will be approximations to the moments of the theoretical distribution. We shall see later, when we come to discuss sampling theory, how the moments, skewness, or other parameters of the parent population may, in some cases at least, be estimated from the corresponding values for the sample.

2.7 The Cauchy Distribution. The Cauchy distribution is a classical example of a probability distribution although its use in present-day statistics is relatively unimportant. Its equation is

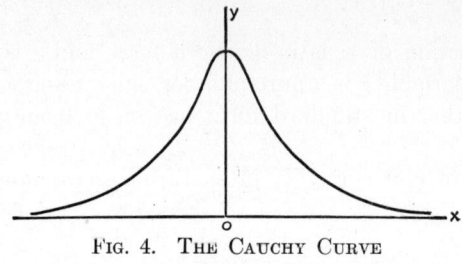

$$(2.19) \qquad y = \frac{b}{\pi(b^2 + x^2)},$$
$$-\infty \leq x \leq \infty,$$
$$b > 0$$

The curve is symmetrical, having its center at $x = 0$.

FIG. 4. THE CAUCHY CURVE

A simple derivation of this function is as follows. For a given real constant b locate the point $(0, b)$ as in the figure below. Let lines be drawn at random through $(0, b)$ and let θ be the variable angle between any such line and the negative direction of the y-axis; θ varies between the limits $-\pi/2$ and $\pi/2$. The hypothesis is that all values of θ in this range are equally likely. Denote the intercepts on the horizontal axis by x. Clearly,

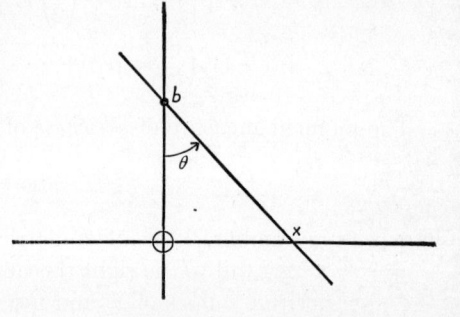

$$-\infty < x < \infty.$$

The relation between θ and x is

$$\theta = \tan^{-1}\frac{x}{b}$$

Under the hypothesis, the probability that an angle Obx will be contained between θ and $\theta + d\theta$ is $d\theta/\pi$. By differentiation we find the relation between $d\theta$ and dx to be

$$(2.20) \qquad \frac{d\theta}{\pi} = \frac{b\,dx}{\pi(b^2 + x^2)}$$

Therefore, the points of intersection of the lines with the x-axis are distributed so that the probability that a value of x will fall in the range dx is given by the right-hand member of (2.20). Hence the probability function for the variable x is

$$f(x) = \frac{b}{\pi(b^2 + x^2)}$$

and the probability that x lies in a finite interval (c, d) is given by

Sec. 8   Moments of the Bernoulli Distribution   29

$$P(c, d) = \int_c^d \frac{b\,dx}{\pi(b^2 + x^2)}$$

since the integral of the right-hand member of (2.20) from $-\infty$ to ∞ is equal to unity, as can easily be verified. However, we cannot speak here of the mean value of x or of moments of higher order, since the integral

$$\int_{-\infty}^{\infty} \frac{x^k\,dx}{(b^2 + x^2)}$$

has no meaning for $k = 1, 2, \cdots$.   ? $\nu_k = 0$ for k odd

If a machine gun were mounted on a swivel at $(0, b)$ so as to be perfectly free to turn, and if it fired bullets into a very long straight wall stretching along the x-axis, the distribution of bullet holes would be a Cauchy distribution, on the assumption that all angular positions of the gun were equally likely.

2.8 Moments of the Bernoulli Distribution. By definition,

(2.21) $$\nu_1 = E(x) = \sum x_i f(x_i)$$

where

$$x_i = 0, 1, 2, \cdots s, \qquad f(x_i) = \binom{s}{x_i} p^{x_i} q^{s-x_i}$$

Then

$$\nu_1 = \sum_{k=1}^{s} k \binom{s}{k} p^k q^{s-k}$$

$$= \sum_{1}^{s} \frac{s!}{(k-1)!(s-k)!} p^k q^{s-k}$$

$$= sp \sum_{1}^{s} \frac{(s-1)!}{(k-1)!(s-k)!} p^{k-1} q^{s-k}$$

$$= sp(q+p)^{s-1}$$

Since $q + p = 1$,

(2.22) $$\nu_1 = E(x) = sp$$

Similarly,

$$\nu_2 = \sum_{k=1}^{s} k^2 \binom{s}{k} p^k q^{s-k}$$

$$= \sum_{1}^{s} \{k(k-1) + k\} \frac{s!}{k!(s-k)!} p^k q^{s-k}$$

$$= \sum_{2}^{s} \frac{s!}{(k-2)!(s-k)!} p^k q^{s-k} + sp$$

$$= s(s-1)p^2(q+p)^{s-2} + sp$$

$$= s(s-1)p^2 + sp$$

$$= s^2 p^2 + spq$$

Hence

(2.23) $$\mu_2 = E(x - sp)^2 = \nu_2 - \nu_1^2 = spq$$

Higher moments may be found similarly. They may also be calculated from the recursion formula, due to Romanovsky,

$$\mu_{r+1} = pq\left[sr\mu_{r-1} - \frac{d\mu_r}{dq}\right] \tag{2.24}$$

A simple proof of (2.24) has been given by A. T. Craig.[3] Note that μ_r is here expressed as a function of s and q by means of the relation $p = 1 - q$.

Thus, knowing that $\mu_0 = 1$, $\mu_1 = 0$, we have:

$k = 1,\quad \mu_2 = pq(s - 0) = spq = sq(1 - q)$
$k = 2,\quad \mu_3 = pq[0 - (s - 2sq)]$
$\qquad\qquad = spq(2q - 1) = spq(q - p) = sq(1 - q)(2q - 1)$
$k = 3,\quad \mu_4 = pq(3s^2pq + 6sq^2 - 6sq + s)$
$\qquad\qquad = spq(3spq - 6pq + 1)$
$\qquad\qquad = spq[1 + 3pq(s - 2)]$

Hence

$$\gamma_1 = \alpha_3 = \frac{q - p}{\sqrt{spq}} \tag{2.25}$$

$$\alpha_4 = \frac{1}{spq} + \frac{3(s - 2)}{s} \tag{2.26}$$

$$\gamma_2 = \alpha_4 - 3 = \frac{1}{spq} - \frac{6}{s} \tag{2.27}$$

For the symmetrical binomial curve, for which $p = q = \tfrac{1}{2}$,

$$\gamma_1 = 0, \qquad \gamma_2 = -\frac{2}{s} \tag{2.28}$$

Equations (2.22) and (2.23) give the mean and variance with respect to the number of successes x in s trials. In some statistical investigations the data are expressed in terms of percentages or rates. When we may assume a constant probability underlying the frequency ratios obtained from observations we have a binomial distribution as before but on a different scale. Instead of the variable being x it is now x/s. In this case we have

$$E\left(\frac{x}{s}\right) = \frac{1}{s}E(x) = \frac{sp}{s} = p \tag{2.29}$$

For the analogous concept relating to the variance we have

$$E\left(\frac{x}{s} - p\right)^2 = \frac{1}{s^2}E(x - sp)^2 = \frac{spq}{s^2} = \frac{pq}{s} \tag{2.30}$$

Therefore, we see from (2.22) and (2.23) that the *number* of successes per set of s trials is distributed about an expected value sp with a standard deviation $(spq)^{1/2}$. From (2.29) and (2.30) we see that the *proportion* of successes in a set of s trials is distributed about an expected value p with a standard deviation $(pq/s)^{1/2}$.

Sec. 8 Moments of the Bernoulli Distribution

It is important to observe that for a fixed value of p the standard deviation of x increases as s increases and is proportional to $(s)^{1/2}$, whereas the standard deviation of x/s decreases as s increases, since it is proportional to $(1/s)^{1/2}$.

Problems

1. A dust storm contains particles of two kinds identical except as to color, brown and yellow particles existing in the ratio 3:2. If five particles of this dust enter my eye at random determine the probability that two of them are brown and the other three are yellow. (See *American Mathematical Monthly*, **41**, 1934, p. 337.)

2. Six coins are tossed once, or what amounts to the same thing, one coin is tossed six times. Find the probability of obtaining heads
  (a) exactly three times
  (b) at most three times
  (c) at least three times
  (d) at least once.

3. (a) What is the probability of throwing seven in a single toss of two dice?
  (b) In six tosses of two dice find the probability of throwing seven at least once.

4. Toss six coins 64 times and record the number of times heads appear 0, 1, 2, 3, 4, 5, 6 times. (Instead of tosses, the coins may be shaken in a box.) Compare the resulting distribution of frequencies with the terms of the expansion of $64(\frac{1}{2} + \frac{1}{2})^6$.

5. A bag contains white and black balls in the proportion 2:3. Let the drawing of a white ball be called a success. Three balls are drawn separately and after each drawing the ball is returned to the bag and thoroughly mixed with the others so that the fundamental probability of success remains constant during the trials. Find the probabilities of 0, 1, 2, 3 successes. If this experiment were repeated 125 times what is the theoretical frequency of each of the possible number of successes?

6. (a) Find the values of $\binom{18}{x}$ for $x = 0$ to $x = 18$ inclusive. (To the instructor: Pascal's Triangle provides a simple scheme for constructing a table of binomial coefficients.)
  (b) Evaluate $2^x/3^{18}$ for $x = 0$ to $x = 18$ inclusive.
  (c) Show that $(\frac{1}{3} + \frac{2}{3})^{18}$ may be written
$$\sum_{x=0}^{18} f(x) \text{ where } f(x) = \binom{18}{x} 2^x/3^{18}.$$
  (d) Using the results of (a) and (b), find the values of $f(x)$ for $x = 0$ to $x = 18$. Save your results for future reference.

7. Expand the binomial $N(\frac{1}{3} + \frac{2}{3})^s$ for $s = 2$ and $s = 8$. Find the theoretical frequencies in each case by taking N as the smallest number necessary to express the terms of each expansion as integers.

8. Find the mean and standard deviation for each of the distributions in Problem 7.

9. Find $\bar{x}$, σ, α_3, α_4 for each of the following binomials:
$$(\tfrac{1}{2} + \tfrac{1}{2})^7, \ (\tfrac{1}{6} + \tfrac{5}{6})^4, \ (\tfrac{1}{3} + \tfrac{2}{3})^{18}.$$

10. For a certain binomial distribution
$$\sigma = 2.66, \ \alpha_3 = 0.318. \quad \text{Find } p, q, \text{ and } s.$$

11. Assume that .04 is the theoretical rate of mortality in a certain age group. Suppose an insurance company is carrying $s = 1000$ such cases. What is the expected dispersion (standard deviation) in death rates from the theoretical rate $p = .04$? What would it be if $s = 10,000$?

12. The value of x for which $\binom{s}{x} p^x q^{s-x}$ is the largest is called the mode of a Bernoulli distribution. Show that the mode is the positive integral value (or values) of x for which
$$sp - q \le x \le sp + p$$

Hint. Using equation (2.1), write down the conditions that $p(x+1, s)/p(x, s) \le 1$ and $p(x-1, s)/p(x, s) \le 1$ simultaneously.

13. Suppose the law of distribution of the happening of an event in s successive trials is given by the terms of the expansion of
$$(q + p)^s = \sum_{x=0}^{s} \binom{s}{x} p^x q^{s-x} = \sum_{x=0}^{s} P_x$$

(a) If $s = 100$ what values of p and q will make $P_0 = P_1$; $P_9 = P_{10}$?
(b) Give approximate values of the P's in (a).

14. A tosses three pennies and B two, and the winner is the one with the greatest number of heads. In case of a tie they continue until a definite decision is reached. (a) What are, at the start, the respective probabilities of winning in a single game (a game is a set of tosses leading to a decision)? (b) How much money should A put up on a game to each dollar that B puts up, to make the game fair? *Ans.* (a) $\frac{8}{11}$, $\frac{3}{11}$; (b) $2.67.

Note that here our collective, to which the probabilities relate, is an infinite sequence of events each one of which consists of a finite or infinite number of tosses. The probability that any one game will continue indefinitely is, however, zero. Moreover, in almost every long sequence of these games the number of games will be large compared with the largest number of tosses in any one game.

15. A tosses a coin, agreeing beforehand to give B two dollars if it turns up "head," four dollars if "head" does not turn up till the second toss, eight dollars if not until the third toss, and in general 2^{x+1} dollars if x "tails" in succession appear before "head" appears. If, however, "tail" should appear ten times running, the game will end there with B receiving 2^{11} dollars. Assuming that the coin is unbiased and the tossing random, what is B's expectation? *Ans.* $12.00.

This is a variant of the famous "Petersburg paradox," on which a great deal has been written. The paradox arises from the fact that, without the agreement to stop at 10 tosses in any case, B's expectation, contrary to common sense, is infinite. He has an extremely small chance of winning an enormous amount, an amount which would certainly be beyond any A's capacity to pay.

We can, however, define a "fair" game, as Feller[4] has shown, in a way which leads to a definite solution of the Petersburg problem.

Let B_k be B's entrance fee on the kth trial (a trial being a set of tosses, however long, ending with the first head) and $T_n = \sum_{k=1}^{n} B_k$, the accumulated fees up to the nth trial. Let S_n be the sum of B's winnings up to the nth trial. Then if for any given $\epsilon > 0$, the probability that $|S_n - T_n| < \epsilon T_n$ tends to 1 as $n \to \infty$, the game can be called fair. The value of B_k turns out to be $\log_2 k$, so that $T_n = \log_2 n!$ or approximately $(n \log_e n - n)/\log_e 2$ when n is large. Thus, for $n = 100$, T_n is about $520, corresponding to an average of $5.20 per game.

This definition of a "fair" game depends on what happens in the long run (as $n \to \infty$). The assumption is that B is willing to play a very large number of games, large enough to make it practically certain that if the game is fair $|S_n - T_n|$ will be very small compared with T_n.

The subject of games has received much attention from mathematicians in recent years, partly because of a parallel to certain economic situations (see *The Theory of Games and Eco-*

Sec. 9 Approximating the Binomial with Normal Curve

nomic Behaviour by J. von Neumann and O. Morgenstern), and partly because of its importance in modern warfare.

2.9 Approximating the Binomial with the Normal Curve. If we plot the terms of $(q + p)^s$ as ordinates against the values of $x/\sqrt{s}$ as abscissas and draw the corresponding histogram we find that it approaches a smooth curve as s is taken larger and larger. Thus in Figure 5 (where the vertical sides of the rectangles are omitted since they contribute nothing to the interpretation) we see how the staircase outline of the histogram approaches closer to a continuous curve as s is taken larger.

The limiting values of γ_1 and γ_2 for the binomial as $s \to \infty$ are those of the normal curve. Thus from

$$\gamma_1 = \frac{q-p}{\sqrt{spq}}$$

and

$$\gamma_2 = \frac{1}{spq} - \frac{6}{s}$$

we see that $\gamma_1 \to 0$ and $\gamma_2 \to 0$ as $s \to \infty$. This suggests the possibility of approximating the binomial with the normal curve. As a matter of fact, it can be proved, under certain conditions of approximation, that $(q + p)^s$ approaches the normal curve as a limit as $s \to \infty$. A complete proof will not be given here but a word or two about it may be appropriate. In using the normal curve to approximate the binomial we are particularly interested in a range of three or four standard deviations from the mean. This fact suggests the reasonableness of assuming that the number of successes x' above or below sp be considered as the same order of magnitude as σ. This means that $x'/(spq)^{1/2}$ will remain finite as $s \to \infty$. Now $(spq)^{1/2}$ is of order $(s)^{1/2}$ if neither p nor q is extremely small. Hence the propriety of assuming (in the proof) that $x'/(s)^{1/2}$ will remain finite. This is the reason for plotting the histograms (Figure 5) in terms of $x/(s)^{1/2}$.

We may expect, therefore, that the fitted normal curve will give a fair approximation to the binomial except possibly at the extremities of the range. When the terms of the binomial are arranged symmetrically with respect to the mean, that is, when $p = q$, the approximation is considerably better than when either p or q is small compared with the other.

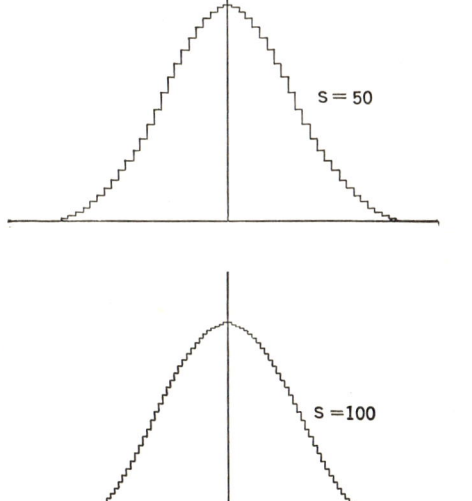

FIG. 5. SHOWING APPROACH OF $(q + p)^s$ TO SMOOTH CURVE AS $s \to \infty$

The Binomial Distribution

Because of the central role played by the normal law in statistical theory, we append a proof that the limiting form of the binomial curve is the normal curve. The proof is, however, suggestive rather than rigorous.

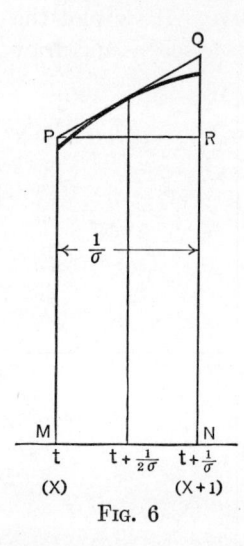

The variable is first changed to t, where

$$t = (x - sp)/\sigma, \quad \sigma = (spq)^{1/2},$$

so that the "step" of t is $1/\sigma$. This step becomes indefinitely small as $s \to \infty$. The slope of the straight line joining the tops of two successive t ordinates is then equated to the slope of a continuous approximating curve at the midpoint. To maintain the area under the curve unaltered, the ordinates are multiplied by σ at the same time as the abscissae are divided by σ. The slope of PQ is

$$\frac{NQ - MP}{MN} = \frac{f(t + 1/\sigma) - f(t)}{1/\sigma}$$

where

$$f(t) = \frac{\sigma s!}{x!(s-x)!} p^x q^{s-x}, \quad x = sp + \sigma t$$

Fig. 6

Now

$$\frac{f(t + 1/\sigma)}{f(t)} = \frac{p(x+1, s)}{p(x, s)} = \frac{s-x}{x+1} \cdot \frac{p}{q}$$

Hence

$$\frac{f(t + 1/\sigma) - f(t)}{f(t + 1/\sigma) + f(t)} = \frac{(s-x)p - (x+1)q}{(s-x)p + (x+1)q}$$

$$= \frac{sp - q - x}{sp + q + (q-p)x}$$

$$= -\frac{q + \sigma t}{q + 2\sigma^2 + (q-p)\sigma t}$$

Now the ordinate of the approximating curve midway between t and $t + 1/\sigma$ is nearly $\frac{1}{2}[f(t + 1/\sigma) + f(t)]$, so that, if y is the ordinate of this approximating curve, we can suppose that

$$\left(\frac{1}{y}\frac{dy}{dt}\right)_{t+1/2\sigma} = \lim_{\sigma \to \infty} \left(\frac{\text{slope of } PQ}{\text{mid-ordinate}}\right)$$

$$= \lim_{\sigma \to \infty} \frac{\sigma\{f(t+1/\sigma) - f(t)\}}{\frac{1}{2}\{f(t+1/\sigma) + f(t)\}}$$

$$= \lim_{\sigma \to \infty} \frac{-2\sigma(q + \sigma t)}{q + 2\sigma^2 + (q-p)\sigma t}$$

Substituting $t - 1/2\sigma$ for t, we have

$$\left(\frac{1}{y}\frac{dy}{dt}\right)_t = \lim_{\sigma \to \infty} \frac{-2\sigma(q + \sigma t - \frac{1}{2})}{q + 2\sigma^2 + (q-p)\sigma t - \frac{q-p}{2}}$$

Sec. 9   Approximating the Binomial with Normal Curve

$$= \lim_{\sigma \to \infty} \frac{-2\sigma^2 \left\{ \frac{q-p}{2\sigma} + t \right\}}{2\sigma^2 \left\{ 1 + \frac{1}{4\sigma^2} + \frac{q-p}{2\sigma} t \right\}}$$

$$= \lim_{\sigma \to \infty} \frac{-t - \frac{q-p}{2\sigma}}{1 + \frac{q-p}{2\sigma} t + \frac{1}{4\sigma^2}}$$

$$= -t$$

so that

$$\log y = -\frac{t^2}{2} + c$$

or

(2.31) $$\qquad y = \phi(t) = A e^{-t^2/2}$$

It may be noted that since $\gamma_1 = (q-p)/\sigma$, a closer approximation to the binomial curve when q is not equal to p is given by

$$\frac{1}{y}\frac{dy}{dt} = -\frac{t + \gamma_1/2}{1 + \gamma_1 t/2} = -\frac{2}{\gamma_1} + \frac{2/\gamma_1 - \gamma_1/2}{1 + \gamma_1 t/2}$$

On integration this gives

(2.32) $$\qquad y = A e^{-2t/\gamma_1}(1 + \gamma_1 t/2)^{(4/\gamma_1^2)-1}$$

which is a skew curve known as Pearson's Type III (see § 5.6). As $s \to \infty$, $\gamma_1 \to 0$ and this curve tends to the normal curve.

In (2.31), since t ranges from $-\infty$ to ∞ as x goes from 0 to ∞, we must have $\int_{-\infty}^{\infty} \phi(t)\, dt = 1$, whence $A = (2\pi)^{-1/2}$. A proof of this is given in Chapter III (see § 3.2). We have, therefore, the standard equation of the normal curve,

(2.33) $$\qquad \phi(t) = \frac{1}{\sqrt{2\pi}} e^{-t^2/2}$$

Exercise

Fit a normal curve to the binomial $(\frac{1}{3} + \frac{2}{3})^{18}$. Directions: This binomial may be written

$$\sum_{x=0}^{18} f(x), \quad \text{where} \quad f(x) = \binom{18}{x} \frac{2^x}{3^{18}}$$

(See Problem 6, § 2.8.) Next recall that the equation of the normal curve is

$$y = \frac{N}{\sigma} \phi(t)$$

where $$\phi(t) = \frac{1}{\sqrt{2\pi}} e^{-t^2/2} \quad \text{and} \quad t = \frac{(x - \bar{x})}{\sigma}$$

If we set $N = 1$, $\bar{x} = sp$, and $\sigma = (spq)^{1/2}$ we shall expect that y will give, approximately, the values of $f(x)$ for the various values of x. As in Chapter VI of Part I the following outline is suggested for organizing the computations.

x	t	$\phi(t)$	y	$f(x)$

Construct the histogram and draw the curve. It is suggested that paper ruled "20 to the inch" be used. By comparing the last two columns and also judging from the figure, does the fit seem to be good, even though s is rather small and $q = \frac{1}{2}p$?

Note that judgments by eye as to goodness of fit are likely to be deceptive. As will be seen later, there is a better method of forming such a judgment by means of the chi-square test.

The above exercise will help the student appreciate a theorem which will now be introduced. The sum of successive terms of the binomial equals the area of the corresponding rectangles in its histogram. We may obtain an approximation to this sum by finding the area under the fitted normal curve which these rectangles occupy. Graphically, the values $x = 0, 1, 2, \cdots, s$ are the mid-points of the bases of these rectangles. Therefore, if we are summing the terms of the binomial in which x ranges from $x = d_1$ to $x = d_2$, inclusive, the corresponding area under the curve will be from $x = d_1 - \frac{1}{2}$ to $x = d_2 + \frac{1}{2}$. We must convert these values into standard units in order to enter a table of areas of the normal curve. Hence we have the following theorem.

2.10 The DeMoivre-Laplace Theorem.

Theorem 2.1. *The sum of those terms of the binomial $(q + p)^s$ in which the number of successes x ranges from d_1 to d_2, inclusive, is approximately*

$$(2.34) \qquad Q = \int_{t_1}^{t_2} \phi(t)\, dt$$

where

$$t_1 = \frac{d_1 - \frac{1}{2} - sp}{\sigma}, \qquad t_2 = \frac{d_2 + \frac{1}{2} - sp}{\sigma}, \qquad \sigma = (spq)^{1/2}$$

A careful and ingenious, but rather long, proof of the DeMoivre-Laplace Theorem is given in Uspensky's book.[5] The great merit of this proof is that it provides an upper limit to the error involved in making the approximation, at least for reasonably large values of s. The result may be stated as follows and is exact:

Theorem 2.2.

$$(2.35) \qquad Q = \int_{t_1}^{t_2} \phi(t)\, dt + \frac{q - p}{6\sigma}\left[(1 - t^2)\phi(t)\right]_{t_1}^{t_2} + \Omega$$

Sec. 10 The DeMoivre-Laplace Theorem

where

(2.36) $$|\Omega| < \frac{0.12 + 0.18\,|p - q|}{\sigma^2} + e^{-3\sigma/2} \quad \text{for } \sigma \geq 5.$$

If $t_1 = -t_2$, this reduces to

(2.37) $$Q = 2\int_0^{t_2} \phi(t)\,dt + \Omega$$
$$= 2\Phi(t_2) - 1 + \Omega$$

where

(2.38) $$\Phi(x) = \frac{1}{\sqrt{2\pi}} \int_{-\infty}^x e^{-t^2/2}\,dt$$

Values of $\Phi(x)$ are given in the Appendix, Table 1. (The table gives $\Phi(x) - 0.5$, since the integral is taken from 0 to x. See also § 2.13.)

Example 1. Suppose $p = .2$ is the probability of success in a single trial. Estimate the probability of obtaining less than five or more than fifteen successes in fifty trials.

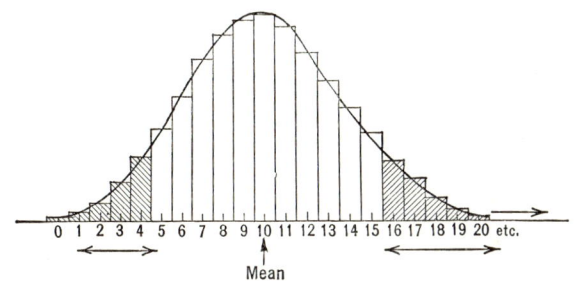

FIG. 7. BINOMIAL $(.8 + .2)^{50}$

Solution. The required probability, indicated by the shaded area in Figure 7, is $P = 1 - Q$ where Q is the probability of obtaining more than 4 and less than 16 successes. In using Theorem 2.1, we have

$$sp = 10, \quad \sigma = 2.828, \quad t_1 = -1.944, \quad t_2 = 1.944$$

Therefore,

$$P = 1 - Q = 1 - 2\int_0^{1.944} \phi(t)\,dt = .0519$$

The exact propability is obtained by evaluating and adding the sixth to the sixteenth terms of $(.8 + .2)^{50}$ and subtracting the result from unity. However, instead of computing these terms separately, a systematic procedure may be set up by which each term is made to depend upon the preceding term. Thus we may write a binomial as follows:

$$(q + p)^s = q^s(1 + k)^s = q^s\left\{1 + sk + \frac{s(s-1)}{2!}k^2 + \frac{s(s-1)(s-2)}{3!}k^3 + \cdots + k^s\right\}$$

where $k = p/q$. Then q^s may be computed by logarithms and its product with the terms in the brackets may be obtained on computing machines by a continuous process. Thus for the terms within the brackets,

the second term is first term multiplied by sk

the third term is second term multiplied by $\frac{s-1}{2}k$

the fourth term is third term multiplied by $\dfrac{s-2}{3}k$

. . . .

the rth term is $(r-1)$st term multiplied by $\dfrac{s-(r-2)}{r-1}k$

In this way we find $Q = .9497$, so the required probability is $P = .0503$. For most practical purposes the approximation by use of Theorem 2.1 would be satisfactory.

Uspensky's limit of error is here somewhat uncertain, since σ is less than 5. Inequality (2.36) gives a value of 0.04 as an upper limit for $|\Omega|$. In this case, the approximation is actually much better than the formula would suggest.

Example 2. Find the probability that in throwing 100 coins one will obtain a number of heads which will differ from the expected number by less than five.
Solution.

$$t_1 = -\frac{4.5}{5} = -.9$$

$$t_2 = \frac{4.5}{5} = .9$$

Hence the required probability is given by

$$Q = 2\int_0^{.9} \phi(t)\,dt = .632$$

Here $|\Omega| < .0054$, so that we can be quite certain that the probability lies between 0.626 and 0.637.

2.11 Simple Sampling of Attributes. It is a matter of common experience that certain fluctuations between observation and expectation under a given hypothesis may be explained on the basis of chance. For example, in throwing 100 coins an observed result of 45 heads and 55 tails does not warrant the conclusion that the coins are biased. In such cases a very natural question arises as to what sampling deviations may be allowed before we conclude that they indicate the operation of definite and assignable causes, that is, that the results are inconsistent with the given hypothesis. The theory dealing with such fluctuations in relative frequencies is called sampling of attributes.

Suppose we are given a sample of s individuals of which x have a certain character or attribute. The question then arises: Is this result consistent with the hypothesis that the sample is drawn from a population having the fraction p with the given character? Could it reasonably have arisen on the basis of chance or is it significant of other than chance factors? In answering this question our common-sense judgment is greatly aided by a probability scale for chance fluctuations under the given hypothesis. We therefore restate our question more precisely as follows:

Suppose the probability of an event is known from theoretical considerations to be equal to p. What is the probability that in s trials the number of successes will differ numerically from the expected number sp by as much as (or more than) an observed amount d?

Sec. 11 Simple Sampling of Attributes

The required probability may be estimated by means of the following corollaries to the DeMoivre-Laplace Theorem.

Theorem 2.3. *The probability that the number of successes x in s trials will differ from the expected number sp by more than d is approximately given by $P_\delta = 1 - Q_\delta$ where*

$$Q_\delta = 2 \int_0^\delta \phi(t)\, dt \quad \text{and} \quad \delta = \frac{d + \frac{1}{2}}{\sigma}$$

Theorem 2.4. *If the words "more than" in Theorem 2.3 be replaced by "as much as," then $\delta = (d - \frac{1}{2})/\sigma$.*

The proofs are obvious if we admit that the normal curve fits the histogram of the point binomial.

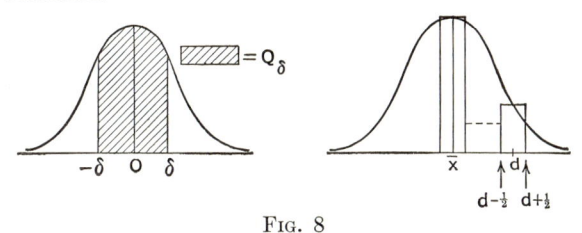

Fig. 8

In another slightly different form involving relative frequencies, Q_δ gives an approximation to the probability that the difference between an observed relative frequency of success x/s and the true probability p satisfies the relation

(2.39) $$\left| \frac{x}{s} - p \right| \leq \delta \left(\frac{pq}{s} \right)^{1/2}$$

for every assigned positive value of δ.

In using Theorem 2.3, Table 1 gives a general idea of the magnitudes of probabilities for certain deviations. It is divided into two sections: the first section lists probabilities for specially selected deviations, the second section lists deviations for specially selected probabilities.

TABLE 1. ABRIDGED NORMAL PROBABILITY SCALE

Deviation δ	Chance of Deviation Outside $\pm \delta$	Deviation δ	Chance of Deviation Outside $\pm \delta$
0.5	.617	.67	.50
1.0	.317	1.28	.20
1.5	.134	1.64	.10
2.0	.064	1.96	.05
2.5	.0124	2.33	.02
3.0	.0027	2.58	.01
3.5	.00047	3.29	.001

A computed probability is used to scale our judgment as to whether the deviation in question can be explained on the basis of chance. If it cannot be so explained, it is said to be "significant" of other than chance causes. In passing judgment on a deviation it is sometimes difficult to give a definite answer. Good judgment in these matters is sharpened by experience in the particular field. However, it is customary in much experimental work to describe an effect as "significant" if the probability of its arising by chance, on the hypothesis that its true value in the parent population is zero, is less than 0.05, and as "highly significant" if this probability is less than 0.01. This is the convention adopted by R. A. Fisher and is the one we shall follow as a rule. The level of significance to be used in any particular case will frequently depend, however, on the seriousness of drawing the wrong conclusions. If human lives are dependent on the reality of an effect, it is unlikely that one would be satisfied with a probability of 1 in 20 of being wrong in claiming that the effect exists. This point will be discussed later in connection with sampling theory and statistical inference.

Example 3. (*Rietz*) A group of scientific men reported 1705 sons and 1527 daughters. The examination of these numbers brings up the following fundamental questions of simple sampling. Do these data conform to the hypothesis that $\frac{1}{2}$ is the probability that a child to be born will be a boy? That is, can the deviations be reasonably regarded as fluctuations in simple sampling under this hypothesis? In another form, what is the probability in throwing 3232 coins that the number of heads will differ from $(3232/2) = 1616$ by as much as $d = 1705 - 1616 = 89$?

Solution. $s = 3232$, $(pqs)^{1/2} = 28.425$, $\delta = \dfrac{88.5}{28.425} = 3.113$, $P_\delta = 1 - 2\int_0^{3.113} \phi(t)\, dt = 1 - .9981 = .0019$.

Hence we conclude that these data cannot be explained on the basis of chance, that is, they are inconsistent with a hypothetical sex ratio of $\frac{1}{2}$.

In the statement of the DeMoivre-Laplace Theorem, d_1 and d_2 were integers. In Theorem 2.3 d need not be an integer, since sp is not necessarily integral.

The more exact statement of Theorem 2.3, due to Uspensky, is as follows:

Theorem 2.5. *The probability of the inequality* $|x - sp| \leq d$ *is given by*

$$(2.40) \qquad Q_{\delta_1} = 2\int_0^{\delta_1} \phi(t)\, dt + \frac{1 - \theta_1 - \theta_2}{\sigma} \phi(\delta_1) + \Omega_1$$

where

$$\delta_1 = d/\sigma,$$

$$(2.41) \qquad |\Omega_1| < \frac{0.20 + 0.25\,|p - q|}{\sigma^2} + e^{-3\sigma/2}$$

for $\sigma \geq 5$, and θ_1 and θ_2 are the fractional parts respectively of $sq + d$ and $sp + d$.

That is, if d_1 is the integer equal to or next above $sp - d$, and d_2 is the integer equal to or next below $sp + d$,

(2.42) $$sp - d = s - (sq + d) = d_1 - \theta_1$$
(2.43) $$sp + d = d_2 + \theta_2$$

The sign of equality in Theorem 2.5 can occur only if $sp + d$ or $sq + d$ is an integer.

If in Theorem 2.3 we put $\delta = \delta_1 + 1/2\sigma$, and if s is large enough for $1/2\sigma$ to be small, compared with $\phi(\delta_1)$, we obtain

(2.44) $$Q_\delta = 2 \int_0^{\delta_1} \phi(t)\, dt + 2\frac{1}{2\sigma}\phi(\delta_1)$$

approximately, which indicates that Q_{δ_1} differs from Q_δ only by terms depending on θ_1/σ and θ_2/σ and by the error term Ω_1.

Note that if s tends to infinity while δ_1 remains fixed, the probability that $|x - sp| \le \delta_1\sigma$ tends to the limit

$$2\int_0^{\delta_1} \phi(t)\, dt = 2\Phi(\delta_1) - 1$$

where $\Phi(x)$ is the distribution function of the normal law.

This is a very special case of an extremely general theorem, known as the *Central Limit Theorem*, of which something more will be said in Chapter IV.

2.12 Bernoulli's Theorem. If an event occurs x times in s trials and if p is the probability of success in a single trial, the probability that the relative frequency of success x/s will differ from p by less than any given arbitrary positive quantity ϵ tends to 1 as s increases indefinitely.

On the frequency definition of probability this theorem is a mere tautology. If, however, we suppose that probabilities can be assigned *without* performing an indefinitely long sequence of trials, the theorem provides a link between the probabilities so assigned and the results of often-repeated trials.

If ϵ is given and $|x/s - p| \le \epsilon$, x may lie between $sp - s\epsilon$ and $sp + s\epsilon$, inclusive.

Taking $\delta_1 = s\epsilon/\sigma$, the probability that $|x/s - p| \le \epsilon$ is, from (2.40), given by

$$Q_{\delta_1} = 2\int_0^{\delta_1} \phi(t)\, dt + \frac{1 - \theta_1 - \theta_2}{\sigma}\phi(\delta_1) + \Omega_1$$

and as $s \to \infty$

$$Q_{\delta_1} \to 2\int_0^{\infty} \phi(t)\, dt = 1$$

This proves the theorem.

Example 4. If $p = \frac{3}{5}$ and $s = 6520$, what is the probability that the relative frequency of success will not differ from $\frac{3}{5}$ by more than 0.01?

Here $\sigma = \sqrt{spq} = 39.56$, $\epsilon = 0.01$, $sp - s\epsilon = 3912 - 65.2 = 3846.8$, $sp + s\epsilon = 3977.2$. Hence $\theta_1 = \theta_2 = 0.2$, $\delta_1 = 65.2/39.56 = 1.648$, and the required probability $= 2\Phi(1.648) + (0.6/39.56)\phi(1.648) - 1 + \Omega_1 = 0.90220 + \Omega_1$. Here $|\Omega_1| < (0.20 + 0.05)/1565 = .00016$, so that the calculated probability is certainly not in error by more than two units in the fourth decimal place.

Example 5 (Wolf's Dice Experiments). From time to time, attempts have been made to verify the calculations of probability theory by making actual experimental trials with dice, balls, or other apparatus. Among the most extensive of such trials is one made in 1850 by the Swiss astronomer Wolf,[6] in the course of which two dice were thrown 100,000 times.

One result was that the frequency of unlike pairs was 83,533 as compared with a theoretical value of $\frac{5}{6} \times 100{,}000$. The probability of a discrepancy not greater than that actually obtained is Q_{δ_1} where

$$sp = 83{,}333\tfrac{1}{3} \qquad \theta_1 = \frac{1}{3}, \qquad \theta_2 = 0, \qquad \sigma = \frac{(500{,}000)^{1/2}}{6} = 117.85$$

$$\delta_1 = \frac{199\tfrac{2}{3}}{\sigma} = 1.6943$$

so that

$$Q_{\delta_1} = 2\Phi(1.6943) - 1 + \frac{2}{3\sigma}\phi(1.6943) + \Omega_1$$
$$= 0.90962 + 0.00054 + \Omega_1$$

with $|\Omega_1| < 0.000026$. The required probability is, therefore, 0.9102, almost exactly. Since this differs from 1 by about 0.09, we can hardly say that the result was surprising. A larger discrepancy would have occurred about once in 11 times with perfect dice. Some others of Wolf's results, however, indicate that his dice were, in fact, decidedly imperfect. All such experimental trials merely serve to demonstrate the accuracy or lack of accuracy of the apparatus used. They can have no bearing on the validity of the axioms of probability theory.

2.13 Tables of the Normal Law. The normal law, as we shall see later, occupies a central position in the theory of probability and mathematical statistics. It is the limiting form assumed, not merely by the binomial law, but by a very large class of frequency functions as the size of the sample increases, and moreover the assumption of a normal distribution of errors of observation is fundamental in many widely used techniques of statistical inference. The normal law (or error law, or probability integral) has, therefore, been extensively tabulated, but there is considerable diversity of arrangement among the tables.

The distribution function for the normal law is

$$\Phi(x) = \int_{-\infty}^{x} \phi(t)\, dt = \tfrac{1}{2} + \int_{0}^{x} \phi(t)\, dt$$

where

$$\phi(t) = \frac{1}{\sqrt{2\pi}} e^{-t^2/2}$$

Table I in the Appendix to this book lists $\phi(t)$ and $\int_0^t \phi(t)\, dt$, so that $\Phi(t)$ is given by adding 0.5 to the tabular values. Part III of Glover's *Tables of Applied Mathematics in Finance, Insurance, Statistics* also gives $\phi(t)$ and $\int_0^t \phi(t)\, dt$, as well as the derivatives of $\phi(t)$ from the 2nd to the 8th.

Sec. 14 The Poisson Exponential Approximation

Some books, including Peirce's *Short Table of Integrals*, tabulate

$$g(x) = \frac{2}{\sqrt{\pi}} \int_0^x e^{-t^2}\, dt$$

It is readily seen by changing the variable of integration to $u = \sqrt{2}\,t$ that

$$g(x) = 2\Phi(\sqrt{2x}) - 1$$

Again, Pearson's *Tables for Statisticians and Biometricians*, Part I, Table II, denotes $\phi(x)$ by z and $\int_{-x}^{x} \phi(t)\, dt$ by α. The quantity tabulated is $\frac{1}{2}(1 + \alpha) = \Phi(x)$.

In Fisher's *Statistical Methods for Research Workers*, 10th Edition, page 77, the table gives values of x for selected values of P, where

$$P = 1 - \int_{-x}^{x} \phi(t)\, dt = 1 - 2\int_0^x \phi(t)\, dt$$
$$= 2[1 - \Phi(x)].$$

This arrangement is convenient for many purposes, but if it is required to determine areas under a normal curve the table has to be read "inside out."

Tables of the normal law are sometimes disguised as *probits*, e.g., in *Statistical Tables* by Fisher and Yates, Table IX. If A is the percentage area up to the ordinate at x, $A = 100\Phi(x)$, and the probit corresponding to A is $5 + x$. The 5 is added to avoid negative values in all cases that are likely to occur in practice. Thus for $A = 10$, $\Phi(x) = 0.1$, $x = -1.282$, and the probit is $5 - 1.282 = 3.718$. *Kelley's Statistical Tables* (Harvard Univ. Press, 1948) give x and $\phi(x)$ to 8 decimal places corresponding to values of $\Phi(x)$ at every 0.0001 between 0.5 and 1. In these tables $\Phi(x)$ is denoted by p and $\phi(x)$ by z.

The most extensive and accurate tables of the normal law now available (*Tables of Probability Functions, Vol. II*) were prepared under the Federal Government Work Projects Administration and published by the National Bureau of Standards, 1942. These give $\phi(x)$ and $2\Phi(x) - 1$ to 15 decimal places at intervals of 0.0001 between 0 and 1, at intervals of 0.001 between 1 and 7.8, and at larger intervals up to $x = 8$. An auxiliary table continues as far as $x = 10$ to 7 significant figures. Vol. I of these tables gives values of comparable accuracy for the error function $2/\sqrt{\pi}\, e^{-x^2}$ and its integral.

2.14 The Poisson Exponential Approximation. If p (or q) is small the normal curve cannot ordinarily be used with confidence to approximate the terms of the binomial $(q + p)^s$. If s is large but sp is of moderate size (of the order of 10), a useful approximation to

(2.45) $$p(x, s) = \frac{s!}{x!(s - x)!} p^x q^{s-x}$$

may be given by means of the Poisson exponential function. Statistical examples of this situation are sometimes called rare events and occur in widely different fields; for example, the number born blind per year in a large city, the number of organisms of a given size S on a given glass slide that escape death by X-rays after being exposed for t seconds, the number of times in a certain year that the volume of trading on the New York Stock Exchange exceeds M million shares, the frequency of certain "peaks" in a given time interval such as occur in telephone "traffic," and other problems in demands for services.

The word "rare" means "individually rare." In a large population several such events may occur, but the probability of occurrence of each individual event is small.

The approximation is sometimes used with values of p as high as 0.05, but s should not then be larger than, say, 200, and even so the approximation may be 3 or 4 per cent in error.

Suppose, then, that p is the probability for the occurrence of the rare event in question, and assume that $q = 1 - p$ is nearly unity. From (2.45)

$$p(x, s) = \frac{s(s-1)\cdots(s-x+1)}{x!} p^x(1-p)^{s-x}$$

$$= \frac{s^x\left(1-\frac{1}{s}\right)\left(1-\frac{2}{s}\right)\cdots\left(1-\frac{x-1}{s}\right)}{x!}\left(\frac{m}{s}\right)^x\left(1-\frac{m}{s}\right)^{s-x}$$

where $m = sp$. Hence

(2.46) $\quad p(x, s) = \left(1-\frac{1}{s}\right)\left(1-\frac{2}{s}\right)\cdots\left(1-\frac{x-1}{s}\right)\cdot\frac{m^x}{x!}\left(1-\frac{m}{s}\right)^s\left(1-\frac{m}{s}\right)^{-x}$

Now if x is fixed and $s \to \infty$ while $p \to 0$ in such a way that m remains finite, the factors $1 - 1/s, \cdots, 1 - (x-1)/s, (1 - m/s)^{-x}$ all $\to 1$. Also, it is well known that

$$\lim_{s \to \infty} (1 - m/s)^s = e^{-m}$$

so

(2.47) $\quad\quad\quad\quad\quad\quad \lim_{s \to \infty} p(x, s) = \frac{m^x e^{-m}}{x!}$

which is *Poisson's exponential function*. For rare events it gives an *approximation* to the true probability of x successes in s trials. Tables of this function are to be found in Pearson's *Tables for Statisticians and Biometricians*, Part I, Table LI, and in Fry's *Probability and its Engineering Uses*. More extensive tables have been compiled by Molina.[7]

Uspensky has given a formula which indicates the accuracy of the approximation, namely,

(2.48) $\quad\quad\quad\quad\quad\quad p(x, s) = \beta \frac{m^x e^{-m}}{x!}$

where

$$\beta = [1 - \theta g(x)]e^{h(x)}, \quad 0 < \theta < 1$$

$$g(x) = \frac{(s-x)m^3}{3(s-m)^3} + \frac{x^3}{2s(s-x)}$$

Sec. 14 The Poisson Exponential Approximation

and
$$h(x) = \frac{mx}{s} - \frac{m^2}{2s^2}(s-x) - \frac{x(x-1)}{2s} = p\left[\frac{x}{2}\left(p + \frac{1}{m}\right) - \frac{(x-m)^2}{2m}\right]$$

Thus, for $p = 1/100$, $s = 1000$, $m = 10$, the Poisson approximation for $x = 10$ is $10^{10}e^{-10}/10! = 0.1251$. Here $g(10) = 0.000845$, $h(10) = 0.0055$, so that $\beta = 1.005515(1 - 0.000845\theta)$, that is, β lies between 1.004665 and 1.005515, or $p(1000, 10)$ lies between 0.12568 and 0.12579. The exact value, obtained by using logarithms of factorials, is 0.12574, which is about halfway between the limits assigned.

The terms of the series

(2.49) $$e^{-m}\left[1 + m + \frac{m^2}{2!} + \frac{m^3}{3!} + \cdots + \frac{m^x}{x!} + \cdots\right]$$

give the approximate probabilities of exactly $0, 1, 2, \cdots x \cdots$ occurrences of the rare event in s trials. Hence the probability that the number of successes is *at least equal to* x is approximately given by

(2.50) $$Q_m(x) = \sum_{r=x}^{\infty} \frac{m^r e^{-m}}{r!}$$

This function is tabulated by Fry and by Molina.

According to Uspensky, the true probability of at least x successes in s trials is given by

(2.51) $$P_{ms}(x) = Q_m(x) + \Delta$$

where
$$|\Delta| < (e^x - 1)Q_m(x+1), \quad \text{if } Q_m(x+1) \geq \tfrac{1}{2}$$
$$|\Delta| < (e^x - 1)[1 - Q_m(x+1)], \quad \text{if } Q_m(x+1) \leq \tfrac{1}{2}$$

and
$$\chi = \frac{m + \frac{1}{4} + \frac{m^3}{s}}{2(s-m)}$$

Thus, with the data above,
$$Q_{10}(10) = 0.54207, \quad \chi = 0.00568$$
$$|\Delta| < 0.005696(1 - 0.41696) = 0.00332$$

so that $P_{10,1000}(10)$ lies between 0.5388 and 0.5454. The true value is very close to 0.5421.

Certain simple and interesting results may be obtained for the moments of the distribution given by (2.47) when x takes all integral values from $x = 0$ to $x = s$. First we observe that from (2.49)

$$\sum_{x=0}^{s} \frac{m^x e^{-m}}{x!} = 1$$

approximately if s is large. Then

$$E(x) = \nu_1 = \sum_{x=0}^{s} xf(x)$$
$$= me^{-m}\left[1 + m + \frac{m^2}{2!} + \cdots + \frac{m^{s-1}}{(s-1)!}\right]$$
$$\approx me^{-m}e^{m}$$
(2.52) $\qquad = m = sp$, approximately

And
$$\nu_2 = \sum_{0}^{s} x^2 f(x)$$
$$= \sum_{0}^{s}[x(x-1) + x]f(x)$$
$$= m(m+1), \text{ approximately}$$

The theoretical Poisson approximation is the limiting distribution when $s \to \infty$. For this limiting distribution the above values of ν_1 and ν_2 are exact. From these results, we have

$$\text{Mean} = m = sp$$
$$\mu_2 = m(m+1) - m^2$$
(2.53) $\qquad\qquad = m$
(2.54) $\qquad\qquad \therefore \sigma = (m)^{1/2}$

It may also be shown that
$$\nu_3 = m(m^2 + 3m + 1)$$
$$\nu_4 = m(m^3 + 6m^2 + 7m + 1)$$

whence we find that

(2.55) $\qquad\qquad \mu_3 = m$
(2.56) $\qquad\qquad \mu_4 = 3m^2 + m$

and

(2.57) $\qquad\qquad \gamma_1 = \frac{1}{m^{1/2}}, \qquad \gamma_2 = \frac{1}{m}$

It is a rather striking result that each of the mean, variance, and μ_3 is equal to m.

The importance of the Poisson approximation in dealing with certain problems in telephone engineering and other fields is discussed in Fry's book, *Probability and Its Engineering Uses*. The interested student might investigate and prepare a special report on some of these applications.

A recursion formula for the moments of the Poisson distribution is readily obtained. Thus

$$\mu_r = \sum_{x=0}^{\infty} (x-m)^r \frac{m^x e^{-m}}{x!}$$

Hence
$$\frac{d\mu_r}{dm} = \sum_{x=0}^{\infty}\left[-r(x-m)^{r-1} + (x-m)^r\left(\frac{x}{m}-1\right)\right]\frac{m^x e^{-m}}{x!}$$
$$= -r\mu_{r-1} + \frac{1}{m}\mu_{r+1}$$

or

(2.58) $\qquad \mu_{r+1} = mr\mu_{r-1} + m\dfrac{d\mu_r}{dm}$

Putting $\mu_0 = 1$, $\mu_1 = 0$, we get successively,

$\mu_2 = m$
$\mu_3 = m$
$\mu_4 = 3m^2 + m$
$\mu_5 = 4m^2 + 6m^2 + m = 10m^2 + m,$ etc.

2.15 Poisson and Lexis Schemes. In the Bernoulli scheme (§ 2.1), we considered s trials of an event with a constant probability p of success in a single trial. Variants of this scheme are associated with the names of Poisson and Lexis.

In the *Poisson scheme*, the probability of success p_i, at the ith trial, varies from trial to trial. If x is the number of successes,

(2.59) $\qquad E(x) = \sum_{i=1}^{s} E(z_i) = \sum_i p_i$

where z_i takes the values 1 and 0 with probabilities p_i and q_i respectively.

Also, since the trials are independent, the variance of x is

(2.60) $\qquad \text{Var}(x) = \sum_i \text{var}(z_i) = \sum_i p_i q_i = \sum_i p_i - \sum_i p_i^2$

Let $p = $ mean of the $p_i = 1/s \sum_i p_i$, and let

$\sigma_p^2 = $ variance of the p_i
$\qquad = \dfrac{1}{s}\sum_i (p_i - p)^2$
$\qquad = \dfrac{1}{s}\sum_i p_i^2 - \dfrac{1}{s^2}\left(\sum_i p_i\right)^2$

Then

(2.61) $\qquad \text{Var}(x) = sp - s(\sigma_p^2 + p^2) = spq - s\sigma_p^2$

and hence is *less* than if all the p_i are equal to p.

In the *Lexis scheme*, we consider n sets of s trials each, the probability of success being constant within each set but varying from one set to another. The number of successes in the jth set is x_j and its expected value is sp_j. The expectation of the total number of successes is

(2.62) $\qquad E(x) = s\sum_{j=1}^{n} p_j = snp$

where $p = 1/n \sum_j p_j$, so that the expected number of successes per set of s trials is sp.

In the jth set,
$$E(x_j - sp_j)^2 = sp_j q_j$$
so that
$$E(x_j - sp)^2 = E(x_j - sp_j + sp_j - sp)^2 = sp_j q_j + (sp_j - sp)^2$$

The variance of x is therefore given by
$$\text{Var}(x) = s \sum_j p_j q_j + s^2 \sum_j (p_j - p)^2$$
$$= s \sum p_j - s \sum p_j^2 + s^2 \sum (p_j - p)^2$$

Putting $\sum_{j=1}^n p_j = np$, $\sum_{j=1}^n (p_j - p)^2 = n\sigma_p^2$, we obtain

(2.63)
$$\text{Var}(x) = snp - (sn\sigma_p^2 + snp^2) + s^2 n\sigma_p^2$$
$$= snpq + s(s-1)n\sigma_p^2$$

so that the variance of the number of successes per set of s trials is

(2.64) $$\text{Var}(x/n) = spq + s(s-1)\sigma_p^2$$

and hence is *greater* than if the probability of success remained constant from set to set. The second term depends on the variation of probability from set to set, a variation which in the applications may possess physical significance.

If σ^2 is the variance of the number of successes in an experimental set of s trials, and if σ_B^2 is the variance calculated on the assumption of a Bernoulli distribution, the ratio

(2.65) $$L = \sigma/\sigma_B$$

is called the *Lexis ratio*. The dispersion is said to be subnormal if $L < 1$ and supernormal if $L > 1$.

2.16 The Hypergeometric Distribution. If we have a finite population of size n, composed, say, of black and white balls, and if we draw a sample of s balls *without* replacements, the probability of drawing a white ball at any trial no longer remains constant but depends on the results of earlier trials.

In fact, if p is the original proportion of white balls in the population, the chance of obtaining x white and $s - x$ black balls in s trials is given by

(2.66) $$h_n(x, s) = \frac{\binom{np}{x}\binom{nq}{s-x}}{\binom{n}{s}}$$
$$= \frac{(np)!\,(nq)!\,s!\,(n-s)!}{x!\,(np-x)!\,(s-x)!\,(nq-s+x)!\,n!}$$

Sec. 16　The Hypergeometric Distribution

By using Stirling's approximation for the factorials containing n (§ 3.3), it is easily seen that

(2.67) $$\lim_{n \to \infty} h_n(x, s) = \frac{s!}{x!\,(s-x)!} p^x q^{s-x} = p(x, s)$$

Hence sampling with replacements from a finite population gives the same distribution of successes in s trials as sampling without replacements from an infinite population. This, of course, is to be expected since removing a finite sample from an infinite population will not affect the chance of success in a new trial.

The function $h_n(x, s)$ may be written

(2.68) $$h_n(x, s) = A \frac{s!}{x!\,(s-x)!} \frac{(np)!}{(np-x)!} \frac{(nq-s)!}{(nq-s+x)!}$$

where $A = (nq)!\,(n-s)!/(nq-s)!\,n!$ Hence the probability of x successes in s trials is given by the coefficient of u^x in the expression

(2.69) $$A\left[1 + s\frac{np}{nq-s+1}u + \frac{s(s-1)}{1\cdot 2}\frac{np(np-1)u^2}{(nq-s+1)(nq-s+2)} + \cdots \right.$$
$$\left. + \frac{np(np-1)\cdots(np-s+1)}{(nq-s+1)(nq-s+2)\cdots nq}u^s\right]$$

The part of this expression in square brackets may be written as a *hypergeometric function*.

The hypergeometric function is defined by the infinite series

(2.70) $$F(\alpha, \beta, \gamma; u) = 1 + \frac{\alpha\beta}{1\cdot\gamma}u + \frac{\alpha(\alpha+1)\beta(\beta+1)}{1\cdot 2\gamma(\gamma+1)}u^2 + \cdots$$

If $\alpha = -s$, $\beta = -np$, $\gamma = nq - s + 1$, this series terminates, since s is an integer, and agrees with the bracketed expression in (2.69). Therefore

(2.71) $$\sum_{x=0}^{s} h_n(x, s) u^x = A F(-s, -np, nq - s + 1; u)$$

and for this reason the discrete distribution given by the values of $h_n(x, s)$ for $x = 0, 1, 2, \cdots s$ is called a *hypergeometric distribution*. Putting $u = 1$ in (2.71), we have

(2.72) $$1 = \sum_{x=0}^{s} h_n(x, s) = A F(-s, -np, nq - s + 1; 1)$$

Differentiating (2.71) with respect to u, we have

$$\sum_{x=0}^{s} h_n(x, s) x u^{x-1} = A \frac{d}{du} F(-s, -np, nq - s + 1; u)$$

Putting $u = 1$, this gives

(2.73) $$E(x) = \sum_{x=0}^{s} x h_n(x, s) = A \cdot F'(-s, -np, nq - s + 1; 1)$$

where F' stands for dF/du. In the same way

(2.74) $\quad E\{x(x-1)\} = AF''(-s, -np, nq - s + 1; 1)$

and so on.

Now $F(\alpha, \beta, \gamma; u)$ satisfies the differential equation

(2.75) $\quad u(1-u)F'' + \{\gamma - (\alpha + \beta + 1)u\}F' - \alpha\beta F = 0$

so that when $u = 1$,

$$(\gamma - \alpha - \beta - 1)F' = \alpha\beta F$$

or, substituting for α, β, γ,

(2.76) $\quad F' = spF$

Hence from (2.72) and (2.73),

(2.77) $\quad E(x) = sp$

which shows that the expected value for x is exactly the same in this problem as in the simple Bernoulli scheme.

Differentiating (2.75) and then putting $u = 1$, we get

$$-F''' + (\gamma - \alpha - \beta - 1)F'' - (\alpha + \beta + 1)F' - \alpha\beta F' = 0$$

or

$$(\gamma - \alpha - \beta - 2)F'' = (\alpha\beta + \alpha + \beta + 1)F'$$

Substituting for α, β, γ, we find

(2.78) $\quad (n-1)F'' = (np-1)(s-1)F' = (np-1)(s-1)spF$

Therefore

$$E(x^2 - x) = \frac{(np-1)(s-1)}{n-1} sp$$

so that

(2.79) $\quad E(x^2) = \{(np-1)(s-1)/(n-1) + 1\} sp$

whence the variance of x is given by

(2.80) $\quad E(x^2) - \{E(x)\}^2 = sp\{(np-1)(s-1)/(n-1) + 1 - sp\}$

$$= spq \frac{n-s}{n-1}$$

$$= \frac{n-s}{n-1} \sigma_B^2$$

Consequently, for $s > 1$, the variance is less than it would be if the population were infinite, or if the drawings were made with replacements.

Problems

1. Use Theorem 2.1 to approximate the following sums:
(a) the terms of $(\frac{1}{3} + \frac{2}{3})^{90}$ in which $50 \leq x \leq 70$.
(b) the terms of $(.946 + .054)^{521}$ in which $x \geq 33$.

Problems

2. Fit a normal curve to the point binomial $(\frac{1}{2} + \frac{1}{2})^4$.

3. Fit a normal curve to $(\frac{1}{2} + \frac{1}{2})^6$.

4. Suppose you are studying IQ's and it is known that 20% in the universe with which you are dealing have an IQ below M, so that $\frac{1}{5}$ is the probability that an individual chosen at random has an IQ below M. (M itself has no bearing on the solution of the problem.) If a teacher had a class of fifty which could be regarded as a random sample from this universe, would it be exceptional if she found fewer than five or more than fifteen with IQ's below M? (See Example 1.)

5. (*Camp*) A dean's report showed the following figures:

Subject	Honor Grades Number	Honor Grades %	Failures Number	Failures %	Number Examined
German	187	36	33	6.3	521
Mathematics	162	35	38	8.2	466
Music	11	50	0	0.0	22
All Subjects		38		5.4	

Taking $p = .38$ for honor grades and $p = .054$ for failures find the probability: (*a*) that in selecting 521 students at random (from a supposedly infinite number), one would obtain as few honor grades as were obtained in German; (*b*) as many failures; (*c*) in selecting 466 at random, one would obtain as few honor grades as were obtained in mathematics; (*d*) as many failures; (*e*) in selecting 22 at random, one would obtain no failures (as in music); (*f*) eleven or more honor grades.

Hints. (*a*) Find sum of terms of $(.62 + .38)^{521}$ in which $x \leq 187$.

(*b*) See Problem 1 (*b*) above.

(*e*) Evaluate $(0.946)^{22}$ by logarithms.

6. (*Burgess*) If analyzed past experience shows that 4% of all insured white males of exact age 65 have died within a year, and it is found that 60 of a similar group of 1000 actually die within a year, should the group be regarded as essentially different from the general mass — that is, is the departure from the expected mortality greater than might be expected as a result of chance variation alone?

7. (*Richardson*) In a coin tossing experiment in which a coin was tossed 400 times, 250 heads appear. Do you believe the experiment was honestly performed?

8. (*Lovitt* and *Holtzclaw*) Would you be willing to bet 10 to 1 that an opponent could not throw the sum 7 with two dice at least 23 times in a hundred throws with two dice?

9. A factory produces units of a standardized article at the rate of 1000 per day, with a probability of 0.05 that any one unit selected at random will be defective. Find the probability that the number of defective units produced in one day will be not less than 40 nor more than 60. *Ans.* 0.863.

10. Professor J. E. Kerrich in *An Experimental Introduction to the Theory of Probability*, Einar Munksgaard, Copenhagen, 1946, has discussed very fully some experiments he made during a period of enforced leisure in a Danish internment camp. In one of these, a coin was spun 10,000 times, and the number of heads was 5067. Estimate the probability of a discrepancy at least as great as this, if the true probability of "head" with the coin used was precisely 0.5.

11. A coin is tossed s times. It is desired that the relative frequency of the appearance of heads shall not be greater than .51 or less than .49. Find the smallest value of s that will insure the above results with a degree of certainty $Q_\delta = .90$.

Solution. We must determine s such that $Q_\delta = .90$ that
$$\left|\frac{x}{s} - \frac{1}{2}\right| \leq .01$$
We have
$$\delta\left(\frac{pq}{s}\right)^{1/2} = .01$$
$$\delta = .02\sqrt{s}$$
since $p = q = \frac{1}{2}$. Also
$$Q_\delta = 2\int_0^\delta \phi(t)\,dt = .90$$
whence from the tables we find $\delta = 1.645$. Therefore,
$$.02\sqrt{s} = 1.645$$
and
$$s = 6745, \quad \text{approximately.}$$

The exact solution is not readily obtainable, but we can take a trial value of s and see with what probability the required condition is satisfied.

Thus if we let $s = 6800$, we find $s\epsilon = 68$,
$$\theta_1 = \theta_2 = 0, \qquad \sigma = 41.23, \qquad \delta_1 = 1.649,$$
and
$$Q_{\delta_1} = 2\Phi(1.649) + \frac{1}{41.23}\phi(1.649) - 1 + \Omega_1$$
where
$$|\Omega_1| < \frac{0.20}{1700} = .00012$$

Since $Q_{\delta_1} = 0.90334 + \Omega_1$, it is evident that the probability of the desired result is at least 0.90 when $s = 6800$.

12. A coin is tossed s times. It is desired that the relative frequency of the appearance of heads shall **not** be greater than $.502$ or less than $.498$. Find the smallest value of s that will insure the foregoing results with a degree of certainty $Q_\delta = \frac{15}{16}$.

13. (*Camp*) A census report showed that in general 59.58% of New York City children went to school, but that only 56.8% of the Negro children went to school. The number of Negro children was $20,000$. Was the difference due to chance?

14. A tosses a coin, agreeing to pay B a dollar if it falls "head," and B agrees to pay A a dollar if it falls "tail." They continue this game for 1000 tosses, keeping score, but not settling up until the end of the series. If A has m dollars and B n dollars, calculate the probability that the loser can pay what he owes.

Show that this probability is approximately equal to $\Phi(m/\sqrt{1000}) + \Phi(n/\sqrt{1000}) - 1$, and calculate it for $m = 20$, $n = 30$. *Ans.* 0.565.

15. Within what limits will the number of heads lie, with 95% probability, in 1000 tosses of a coin which is practically unbiased?

Assume that "practically unbiased" means that the true probability of "head" with this coin does not differ from 0.5 by more than 0.001. *Ans.* 470 to 530.

Hint. Take $p = 0.499$, calculate δ from the relation $Q_\delta = 0.95$, and hence find $\epsilon = \delta\sqrt{pq/1000}$. Limits of x are then given by $|x/1000 - 0.499| \leq \epsilon$. Slightly different limits are given if $p = 0.501$. Take limits including both sets and verify that Q_{δ_1} is actually ≥ 0.95.

16. A company uses many thousands of electric lamps annually, burning continuously day and night. Assume that under such conditions the life of a lamp may be regarded as a variable normally distributed about a mean of 50 days with a standard deviation of 19 days.

On January 1, 1951, the company put 5000 new lamps into service. How many would you expect to need replacement by (a) February 1, (b) April 1? The lamps may be supposed all put into operation at about the same time of day. *Ans.* (a) 794, (b) 4912.

17. A pair of dice are thrown 3000 times and the two numbers that turn up are different from each other in 2726 of the throws. Does this result suggest a doubt as to the accuracy of the dice?

18. (*Bertrand*) The proprietor of a gambling establishment complains to the makers of a roulette wheel which he has installed that the wheel seems to favor red. In 1000 trials of which he has kept a record, red has shown up 515 times, black 455 times and white 30 times, the theoretical proportions being 18:18:1. The makers reply that the wheel was carefully constructed, and that nothing can be done about the laws of chance. What would be your opinion?

19. Prove that the mode of the Poisson distribution is the integer lying between $m - 1$ and m, unless m happens to be an integer, in which case the values for $m - 1$ and m are equal.

20. "If we spin a halfpenny nothing within our knowledge may be able to decide whether it will come down head or tail, yet if we throw up a million tons of halfpennies we know that there will be 500,000 tons of heads and 500,000 tons of tails." (Sir James Jeans.)

Comment on this statement. Assuming that 160,000 halfpennies go to a ton, what can we really say about the result of this experiment?

21. Show that the tangents to the curve $y = \phi(t)$ at its inflection points intersect the t-axis at $t = \pm 2$.

22. If x has the frequency function

$$f(x) = (2\pi a)^{-1/2} e^{-(x-m)^2/2a}, \quad -\infty < x < \infty$$

show by integration that the mean is m and the variance a.

23. A continuous variate x has the frequency function

$$f(x) = Cx^{1/2}(1 - x)^{3/2}, \quad 0 \leq x \leq 1$$

(a) Show that this function vanishes with infinite slope at $x = 0$, vanishes with zero slope at $x = 1$ and has a single maximum at $x = \frac{1}{4}$. Sketch the curve.

(b) Determine the constant C so that the area under the curve is unity.

(c) Show that $\nu_1 = 3/8$, $\mu_2 = 3/64$, $\gamma_1 = 2\sqrt{3}/9$, $\gamma_2 = -2/3$. *Ans.* $C = 16/\pi$.

24. In a fairy story, the fairy godmother assures the queen that her baby prince will not die until the following condition has been fulfilled. A scroll is prepared, and on the day of birth and every subsequent birthday a letter of the Greek alphabet, chosen at random, is entered on the scroll. On the day that all the letters of the alphabet appear, he will die. What is his expectation of life? There are 24 letters in the Greek alphabet. *Ans.* 89.6 years.

Hint. Suppose that at any stage there are n letters remaining to be picked. The chance that the next letter picked will belong to this group is $n/24$. The chance that it does not, but the following letter does, is $(1 - n/24)n/24$, and so on. Hence show that the expected number of trials before *one* of the group is picked is $24/n$.

Therefore the total expectation is $24(\frac{1}{1} + \frac{1}{2} + \cdots + \frac{1}{24})$.

References

1. J. Shohat, "Stieltjes Integrals in Mathematical Statistics," *Ann. Math. Stat.*, **1**, 1930, p. 73.

2. I. Kaplansky (*J. Amer. Stat. Assoc.*, **40**, 1945, p. 259) has shown by means of examples that kurtosis has not necessarily anything whatever to do with "peakedness." A distribution with a perfectly flat top may have infinite kurtosis, and one with infinite peakedness (in the sense that $f(x) \to \infty$ as $|x| \to 0$) may have a negative excess. Nevertheless, for many distributions encountered in practice, a positive γ_2 does mean a sharper peak with higher tails, than if the distribution were normal.

3. A. T. Craig, *Bull. Amer. Math. Soc.*, **40**, 1934, p. 262.

4. W. Feller, "Note on the Law of Large Numbers and 'Fair' Games," *Ann. Math. Stat.*, **16**, 1945, p. 301.

5. J. V. Uspensky, *Introduction to Mathematical Probability*, 1937, Chapter VII.

6. See an account, with references, in J. M. Keynes, *A Treatise on Probability*, p. 362.

7. E. C. Molina, *Poisson's Exponential Binomial Limit*, 1942.

CHAPTER III

SOME USEFUL INTEGRALS AND FUNCTIONS

To avoid interruption later on we discuss here certain integrals and functions which will be useful in subsequent chapters.

3.1 Some Properties of Definite Integrals. You will recall from elementary calculus that a definite integral is a number defined by a limiting process. This number is designated by

$$\int_a^b f(x)\, dx = F(b) - F(a)$$

where $f(x)$ is a function of the real variable x continuous in the closed interval (a, b), and $F(x)$ is such that $F'(x) = f(x)$ at all points of (a, b).

A function $f(x)$ is said to be *even* if $f(-x) \equiv f(x)$ and *odd* if $f(-x) \equiv -f(x)$. The following properties of definite integrals are frequently useful:

(a) $$\int_a^b f(x)\, dx = \int_a^c f(x)\, dx + \int_c^b f(x)\, dx$$

regardless of the relative positions of a, b, c on the real number scale.

(b) $\int_{-a}^{a} f(x)\, dx = 2\int_0^a f(x)\, dx$, if $f(x)$ is even, and $= 0$ if $f(x)$ is odd

(c) $$\int_0^a f(x)\, dx = \int_0^a f(a - x)\, dx$$

Example.
$$\int_0^{\pi/2} \sin^m \theta\, d\theta = \int_0^{\pi/2} \sin^m \left(\frac{\pi}{2} - \theta\right) d\theta = \int_0^{\pi/2} \cos^m \theta\, d\theta$$

(d) If $f(x)$ can be expanded in a *power series* which converges for all values of x in the interval of integration, the series may be integrated term by term. It is thus often possible to exhibit a definite integral as a convergent series.

(e) If either the upper or lower bound of integration is infinite the integral is said to be *improper*. The value is defined by a limiting process:

$$\int_a^\infty f(x)\, dx = \lim_{b \to \infty} \int_a^b f(x)\, dx$$

and

$$\int_{-\infty}^b f(x)\, dx = \lim_{a \to \infty} \int_{-a}^b f(x)\, dx$$

If the limit exists, the improper integral is said to *converge;* if the limit does not exist, the integral is said to *diverge* and no value is attached to it.

(f) $\int_{-\infty}^{\infty} f(x)\, dx$ is defined as $\int_{-\infty}^{c} f(x)\, dx + \int_{c}^{\infty} f(x)\, dx$ for any finite value of c. Property (b) holds when a is infinite.

(g) Differentiation under the integral sign. Given

$$H(\theta) = \int_a^b f(x, \theta)\, dx$$

where θ is a parameter and a and b are differentiable functions of θ, and where $\partial f(x, \theta)/\partial \theta$ exists and is less in absolute value than some integrable function of x for all admissible θ and for all x in the interval (a, b), then

$$\frac{dH}{d\theta} = \int_a^b \frac{\partial f}{\partial \theta}\, dx + f(b, \theta)\frac{db}{d\theta} - f(a, \theta)\frac{da}{d\theta}$$

When a and b are independent of θ, this reduces to

$$\frac{dH}{d\theta} = \int_a^b \frac{\partial f}{\partial \theta}\, dx$$

3.2 The Gamma Function. The improper integral

(3.1) $$\Gamma(n) = \int_0^\infty x^{n-1} e^{-x}\, dx$$

which converges for $n > 0$, is called the Gamma function of the positive number n. The difference equation

(3.2) $$\Gamma(n+1) = n\Gamma(n)$$

is easily established from (3.1) by integration by parts (see the chapter on the Gamma function in any textbook on advanced calculus). By successive reduction of (3.2) we obtain

$$\Gamma(n+1) = n(n-1) \cdots (n-k)\Gamma(n-k)$$

where k is a positive integer less than n. If n is also a positive integer and $k = n - 1$, then we have

(3.3) $$\Gamma(n+1) = n!$$

since from (3.1), $\Gamma(1) = 1$. Because of (3.3) the Gamma function is sometimes called the factorial function. It may be considered as a generalization of $n!$ when n is fractional. In fact, we can define $n!$ for any value of $n > -1$ by the equation,

(3.4) $$n! = \int_0^\infty x^n e^{-x}\, dx$$

and the use of a separate symbol for the Gamma function is really unnecessary.

Sec. 2 The Gamma Function

However, the symbol is so widely used in books and tables that the student should be familiar with it. The graph of the function is shown in Figure 9. It can be drawn from the following values, some of which follow immediately from (3.2); the others will be established later.

$$\Gamma(0) = \infty \qquad \Gamma(2) = 1$$
$$\Gamma(1) = 1 \qquad \Gamma(3) = 2$$
$$\Gamma(\tfrac{1}{2}) = (\pi)^{1/2} \qquad \Gamma(4) = 6$$

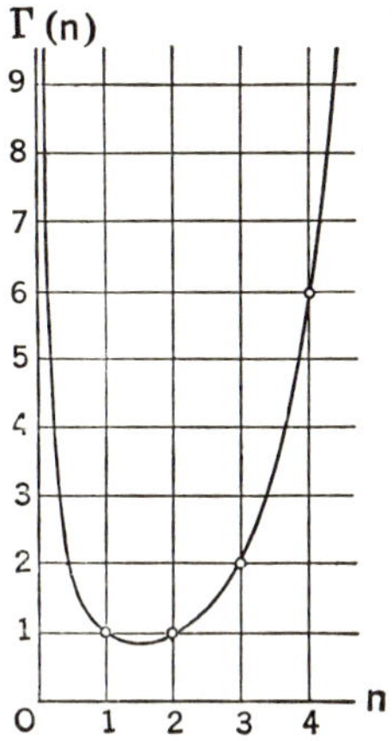

Other forms of (3.1) may be obtained by changes of variable. For example,

(3.5) $\quad \Gamma(n) = 2\int_0^\infty y^{2n-1} e^{-y^2}\, dy, \quad$ by $x = y^2$

Now we can show that

(3.6) $\quad \int_0^\infty e^{-y^2}\, dy = \tfrac{1}{2}(\pi)^{1/2}$

Fig. 9

To establish (3.6) we first observe from (3.5) that

(3.7) $\quad \Gamma(\tfrac{1}{2}) = 2\int_0^\infty e^{-y^2}\, dy$

Since (3.7) is independent of the variable of integration, we may also write

$$\Gamma(\tfrac{1}{2}) = 2\int_0^\infty e^{-x^2}\, dx$$

So

(3.8) $\quad \begin{aligned}[t] [\Gamma(\tfrac{1}{2})]^2 &= 4\int_0^\infty e^{-x^2}\, dx \int_0^\infty e^{-y^2}\, dy \\ &= 4\int_0^\infty \int_0^\infty e^{-(x^2+y^2)}\, dx\, dy \end{aligned}$

the passage from the product of two integrals to the double integral being valid since neither the limits nor the integrand of either integral depend on the variable in the other.

To evaluate (3.8) it will be convenient to change to polar coördinates. First, however, we will make a few remarks about a change of variables in general. Let x and y be the coördinates of a point with respect to a set of rectangular axes in a plane, u and v the coördinates of another point with respect to a similarly chosen set of rectangular axes in some other plane. Suppose we have a function of the variables x and y,

$$z = f(x, y)$$

and we make x and y depend on new variables u and v by the relations

$$x = g(u, v) \qquad \text{and} \qquad y = h(u, v)$$

These relations establish a certain correspondence between the points of the two planes. Let dA be an element of area for the function $f(x, y)$. Then it is shown in advanced calculus * that

$$dA = \left| J\left(\frac{x, y}{u, v}\right) \right| du\, dv$$

where $\left| J\left(\frac{x, y}{u, v}\right) \right|$ is a convenient symbol for the absolute value of the determinant

$$\begin{vmatrix} \frac{\partial x}{\partial u} & \frac{\partial x}{\partial v} \\ \frac{\partial y}{\partial u} & \frac{\partial y}{\partial v} \end{vmatrix} = \frac{\partial x}{\partial u}\frac{\partial y}{\partial v} - \frac{\partial x}{\partial v}\frac{\partial y}{\partial u}$$

and the latter is called the *Jacobian* or *functional determinant* of the transformation.

If, then, we change (3.8) to polar coördinates by letting

(3.9) $$\begin{cases} x = r\cos\theta \\ y = r\sin\theta \end{cases}$$

the Jacobian is

$$\begin{vmatrix} \cos\theta & -r\sin\theta \\ \sin\theta & r\cos\theta \end{vmatrix} = r$$

Therefore, the element of integration $dx\, dy$ becomes $r\, dr\, d\theta$. The limits of integration are now from 0 to ∞ for r and from 0 to $\pi/2$ for θ. From (3.9), $x^2 + y^2 = r^2$. So (3.8) becomes

$$[\Gamma(\tfrac{1}{2})]^2 = 4\int_0^{\pi/2}\int_0^{\infty} e^{-r^2} r\, dr\, d\theta$$
$$= 2\int_0^{\pi/2} d\theta = \pi$$

Hence,

(3.10) $$\Gamma(\tfrac{1}{2}) = (\pi)^{1/2}$$

For a more general form of (3.6) we may let $y = t/(2k)^{1/2}$, $k > 0$, and obtain

(3.11) $$\int_0^{\infty} e^{-t^2/2k}\, dt = \tfrac{1}{2}(2\pi k)^{1/2}$$

and

(3.12) $$\int_{-\infty}^{\infty} e^{-t^2/2k}\, dt = (2\pi k)^{1/2}$$

---

* See *Mathematical Analysis*, Goursat-Hedrick, vol. 1.

Sec. 3   Stirling's Approximation

An alternate derivation of (3.10) may be given as follows. The right-hand member of (3.8) represents the volume V under the bell-shaped surface

(3.13) $\quad\quad z = e^{-(x^2+y^2)}$

and so from (3.8) we have $\Gamma(\frac{1}{2}) = V^{1/2}$. Since (3.13) is a surface of revolution we may take as the element of volume a cylindrical shell of radius r, thickness dr, and height z. Then

$$dV = 2\pi r \, dr \, z = 2\pi r e^{-r^2} \, dr$$

$$V = 2\pi \int_0^\infty e^{-r^2} r \, dr = \pi$$

and consequently we obtain (3.10).

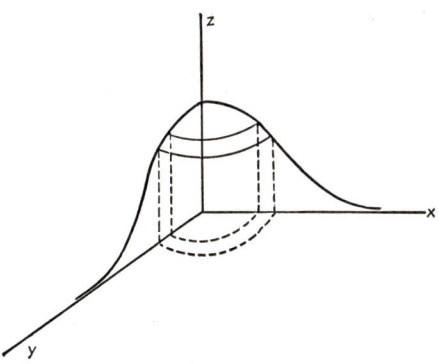

Fig. 10

3.3 Stirling's Approximation.

Tables of $\log n!$, to seven places, are available in Glover's Tables up to $n = 1000$. However, it is often convenient to replace $n!$ in a formula by an expression more amenable to algebraic treatment. The most widely used expression is Stirling's:

(3.14) $\quad\quad n! \approx (2\pi)^{1/2} n^{n+1/2} e^{-n}$

Actually this is only the first term in an *asymptotic series* [1]

(3.15) $\quad\quad n! = (2\pi)^{1/2} n^{n+1/2} e^{-n} \left[1 + \dfrac{1}{12n} + \dfrac{1}{288n^2} + \cdots \right]$

or equivalently, taking the logarithm and using the series for $\log(1+x) = x - x^2/2 + x^3/3 - \cdots$,

(3.16) $\quad \log n! = \frac{1}{2} \log 2\pi + (n + \frac{1}{2}) \log n - n + \dfrac{1}{12n} - \dfrac{1}{360n^3} + \cdots$

The expression on the right starting at $1/12n$ is not a convergent series, but the early terms decrease rapidly for values of n larger than, say, 5, and the error made by stopping at any term is less than the magnitude of the next following term.

We will establish the formula in the following form, which is quite sufficient in practice.

(3.17) $\quad\quad \log n! = \frac{1}{2} \log 2\pi + (n + \frac{1}{2}) \log n - n + \omega_n$

where $0 < \omega_n < 1/12n$.

$$\log n! = \log 1 + \log 2 + \log 3 + \cdots + \log n$$
$$= \sum_{k=2}^{n} \log k$$
$$= \text{sum of shaded rectangles in Figure 11}$$

Each rectangle is made up of the area under the curve $y = \log x$, plus a triangular piece RST, minus the area $RVTU$ between the included portion of the curve and its chord.

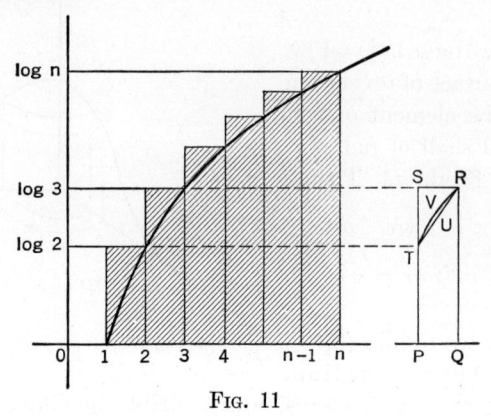

Fig. 11

Thus for the rectangle between $k - 1$ and k,

$$\text{the area} = \int_{k-1}^{k} \log x \, dx + \tfrac{1}{2}[\log k - \log (k - 1)] - \epsilon_k$$

where

$$\epsilon_k = \int_{k-1}^{k} \log x \, dx - \tfrac{1}{2}[\log k + \log (k - 1)]$$
$$= (k - \tfrac{1}{2})[\log k - \log (k - 1)] - 1$$

since $\int \log x \, dx = x \log x - x$. Hence, adding up for all the rectangles,

$$\log n! = \int_{1}^{n} \log x \, dx + \tfrac{1}{2}[\log n - \log (n - 1) + \log (n - 1)$$
$$- \log (n - 2) + \cdots + \log 2 - \log 1] - \sum_{k=2}^{n} \epsilon_k$$
$$= n \log n - n + 1 + \tfrac{1}{2} \log n - \sum_{k=2}^{n} \epsilon_k$$

We can now prove that $\sum_{k=2}^{\infty} \epsilon_k$ converges to a finite quantity α. For

$$\epsilon_k = \left(k - \frac{1}{2}\right) \log \frac{k}{k-1} - 1$$
$$= \left(k - \frac{1}{2}\right) \log \frac{1 + \dfrac{1}{2k-1}}{1 - \dfrac{1}{2k-1}} - 1$$
$$= \left(k - \frac{1}{2}\right) 2 \left[\frac{1}{2k-1} + \frac{1}{3(2k-1)^3} + \cdots\right] - 1$$

on expanding the logarithms of numerator and denominator. Therefore

$$\epsilon_k = \frac{1}{3(2k-1)^2} + \frac{1}{5(2k-1)^4} + \cdots$$

so that

$$0 < \epsilon_k < \frac{1}{3(2k-1)^2}\left[1 + \frac{1}{(2k-1)^2} + \frac{1}{(2k-1)^4} + \cdots\right] = \frac{1}{12k(k-1)}$$

But

$$\sum_{k=2}^{\infty} \frac{1}{k(k-1)} = \sum_{2}^{\infty}\left[\frac{1}{k-1} - \frac{1}{k}\right] = 1$$

so that $\sum_{2}^{\infty} \epsilon_k < \frac{1}{12}$ and so is finite ($= \alpha$). Therefore

$$\sum_{2}^{n} \epsilon_k = \alpha - \sum_{n+1}^{\infty} \epsilon_k = \alpha - \omega_n$$

where

$$0 < \omega_n < \sum_{n+1}^{\infty} \frac{1}{12k(k-1)} = \frac{1}{12n}$$

Hence

$$\log n! = (n + \tfrac{1}{2}) \log n - n + 1 - \alpha + \omega_n$$
$$= \log c + (n + \tfrac{1}{2}) \log n - n + \omega_n$$

where $\log c = 1 - \alpha$, so that

(3.18) $$n! = cn^{n+1/2}e^{-n}e^{\omega_n}$$

It remains to evaluate the constant c.

By making use of *Wallis's formula* (see Example 4 of § 3.5),

(3.19) $$\frac{\pi}{2} = \lim_{n\to\infty} \frac{1}{2n+1}\left[\frac{2\cdot 4\cdot 6\cdots 2n}{1\cdot 3\cdot 5\cdots(2n-1)}\right]^2$$
$$= \lim_{n\to\infty} \frac{2^{4n}(n!)^4}{[(2n)!]^2(2n+1)}$$

and substituting for the factorials from (3.18) we obtain

$$\frac{\pi}{2} = \lim_{n\to\infty} \frac{2^{4n}c^4 n^{4n+2} e^{-4n} e^{4\omega_n}}{c^2(2n)^{4n+1} e^{-4n} e^{2\omega_{2n}}(2n+1)}$$
$$= \lim_{n\to\infty} \frac{c^2 n}{2(2n+1)} = \frac{c^2}{4}$$

Therefore $c = \sqrt{2\pi}$.

3.4 The Beta Function. The definite integral

(3.20) $$B(m, n) = \int_0^1 x^{m-1}(1-x)^{n-1}\, dx$$

is called the Beta function of any two positive numbers m and n. Another useful form is

(3.21) $$B(m, n) = 2 \int_0^{\pi/2} \sin^{2m-1} \theta \cos^{2n-1} \theta \, d\theta$$

which is obtained by letting $x = \sin^2 \theta$ in (3.20).

If we let $x = 1 - y$, (3.20) becomes

$$B(m, n) = \int_0^1 (1 - y)^{m-1} y^{n-1} \, dy$$
$$= \int_0^1 (1 - x)^{m-1} x^{n-1} \, dx$$
$$= B(n, m) \quad \text{Follows at once from 3.1c}$$

Therefore, m and n may be interchanged.

If we let $x = (1 + y)^{-1}$, (3.20) becomes

(3.22) $$B(m, n) = \int_0^\infty \frac{y^{n-1} \, dy}{(1 + y)^{m+n}}$$

and here also, m and n may be interchanged.

A relation between the Beta and Gamma functions may be obtained as follows. From (3.5) we may write

$$\Gamma(n)\Gamma(m) = 4 \int_0^\infty x^{2n-1} e^{-x^2} \, dx \int_0^\infty y^{2m-1} e^{-y^2} \, dy$$
$$= 4 \int_0^\infty \int_0^\infty x^{2n-1} y^{2m-1} e^{-(x^2+y^2)} \, dx \, dy$$

Since the region of integration is the first quadrant of the xy-plane, we have, upon changing to polar coördinates,

$$\Gamma(n)\Gamma(m) = 4 \int_0^{\pi/2} \int_0^\infty r^{2(m+n-1)} e^{-r^2} \sin^{2m-1} \theta \cos^{2n-1} \theta \, r \, d\theta \, dr$$
$$= 4 \int_0^{\pi/2} \sin^{2m-1} \theta \cos^{2n-1} \theta \, d\theta \int_0^\infty r^{2(m+n)-1} e^{-r^2} \, dr$$
$$= B(m, n)\Gamma(m + n)$$

by (3.21) and (3.5). Hence

(3.23) $$B(m, n) = \frac{\Gamma(m)\Gamma(n)}{\Gamma(m + n)} = \frac{(m - 1)!\,(n - 1)!}{(m + n - 1)!}$$
$$= (m + n - 1)^{-1} \binom{m + n - 2}{m - 1}^{-1}$$

3.5 Reduction to Gamma and Beta Functions. By appropriate changes of variables many of the integrals that occur in statistics may be evaluated by expressing them in terms of Gamma and Beta functions.

Example 1. Prove that

$$\int_0^\infty y^{N-1} e^{-Ny^2/2\sigma^2} \, dy = \frac{1}{2} \left(\frac{2\sigma^2}{N} \right)^{N/2} \Gamma\left(\frac{N}{2} \right)$$

Sec. 5   Reduction to Gamma and Beta Functions

Solution. This integral may be written

$$\frac{1}{2}\int_0^\infty (y^2)^{(N-2)/2} e^{-Ny^2/2\sigma^2}\, d(y^2)$$

By the substitution

$$x = \frac{Ny^2}{2\sigma^2}, \qquad d(y^2) = \frac{2\sigma^2}{N}\, dx$$

this becomes

$$\frac{1}{2}\left(\frac{2\sigma^2}{N}\right)^{N/2}\int_0^\infty x^{(N-2)/2} e^{-x}\, dx = \frac{1}{2}\left(\frac{2\sigma^2}{N}\right)^{N/2}\Gamma\!\left(\frac{N}{2}\right)$$

Example 2. Determine k so that

$$k\int_0^\infty e^{-Ns^2/2\sigma^2}(s^2)^{(N-3)/2}\, d(s^2) = 1$$

Solution. By the substitution

$$x = \frac{Ns^2}{2\sigma^2}, \qquad d(s^2) = \frac{2\sigma^2}{N}\, dx$$

this becomes

$$k\left(\frac{2\sigma^2}{N}\right)^{(N-1)/2}\int_0^\infty x^{(N-3)/2} e^{-x}\, dx = 1$$

and so

$$k = \frac{\left(\dfrac{N}{2\sigma^2}\right)^{(N-1)/2}}{\Gamma\!\left(\dfrac{N-1}{2}\right)}$$

Example 3. Determine K so that $K\displaystyle\int_{-\infty}^{\infty}(1+z^2)^{-N/2}\, dz = 1$.

Solution. By the substitution $z = \tan\theta$ this becomes $2K\displaystyle\int_0^{\pi/2}\cos^m\theta\, d\theta$ where $m = N - 2$. From Problem 9 below we find that

$$\frac{1}{K} = \mathrm{B}\!\left(\frac{m+1}{2}, \frac{1}{2}\right) = \frac{\Gamma\!\left(\dfrac{m+1}{2}\right)\Gamma\!\left(\dfrac{1}{2}\right)}{\Gamma\!\left(\dfrac{m+2}{2}\right)}$$

whence

$$K = \frac{\Gamma\!\left(\dfrac{N}{2}\right)}{(\pi)^{1/2}\Gamma\!\left(\dfrac{N-1}{2}\right)}$$

Example 4. Prove *Wallis's formula*, equation (3.19).

Solution. From Problem 9 below, $\displaystyle\int_0^{\pi/2}\sin^m\theta\, d\theta = \tfrac{1}{2}\mathrm{B}[\tfrac{1}{2}(m+1), \tfrac{1}{2}]$. Since, in the interval 0 to $\pi/2$, $0 \leq \sin\theta \leq 1$, we have

$$\int_0^{\pi/2}\sin^{2m-1}\theta\, d\theta > \int_0^{\pi/2}\sin^{2m}\theta\, d\theta > \int_0^{\pi/2}\sin^{2m+1}\theta\, d\theta$$

or $\mathrm{B}(m, \tfrac{1}{2}) > \mathrm{B}(m + \tfrac{1}{2}, \tfrac{1}{2}) > \mathrm{B}(m+1, \tfrac{1}{2})$. Hence, by (3.23),

$$\frac{\Gamma(m)}{\Gamma(m+\tfrac{1}{2})} > \frac{\Gamma(m+\tfrac{1}{2})}{\Gamma(m+1)} > \frac{\Gamma(m+1)}{\Gamma(m+\tfrac{3}{2})} = \frac{m}{m+\tfrac{1}{2}}\frac{\Gamma(m)}{\Gamma(m+\tfrac{1}{2})}$$

The ratio of the two extreme members of this inequality is $m/(m + \tfrac{1}{2})$ and so $\to 1$ as $m \to \infty$. Therefore the ratio of the second to the third also $\to 1$ as $m \to \infty$. So

$$\lim_{m \to \infty} (m + \tfrac{1}{2}) \left[\frac{\Gamma(m + \tfrac{1}{2})}{\Gamma(m + 1)} \right]^2 = 1$$

Now if m is a positive integer,

$$\frac{\Gamma(m + \tfrac{1}{2})}{\Gamma(m + 1)} = \frac{1}{m!} \left(m - \frac{1}{2} \right) \left(m - \frac{3}{2} \right) \cdots \frac{1}{2} \Gamma \left(\frac{1}{2} \right)$$

$$= \frac{1}{m!} \frac{(2m - 1)(2m - 3) \cdots 1}{2^m} \sqrt{\pi}$$

$$= \frac{1}{m!} \frac{2m(2m - 1)(2m - 2) \cdots 1}{2^{2m} m!} \sqrt{\pi}$$

$$= \frac{(2m)! \sqrt{\pi}}{2^{2m} (m!)^2}$$

Therefore

$$\lim_{m \to \infty} \frac{(m + \tfrac{1}{2})[(2m)!]^2 \pi}{2^{4m} (m!)^4} = 1$$

which is equivalent to (3.19).

3.6 Incomplete Beta and Gamma Functions. The integral

(3.24) $$\Gamma_x(n) = \int_0^x e^{-x} x^{n-1} \, dx$$

is called the *incomplete Gamma function*. Similarly

(3.25) $$B_x(m, n) = \int_0^x x^{m-1} (1 - x)^{n-1} \, dx$$

is called the *incomplete Beta function*. Both (3.24) and (3.25) are useful functions in mathematical statistics and they have been tabulated [2] by Karl Pearson and his staff at the Biometric Laboratory, University College, London.

Obviously $\Gamma_\infty(n) = \Gamma(n)$, and $B_\infty(m, n) = B(m, n)$, so that the ordinary Gamma and Beta Functions are often called *complete*.

Note that Pearson's tables give the *ratios*

$$I(u, n) = \frac{\Gamma_x(n + 1)}{\Gamma(n + 1)}, \quad \text{where } x = u\sqrt{n + 1}$$

and

$$I_x(m, n) = \frac{B_x(m, n)}{B(m, n)}$$

which are usually more useful than the incomplete functions themselves.

Problems

1. Show that $\dfrac{\Gamma(n + 1)}{\Gamma(r + 1)\Gamma(n - r + 1)} = \dbinom{n}{r}$.

2. Prove that $\displaystyle\int_{-\infty}^{\infty} \phi(t) \, dt = 1$, where $\phi(t) = (2\pi)^{-1/2} e^{-t^2/2}$.

3. If $f(n) = n^{1/2} B(n/2, \tfrac{1}{2})$, prove that $\displaystyle\lim_{n \to \infty} f(n) = (2\pi)^{1/2}$.

Problems

4. Evaluate $\int_{-2}^{\infty} e^{-3x}(1+x/2)^7 \, dx$ by transforming it into a Gamma function.
Hint. Let $cy = 1 + x/2$ and determine c so that $e^{-3x} = ke^{-y}$.
Ans. $(e^6 7!)/3(6^7)$.

5. Evaluate $\int_6^{\infty} e^{-2x}(x-6)^7 \, dx$. *Ans.* $e^{-12} 2^{-8} 7!$.

6. Evaluate $\int_0^{\infty} e^{-x} x^{1/2} \, dx$, given that $\int_0^{\infty} e^{-x} x^{-1/2} \, dx = (\pi)^{1/2}$.
Hint. $\Gamma(\tfrac{3}{2}) = \tfrac{1}{2}\Gamma(\tfrac{1}{2})$.

7. Find the difference and the ratio between the exact value of 10! and the approximate value obtained by using Stirling's formula.

8. Using (3.23), show that

$$\frac{\Gamma\left(\dfrac{N}{2}\right)}{(\pi)^{1/2} \Gamma\left(\dfrac{N-1}{2}\right)} = \frac{1}{B[\tfrac{1}{2}(N-1), \tfrac{1}{2}]}$$

9. Prove that $\int_0^{\pi/2} \cos^m \theta \, d\theta = \int_0^{\pi/2} \sin^m \theta \, d\theta = \tfrac{1}{2} B[(m+1)/2, \tfrac{1}{2}]$. *Hint.* Use (3.21).

10. Show that $K \int_{-\infty}^{\infty} (1+z^2)^{-N/2} z^2 \, dz = 1/(N-3)$, where $1/K = B[(N-1)/2, \tfrac{1}{2}]$.

11. Show that $K \int_{-\infty}^{\infty} (1+t^2/n)^{-(n+1)/2} t^2 \, dt = n/(n-2)$, where $1/K = n^{1/2} B(n/2, \tfrac{1}{2})$.

12. If $p(s, x) = \binom{s}{x} p^x q^{s-x}$, prove by means of Stirling's approximation that the maximum value of $p(s, x)$ for any x tends, as $s \to \infty$, to $1/\sqrt{2\pi spq}$. *Hint.* The maximum is given for $sp - q \leq x \leq sp + p$. See Problem 12 following §2.8.

13. Prove by using Stirling's approximation that the probability of exactly x successes in s trials, of an event with the constant probability $\tfrac{1}{2}$ of success in a single trial, is $(2/\pi s)^{1/2} e^{-2(x-s/2)^2/s}$, to terms of order $1/s$.

14. Prove that if $f(m, x)$ is the Poisson exponential function $e^{-m} m^x/x!$, and if $Q_n(m) = \sum_{x=n}^{\infty} f(m, x)$, then

$$Q_n(m) = \frac{\Gamma_m(n)}{\Gamma(n)} = I\left(\frac{m}{\sqrt{n}}, n-1\right)$$

Hint. Writing Taylor's theorem in the form

$$f(a+h) = f(a) + hf'(a) + \cdots + \frac{h^{n-1}}{(n-1)!} f^{n-1}(a) + \frac{h^n}{(n-1)!} \int_0^1 f^{(n)}(a+th)(1-t)^{n-1} \, dt$$

put $f(x) = e^x$, $a = 0$, $h = m$. Hence show that

$$1 = \sum_{x=0}^{n-1} e^{-m} \frac{m^x}{x!} + \frac{1}{(n-1)!} \int_0^m e^{-u} u^{n-1} \, du$$

15. Using equation (3.22), show that

$$B(m, n) = \int_0^1 \frac{x^{m-1} + x^{n-1}}{(1+x)^{m+n}} \, dx$$

Hint. Divide the range of integration in (3.22) into two parts, 0 to 1 and 1 to ∞, and in the second part put $y = 1/x$.

16. Obtain an asymptotic series for the computation of the integral $\int_0^x e^{-y^2} \, dy$, for large values of x. (See next page.)

Hint.

$$\int_0^x e^{-y^2}\,dy = \int_0^\infty e^{-y^2}\,dy - \int_x^\infty e^{-y^2}\,dy$$
$$= \tfrac{1}{2}\sqrt{\pi} - \int_x^\infty e^{-y^2}\,dy$$

Write the last integral as $\int_x^\infty (1/y)(ye^{-y^2})\,dy$ and integrate by parts repeatedly. The result is

$$\int_0^x e^{-y^2}\,dy = \tfrac{1}{2}\sqrt{\pi} - \frac{e^{-x^2}}{2x}\left[1 - \frac{1}{2x^2} + \frac{3}{4x^4} - \frac{15}{8x^6} + \cdots + (-1)^n T_{n+1} + R_{n+1}\right]$$

where

$$T_{n+1} = \frac{1\cdot 3\cdot 5 \cdots (2n-1)}{2^n x^{2n}}, \qquad R_{n+1} = (-1)^{n+1}\frac{1\cdot 3\cdots (2n+1)}{2^{n+1}}\int_x^\infty \frac{e^{-y^2}\,dy}{y^{2n+2}}$$

T_{n+1} decreases as n increases, as long as $n \leq x^2$. Show that

$$\frac{|R_{n+1}|}{T_{n+2}} < \int_x^\infty e^{-y^2}\,dy < \tfrac{1}{2}\sqrt{\pi} < 1$$

and hence that the error in stopping at any term of the asymptotic series is numerically less than the next following term.

17. Use the asymptotic series in Problem 16 to evaluate $\int_0^3 \phi(t)\,dt$, and check with Table I in the Appendix.

18. Use Stirling's approximation to verify the statement in § 2.16 (see equation 2.67) that

$$\lim_{n\to\infty} h_n(x,s) = \frac{s!}{x!(s-x)!}p^x q^{s-x}$$

References

1. See, *e.g.*, K. Knopp, *Theory and Application of Infinite Series*, Ch. XIV.
2. *Tables of the Incomplete Gamma Function*, edited by K. Pearson (London, 1922). *Tables of the Incomplete Beta Function*, edited by K. Pearson (London, 1934).

CHAPTER IV

DISTRIBUTIONS OF TWO OR MORE VARIABLES; MOMENT-GENERATING FUNCTIONS; THE LAW OF LARGE NUMBERS

4.1 Joint Distributions of Two Variables. Definitions of a frequency function of one variable and the associated notion of probability were given in § 2.3. Corresponding definitions will now be given for an arbitrary probability distribution of two variables. The continuous variables x and y have the joint frequency function $f(x, y)$ if the double integral of $f(x, y)$ over a region of the (x, y)-plane measures the frequency of occurrence of pairs of values (x, y) in that region. It will be understood that $f(x, y)$ is continuous, single-valued, and non-negative. If values of (x, y) are restricted to a finite region we define $f(x, y)$ to be identically zero outside that region. In the extended region of definition, we set

$$(4.1) \qquad \int_{-\infty}^{\infty} \int_{-\infty}^{\infty} f(x, y) \, dy \, dx = 1$$

Geometrically, this means that the volume under the surface represented by $z = f(x, y)$ is unity. Then $f(x, y) \, dy \, dx$ is the *probability* that simultaneously x lies in the interval $(x, x + dx)$ and y lies in the interval $(y, y + dy)$. Consequently,

$$(4.2) \qquad \int_{a}^{b} \int_{c}^{d} f(x, y) \, dy \, dx$$

represents the probability that x lies between a and b at the same time that y lies between c and d.

We shall distinguish between two cases: (*a*) when the variables are independent in the probability sense, and (*b*) when they are not. Let the probability be $g(x) \, dx$ that x occurs in dx for all y's. Then integrating over all admissible values of y, we have

$$(4.3) \qquad g(x) \, dx = dx \int_{-\infty}^{\infty} f(x, y) \, dy$$

It is clear that the integral in (4.3) gives $g(x)$ because the relative frequency of occurrence of x in any interval (a, b) is the relative frequency of pairs (x, y) belonging to the strip of the xy-plane for which $a < x < b$, and this is

$$\int_{a}^{b} \int_{-\infty}^{\infty} f(x, y) \, dy \, dx = \int_{a}^{b} g(x) \, dx$$

Similarly, if $h(y)\,dy$ is the probability that y occurs in dy for all assignments of x, we have

$$(4.4) \qquad h(y)\,dy = dy \int_{-\infty}^{\infty} f(x, y)\,dx$$

In accordance with convention we shall call $g(x)$ and $h(y)$ the *marginal* distributions.

The independence of x and y is characterized by the following

DEFINITION. *The variables x and y are independent when $f(x, y) \equiv g(x)h(y)$. If $f(x, y)$ cannot be expressed identically as the product of the marginal distributions, then x and y are not independent.*

4.2 Moments. Let the general product moment about the common origin of x and y be defined as follows:

$$(4.5) \qquad \nu_{mn} = \int_{-\infty}^{\infty} \int_{-\infty}^{\infty} f(x, y) x^m y^n \,dy\,dx$$

assuming that the integral exists.

If $m = 0$ and $n = 1$, we have

$$(4.6) \qquad \nu_{01} = \int_{-\infty}^{\infty} \int_{-\infty}^{\infty} f(x, y) y \,dy\,dx$$

Let $f(x, y)$ be a function in which the order of integration may be interchanged. Then ν_{01} becomes

$$\int_{-\infty}^{\infty} \left[\int_{-\infty}^{\infty} f(x, y)\,dx \right] y\,dy = \int_{-\infty}^{\infty} h(y) y\,dy$$

which is the expected value of y. Similarly, the expected value of x is

$$(4.7) \qquad \nu_{10} = \int_{-\infty}^{\infty} \int_{-\infty}^{\infty} f(x, y) x \,dy\,dx = \int_{-\infty}^{\infty} g(x) x\,dx$$

We will now define the general product moment about (ν_{10}, ν_{01}) as follows:

$$(4.8) \qquad \mu_{mn} = \int_{-\infty}^{\infty} \int_{-\infty}^{\infty} (x - \nu_{10})^m (y - \nu_{01})^n f(x, y)\,dy\,dx$$

When $m = n = 1$, we have

$$(4.9) \qquad \mu_{11} = \int_{-\infty}^{\infty} \int_{-\infty}^{\infty} (x - \nu_{10})(y - \nu_{01}) f(x, y)\,dy\,dx$$

which is called the *covariance* of x and y.

When $m = 2$ and $n = 0$, we have the *variance of x*,

$$(4.10) \qquad \mu_{20} = \int_{-\infty}^{\infty} \int_{-\infty}^{\infty} (x - \nu_{10})^2 f(x, y)\,dy\,dx$$

$$= \int_{-\infty}^{\infty} (x - \nu_{10})^2 g(x)\,dx$$

$$= \sigma_x^2$$

Sec. 3   Discrete Variables   69

Similarly, when $m = 0$ and $n = 2$, we have the *variance of y*,

$$\text{(4.11)} \quad \mu_{02} = \int_{-\infty}^{\infty} \int_{-\infty}^{\infty} (y - \nu_{01})^2 f(x, y) \, dy \, dx$$

$$= \int_{-\infty}^{\infty} (y - \nu_{01})^2 h(y) \, dy$$

$$= \sigma_y^2$$

It is left as an exercise for the student to show that

$$\text{(4.12)} \quad \begin{cases} \mu_{11} = \nu_{11} - \nu_{10}\nu_{01} \\ \mu_{20} = \nu_{20} - \nu_{10}^2 \end{cases}$$

The coefficient of correlation between x and y, denoted by ρ_{xy}, is defined by

$$\text{(4.13)} \quad \rho_{xy} = \frac{\mu_{11}}{\sigma_x \sigma_y}$$

Note that if $\rho_{xy} = 0$, x and y are said to be *uncorrelated*. If x and y are independent they are uncorrelated, but the converse is not true. It is possible for ρ_{xy} to be zero even though x and y are highly dependent on each other.

4.3 Discrete Variables. If the variables x and y are *discrete*, we define a *joint distribution function* $F(x, y)$ by

$$\text{(4.14)} \quad F(x, y) = \sum_{x_i} \sum_{y_j} f(x_i, y_j)$$

where the summation is over all values of $x_i \leq x$ and all $y_j \leq y$.

If x is discrete and y continuous,

$$\text{(4.15)} \quad F(x, y) = \sum_{x_i} \int_{-\infty}^{y} f(x_i, y) \, dy$$

and similarly if y is discrete and x continuous,

$$\text{(4.16)} \quad F(x, y) = \sum_{y_j} \int_{-\infty}^{x} f(x, y_j) \, dx$$

Finally, if x and y are both continuous,

$$\text{(4.17)} \quad F(x, y) = \int_{-\infty}^{x} \int_{-\infty}^{y} f(u, v) \, dv \, du$$

All these cases can be included in one formula by writing the joint function as a Stieltjes integral (§ 2.3)

$$\text{(4.18)} \quad F(x, y) = \int_{-\infty}^{x} \int_{-\infty}^{y} dF(u, v)$$

where

$$\text{(4.19)} \quad \int_{-\infty}^{\infty} \int_{-\infty}^{\infty} dF(u, v) = 1$$

Then

$$\nu_{mn} = \int_{-\infty}^{\infty}\int_{-\infty}^{\infty} x^m y^n \, dF(x,y) \tag{4.20}$$

$$\mu_{mn} = \int_{-\infty}^{\infty}\int_{-\infty}^{\infty} (x-\nu_{10})^m (y-\nu_{01})^n \, dF(x,y) \tag{4.21}$$

The variables x and y are independent if and only if $dF(x,y) \equiv dG(x)\,dH(y)$, for all values of x and y.

Example 1. If X and Y are independent variables with distribution functions $F(x)$ and $G(y)$ respectively, find the distribution function of the variable $W = X + Y$.

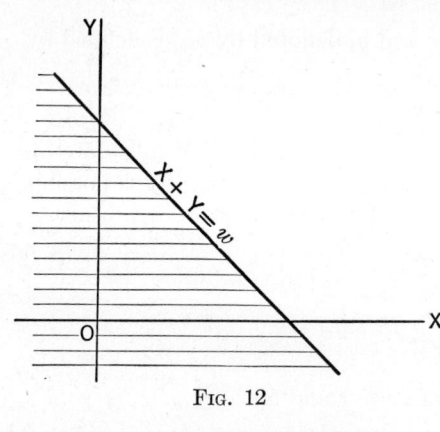

This distribution function, say $H(w)$, is defined as $H(w) = \Pr[W \leq w]$ = probability that a point in the XY-plane lies in the shaded region below the line $X + Y = w$. For any given y, the probability that $X \leq w - y$ is $F(w - y)$. Hence the required probability is

$$\int_{-\infty}^{\infty} F(w-y)\,dG(y)$$

If X and Y have continuous frequency functions $f(x)$ and $g(y)$ respectively, we find, by differentiating, that the frequency function of W is

$$h(w) = \int_{-\infty}^{\infty} f(w-y)g(y)\,dy \tag{4.22}$$

Fig. 12

This is known as the *law of convolution*.

4.4 Joint Distribution of More than Two Variables. The notation and definitions of § 4.3 may be extended to any finite number of variables, although, of course, there is no longer an intuitive geometrical picture. If $x_1, x_2, \cdots x_n$ are the variables, they are independent (see § 1.6) if and only if

$$dF(x_1, x_2, \cdots x_n) = dF_1(x_1)\,dF_2(x_2)\cdots dF_n(x_n) \tag{4.23}$$

If all the separate distributions possess frequency functions, and if there is a joint frequency function, this relation is

$$f(x_1, x_2, \cdots x_n) = f_1(x_1)f_2(x_2)\cdots f_n(x_n) \tag{4.24}$$

4.5 Some Theorems on Expectation. The expectation of $g(x)$ has been defined, equation (2.12), as

$$E\{g(x)\} = \int_{-\infty}^{\infty} g(x)\,dF(x)$$

The following theorems are readily established from this definition, remembering that

$$\int_{-\infty}^{\infty} dF(x) = 1 \tag{4.25}$$

Sec. 5 Some Theorems on Expectation

Theorem 4.1. *The expected value of the product of a variable and a constant is the product of the constant and the expected value of the variable,*

(4.26) $$E(cx) = cE(x)$$

Theorem 4.2. *The expected value of the deviation of a variable from its expected value is zero,*

(4.27) $$E(x - \nu_1) = 0$$

Theorem 4.3. *If x and y are variables with a joint distribution function $F(x, y)$, the expected value of $x + y$ is given by*

(4.28)
$$\begin{aligned}E(x + y) &= \int_{-\infty}^{\infty}\int_{-\infty}^{\infty} (x + y)\, dF(x, y) \\ &= \int_{-\infty}^{\infty}\int_{-\infty}^{\infty} x\, dF(x, y) + \int_{-\infty}^{\infty}\int_{-\infty}^{\infty} y\, dF(x, y) \\ &= E(x) + E(y)\end{aligned}$$

That is, the expected value of the sum of two variables is the sum of their expected values.

This is true whether the variables are independent or not. By an immediate extension, we have

Theorem 4.4. *The expected value of the sum of n variables is the sum of their expected values,*

(4.29) $$E(x_1 + x_2 + \cdots + x_n) = \sum_{i=1}^{n} E(x_i)$$

Theorem 4.5. *If x and y are two independent variables we have, by § 4.3,*

(4.30)
$$\begin{aligned}E(xy) &= \int_{-\infty}^{\infty}\int_{-\infty}^{\infty} xy\, dF(x, y) \\ &= \int_{-\infty}^{\infty}\int_{-\infty}^{\infty} xy\, dG(x)\, dH(y) \\ &= \int_{-\infty}^{\infty} x\, dG(x) \int_{-\infty}^{\infty} y\, dH(y) \\ &= E(x)E(y)\end{aligned}$$

That is, the expected value of the product of two independent variables is the product of their expected values.

This theorem can also be extended to n variables.

Theorem 4.6. *The expected value of the product of n variables is equal to the product of their separate expectations, provided the variables are independent,*[*]

$$E(x_1 x_2 \cdots x_n) = E(x_1) E(x_2) \cdots E(x_n)$$

[*] See § 1.6.

Theorem 4.7. *The expected value of the product of deviations of two independent variables from their respective expected values is zero,*

$$E(x - \nu_{10})(y - \nu_{01}) = 0$$

This is an immediate corollary from Theorem 4.5.

Theorem 4.8. *If x and y are any two variables, the expected value of the product of deviations from their respective expected values is equal to $\rho_{xy}\sigma_x\sigma_y$, that is,*

(4.31) $$E(x - \nu_{10})(y - \nu_{01}) = \rho_{xy}\sigma_x\sigma_y$$

For, by definition, $\mu_{11} = E(x - \nu_{10})(y - \nu_{01})$ and $\rho_{xy} = \mu_{11}/\sigma_x\sigma_y$.

Theorem 4.9. *The variance of the sum of a number of variables is equal to the sum of the variances, if the variables are pairwise uncorrelated.* Thus, if $y = x_1 + x_2 + \cdots + x_n$ where the variable x_i has the expected value $\nu_1^{(i)}$,

(4.32) $$\begin{aligned}\text{Var}(y) &= E[y - \nu_1^{(1)} - \nu_1^{(2)} - \cdots - \nu_1^{(n)}]^2 \\ &= E[\sum_i (x_i - \nu_1^{(i)})^2 + \sum_{i \neq j}\sum (x_i - \nu_1^{(i)})(x_j - \nu_1^{(j)})] \\ &= \sum_i \mu_2^{(i)}\end{aligned}$$

4.6 Moment-generating and Characteristic Functions.[1] If we put $g(x) = e^{hx}$ in (2.12) we define a function of h,

(4.33) $$M(h) = \int_{-\infty}^{\infty} e^{hx}\, dF(x)$$

provided that the integral exists. $M(h)$ is called the *moment-generating function* (*mgf*) of the distribution of x, since if e^{hx} is expanded in a power series and if moments of all orders exist,

(4.34) $$\begin{aligned}M(h) &= \int_{-\infty}^{\infty}(1 + hx + \frac{1}{2!}h^2x^2 + \cdots)\, dF(x) \\ &= 1 + h\nu_1 + \frac{h^2}{2!}\nu_2 + \cdots\end{aligned}$$

so that the coefficient of $h^r/r!$ is the rth moment about zero. It follows that, if we differentiate r times with respect to h and then set $h = 0$, we obtain the rth moment ν_r, that is,

(4.35) $$\nu_r = M^{(r)}(0)$$

For the Cauchy distribution, as we have seen, ν_1 does not exist and hence there is no mgf. But we can avoid such difficulties of convergence by supposing that h is a pure imaginary number, that is, by writing $g(x) = e^{itx}$ where t is real and $i = \sqrt{-1}$. The function

(4.36) $$C(t) = E(e^{itx}) = \int_{-\infty}^{\infty} e^{itx}\, dF(x)$$

always exists for a given distribution since $|e^{itx}| = 1$.

$C(t)$ is called the *characteristic function* (*cf*) of the distribution and is, of course, in general a complex-valued function of t. Obviously $C(0) = 1$, whatever the distribution.

Analogously to (4.34) and (4.35) we have the relations

(4.37) $$C(t) = 1 + it\nu_1 - \frac{t^2}{2!}\nu_2 - \frac{it^3}{3!}\nu_3 + \cdots$$

and

(4.38) $$i^r \nu_r = C^{(r)}(0)$$

For the *Cauchy distribution*,

(4.39) $$C(t) = \frac{1}{\pi}\int_{-\infty}^{\infty} \frac{e^{itx}}{1+x^2}\,dx = \frac{1}{\pi}\int_{-\infty}^{\infty} \frac{\cos tx}{1+x^2}\,dx$$

since $e^{itx} = \cos tx + i \sin tx$ and the function $(\sin tx)/(1 + x^2)$, being an odd function of x, vanishes on integration between $-\infty$ and $+\infty$. It may be shown that (4.39) reduces to e^{-t} when $t > 0$ and to e^t when $t < 0$. Therefore $C(t) = e^{-|t|}$ is the cf of the Cauchy distribution. It should be noted, however, that the first derivative of $C(t)$ is discontinuous at $t = 0$, being -1 at $t = 0+$, and $+1$ at $t = 0-$.

4.7 Some Examples of Moment-generating Functions. (i) *The unit distribution.* This is a highly special discrete distribution in which the total frequency is concentrated at the one point $x = 0$. The distribution function is

(4.40) $$\epsilon(x) = \begin{cases} 0, & x < 0 \\ 1, & x \geq 0 \end{cases}$$

and so has a single step of size 1 at $x = 0$. The mgf is

(4.41) $$M(h) = \int_{-\infty}^{\infty} e^{hx}\,d\epsilon(x) = e^0 = 1$$

since the integral here reduces to a single term.

(ii) *The binomial distribution.* Recall that the probability of x successes in s trials, with constant probability p of success in a single trial, is

(4.42) $$p(x, s) = \binom{s}{x} p^x q^{s-x}, \quad x = 0, 1, \cdots s$$

Let us now introduce s auxiliary variables $z_1, z_2, \cdots z_s$, each of which can take only the two values 0 and 1, with probabilities q and p respectively. The number of successes will then be given by

(4.43) $$x = z_1 + z_2 + \cdots + z_s$$

since each success contributes a 1 and each failure a 0 to this sum.

Each z_i has a distribution function with two steps, one of q at 0 and one of p at 1. Therefore its mgf is

(4.44) $$M_i(h) = \int e^{hz_i} dF(z_i)$$
$$= e^0 q + e^h p = q + pe^h$$

The mgf for x is
$$M(h) = \int e^{h(z_1 + \cdots + z_s)} dF(x)$$
$$= \int e^{hz_1} dF(z_1) \cdots \int e^{hz_s} dF(z_s)$$
$$= M_1(h) M_2(h) \cdots M_s(h)$$

since the various trials are supposed to be independent (see equation 4.23). Hence, since $M_i(h)$ is the same for each z_i,

(4.45) $$M(h) = (q + pe^h)^s$$

From this we can obtain the various moments by means of (4.35). The student should calculate ν_1 to ν_4 and μ_2 to μ_4 as an exercise.

The expectation of z_i is $0q + 1p = p$. Hence from (4.43) and Theorem 4.4 we obtain immediately $E(x) = sp$.

The variance of z_i is $(0 - p)^2 q + (1 - p)^2 p$ which simplifies into pq. Hence by (4.32) the variance of x is spq.

(iii) *The normal (Gaussian) distribution.* In terms of the standardized variable τ the frequency function of the normal law is

(4.46) $$\phi(\tau) = (2\pi)^{-1/2} e^{-\tau^2/2}$$

Therefore the mgf is

(4.47) $$M(h) = (2\pi)^{-1/2} \int_{-\infty}^{\infty} e^{h\tau} e^{-\tau^2/2} d\tau$$

Putting $u = \tau - h$, we have

(4.48) $$M(h) = (2\pi)^{-1/2} e^{h^2/2} \int_{-\infty}^{\infty} e^{-u^2/2} du = e^{h^2/2}$$

For all values of h this may be written
$$M(h) = 1 + \frac{h^2}{2} + \frac{h^4}{2^2 2!} + \frac{h^6}{2^3 3!} + \cdots$$

so that all the odd ν's are 0, and the even ones are given by

(4.49) $$\begin{cases} \nu_2 = 1 \\ \nu_4 = 1 \cdot 3 \\ \nu_6 = 1 \cdot 3 \cdot 5 \\ \nu_8 = 1 \cdot 3 \cdot 5 \cdot 7 \\ \cdots \cdots \end{cases}$$

Because the expected value of τ is 0, the μ's coincide with the respective ν's.

(iv) *The Poisson distribution.* Since the Poisson distribution is obtained from the binomial distribution by letting $p \to 0$ and $s \to \infty$ while $m = sp$

remains finite, we should expect that the moment-generating function of the Poisson distribution would be given by

$$(4.50) \qquad M(h) = \lim_{s \to \infty} \left[1 - \frac{m}{s} + \frac{m}{s} e^h \right]^s$$
$$= e^{-m(1-e^h)}$$

That this passage to the limit is valid rests on a theorem to be found in Cramér's *Mathematical Methods of Statistics*. It states that, if a sequence of characteristic functions has a limit which, as a function of t, is continuous at $t = 0$, then the corresponding sequence of distribution functions also has a limit, and this limit is the distribution function of the limiting characteristic function. Since the characteristic function differs from (4.50) only by having it instead of h, and is clearly continuous at $t = 0$, the conditions of the theorem are satisfied.

The moments of the Poisson distribution are therefore given by

$$(4.51) \qquad \begin{cases} \nu_1 = e^{-m} \left[\dfrac{d}{dh} \left(e^{me^h} \right) \right]_{h=0} \\ \qquad = e^{-m} m e^m = m \\ \nu_2 = e^{-m} \left[\dfrac{d^2}{dh^2} \left(e^{me^h} \right) \right]_{h=0} \\ \qquad = m^2 + m, \quad \text{etc.} \end{cases}$$

(v) *The rectangular distribution*

$$(4.52) \qquad f(x) = \frac{1}{2a}, \quad -a < x < a, \quad a > 0$$
$$f(x) = 0, \quad |x| > a$$

This distribution has discontinuities at $x = \pm a$.

$$(4.53) \qquad M(h) = \frac{1}{2a} \int_{-a}^{a} e^{hx} \, dx = \frac{1}{ah} \sinh ah$$
$$= 1 + \frac{a^2 h^2}{3!} + \frac{a^4 h^4}{5!} + \cdots$$

for all real values of h. Hence the odd moments are all zero, as is obvious from the symmetry of the distribution. Also, since $\nu_1 = 0$,

$$(4.54) \qquad \mu_2 = \frac{a^2}{3}, \quad \mu_4 = \frac{a^4}{5}, \quad \text{etc.}$$

4.8 Change of Scale and Origin. If the origin is shifted to the right by an amount a, which is equivalent to replacing x by $x' = x - a$, the distribution function $F(x)$ becomes $F(x' + a)$. The moment-generating function is now

$$(4.55) \qquad M_1(h) = \int_{-\infty}^{\infty} e^{hx'} \, dF(x' + a)$$

$$= \int_{-\infty}^{\infty} e^{h(x-a)} \, dF(x)$$
$$= e^{-ah} M(h)$$

so that the effect is to multiply the moment-generating function by e^{-ah}.

If the scale, that is, the unit of x, is decreased in the ratio $b:1$ which is equivalent to replacing the variable x by $x' = bx$, the distribution function becomes $F(x'/b)$. The mgf is

(4.56) $$M_2(h) = \int_{-\infty}^{\infty} e^{hx'} \, dF\left(\frac{x'}{b}\right)$$
$$= \int_{-\infty}^{\infty} e^{bhx} \, dF(x)$$
$$= M(bh)$$

so that the effect is to replace h by bh.

Hence for the normal distribution with frequency function

(4.57) $$f(x) = \frac{1}{\sigma\sqrt{2\pi}} e^{-(x-\nu_1)^2/2\sigma^2}$$

the mgf is

(4.58) $$M(h) = e^{\nu_1 h} e^{\frac{1}{2}\sigma^2 h^2}$$

since this distribution is obtained from the standardized normal curve by shifting the origin a distance ν_1 to the *left* and decreasing the unit in the ratio $\sigma:1$. The characteristic function is

(4.59) $$C(t) = e^{i\nu_1 t} e^{-\frac{1}{2}\sigma^2 t^2}$$

4.9 Uniqueness Theorem for Characteristic Functions. It may be shown (see Cramér's *Mathematical Methods of Statistics*, page 93) that a distribution is uniquely determined by its characteristic function. It is not true that a distribution is uniquely determined when all its moments are known, although examples to the contrary are rather special and complicated.

An interesting dual relation exists between the frequency function and the characteristic function. If the frequency function $f(x)$ exists for all x, except at most at a finite number of points,

(4.60) $$C(t) = \int_{-\infty}^{\infty} e^{itx} f(x) \, dx$$

and $C(t)$ tends to zero as t tends to $\pm \infty$.

Conversely,

(4.61) $$f(x) = \frac{1}{2\pi} \int_{-\infty}^{\infty} e^{-itx} C(t) \, dt$$

and $f(x)$ is said to be the *Fourier transform*[2] of $C(t)$.

For example, if $C(t) = e^{-\frac{1}{2}\sigma^2 t^2}$

Sec. 10 Cumulants and Cumulant-generating Function

$$f(x) = \frac{1}{2\pi} \int_{-\infty}^{\infty} e^{-itx} e^{-\frac{1}{2}\sigma^2 t^2} \, dt$$

$$= \frac{1}{2\pi} e^{-x^2/2\sigma^2} \int_{-\infty}^{\infty} e^{-\frac{1}{2}(\sigma t + ix/\sigma)^2} \, dt$$

Putting $u = \sigma t + ix/\sigma$, $du = \sigma/dt$, we have

$$f(x) = \frac{1}{2\pi\sigma} e^{-x^2/2\sigma^2} \int_{-\infty + ix/\sigma}^{\infty + ix/\sigma} e^{-u^2/2} \, du$$

$$= \frac{1}{2\pi\sigma} e^{-x^2/2\sigma^2} \lim_{A \to \infty} \int_{-A + ix/\sigma}^{A + ix/\sigma} e^{-u^2/2} \, du$$

Since the integrand has no poles in any finite part of the plane the integral around a rectangle joining the points A, $A + ix/\sigma$, $-A + ix/\sigma$, $-A$, will be zero. Since also the integrand $\to 0$ when $A \to \infty$ along the two ends of the rectangle, the integral from $-A + ix/\sigma$ to $A + ix/\sigma$ is the same as from $-A$ to A, i.e., $\sqrt{2\pi}$ in the limit. Hence

$$f(x) = \frac{1}{\sigma\sqrt{2\pi}} e^{-x^2/2\sigma^2}$$

as we should expect from (4.59) and (4.57).

4.10 Cumulants and the Cumulant-generating Function. Certain functions of the moments have been shown by Thiele,[3] Fisher [4] and other writers to be of particular importance in sampling theory. These functions were first called *semi-invariants* and later, by Fisher, *cumulants*. They are usually (following Fisher) denoted by the Greek letter kappa (κ).

If the logarithm of the moment-generating function as a function of h is expanded into a power series which converges for some range of h containing the origin as an interior point, then κ_r is the coefficient of $h^r/r!$ in this series, and $\log M(h)$ is the *cumulant-generating function* (cgf) $K(h)$; that is,

(4.62) $\qquad K(h) = \log M(h) = \kappa_1 h + \kappa_2 \frac{h^2}{2!} + \kappa_3 \frac{h^3}{3!} + \cdots$

Since $M(0) = 1$, there is no constant term. If we move the origin a distance ν_1 to the right, the mgf becomes $M(h)e^{-\nu_1 h} = M_1(h)$, where

$$M_1(h) = 1 + \mu_2 \frac{h^2}{2!} + \mu_3 \frac{h^3}{3!} + \cdots$$

since μ_r is now the same as ν_r.
Since

$$\frac{dK_1(h)}{dh} = \frac{1}{M_1(h)} \cdot \frac{dM_1(h)}{dh}$$

we have

(4.63) $\qquad \left(1 + \mu_2 \frac{h^2}{2!} + \mu_3 \frac{h^3}{3!} + \cdots\right)\left(\kappa_1 + \kappa_2 h + \kappa_3 \frac{h^2}{2!} + \cdots\right)$

$$= \mu_2 h + \mu_3 \frac{h^2}{2!} + \mu_4 \frac{h^3}{3!} + \cdots$$

and, on equating coefficients of like powers of h,

(4.64)
$$\begin{cases} \kappa_1 = 0 \\ \kappa_2 = \mu_2 \\ \kappa_3 = \mu_3 \\ \kappa_4 + 3\mu_2\kappa_2 = \mu_4 \\ \kappa_5 + 6\mu_2\kappa_3 + 4\mu_3\kappa_2 = \mu_5 \\ \cdots \cdots \cdots \cdots \cdots \end{cases}$$

Solving these equations for the kappas, we get

(4.65)
$$\begin{cases} \kappa_2 = \mu_2 \\ \kappa_3 = \mu_3 \\ \kappa_4 = \mu_4 - 3\mu_2^2 \\ \kappa_5 = \mu_5 - 10\mu_3\mu_2 \\ \cdots \cdots \cdots \cdots \end{cases}$$

The only effect of the translation on the kappas is to change κ_1 from ν_1 to 0. Hence we can complete (4.65) by adding, for the original distribution,

(4.66) $\qquad\qquad\qquad \kappa_1 = \nu_1$

Some examples of cumulants will now be given.

Example 2 (Normal distribution).
$$\begin{aligned} K(h) &= \log[e^{\nu_1 h}e^{\frac{1}{2}\sigma^2 h^2}] \\ &= \nu_1 h + \tfrac{1}{2}\sigma^2 h^2 \\ \kappa_1 &= \nu_1 \\ \kappa_2 &= \sigma^2 \end{aligned}$$

and all remaining cumulants are zero.

Example 3 (Poisson distribution).
$$\begin{aligned} M(h) &= e^{m(e^h - 1)} \\ K(h) &= m(e^h - 1) \\ &= m\left(h + \frac{h^2}{2!} + \frac{h^3}{3!} + \cdots\right) \end{aligned}$$

Hence each cumulant has the value m.

4.11 Additive Property of Cumulants. The principal property of cumulants is expressed in the following theorem:

Theorem 4.10. *If* $L = \sum_{j=1}^{N} c_j x_j$ *is a linear function of N independent variates, the cumulant-generating function for L is given by*

(4.67) $\qquad\qquad\qquad K(h) = \sum_{j=1}^{N} K_j(c_j h)$

where $K_j(h)$ is the cgf for x_j.

This follows at once from the corresponding property for moment-generating functions (see Problem 6),

Sec. 11   Additive Property of Cumulants

(4.68) $$M(h) = \prod_{j=1}^{N} M_j(c_j h).$$

when we remember that $K(h) = \log M(h)$.

Thus, if x and y are independent variables, the cgf for $x + y$ is the sum of the cgf for x and y separately.

Some important reproductive properties of certain distributions follow from Theorem 4.10.

Theorem 4.11. *If $x_1, x_2, \cdots x_N$ are independent and normally distributed variables with means $m_1, m_2, \cdots m_N$ and variances $\sigma_1^2, \sigma_2^2, \cdots \sigma_N^2$, and if $L = \sum_{j=1}^{N} c_j x_j$ is a linear function of the x_j, then L is normally distributed with mean* **

$$\sum_{j=1}^{N} c_j m_j \quad \text{and variance} \quad \sum_{j=1}^{N} c_j^2 \sigma_j^2$$

Proof: The cgf of the variable x_j is

$$K_j(h) = m_j h + \tfrac{1}{2}\sigma_j^2 h^2$$

Hence, for L, the cgf is

(4.69) $$K(h) = h \sum_{j=1}^{N} c_j m_j + \tfrac{1}{2} h^2 \sum_{j=1}^{N} c_j^2 \sigma_j^2$$

Therefore

$$\nu_1 = \sum c_j m_j, \quad \text{and} \quad \mu_2 = \sigma^2 = \sum c_j^2 \sigma_j^2$$

all the higher cumulants being zero. Hence, by the uniqueness theorem, the distribution of L is normal.

Theorem 4.12. *If $x_1, x_2, \cdots x_N$ are independent normally distributed variables with means $m_1, m_2, \cdots m_N$ and with a common variance σ^2, and if $L = (1/\sqrt{N}) \sum_{j=1}^{N} x_j$, then L is normally distributed with the same variance.*

This is an immediate corollary of Theorem 4.11, with $c_j = 1/\sqrt{N}$ and $\sigma_j = \sigma$.

Theorem 4.13. *If the independent variables $x_1, x_2, \cdots x_N$ have binomial distributions with a common parameter p, but with $s = s_1, s_2, \cdots s_N$, respectively, and if $X = \sum_{j=1}^{N} x_j$, then X has a binomial distribution with parameters p and $S = \sum_{j=1}^{N} s_j$.*

---

* The word "mean," as mentioned at the end of § 2.5, is often used as synonymous with "expectation," since the mean of a random sample tends to the expectation as the size of the sample increases.

Proof:

$$K_j(h) = \log(q + pe^h)^{s_j}$$
$$= s_j \log(q + pe^h)$$

by equation (4.45). Then

(4.70) $$K(h) = \sum_{j=1}^{N} s_j \log(q + pe^h)$$
$$= S \log(q + pe^h)$$

Theorem 4.14. *If the independent variables $x_1, x_2, \cdots x_N$ have Poisson distributions with parameters $m_1, m_2, \cdots m_N$, and if $X = \sum_{j=1}^{N} x_j$, then X has a Poisson distribution with parameter $M = \sum_{j=1}^{N} m_j$.*

Proof:

$$K_j(h) = m_j(e^h - 1)$$

Therefore

(4.71) $$K(h) = \sum_j m_j(e^h - 1) = M(e^h - 1)$$

Theorem 4.15. *The Poisson distribution tends to the normal distribution as $m \to \infty$.*

Proof: If we change the variable to the standard form $\tau = (x - m)/m^{1/2}$, the effect on the mgf is, by (4.55) and (4.56), to multiply $M(h)$ by e^{-mh}, and then to replace h by $m^{-1/2}h$.

Hence the mgf is

$$M(h) = e^{-m^{1/2}h} \exp[m(e^{hm^{-1/2}} - 1)]$$

and the cgf is

(4.72) $$K(h) = -m^{1/2}h + m(e^{hm^{-1/2}} - 1)$$
$$= \frac{h^2}{2!} + m^{-1/2}\frac{h^3}{3!} + m^{-1}\frac{h^4}{4!} + \cdots$$

Hence $\kappa_1 = 0$, $\kappa_2 = 1$, $\kappa_r = m^{(1-r/2)}$, $r \geq 2$. The limit of κ_r as $m \to \infty$ is therefore 0 for $r > 2$, so that the cumulants tend to the values for the normal curve.

4.12 Sheppard's Corrections. A continuous distribution may be specified by the frequencies corresponding to each of a set of class-intervals covering the range of the variable. If moments and cumulants are calculated, assuming that the frequencies are concentrated at the mid-points of the respective intervals, there will be, in many cases, an error due to this grouping. In certain circumstances it is possible, as Sheppard showed, to allow for the error of grouping. The corrections, as applied to the cumulants, are as follows:

If $\kappa_r{}'$ is the rth cumulant of the ungrouped distribution, and κ_r the rth cumulant of the grouped distribution with class interval c, the corrected cumulants are

(4.73) $$\begin{cases} \kappa_r' = \kappa_r, & r \text{ odd} \\ \kappa_r' = \kappa_r - \dfrac{B_r}{r} c^r, & r \text{ even} \end{cases}$$

where B_r is the rth *Bernoulli number*.

This number [5] is defined as the coefficient of $t^r/r!$ in the expansion of

$$t(e^t - 1)^{-1}$$

Thus, $B_0 = 1$, $B_1 = -\tfrac{1}{2}$, $B_2 = \tfrac{1}{6}$, $B_4 = -\tfrac{1}{30}$, $B_6 = \tfrac{1}{42}$, etc., and all the B's of odd subscript beyond 1 are zero, so that

(4.74) $$\begin{cases} \kappa_2' = \kappa_2 - \dfrac{c^2}{12} \\ \kappa_4' = \kappa_4 + \dfrac{c^4}{120} \\ \kappa_6' = \kappa_6 - \dfrac{c^6}{252} \quad \text{etc.} \end{cases}$$

For a proof of the validity of these corrections, under the rather restrictive conditions in which they apply, the reader may refer to Kendall's *Advanced Theory of Statistics*, Vol. I.[6]

These conditions are that the frequency function $f(x)$ is continuous, bounded, and tends monotonically to zero in the directions in which the range is infinite, that the absolute moment of order r, $\int_{-\infty}^{\infty} |x^r| f(x)\, dx$, exists, and that the limit of $x^r[d^j f(x)/dx^j]$ is 0 for all j up to and including r when $x \to \pm\infty$. If the range has finite terminal points, $f(x)$ and its first m derivatives must vanish there, m being a number (of the order of r) such that the mth derivative of $f(x)$ multiplied by c^{m+1} is small at all points of the range. This last condition means that the distribution must have contact of a sufficiently high order with the x axis at the ends of the range.

Sheppard's corrections apply also in a rather different situation. We think of the true continuous distribution as stretching over an unknown range, with an interval-grid superimposed on it in a random manner, and determine the corrections to be applied to the grouped moments so as to bring them *on the average* nearer to the true moments. The condition about high order contact at the ends of the range is not now essential, but if it is not satisfied (if, for example, the distribution starts off abruptly at the beginning of the range) the grouping error may vary a great deal with the random position of the interval-grid. Sheppard's corrections will still apply on the average but may not be at all satisfactory in some particular positions of the interval-grid.

In the following discussion it is assumed that the random distribution of the interval grid is *rectangular*. That is, if x_i is the nearest mid-interval point to any given x, then $x_i = x + \epsilon_i$, where ϵ_i ranges from $-c/2$ to $c/2$ with a constant probability density, independent of the distribution of x. This is a special assumption, but it places no limitation on the frequency function of x itself.

If $K(h)$, $K'(h)$, $K''(h)$ are the cumulant-generating functions for x_i, x, and ϵ_i respectively,
$$K(h) = K'(h) + K''(h)$$
Now by (4.53) $K''(h) = \log \sinh \theta/2 - \log \theta/2$ where $\theta = ch$.

By the definition of the Bernoulli numbers B_r,

(4.75) $$\sum_{r=0}^{\infty} \frac{B_r \theta^r}{r!} = \theta(e^\theta - 1)^{-1} = \frac{\theta}{2}\left(\coth \frac{\theta}{2} - 1\right)$$

so that
$$\sum_{2}^{\infty} \frac{B_r \theta^r}{r!} + 1 - \frac{\theta}{2} = \frac{\theta}{2}\left(\coth \frac{\theta}{2} - 1\right)$$
Dividing by θ, we obtain
$$\sum_{2}^{\infty} \frac{B_r \theta^{r-1}}{r!} = \frac{1}{2} \coth \frac{\theta}{2} - \frac{1}{\theta}$$

Integrating from 0 to θ, we have
$$\sum_{2}^{\infty} \frac{B_r \theta^r}{r \cdot r!} = \log \sinh \frac{\theta}{2} - \log \frac{\theta}{2}$$

the constant $\log 2$ being introduced to make both sides tend to 0 as $\theta \to 0$. Hence

(4.76) $$K'(h) = K(h) - \sum_{2}^{\infty} \frac{B_r (ch)^r}{r \cdot r!}$$

whence
$$\kappa_r' = \kappa_r - \frac{c^r}{r} B_r$$

as stated above.

In practice, Sheppard's corrections are usually applied, not to theoretical distributions, but to sample data. (See, for example, a discussion in Part One of this work.*) It is by no means certain that the use of these corrections will improve the estimates of the moments of the parent population, but very frequently it will do so. Since, for small samples, the sampling errors of the moments will greatly exceed the corrections, it is not worth while applying Sheppard's corrections unless the sample consists of at least a few hundred individuals. Moreover, the corrections should not be used unless the distribution tails off gradually at both ends.

4.13 Orthogonal Linear Transformations. Let the n variates x_i be subjected to a linear transformation

(4.77) $$y_i = \sum_j c_{ij} x_j, \quad (i, j = 1, 2, \cdots n)$$

---

* Kenney, J. F. and Keeping, E. S., *Mathematics of Statistics, Part One*, D. Van Nostrand Co., Inc., New York, 1954.

Sec. 13 Orthogonal Linear Transformations

where c_{ij} are arbitrary constants. If these constants are so chosen that

(4.78) $$\sum_{k=1}^{n} c_{ik} c_{jk} = \begin{cases} 1, & \text{if } i = j, \\ 0, & \text{if } i \neq j, \end{cases}$$

the transformation is said to be *orthogonal*.

If the determinant of the coefficients in (4.77) is multiplied by itself (with rows and columns transposed), it is easily seen[*] that, because of (4.78),

$$\begin{vmatrix} c_{11} & c_{12} & \cdots & c_{1n} \\ c_{21} & c_{22} & \cdots & c_{2n} \\ \cdot & & & \cdot \\ \cdot & & & \cdot \\ c_{n1} & c_{n2} & \cdots & c_{nn} \end{vmatrix} \begin{vmatrix} c_{11} & c_{21} & \cdots & c_{n1} \\ c_{12} & c_{22} & \cdots & c_{n2} \\ \cdot & & & \cdot \\ \cdot & & & \cdot \\ c_{1n} & c_{2n} & \cdots & c_{nn} \end{vmatrix} = \begin{vmatrix} 1 & 0 & \cdots & 0 \\ 0 & 1 & \cdots & 0 \\ \cdot & \cdot & \cdots & \cdot \\ 0 & 0 & \cdots & 1 \end{vmatrix} = 1$$

so that the determinant itself is equal to ± 1. By multiplying the determinants in the reverse order, which will obviously give the same result, we obtain the relations

(4.79) $$\sum_{k=1}^{n} c_{ki} c_{kj} = \begin{cases} 1, & \text{if } i = j \\ 0, & \text{if } i \neq j \end{cases}$$

The proof requires a knowledge of matrix theory, given in Chapter X. If C is the matrix of the coefficients c_{ij}, and C' its transpose, then by (4.78) C' is the inverse of C. It follows that $CC' = C'C$, which means that these products are equal, element by element.

Hence in the determinant $|c_{ij}|$ the sum of the squares of the elements in any row or any column is equal to unity, while the sum of the products of corresponding elements in any two rows or any two columns is equal to zero.

It follows that

(4.80) $$\sum_{i=1}^{n} y_i^2 = \sum_{j=1}^{n} x_j^2$$

The Jacobian of the y's with respect to the x's will be the determinant $|c_{ij}|$. By changing the sign of one of the y's, if necessary, we can ensure that the determinant is equal to 1, and hence

(4.81) $$J\left(\frac{y_1, \cdots y_n}{x_1, \cdots x_n}\right) = J\left(\frac{x_1, \cdots x_n}{y_1, \cdots y_n}\right) = 1$$

Geometrically, this transformation is equivalent to a rotation of the coördinate axes about the origin. In such a rotation distance from the origin remains invariant.

Theorem 4.16. *If the variates x_i are independently and normally distributed about zero with the same variance σ^2, the y_i are also independently and normally distributed about zero with variance σ^2.*

---

[*] The determinants are multiplied according to the rule for matrices (§10.6). For fuller details a book such as Aitken's *Determinants and Matrices* (Oliver and Boyd) may be consulted.

Proof: The joint frequency function of the x_j is
$$f(x_1, x_2, \cdots x_n)\, dx_1 \cdots dx_n = (2\pi\sigma^2)^{-\frac{1}{2}n} e^{-\Sigma x_j^2/2\sigma^2}\, dx_1 \cdots dx_n$$
Therefore, by (4.80) and (4.81), the joint frequency function of the y_i is
$$f(y_1, y_2 \cdots y_n)\, dy_1 \cdots dy_n = (2\pi\sigma^2)^{-\frac{1}{2}n} e^{-\Sigma y_i^2/2\sigma^2}\, dy_1 \cdots dy_n$$
But the right-hand side is the product of n factors like
$$(2\pi\sigma^2)^{-1/2} e^{-y_i^2/2\sigma^2}\, dy_i$$
and so the y_i are independent and normally distributed, with variance σ^2.

Example. The transformation

(4.82)
$$\begin{cases} y_1 = (x_1 + x_2 + \cdots + x_n)/\sqrt{n} \\ y_2 = (x_1 - x_2)/\sqrt{2} \\ y_3 = (x_1 + x_2 - 2x_3)/\sqrt{6} \\ y_4 = (x_1 + x_2 + x_3 - 3x_4)/\sqrt{12} \\ \cdots \cdots \cdots \cdots \\ y_n = [x_1 + x_2 + \cdots + x_{n-1} - (n-1)x_n]/\sqrt{n(n-1)} \end{cases}$$

is orthogonal. It is easy to see that in each y the sum of squares of the coefficients is 1, and that, for any two different y's, the product of the coefficients pair by pair is equal to 0.

4.14 The Bienaymé-Tchebycheff Inequality. Let X be a random variable, taking real values $X_1, X_2, \cdots X_N$ with respective probabilities $p(X_1), p(X_2), \cdots p(X_n)$, or, if X is continuous, taking values between X and $X + dX$ with probability $p(X)\, dX$.

What we mean by saying that X is a *random variable* * is merely that we can associate in some way with every value of X a real, non-negative number $p(X)$, such that $\int_{-\infty}^{\infty} dP(X) = 1$, where this integral means $\int_{-\infty}^{\infty} p(X)\, dX$, if X is continuous, or $\sum_i p(X_i)$, if X takes on the discrete values X_i.

The expected value of X is
$$\nu_1 = \int_{-\infty}^{\infty} X\, dP(X)$$
and its variance is
$$\sigma^2 = \int_{-\infty}^{\infty} (X - \nu_1)^2\, dP(X)$$

Let c be any assigned real positive constant. The probability that $|X - \nu_1| \geq c$ is $\int_{(s)} dP(X)$, integrated over the set s of all values of X satisfying the given inequality. Clearly

---

* The terms "random variable," "chance variable," "chance quantity," "statistical variable," "stochastic variable," and "variate," are used synonymously in the literature. Symbols x and X will both be used at times in this book to denote random variables.

$$\sigma^2 \geq \int_{(s)} (X - \nu_1)^2 \, dP(X) \geq c^2 \int_{(s)} dP(X)$$

and we have

Theorem 4.17.

(4.83) $$\Pr\{|X - \nu_1| \geq c\} \leq \frac{\sigma^2}{c^2}$$

which is the Bienaymé-Tchebycheff inequality. It asserts that whatever the nature of the distribution (if it has a finite variance) the probability that a random value of X will differ from its expected value by as much as δ times its standard deviation is not more than $1/\delta^2$.

4.15 The Weak Law of Large Numbers (*Bernoulli's Theorem*). If x is the number of successes in s trials of an event with constant probability p, we have seen that the expectation of x is sp and its variance $\sigma^2 = spq$. Therefore by (4.83)

$$\Pr\{|x - sp| \geq c\} \leq \frac{spq}{c^2} \leq \frac{s}{4c^2}$$

since pq is always $\leq \frac{1}{4}$.

Let $y = x/s$, the relative frequency of success. Then

$$\Pr\left\{|y - p| \geq \frac{c}{s}\right\} \leq \frac{s}{4c^2}$$

or, putting $t = c/s$,

(4.84) $$\Pr\{|y - p| \geq t\} \leq \frac{1}{4st^2}$$

Hence for any given positive number ϵ, however small, we can always find s so large that $\Pr\{|y - p| \geq t\} < \epsilon$, for any $t > 0$. This is the *weak law of large numbers* in one form.

For example, if $\epsilon = 0.001$ and $t = 0.01$, we have to find s so that $1/.0004s < .001$. This means that it suffices to have $s > 2,500,000$.

The theorem may be stated also as follows.

(4.85) $$\lim_{s \to \infty} \Pr\{|x/s - p| \geq \delta\} = 0$$

for any assigned $\delta > 0$, which means that $y = x/s$ tends *in probability* or *stochastically* to the value p as s increases indefinitely. Note that if A_s stands for the event $|x/s - p| \geq \delta$ we have proved that the probability of A_s is at most $(4s\delta^2)^{-1}$, and so $\to 0$ as $s \to \infty$. But the probability of this event for some $s \geq N$ is given by

$$\Pr(A_N + A_{N+1} + \cdots) \leq P(A_N) + P(A_{N+1}) + \cdots$$
$$\leq \frac{1}{4\delta^2}\left(\frac{1}{N} + \frac{1}{N+1} + \cdots\right)$$

and, since the series diverges, this tells us nothing about the probability. However, there is a stronger form of the law of large numbers.

4.16 The Strong Law of Large Numbers.[7] Let $x_1, x_2, \cdots x_n$ be independent random variables with the same distribution, characterized by

$$\kappa_1 = a, \qquad \kappa_2 = b, \qquad \kappa_3 = c, \qquad \kappa_4 = d$$

If $y = 1/n \sum_{i=1}^{n} x_i$, we have by Theorem 4.10 that the cgf of y is

(4.86) $$K(h) = \sum_{i=1}^{n} K_i\left(\frac{h}{n}\right)$$

where

$$K_i(h) = \kappa_1 t + \kappa_2 \frac{h^2}{2!} + \cdots$$

Hence

(4.87) $$K(h) = n\left[a\frac{h}{n} + \frac{b}{2}\left(\frac{h}{n}\right)^2 + \frac{c}{6}\left(\frac{h}{n}\right)^3 + \frac{d}{24}\left(\frac{h}{n}\right)^4 + \cdots\right]$$
$$= ah + \frac{b}{n}\frac{h^2}{2} + \frac{c}{n^2}\frac{h^3}{6} + \frac{d}{n^3}\frac{h^4}{24} + \cdots$$

so that the first four cumulants for the distribution of y are $a, b/n, c/n^2, d/n^3$. It follows that

(4.88) $$E\{(y-a)^4\} = d/n^3 + 3b^2/n^2$$

Now if $P(y)$ is the distribution function of y, and $g(y)$ is a given non-negative function of y,

(4.89) $$E\{g(y)\} = \int g(y)\, dP(y) \geq \int_{g(y) \geq \epsilon} g(y)\, dP(y) \geq \epsilon \int_{g(y) \geq \epsilon} dP(y)$$

for arbitrary positive ϵ. Since the last integral in (4.89) is the probability that $g(y) \geq \epsilon$, we have

$$\Pr\{g(y) \geq \epsilon\} \leq E\{g(y)\}/\epsilon$$

Letting $g(y) = (y-a)^4$, and $\delta = \epsilon^{1/4}$, we have

(4.90) $$\Pr\{|y-a| \geq \delta\} \leq E(y-a)^4/\delta^4 = (d + 3nb^2)/\delta^4 n^3$$

This is a modification of the Bienaymé-Tchebycheff inequality, which is generally sharper than the latter, assuming that the fourth moment exists, because of the higher power of n in the denominator. The Bienaymé-Tchebycheff inequality states, in this case, that

(4.91) $$\Pr\{|y-a| \geq \delta\} \leq \frac{b}{n\delta^2}$$

From (4.90),

$$\sum_{n=N}^{\infty} \Pr\{|y-a| \geq \delta\} \leq \sum_{n=N}^{\infty}\left(\frac{k_1}{n^2} + \frac{k_2}{n^3}\right)$$

where $k_1 = 3b^2/\delta^4$, $k_2 = d/\delta^4$. Both series $\sum 1/n^2$ and $\sum 1/n^3$ converge, so that

Sec. 16 The Strong Law of Large Numbers

(4.92)
$$\lim_{N \to \infty} \sum_{n=N}^{\infty} \Pr\{|y_n - a| \geq \delta\} = 0$$

where
$$y_n = \frac{1}{n}(x_1 + x_2 + \cdots + x_n)$$

This is a stronger form of the law of large numbers, since it states that the *total* probability for $n = N$, or $N + 1$, or $N + 2$, and so on indefinitely, tends to zero as N increases.

Let A_{nk} denote the event "$|y_n - a| \geq 1/k$," $k = 1, 2, 3 \cdots$ and let B_k denote the event "$|y_n - a| \geq 1/k$ for infinitely many values of n." Note that the truth of B_k does not imply that this inequality holds for *all* values of n, or even for all values greater than some fixed N.

Now, with the notation of § 1.6, the event $A_{n1} + A_{n2}$ means either or both of the events A_{n1} and A_{n2}. Hence the event B_k is certainly included within the events represented by

$$A_{nk} + A_{n+1, k} + A_{n+2, k} + \cdots$$

for every value of n.

It follows from one of the fundamental theorems of probability that

$$\Pr(B_k) \leq \Pr(A_{nk} + A_{n+1, k} + \cdots)$$
$$\leq \sum_{j=n}^{\infty} \Pr(A_{jk})$$

By (4.92), $\lim_{n \to \infty} \sum_{j=n}^{\infty} \Pr(A_{jk}) = 0$, for any value of k. It follows that

$$\Pr(B_k) = 0$$

Now let B denote the event $\lim_{n \to \infty} y_n \neq a$. If this is true, at least one of the events B_k must be true for some finite k, and we may write

$$B = B_1 + B_2 + B_3 + \cdots$$

Therefore
$$\Pr(B) \leq \Pr(B_1) + \Pr(B_2) + \cdots$$

and since $\Pr(B_k) = 0$ for every k, it follows that

(4.93)
$$\Pr(B) = 0$$

In other words, we have the result, due to Kolmogoroff, expressed in the following theorem:

Theorem 4.18.

(4.94)
$$Pr\{\lim_{n \to \infty} y_n = a\} = 1$$

This is the *strong law of large numbers*. It implies that in almost every unending sequence of variables $y_1, y_2 \cdots$, where $y_n = (1/n)(x_1 + x_2 + \cdots + x_n)$ and the x's are independent random variables with the same distribution, the sequence tends to a limit a. It does not imply the strict mathematical convergence of y_n to a, although such convergence would imply both the strong law and the weak law.

The probability mentioned in (4.94) is that of a limit, and hence is difficult to interpret in any elementary sense. The axiomatic approach is perhaps the only safe one.

It may be noted that the assumption of a finite fourth moment for the distribution of the variables x_i is not necessary. If the variables are independent the existence of a first moment alone is sufficient, but a very different proof is needed in this case.

4.17 The Central Limit Theorem. Let $X_1, X_2, \cdots X_r \cdots$ be independent random variables, all with the same distribution function[1] $F(x)$. We can suppose the origin and units chosen so that $E(X_i) = 0$ and $E(X_i^2) = 1$.

Let the characteristic function of any X_i be

$$C(t) = \int_{-\infty}^{\infty} e^{itx} \, dF(x)$$

If all moments of X_i up to the nth exist, that is, if $\int_{-\infty}^{\infty} |x|^n \, dF(x)$

exists, then $C(t)$ possesses continuous derivatives of all orders up to and including the nth. Since we are supposing that $E(X_i^2) = 1$, so that n is at least 2, we may write, by (4.37),

$$C(t) = 1 - \frac{t^2}{2} + o(t^2)$$

where by $o(t^2)$ we mean terms of order less than t^2, that is, a function such that $o(t^2)/t^2 \to 0$ as $t \to 0$. Let

(4.95) $$Z_n = \frac{1}{\sqrt{n}} (X_1 + X_2 + \cdots + X_n)$$

The characteristic function of Z_n is $\left\{ C\left(\frac{t}{\sqrt{n}}\right) \right\}^n = C_n(t)$ say, where

(4.96) $$C_n(t) = \left\{ 1 - \frac{t^2}{2n} + o\left(\frac{t^2}{n}\right) \right\}^n$$

Now for fixed positive t, $\lim_{n \to \infty} n/t^2 \cdot o(t^2/n) = 0$. Therefore $|2n \, o(t^2/n)| < \epsilon$, for sufficiently large n, where ϵ is any positive quantity, as small as we like. But

$$C_n(t) = \left[1 - \frac{t^2 - 2n \, o(t^2/n)}{2n} \right]^n$$

---

[1] That is, $Pr\{X_r \leq x\} = F(x)$.

Sec. 17 The Central Limit Theorem

and hence
$$\left[1 - \frac{t^2 + \epsilon}{2n}\right]^n < C_n(t) < \left[1 - \frac{t^2 - \epsilon}{2n}\right]^n$$

Proceeding to the limit as $n \to \infty$,
$$e^{-(t^2+\epsilon)/2} < \lim_{n \to \infty} C_n(t) < e^{-(t^2-\epsilon)/2}$$

or

(4.97) $$\lim_{n \to \infty} C_n(t) = e^{-t^2/2}$$

Since $e^{-t^2/2}$ is the characteristic function of the standardized normal distribution, and because of the uniqueness theorem for characteristic functions, we can state that the limit of the distribution function for Z_n is $\Phi(x)$, the distribution function of the normal law, that is,

(4.98) $$\lim_{n \to \infty} \Pr\{Z_n \le x\} = \Phi(x)$$

This is a form of the *Central Limit Theorem*.

We can easily remove the restrictions that $E(X_i) = 0$ and $E(X_i^2) = 1$. If $E(X_i) = \mu$ and $E\{(X_i - \mu)^2\} = \sigma^2$, we simply change the variable to $X_i' = (X_i - \mu)/\sigma$, and then, from (4.95) and (4.98), we have

$$\lim_{n \to \infty} \Pr\left\{\frac{\sum X_i - n\mu}{\sigma \sqrt{n}} \le x\right\} = \Phi(x)$$

that is, if $\sum X_i = n\bar{X}$, we have

Theorem 4.19.

(4.99) $$\lim_{n \to \infty} \Pr\left\{\sqrt{n}\left(\frac{\bar{X} - \mu}{\sigma}\right) \le x\right\} = \Phi(x)$$

The conditions as stated above for the Central Limit Theorem, although sufficient, are not necessary. The theorem has been proved many times, under conditions of greater and greater generality.

For instance, it is not necessary that all the X_i should have the same distribution. If the variance of X_i is σ_i^2, and if

(4.100) $$s_n^2 = \sum_1^n \sigma_i^2$$

then, if $E(X_i) = 0$,

(4.101) $$\Pr\left\{\frac{X_1 + X_2 + \cdots + X_n}{s_n} \le x\right\} \to \Phi(x)$$

as $n \to \infty$, provided that

(4.102) $s_n \to \infty$ and therefore $\dfrac{\sigma_i}{s_n} \to 0$ as $n \to \infty$

and that all the X_i are of the same order of magnitude. This is, roughly speaking, the *Lindeberg condition*.

Again, if the third moment exists for the distribution of the X_i, and if

(4.103) $$r_n^3 = \sum_{i=1}^{n} \int_{-\infty}^{\infty} |x|^3 \, dF_i(x)$$

then it can be proved that if

(4.104) $$\lim_{n \to \infty} \frac{r_n}{s_n} = 0$$

the Central Limit Theorem holds. This is the *Liapounoff condition*.[8]

The theorem has been stated in its most general form by W. Feller,[9] who has given conditions for the existence of a sequence of constants $a_1, a_2, \cdots$ and another sequence $b_1, b_2, \cdots$, such that

(4.105) $$\lim_{n \to \infty} \Pr\left\{ \frac{X_1 + \cdots + X_n - a_n}{b_n} \leq x \right\} = \Phi(x)$$

It is not even necessary that the variables $X_1, \cdots X_n$ should be independent. A form of the Central Limit Theorem will still hold even if the X_i are dependent, provided that any two are independent if their subscripts differ by more than a fixed number m. It is very remarkable what a wide variety of distributions tend in the limit to the normal form. This fact, together with the mathematical tractability of the normal law, accounts for the central position of the normal distribution in mathematical statistics.

Problems

1. If X and Y are independent variables with frequency functions given respectively by
$$f(x) = C_1 x^l e^{-x/2}, \quad x \geq 0$$
$$g(y) = C_2 y^m e^{-y/2}, \quad y \geq 0$$

prove by means of the law of convolution (equation 4.22) that the frequency function of $X + Y$ is
$$h(w) = C_3 w^{l+m+1} e^{-w/2}$$

2. If X and Y are variables with a joint frequency function $f(x, y)$, and if $U = Y/X$, apply the method of the example in § 4.3 to find the frequency function of U.

Hint.
$$\Pr\{U \leq u\} = \Pr\{Y \leq uX\} \quad \text{if } X > 0$$
$$\text{or} = \Pr\{Y \geq uX\} \quad \text{if } X < 0$$

Draw a diagram showing the areas in the XY-plane corresponding to $U \leq u$, and hence write down the distribution function of U. Differentiate to get the frequency function. Show that
$$h(u) = \int_{-\infty}^{\infty} |x| f(x, ux) \, dx$$

3. In Problem 2 suppose that X and Y are independently and uniformly distributed on the interval $(0, 1)$ so that $f(x, y) = 1$ everywhere inside a unit square and 0 outside. Prove that
$$h(u) = 0, \quad u < 0$$
$$h(u) = \tfrac{1}{2}, \quad 0 < u < 1$$
$$h(u) = \frac{1}{2u^2}, \quad u > 1$$

Problems

4. In Problem 2 suppose that X and Y are independently and normally distributed about 0 with unit variance. Prove that

$$h(u) = \frac{1}{\pi(1 + u^2)}$$

so that U has a Cauchy distribution.

5. Prove that the characteristic function of the *Laplace* (double exponential) *distribution*

$$f(x) = \tfrac{1}{2}e^{-|x|}, \quad -\infty < x < \infty$$

is

$$C(t) = \frac{1}{1 + t^2}$$

6. Prove that if $x_1, x_2, \cdots x_N$ are independent variates, and if $C_1, C_2, \cdots C_N$ are arbitrary constants, not all zero, the mgf of $L = C_1 x_1 + C_2 x_2 + \cdots C_N x_N$ is given by

$$M(h) = \prod_{j=1}^{N} M_j(C_j h)$$

where $M_j(h)$ is the mgf of x_j.

Hint. Use § 4.4.

7. The *factorial moment* of order r of the discrete distribution $f(x)$ is defined by

$$\nu_{(r)} = \sum_x x^{(r)} f(x)$$

where

$$x^{(r)} \equiv x(x - 1)(x - 2) \cdots (x - r + 1)$$

Show that the *factorial moment-generating function* is

$$H(h) = \sum_x (1 + h)^x f(x)$$

8. Find the moment-generating function for the triangular distribution defined by

$$f(x) = x, \quad 0 \leq x \leq 1$$
$$f(x) = 2 - x, \quad 1 \leq x \leq 2$$

Ans. $(e^h - 1)^2/h^2$.

9. Calculate the first four cumulants of the binomial distribution.

10. If $f(x) = (2/b)(1 - x/b), 0 \leq x \leq b$, show that $\int_0^b f(x)\, dx = 1$ and prove that the mgf is

$$\sum_{r=0}^{\infty} \frac{2b^r}{(r + 1)(r + 2)} \frac{h^r}{r!}$$

Hence find the expectation and variance of x. *Ans.* $b/3, b^2/18$.

11. Find the effect on the mgf of the binomial distribution, $(q + pe^h)^s$, of changing the variable from x to

$$u = \frac{x - sp}{(spq)^{1/2}}$$

12. If x_1 and x_2 are independent variates, each having a rectangular distribution with range 1, show that $x_1 + x_2$ has a triangular distribution.

13. Suppose X has a continuous distribution function $F(x)$. What are the distribution functions of (a) $Y = e^X$, (b) $Y = \sin X$, (c) $Y = F(X)$.

Hint. $\Pr\{e^X \leq x\} = \Pr\{X \leq \log x\}$.

Ans. (a) $F(\log x), 0 < x < \infty; 0$ for $x < 0$.

(b) $\sum_{n=-\infty}^{\infty} [F(2n\pi + \sin^{-1} x) - F\{(2n-1)\pi - \sin^{-1} x\}]$.

(c) $x, 0 < x < 1; 0, x \leq 0; 1, x \geq 1$.

14. If $F(x) = 0$ when $x \leq 0$, and $F(x) = 1 - e^{-2x}$ when $x > 0$, show that $M(h) = 2/(2-h)$, $h < 2$, and find the mean, standard deviation, skewness, and excess of kurtosis of this distribution. *Ans.* $\frac{1}{2}, \frac{1}{2}, 2, 6$.

15. Let X be rectangularly distributed on the interval 0 to 1, so that $\Pr\{x_1 < X \leq x_2\} = x_2 - x_1$, where $0 \leq x_1 < x_2 \leq 1$.

Let the decimal expansion of X be $0.a_1 a_2 a_3 \cdots$ and suppose that every terminating decimal greater than zero is replaced by the equivalent non-terminating one (*e.g.*, 0.5 is replaced by $0.4999\cdots$). The distribution of a_1 is a discrete distribution in which each integer value 0 to 9 occurs with probability $1/10$, since $a_1 = k$ when $k/10 < X \leq (k+1)/10$.

Prove that (a) the distribution of a_n is the same as the *conditional* distribution of a_n when $a_1, a_2, \cdots a_{n-1}$ are fixed.

(b) If $X' = 0.a_1 a_3 a_5 \cdots$, the distribution of X' is rectangular on 0, 1.

(c) If $X'' = 0.a_2 a_4 a_6 \cdots$, the distribution of X'' is the same as that of X', the two are independent, and the joint distribution is a uniform distribution over the unit square.

16. If X_1 and X_2 are independently and rectangularly distributed on the interval 0 to 1, find the distribution function and density function for $Y = X_2/X_1$.

Hint. Draw a diagram, shading the area within the unit square for which $X_2/X_1 \leq x$. The distribution function is equal to the shaded area. There are separate cases for $x < 1$ and $x > 1$.

17. If X_1 and X_2 are independently and rectangularly distributed on the interval 0 to 1, find the distribution function and density function for $Y = \max(X_1, X_2)$, that is, Y is equal to the greatest of X_1 and X_2.

18. If X_1 and X_2 are normally and independently distributed with mean 0 and variance 1, and if

$$Y_1 = m_1 + l_{11} X_1 + l_{12} X_2$$
$$Y_2 = m_2 + l_{21} X_1 + l_{22} X_2$$

show that Y_1 and Y_2 are normally distributed with means m_1 and m_2, variances $\mu_{20} = l_{11}^2 + l_{12}^2$, $\mu_{02} = l_{21}^2 + l_{22}^2$ and covariance $\mu_{11} = l_{11} l_{21} + l_{12} l_{22}$.

The joint probability distribution of Y_1 and Y_2 is called the *bivariate normal distribution*. It is characterized by five parameters, $m_1, m_2, \mu_{10}, \mu_{01}, \mu_{11}$.

19. Prove that the density function for the bivariate normal distribution of Problem 18 is

$$\frac{1}{2\pi\{\mu_{20}\mu_{02}(1-\rho^2)\}^{1/2}} \exp\left[-\frac{1}{2(1-\rho^2)}\left\{\frac{(y_1-m_1)^2}{\mu_{20}} + \frac{(y_2-m_2)^2}{\mu_{02}} - \frac{2\rho^2(y_1-m_1)(y_2-m_2)}{\mu_{11}}\right\}\right]$$

where $\rho^2 = \mu_{11}^2/\mu_{20}\mu_{02}$.

Hint. The joint density function for x_1 and x_2 is $(1/2\pi)e^{-\frac{1}{2}(x_1^2 + x_2^2)}$. Put

$$y_1 = m_1 + l_{11} x_1 + l_{12} x_2$$
$$y_2 = m_2 + l_{21} x_1 + l_{22} x_2$$

and assume that $\begin{vmatrix} l_{11} & l_{12} \\ l_{21} & l_{22} \end{vmatrix}$ is not zero.

If this determinant is zero, the distribution is said to be *singular*. In this case we can write

$$y_1 = m_1 + x_3, \qquad y_2 = m_2 + \frac{l_{21}}{l_{11}} x_3$$

where $x_3 = l_{11} x_1 + l_{12} x_2$.

20. Prove that, if $y = \sum_{1}^{N} c_i x_i$ is a linear function of correlated variates x_i which all possess finite variances σ_i^2, then the variance of y is given by

$$\text{Var}(y) = \sum_i c_i^2 \sigma_i^2 + \sum_{i \neq j} c_i c_j \rho_{ij} \sigma_i \sigma_j$$

where ρ_{ij} is the coefficient of correlation between x_i and x_j. (Cf. Theorem 4.11, which corresponds to the case $\rho_{ij} = 0$.)
Hint. As in (4.32),

$$\text{Var}(y) = E\{\sum_i c_i(x_i - \nu_1^{(i)})^2\}$$

Use Theorem 4.8.

21. Calculate the factorial mgf and the rth factorial moment for the Poisson distribution. (See Problem 7.)

22. A discrete distribution is defined by $f(x) = p(1 - p)^x$, where $0 < p < 1$ and $x = 0, 1, 2, 3 \cdots$. Calculate the factorial mgf and the rth factorial moment for this distribution.

23. A sample of N is taken from a population having the distribution defined by $f(x) = p(1 - p)^x$, $0 < p < 1$, $x = 0, 1, 2, 3, \cdots$. The frequencies of $0, 1, 2, 3, \cdots$ in the sample are $f_0, f_1, f_2, f_3, \cdots$, where $\sum_{i=0}^{\infty} f_i = N$.

Calculate the probability of this observed sample, and find for what value of p this probability is a maximum. The value so defined is known as a *maximum likelihood estimate* of p. It is, of course, a function of the sample frequencies. *Ans.* $p = (1 + \bar{x})^{-1}$, where $\bar{x}$ is the mean value of x for the sample.

References

1. Some of the material on moment-generating functions in this chapter is adapted from an article by J. F. Kenney, "Characteristic Functions in Statistics," *National Mathematics Magazine*, **17**, 1942, pp. 1–32. See also J. H. Curtiss, "Generating Functions in the Theory of Statistics," *Amer. Math. Monthly*, **48**, 1941, pp. 374–386.

2. A comprehensive table of functions and their Fourier transforms is given in Campbell and Foster, *Fourier Integrals for Practical Applications* (Van Nostrand, 1948).

3. T. N. Thiele, "The Theory of Observations," 1903, reprinted in *Ann. Math. Stat.*, **2**, 1931, pp. 165–307.

4. R. A. Fisher, *Statistical Methods for Research Workers*, 10th ed., 1947, p. 73.

5. See, *e.g.*, K. Knopp, *Theory and Application of Infinite Series*, p. 183.

6. M. G. Kendall, *The Advanced Theory of Statistics*, Vol. I, 1947, pp. 68–79.

7. For the treatment of this section, the authors are indebted to lecture notes by Prof. H. Robbins, Institute of Statistics, University of North Carolina.

8. See, *e.g.*, a discussion in Cramér, *Methods of Mathematical Statistics*, pp. 213–219.

9. W. Feller, *Math. Zeit.*, **40**, 1935, p. 521 and *Math. Zeit.*, **42**, 1937, p. 301.

CHAPTER V

THE GAMMA, BETA, AND CHI-SQUARE DISTRIBUTIONS; THE PEARSON AND GRAM-CHARLIER SYSTEMS OF CURVES; CURVE FITTING

5.1 The Gamma Distribution. A continuous variable x, distributed with probability density

(5.1) $\quad f(x) = e^{-x} x^{m-1} / \Gamma(m), \quad 0 \leq x < \infty, \quad m > 0$

may be called, following Weatherburn,[1] a *Gamma variate* with parameter m, or, for short, a $\gamma(m)$ *variate*.

The curve of $f(x)$ is asymptotic to the x axis, and touches it at $x = 0$ if $m > 2$. This curve belongs to Type III of the Pearson system of curves which will be described later.

The rth moment about the origin is given by

(5.2) $\quad \nu_r = \dfrac{1}{\Gamma(m)} \displaystyle\int_0^\infty e^{-x} x^{m-1+r} \, dx$

$\qquad\qquad = \dfrac{\Gamma(m+r)}{\Gamma(m)} = m(m+1) \cdots (m+r-1)$

Hence

$\qquad\qquad \nu_1 = m$
$\qquad\qquad \nu_2 = m(m+1), \quad$ etc.

and

(5.3) $\quad \begin{cases} \mu_2 = m \\ \mu_3 = 2m \\ \mu_4 = 3m^2 + 6m \\ \quad \cdots \cdots \end{cases}$

Skewness and excess of kurtosis are therefore given by

(5.4) $\quad \gamma_1 = 2m^{-1/2}, \quad \gamma_2 = 6m^{-1}$

The mgf is

(5.5) $\quad M(h) = \dfrac{1}{\Gamma(m)} \displaystyle\int_0^\infty e^{(h-1)x} x^{m-1} \, dx$

$\qquad\qquad = \dfrac{1}{\Gamma(m)} \displaystyle\int_0^\infty e^{-u} \left(\dfrac{u}{1-h}\right)^{m-1} \dfrac{du}{1-h}, \quad h < 1$

$\qquad\qquad = (1 - h)^{-m}$

Hence the cgf is

(5.6) $\quad K(h) = -m \log(1 - h)$

$\qquad\qquad = m \left[h + \dfrac{h^2}{2} + \dfrac{h^3}{3} + \cdots \right]$

for $|h| < 1$.

The rth cumulant is therefore
(5.7) $$\kappa_r = m(r-1)! = m\Gamma(r)$$

Theorem 5.1. *If $x_1, x_2, \cdots x_N$ are independent Gamma variates with parameters $m_1, m_2, \cdots m_N$, then $X = \sum_{i=1}^{N} x_i$ is a Gamma variate with parameter $M = \sum_{i=1}^{N} m_i$.*

Proof: The cgf of X is
$$K(h) = \sum_i K_i(h) = -\sum_i m_i \log(1-h)$$
$$= -M \log(1-h)$$

Theorem 5.2. *If x is a normal variate with mean ν_1 and standard deviation σ, and if $v = (x-\nu_1)^2/2\sigma^2$, then v is a Gamma variate with parameter $\frac{1}{2}$.*

Proof: The frequency function for x is
$$f(x) = \frac{1}{\sigma\sqrt{2\pi}} e^{-v}$$

The probability of a value of v between v and $v+dv$ is
$$f(v)\,dv = 2f(x)\,dx$$
since as x goes from $-\infty$ to $+\infty$, v goes from ∞ to 0 and back again from 0 to ∞.

Since
$$dv = \frac{x-\nu_1}{\sigma^2}\,dx = (2v)^{1/2}\sigma^{-1}\,dx$$
we have
$$f(v) = \frac{2}{\sigma\sqrt{2\pi}} e^{-v} \frac{\sigma}{(2v)^{1/2}}$$
$$= v^{-1/2} e^{-v} / \Gamma(\tfrac{1}{2})$$
which is the frequency function of a $\gamma(\frac{1}{2})$ variate.

5.2 The Beta Distributions. A continuous variable x, distributed with a probability density
(5.8) $$f(x) = x^{l-1}(1-x)^{m-1}/\mathrm{B}(l,m), \qquad 0 \le x \le 1$$
will be called a *Beta variate* with parameters l and m or, for short, a $\beta(l,m)$ variate.

Since by (3.22),
(5.9) $$\mathrm{B}(l,m) = \int_0^\infty x^{m-1}(1+x)^{-l-m}\,dx$$
we can also speak of a continuous variable with probability density
(5.10) $$f(x) = x^{l-1}(1+x)^{-l-m}/\mathrm{B}(l,m), \qquad 0 \le x < \infty$$

as a Beta variate. To distinguish the two cases we will call it a *Beta-prime variate* or $\beta'(l, m)$ *variate*. The curve of $f(x)$ given by (5.8) belongs to Pearson's Type I, and that given by (5.10) to Type VI.

If $l > 2$, the curve of (5.8) is tangential to the axis at the origin, and if $m > 2$ it is tangential at $x = 1$. The rth moment about zero is given by

$$(5.11) \quad \nu_r = \frac{1}{\mathrm{B}(l, m)} \int_0^1 x^{l+r-1}(1 - x)^{m-1}\, dx$$

$$= \frac{\mathrm{B}(l + r, m)}{\mathrm{B}(l, m)} = \frac{l(l + 1) \cdots (l + r - 1)}{(l + m)(l + m + 1) \cdots (l + m + r - 1)}$$

Hence

$$(5.12) \quad \begin{cases} \nu_1 = \dfrac{l}{l + m}, & \nu_2 = \dfrac{l(l + 1)}{(l + m)(l + m + 1)} \\[2mm] \mu_2 = \nu_2 - \nu_1^2 = \dfrac{lm}{(l + m)^2(l + m + 1)}, & \text{etc.} \end{cases}$$

The curve of (5.10) is asymptotic to the x axis, and touches it at $x = 0$ if $l > 2$. The rth moment about zero is given by

$$(5.13) \quad \nu_r = \frac{1}{\mathrm{B}(l, m)} \int_0^\infty x^{l+r-1}(1 + x)^{-l-m}\, dx$$

$$= \frac{\mathrm{B}(l + r, m - r)}{\mathrm{B}(l, m)} = \frac{l(l + 1) \cdots (l + r - 1)}{(m - 1)(m - 2) \cdots (m - r)}$$

if $r < m$. Therefore

$$(5.14) \quad \begin{cases} \nu_1 = \dfrac{l}{m - 1}, & \nu_2 = \dfrac{l(l + 1)}{(m - 1)(m - 2)} \\[2mm] \mu_2 = \dfrac{l(l + m - 1)}{(m - 1)^2(m - 2)}, & \text{etc.} \end{cases}$$

The method of proof used in the following two theorems is one that is frequently useful in obtaining new distributions.

Theorem 5.3. *If x and y are independent Gamma variates with parameters l and m respectively, then $x/(x + y)$ is a Beta variate with parameters l, m.*

Proof: The joint probability density for x and y is

$$(5.15) \quad f(x, y) = \frac{1}{\Gamma(l)\Gamma(m)} e^{-(x+y)} x^{l-1} y^{m-1}$$

where $0 \leq x < \infty$, $0 \leq y < \infty$.

We introduce new variables u and v, given by

$$(5.16) \quad u = x + y, \qquad v = x/(x + y),$$

or $x = uv$, $y = u(1 - v)$, and find the joint probability density for u and v. Then by integrating out either variable we have the probability density for the other one.

The Jacobian of the transformation is

Sec. 2 The Beta Distributions 97

(5.17) $$J\left(\frac{x, y}{u, v}\right) = \begin{vmatrix} v & u \\ 1 - v & -u \end{vmatrix} = -u$$

Hence $dx\, dy = u\, du\, dv$, and the probability density is given by
$$g(u, v)\, du\, dv = f(x, y)\, dx\, dy = f(x, y)u\, du\, dv$$
or

(5.18) $$g(u, v) = \frac{u}{\Gamma(l)\Gamma(m)} e^{-u}(uv)^{l-1}u^{m-1}(1 - v)^{m-1}$$
$$= \frac{1}{\Gamma(l)\Gamma(m)} e^{-u}u^{l+m-1}v^{l-1}(1 - v)^{m-1}$$

The range of u is from 0 to ∞ and of v from 0 to 1. The distribution of u is therefore given by

(5.19) $$f(u) = \int_0^1 g(u, v)\, dv = \frac{e^{-u}u^{l+m-1}}{\Gamma(l + m)}$$

showing that u is a $\gamma(l + m)$ variate, as already proved in Theorem 5.1.
The distribution of v is given by

(5.20) $$h(v) = \int_0^\infty g(u, v)\, du = \frac{v^{l-1}(1 - v)^{m-1}}{B(l, m)}$$

showing that v is a $\beta(l, m)$ variate.

Theorem 5.4. *If x and y are independent Gamma variates with parameters l and m respectively, then x/y is a Beta-prime variate with parameters l, m.*

Proof: Let $u = x + y$, $v = x/y$. Then
$$J\left(\frac{u, v}{x, y}\right) = \begin{vmatrix} 1 & 1 \\ \frac{1}{y} & -\frac{x}{y^2} \end{vmatrix} = -\frac{x + y}{y^2} = -\frac{(1 + v)^2}{u}$$

Therefore
$$J\left(\frac{x, y}{u, v}\right) = -\frac{u}{(1 + v)^2}$$
and
$$dx\, dy = \frac{u}{(1 + v)^2} du\, dv$$

The joint probability density of u and v is

(5.21) $$g(u, v) = \frac{1}{\Gamma(l)\Gamma(m)} e^{-u}\left(\frac{uv}{1 + v}\right)^{l-1}\left(\frac{u}{1 + v}\right)^{m-1} \frac{u}{(1 + v)^2}$$
$$= \frac{1}{\Gamma(l)\Gamma(m)} e^{-u}u^{l+m-1}v^{l-1}(1 + v)^{-l-m}$$

The range of u is from 0 to ∞ and of v from 0 to ∞. Hence the probability density for v is

(5.22) $$h(v) = \int_0^\infty g(u, v)\, du = \frac{v^{l-1}(1 + v)^{-l-m}}{B(l, m)}$$

which is the frequency function of a $\beta'(l, m)$ variate.

5.3 The Chi-square Distribution.

Theorem 5.5. *If x_i, $i = 1, 2, \cdots n$, are independent, normally distributed variables, with means μ_i and variances σ_i^2, then the quantity defined by*

$$\frac{1}{2}\chi^2 = \sum_{i=1}^{n} \frac{(x_i - \mu_i)^2}{2\sigma_i^2} \tag{5.23}$$

is a Gamma variate with parameter $n/2$.

Proof: By Theorem 5.2, $\frac{1}{2}\chi^2 = \sum u_i$, where u_i is a $\gamma(\frac{1}{2})$ variate. Hence, by Theorem 5.1, $\frac{1}{2}\chi^2$ is a $\gamma(n/2)$ variate.

The probability density is therefore given by

$$f(\tfrac{1}{2}\chi^2)\, d(\tfrac{1}{2}\chi^2) = \frac{1}{\Gamma\left(\dfrac{n}{2}\right)} e^{-\frac{1}{2}\chi^2}(\tfrac{1}{2}\chi^2)^{(n/2)-1}\, d(\tfrac{1}{2}\chi^2) \tag{5.24}$$

The rth moment of the distribution of χ^2 is

$$\nu_r = 2^r \frac{\Gamma\!\left(r + \dfrac{n}{2}\right)}{\Gamma\!\left(\dfrac{n}{2}\right)} = n(n+2)(n+4)\cdots(n+2r-2) \tag{5.25}$$

since the effect of multiplying the variable by 2 is to multiply the rth moment about zero by 2^r.

The rth cumulant is, by (5.7),

$$\kappa_r = 2^r \Gamma(r)\, \frac{n}{2} = 2^{r-1}(r-1)!\, n \tag{5.26}$$

Consequently

$$\begin{cases} \mu_2 = 2n \\ \mu_3 = 8n \\ \mu_4 = 12n^2 + 48n, \quad \text{etc.,} \end{cases} \tag{5.27}$$

and

$$\begin{cases} \kappa_1 = n \\ \kappa_2 = 2n \\ \kappa_3 = 8n \\ \kappa_4 = 48n, \quad \text{etc.} \end{cases} \tag{5.28}$$

The distribution has a positive skewness $(8/n)^{1/2}$ and a positive kurtosis $12/n$, both tending to zero as n increases. The number n, which is the number of squares of independent normal standardized variates added to produce χ^2, is called the number of "degrees of freedom" (§ 7.3).

The chi-square distribution is one of the most important in mathematical statistics. Some of the reasons for this will appear later. Meanwhile we note that the chi-square distribution shares the reproductive property of the Gamma variates.

Theorem 5.6. *If x and y are independently distributed as χ^2 with n_1 and n_2*

degrees of freedom respectively, then $x + y$ is distributed as χ^2 with $n_1 + n_2$ degrees of freedom.

This is an immediate corollary of Theorems 5.1 and 5.5. The converse theorem is often useful, namely,

Theorem 5.7. *If the sum of two independent positive variates is a $\chi^2(n_1 + n_2)$ variate, and one of them is a $\chi^2(n_1)$ variate, then the other is a $\chi^2(n_2)$ variate.*

Proof: The mgf of a $\gamma(n_1/2)$ variate is $(1-h)^{-n_1/2}$. Hence if $M(h)$ is the mgf of the second variate,

$$(1-h)^{-(n_1+n_2)/2} = (1-h)^{-n_1/2} M(h)$$

whence

$$M(h) = (1-h)^{-n_2/2}$$

Theorem 5.8. *For large values of n, $\sqrt{2\chi^2}$ is approximately normally distributed about $\sqrt{2n}$ with unit variance.*

Proof: The mgf of χ^2 is $(1-2h)^{-n/2}$. Hence the mgf of the standardized variable $(\chi^2 - n)/\sqrt{2n}$ is

$$e^{-nh/\sqrt{2n}}\left(1 - \frac{2h}{\sqrt{2n}}\right)^{-n/2} = \left\{e^{h\sqrt{2/n}}\left(1 - \sqrt{\frac{2}{n}}h\right)\right\}^{-n/2}$$

$$= \left\{1 - \frac{h^2}{n} - \left(\frac{2}{n}\right)^{3/2}\frac{h^3}{3} - \cdots\right\}^{-n/2}$$

For a fixed value of h we can take n so large that this $\to e^{h^2/2}$, which is the mgf of the standardized normal law.

Hence $(\chi^2 - n)/(2n)^{1/2}$ tends to a normal distribution with mean zero and unit variance.

Now the distribution function of $\sqrt{2\chi^2} - \sqrt{2n}$ is equal to the probability that

$$\sqrt{2\chi^2} - \sqrt{2n} \leq x = \Pr\{\chi^2 \leq \tfrac{1}{2}[x + (2n)^{1/2}]^2\}$$
$$= \Pr\{(\chi^2 - n)/(2n)^{1/2} \leq x + \tfrac{1}{2}x^2/(2n)^{1/2}\}$$

As $n \to \infty$, this tends to the limit of the probability that $(\chi^2 - n)/(2n)^{1/2} \leq x$, which is $\Phi(x)$ defined in (2.38), as just proved. Hence $(2\chi^2)^{1/2} - (2n)^{1/2}$ is approximately a standard normal variate, for large n.

The above investigation does not indicate how good the approximation is for moderate values of n. Fisher has shown that it is improved by putting $\sqrt{2n-1}$ instead of $\sqrt{2n}$. This approximation is often used to calculate χ^2, for values of n larger than about 30.

A still better approximation is that of Wilson and Hilferty [2] who showed that $(\chi^2/n)^{1/3}$ is very nearly normally distributed about $1 - 2/9n$ with a variance of $2/9n$.

Thus, to calculate the 95% point for χ^2, that is, the value of u such that $\Pr\{\chi^2 \leq u\} = 0.95$, we write

$$(5.29) \qquad \chi^2 \approx n\left[1 - \frac{2}{9n} + t\left(\frac{2}{9n}\right)^{1/2}\right]^3$$

where $t = 1.645$, corresponding to $\Phi(t) = 0.95$. For $n = 30$, this gives $\chi^2 = 43.77$, which is correct. The Fisher approximation is 43.49.

5.4 Distribution of Sums of Squares. The following theorems are often useful in determining the frequency function for a variate.

Theorem 5.9 (*Fisher's Theorem*). *Let A be a sum of squares of n independent normal standardized variates x_i, and suppose $A = B + C$, where B is a quadratic form in the x_i, distributed as χ^2 with h degrees of freedom. Then C is distributed as χ^2 with $n - h$ degrees of freedom, and is independent of B.*

Proof: A is distributed as χ^2 with n df. B is a sum of squares of h orthogonal linear functions, $y_1, y_2, \cdots y_h$, of the x_i. By § 4.13 we can find $n - h$ further functions $y_{h+1}, \cdots y_n$, which are orthogonal among themselves and also to $y_1, y_2, \cdots y_h$, and are such that

$$\sum_1^n x_i^2 = \sum_1^n y_j^2$$

Hence $A = B + \sum_{j=h+1}^{n} y_j^2$, so that C is the sum of $n - h$ squares of independent normal variates. It follows that C is distributed as χ^2 with $n - h$ df, independently of B. The theorem can be extended as follows

Theorem 5.10. *If $A = B_1 + B_2 + \cdots + B_k + C$, where $A = \sum_1^n x_i^2$ and $B_i (i = 1, 2, \cdots k)$, is a sum of squares of n_i variates y_i which are independent linear functions of the x_i, and $\sum_1^k n_i < n$, then C is distributed as χ^2 with $n - \sum n_i$ degrees of freedom independently of the B_i.*

A converse of this theorem, given by Cochran,[3] states that, if B and C are distributed as χ^2 with n_1 and n_2 df and if $A = B + C$ is distributed as χ^2 with $n_1 + n_2$ df, then B and C are independent. This is not, in general, true, but if B and C are *not* independent they must be related in a special way. If we think of the joint frequency function $f(x_1, x_2)$ of the variables x_1 and x_2, where $0 \leq x_1 < \infty$ and $0 \leq x_2 < \infty$, as a distribution of mass over the first quadrant of the $x_1 x_2$ plane, then it is clearly possible to remove some of this mass in some places and redistribute it in other places in such a way as to keep both marginal distributions unaltered and also so as to keep the total mass unaltered along any line $x_1 + x_2 =$ constant. (This last condition requires that if mass is removed at any point an equal quantity must be deposited at the mirror image of that point in the diagonal line $x_1 = x_2$, and if mass is deposited anywhere an equal quantity must be removed at the mirror image.)

If originally x_1 and x_2 were independently distributed, so that $f(x_1, x_2) = f_1(x_1) f_2(x_2)$, this would no longer be true after the redistribution, but the distributions of x_1, x_2 and $x_1 + x_2$ would all be unaffected. The theorem is therefore not always true. It is true if B is a sum of squares of independent linear functions.

Problems

1. Sketch the curves of the Gamma distributions with values 1, 2, 3, of the parameter. Since $\Gamma(m) = (m - 1)!$, tables of the Poisson function may conveniently be used here.

2. Prove that the mode of a $\gamma(m)$ variate, $m > 1$, is at $x = m - 1$. Hence show that Pearson's definition of skewness,

$$\text{Sk}_P = \frac{\text{mean} - \text{mode}}{\text{standard deviation}}$$

gives, for this variate, a value one half that of the moment definition,

$$\text{Sk}_M = \gamma_1$$

3. Prove that the mode of a $\beta(l, m)$ variate, $l > 1$, $m > 1$, is at $x = (l - 1)/(l + m - 2)$, and the mode of a $\beta'(l, m)$ variate, $l > 1$, is at $x = (l - 1)/(m + 1)$.

4. Sketch the curves of a $\beta(\frac{3}{2}, 2)$ distribution and of a $\beta'(\frac{3}{2}, 1)$ distribution.

5. Prove that, if x is a $\beta'(l, m)$ variate, then $1/x$ is a $\beta'(m, l)$ variate.

6. Prove that if x and y are independent normal standard variates (that is, with mean zero and variance 1), then $z = x/y$ has a Cauchy distribution. (See Problem 4, Chapter IV.)

Hint. By Theorem 5.2, $x^2/2$ and $y^2/2$ are $\gamma(\frac{1}{2})$ variates. Therefore, by Theorem 5.4, z^2 is a $\beta'(\frac{1}{2}, \frac{1}{2})$ variate. Hence obtain the distribution of z and show that its frequency function is $\pi^{-1}(1 + z^2)^{-1}$. Note that z goes from $-\infty$ to ∞ but z^2 only from 0 to ∞.

7. Prove that if x is a $\beta(l, m)$ variate, then $(1 - x)/x$ and $x/(1 - x)$ are $\beta'(m, l)$ and $\beta'(l, m)$ variates respectively. (See Problem 5.)

8. Prove that if $n = 1$, the distribution of χ (not χ^2) is normal.

Hint. In eq. (5.24) note that $d(\chi^2/2) = \chi \, d\chi$, and that as χ goes from $-\infty$ to ∞, χ^2 goes from ∞ to 0 and back again from 0 to ∞.

5.5 Pearson System. There are two systems of generalized frequency curves in common use: the *Pearson system* and the *Gram-Charlier system*.

During the years 1895–1916 Karl Pearson published papers in which he showed that a set of frequency curves could be obtained by assigning values to the parameters in a certain first order differential equation. The Pearson school claimed that all the different types of frequency distributions that arise in practical statistics can be represented by the solutions of this equation.

With regard to the genesis of the Pearson system, one point of view is to regard it as empirical. The differential equation of the normal curve may be written

(5.30) $$dy/dx = y(m - x)/a$$

where $a > 0$. Pearson generalized this by writing

(5.31) $$dy/dx = y(m - x)/(a + bx + cx^2)$$

Among the solutions of (5.31) there are several types of curves, the shapes depending on the parameters a, b, c, and m. Examples of symmetrical, skewed, U-shaped and J-shaped curves with finite and infinite range in either or both directions, are shown in Figure 13.

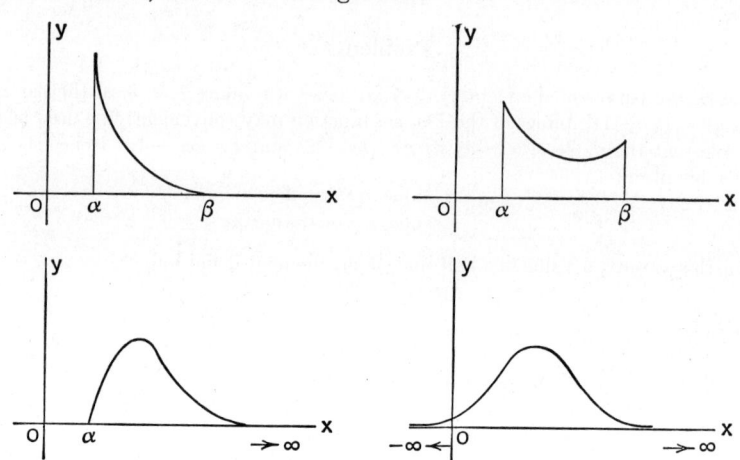

FIG. 13. TYPICAL CURVES OF THE PEARSON SYSTEM

The types of curve are distinguished by the values of $b^2/4ac$, the three main types being

I. $\qquad b^2/4ac < 0, \qquad c_1 \leq x \leq c_2$

where c_1 and c_2 are the roots of $a + bx + cx^2 = 0$.

IV. $\qquad 0 < b^2/4ac < 1, \qquad -\infty < x < \infty$
VI. $\qquad b^2/4ac > 1, \qquad c_1 \leq x < \infty$

where c_1 is the larger root of $a + bx + cx^2 = 0$.

There are two special (symmetrical) types, namely,

II. $\qquad b^2/4ac = 0, \qquad c < 0, \qquad -c_1 \leq x \leq c_1$

where $c_1 = (-a/c)^{1/2}$.

VII. $\qquad b^2/4ac = 0, \qquad c > 0, \qquad -\infty < x < \infty$

There are also two transition types, namely,

III. $\qquad b^2/4ac = \infty, \qquad c = 0, \qquad c_1 \leq x < \infty$

where $c_1 = -a/b$. This is intermediate between Types I and VI.

V. $\qquad b^2/4ac = 1, \qquad c_1 \leq x < \infty$

where $c_1 = -b/2c$. This is intermediate between Types IV and VI.

The normal curve is included in the system as Type O. For this type, b and c are both zero, so that $b^2/4ac$ is indeterminate. There are also some less important particular cases which are sometimes included as additional types.[13]

Sec. 5 Pearson System 103

If a Pearson curve possesses an ordinary mode, it will be at $x = m$. The most useful curves are those for which y vanishes at two values of x, say c_1 and c_2, where c_1 may be $-\infty$ and c_2 may be $+\infty$. If also yx^{r+2} vanishes at both ends of the range, the rth and $(r+1)$th moments exist.

The parameters in (5.31) can be expressed in terms of the moments of the system. Multiplying by x^r and integrating over the range c_1 to c_2, we have

(5.32) $$\int_{c_1}^{c_2} \frac{dy}{dx}(ax^r + bx^{r+1} + cx^{r+2})\, dx = \int_{c_1}^{c_2} y(mx^r - x^{r+1})\, dx$$

Integrating the left-hand side by parts, we obtain

$$\left[y(ax^r + bx^{r+1} + cx^{r+2})\right]_{c_1}^{c_2} - \int_{c_1}^{c_2} y[arx^{r-1} + b(r+1)x^r + c(r+2)x^{r+1}]\, dx$$

and by hypothesis the first term vanishes at c_1 and c_2. Also

(5.33) $$\nu_r = \int_{c_1}^{c_2} yx^r\, dx$$

so that

(5.34) $$ar\nu_{r-1} + b(r+1)\nu_r + c(r+2)\nu_{r+1} = -m\nu_r + \nu_{r+1}$$

Putting $r = 0$ in (5.34) we get

$$b + 2c\nu_1 = -m + \nu_1$$

or

(5.35) $$\nu_1 = (m+b)/(1-2c)$$

Putting $r = 1$ we get

$$a + 2b\nu_1 + 3c\nu_2 = -m\nu_1 + \nu_2$$

or

(5.36) $$\nu_2 = \frac{a + (m+2b)\nu_1}{1 - 3c}$$

If we suppose the variable changed to the standardized form $t = (x - \nu_1)/\sigma$, we shall have in terms of the new variable $\nu_1 = 0$, $\nu_2 = \mu_2 = 1$, $\alpha_r = \mu_r = \nu_r$. Hence $b = -m$, $a = 1 - 3c$, and equation (5.34) becomes

(5.37) $$(1 - 3c)r\alpha_{r-1} - mr\alpha_r + \{c(r+2) - 1\}\alpha_{r+1} = 0$$

Giving r the values 2 and 3, we get

$$2m + (1 - 4c)\alpha_3 = 0$$
$$3(1 - 3c) - 3m\alpha_3 - (1 - 5c)\alpha_4 = 0$$

whence

(5.38) $$\gamma_1 = \alpha_3 = \frac{2m}{4c - 1}, \qquad \gamma_2 = \alpha_4 - 3 = \frac{6(m^2 - 4c^2 + c)}{(4c - 1)(5c - 1)}$$

These relations give the skewness and excess of kurtosis of any of the Pearson curves for which the fourth moment exists. The relations (5.38) may be expressed in the more convenient forms [5]

(5.39) $\quad b = -m = \dfrac{\gamma_1}{2(1+2\delta)}, \quad c = \dfrac{\delta}{2(1+2\delta)}, \quad a = 1 - 3c$
where
$$\delta = (2\gamma_2 - 3\gamma_1^2)/(\gamma_2 + 6)$$
so that when the skewness and kurtosis are known the distribution is determined completely.

In Pearson's *Tables for Statisticians and Biometricians*, Part I, pp. 66 and 67, there are diagrams showing the range of values of $\beta_1(=\sqrt{\gamma_1})$ and $\beta_2(=\gamma_2+3)$ corresponding to the various types. In some regions only U-shaped or J-shaped curves exist. This diagram is reproduced in extended form at the beginning of Part II of the *Tables*.

The Pearson differential equation (5.31) has some theoretical support. If we think of an urn containing n black and white balls, of which np are white and nq black, and if we imagine a sample of s balls drawn without replacements, then according to (2.66) the probability that x of the balls are white is

$$h_n(x, s) = \binom{np}{x}\binom{nq}{s-x} \bigg/ \binom{n}{s}$$

By representing the successive values of $h_n(x, s)$ for $x = 0, 1, 2, \cdots s$ as ordinates of a frequency polygon, it is possible to show [4] that the slope at the mid-point of any side, divided by the ordinate at that point, is equal to a fraction whose numerator is a linear function of x and whose denominator is a quadratic function. On equating this fraction to $(1/y)(dy/dx)$ we obtain (5.31). We have already seen (section 2.9) that even the binomial distribution, when p is not equal to q, approximates to the Pearson Type III form rather than the normal form, although, of course, the Type III curve tends to the normal curve as $s \to \infty$.

5.6 Some Pearson Types.

Type I. The differential equation is

(5.40) $\quad \dfrac{1}{y}\dfrac{dy}{dx} = \dfrac{x-m}{c(x-c_1)(c_2-x)} = \dfrac{m_1}{x-c_1} - \dfrac{m_2}{c_2-x}$

where
$$m_1 = -\dfrac{m-c_1}{c(c_2-c_1)}, \quad m_2 = -\dfrac{c_2-m}{c(c_2-c_1)}$$

both m_1 and m_2 being positive since c is negative.

Integrating, we obtain

(5.41) $\quad\quad\quad\quad y = A(x-c_1)^{m_1}(c_2-x)^{m_2}$

If we change the variable to $u = (x-c_1)/(c_2-c_1)$, so that $1-u = (c_2-x)/(c_2-c_1)$, we have

(5.42) $\quad\quad\quad\quad y = Bu^{m_1}(1-u)^{m_2}$

which shows that u is a Beta variate with parameters m_1+1, m_2+1, and that $1/B = \mathrm{B}(m_1+1, m_2+1)$.

The curve is tangential to the axis at $x = c_1$ if $m_1 > 1$, perpendicular to the axis there if $0 < m_1 < 1$ and asymptotic to the line $x = c_1$ if $m_1 < 0$. Similarly the behavior at $x = c_2$ depends on the value of m_2.

Type VI. The differential equation is

(5.43) $$\frac{1}{y}\frac{dy}{dx} = \frac{m - x}{c(x - c_1)(x - c_2)} = \frac{m_1}{x - c_1} - \frac{m_2}{x - c_2}$$

where $c_2 < c_1 \leq x$, $m_1 = (m - c_1)/c(c_1 - c_2)$, $m_2 = (m - c_2)/c(c_1 - c_2)$. Both m_1 and m_2 are positive, since $c > 0$. Hence

(5.44) $$y = A(x - c_1)^{m_1}(x - c_2)^{-m_2}$$

Putting $u = (x - c_1)/(c_1 - c_2)$, $1 + u = (x - c_2)/(c_1 - c_2)$, we get

(5.45) $$y = Bu^{m_1}(1 + u)^{-m_2}$$

so that u is a Beta-prime variate with parameters $m_1 + 1$, and $m_2 - m_1 - 1$.

Type III. The differential equation is

(5.46) $$\frac{1}{y}\frac{dy}{dx} = \frac{m - x}{b(x - c_1)} = -m_1 + \frac{m_2}{x - c_1}$$

where $c_1 \leq x < \infty$, $m_1 = 1/b$, $m_2 = (m - c_1)/b$. Therefore

(5.47) $$y = Ce^{-m_1 x}(x - c_1)^{m_2}$$

Putting $u = m_1(x - c_1)$, we get

(5.48) $$y = Bu^{m_2}e^{-u}$$

whence u is seen to be a Gamma variate with parameter $m_2 + 1$ and $\Gamma(m_2 + 1) = 1/B$.

If the variable is standardized, $b = -m$, $a = 1$, and $c_1 = -a/b = 1/m$. Also by (5.38) the skewness is given by $\gamma_1 = -2m$, so that

$$m_1 = 2/\gamma_1, \qquad m_2 + 1 = 4/\gamma_1^2$$

Hence the distribution can be expressed in a form in which the skewness is the only parameter, namely,

(5.49) $$y = K(t + A)^{A^2-1}e^{-At}, \qquad -A \leq t < \infty$$

where $A = 2/\gamma_1$ and t is the standardized variable.

For a Type III curve the δ of (5.39) is zero, so that γ_1 and γ_2 are connected by the relation

(5.50) $$2\gamma_2 = 3\gamma_1^2$$

The constant K in (5.49) is determined from the condition

(5.51) $$\int_{-A}^{\infty} y\, dt = 1$$

Putting $A(t + A) = u$, we get

$$Ke^{A^2}A^{-A^2}\int_0^\infty e^{-u}u^{A^2-1}\,du = 1$$

whence

(5.52) $$K = A^{A^2}e^{-A^2}/\Gamma(A^2)$$

The distribution of $2u$ is therefore identical with that of χ^2 with $2A^2$ degrees of freedom. In general, of course, $2A^2$ is not an integer.

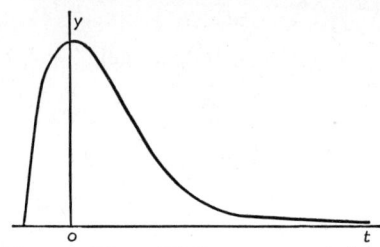

The designation "Type III" is usually restricted to the case for which $A^2 \neq 1$. When $A^2 > 1$, that is, when $|\gamma_1| < 2$, the curve is bell-shaped as shown in Figure 14.

In the Pearson system, the distance from the mode to the mean is $-m = \gamma_1/2(1 + 2\delta)$, and is a measure of skewness. Under the conditions imposed for Type 0, $m = 0$. For Type III, however, $m = -\gamma_1/2$ and therefore we have

FIG. 14. TYPE III CURVE WHEN $|\gamma_1| < 2$

$$\text{mean} - \text{mode} = \frac{\gamma_1}{2}$$

Because of this relation $\gamma_1/2$ is sometimes used as a measure of skewness in observed distributions. The curve for $\gamma_1 = -k$ ($k =$ a constant) is a reflection of that for $\gamma_1 = k$ through the line $t = 0$.

When $A^2 < 1$, that is, when $|\gamma_1| > 2$, the curve is J-shaped with an infinite ordinate at $t = -A$. When $A^2 > 2$, the curve is tangential to the t axis at $t = -A$.

Tables of ordinates and areas of the Type III curve have been published by Salvosa * in the *Annals of Mathematical Statistics*, **1**, 1930, p. 191.

Type VII. The differential equation is of the form

(5.53) $$\frac{1}{y}\frac{dy}{dx} = \frac{m-x}{c(x^2+k^2)}, \qquad -\infty < x < \infty$$

where $k^2 = a/c$. If the variable is standardized, $m = b = 0$ and $k^2 = 1/c - 3$. We obtain on integration, calling the standardized variable u,

$$\log y = -\frac{1}{2c}\log(u^2 + k^2) + A$$

or

(5.54) $$y = B(u^2 + k^2)^{(k^2+3)/2}$$

* These tables have been republished by Edwards Bros., Ann Arbor, Michigan.

This is a symmetrical curve, asymptotic to the x axis in both directions. Putting $u = kt(k^2 + 2)^{-1/2}$, $n = k^2 + 2$, we find that the distribution of t is given by

$$(5.55) \qquad f(t) = B_1(1 + t^2/n)^{-(n+1)/2},$$

which is a very important distribution in statistics, usually known as *Student's t-distribution*. Its genesis will be discussed later in connection with sampling theory.

A systematic treatment of all the curves in the Pearson system has been given in a paper by C. C. Craig.[5]

5.7 Gram-Charlier and Edgeworth Series. Distributions are often encountered which are approximately normal and whose frequency functions may be represented by a series of terms of which the first corresponds to the normal law while the others rapidly decrease in importance. We shall assume that the variable has been standardized, and denote it by $t = (x - \nu_1)/\sigma$.

By repeatedly differentiating the function $e^{-t^2/2}$ we obtain

$$\frac{d}{dt}(e^{-t^2/2}) = -te^{-t^2/2}$$

$$\frac{d^2}{dt^2}(e^{-t^2/2}) = (t^2 - 1)e^{-t^2/2}$$

$$\frac{d^3}{dt^3}(e^{-t^2/2}) = -(t^3 - 3t)e^{-t^2/2}$$

and in general

$$(5.56) \qquad \frac{d^n}{dt^n}(e^{-t^2/2}) = (-1)^n H_n(t) e^{-t^2/2}$$

where $H_n(t)$ is a polynomial in t, of degree n, called the *nth Hermite polynomial*. By repeated integration by parts it is easy to show that

$$(5.57) \qquad (2\pi)^{-1/2} \int_{-\infty}^{\infty} H_m(t) \cdot H_n(t) e^{-t^2/2} \, dt = \begin{cases} n! & \text{if } m = n \\ 0 & \text{if } m \neq n \end{cases}$$

Hence if $\phi(t)$ stands for $(2\pi)^{-1/2} e^{-t^2/2}$ and if we assume that a given frequency function can be expanded in a series

$$(5.58) \qquad f(t) = c_0 \phi(t) + c_1 \phi'(t) + \cdots + c_n \phi^{(n)}(t) + \cdots$$

we can formally obtain the constants in the series by means of (5.57). Multiplying (5.58) by $H_n(t)$ and integrating term by term, we have

$$(5.59) \qquad \int_{-\infty}^{\infty} f(t) H_n(t) \, dt = \sum_j c_j \int_{-\infty}^{\infty} \phi^{(j)}(t) H_n(t) \, dt = (-1)^n n! \, c_n$$

since all terms in the sum except that for which $j = n$ give zero on integration. Substituting $H_0 = 1$, $H_1 = t$, $H_2 = t^2 - 1$, $H_3 = t^3 - 3t$, $H_4 = t^4 - 6t^2 + 3$, we obtain

(5.60)
$$\begin{cases} c_0 = \int_{-\infty}^{\infty} f(t)\, dt = 1 \\ c_1 = -\int_{-\infty}^{\infty} tf(t)\, dt = 0 \\ c_2 = \int_{-\infty}^{\infty} (t^2 - 1)f(t)\, dt = 0 \\ c_3 = -\alpha_3/3! = -\gamma_1/6 \\ c_4 = (\alpha_4 - 6 + 3)/4! = \gamma_2/24 \end{cases}$$

Therefore

(5.61) $$f(t) = \phi(t) - \frac{\gamma_1}{6} \phi^{(3)}(t) + \frac{\gamma_2}{24} \phi^{(4)}(t) - \cdots$$

This is the *Gram-Charlier A series*. It has been shown[6] that the series is not convergent except under rather restrictive conditions. However, the important thing is not whether the series converges but whether a few terms provide a good approximation to $f(t)$. We know that, if a variable x is the sum of n independent random variables, then, under the conditions of the Central Limit Theorem, the distribution function of $t = (x - \nu_1)/\sigma$ is for large n approximately equal to $\Phi(t)$. Also, if the independent variables all possess continuous frequency functions, the frequency function of x is, under rather general conditions, approximately equal to $\phi(t)$. The question now is whether the approximation will be improved by including additional terms beyond the first in (5.61). It appears that from this point of view the coefficients in (5.61) do not steadily decrease as the order of the derivative increases. In fact, while c_3, c_4, c_5 are of orders $n^{-1/2}$, n^{-1}, $n^{-3/2}$ respectively, c_6 is again of order n^{-1}. Hence if we decide to include the term in $\phi^{(4)}(t)$ we should also include the term in $\phi^{(6)}(t)$ since it is of the same order of magnitude.

Edgeworth introduced a more satisfactory series, which is a straightforward expansion in powers of n, and is an asymptotic series with a remainder term of the same order as the first term neglected. It may be written

(5.62) $$f(t) = \phi(t) - \frac{\gamma_1}{3!} \phi^{(3)}(t) + \left\{ \frac{\gamma_2}{4!} \phi^{(4)}(t) + \frac{10\gamma_1^2}{6!} \phi^{(6)}(t) \right\} + \cdots$$

The mode of this distribution is at $-\frac{1}{2}\gamma_1$ approximately.

Tables giving the area and ordinate of the standardized normal curve, as well as the derivatives of all orders from the 2nd to the 8th, may be found in Glover's *Tables of Applied Mathematics in Finance, Insurance, Statistics*. Four-figure tables of the 2nd, 3rd, and 4th derivatives are given in the Chemical Rubber Company's *Handbook of Chemistry and Physics*.

5.8 Curve Fitting. The attempt is often made to fit one of the known theoretical distributions to an empirical distribution obtained from a sample. If the fit is satisfactory, it is a reasonable hypothesis, not disproved by the data, that the parent population from which the sample was obtained does,

Sec. 8 Curve Fitting

in fact, follow the theoretical distribution in respect of the particular quality measured.

The usual procedure in fitting is the "method of moments" advocated by Karl Pearson and his school. The first few moments of the given distribution are calculated and used to estimate the corresponding moments for the hypothetical parent population. A suitable type of theoretical curve is selected on the basis of these moments, and the parameters of the curve are determined. The curve may then be drawn and compared with the empirical distribution of the sample. The goodness of fit is judged by means of the chi-square criterion which will be discussed later, in § 5.14.

In Chapter XII it will be shown that this method of moments is not (except for the normal, binomial, and Poisson distributions) the most efficient method of estimating the parameters, efficiency being judged by the smallness of the sampling variance of the statistics used for estimation. Moreover, the chi-square criterion is not strictly appropriate unless the estimation is done by a method having maximum efficiency, such as the method of maximum likelihood. However, for theoretical distributions which do not depart very widely from the normal curve, the method of moments is so convenient that it may be worth using, even at some sacrifice of efficiency. For a further discussion, see §§ 12.5 to 12.7.

The number of parameters, and hence the number of moments to be calculated, depends on the type of curve selected. The Poisson curve has only one parameter, the normal and binomial curves two, the Pearson Type III three, and the main Pearson types four parameters. Four are also required for the Edgeworth series if we stop at the third approximation. It is seldom worth while going further than this because of the relatively great sampling errors in the higher moments.

In calculating the moments for a grouped distribution Sheppard's corrections (see § 4.12) may usefully be employed where the sample is at least 400 or 500 and the distribution tails off gradually at both ends.

In order to estimate the moments of the parent population we must appeal to some results from the theory of sampling which will be discussed in Chapter VII. It may be proved that unbiased estimates of the cumulants $\kappa_1, \kappa_2, \kappa_3, \kappa_4$, from a sample of size N are provided by certain sample statistics k_1, k_2, k_3, k_4, defined as follows:

(5.63) $k_1 = m$

(5.64) $k_2 = \dfrac{N}{N-1} m_2 = \dfrac{Ns^2}{N-1}$

(5.65) $k_3 = \dfrac{N^2}{(N-1)(N-2)} m_3$

(5.66) $k_4 = \dfrac{N^2}{(N-1)(N-2)(N-3)} [(N+1)m_4 - 3(N-1)s^4]$

where m is the sample mean ($\bar{X}$), s is the sample standard deviation, and m_2, m_3, m_4 are sample moments about the mean. The k-statistics are said to provide *unbiased* estimates of the corresponding kappas because

(5.67) $$E(k_i) = \kappa_i, \quad i = 1, 2, \cdots$$

Estimates of γ_1 and γ_2 are provided by the statistics g_1 and g_2, defined by

(5.68) $$g_1 = k_3/k_2^{3/2}$$
(5.69) $$g_2 = k_4/k_2^2$$

and these are unbiased when the parent population is normal.

Having estimated the cumulants for the parent population, we have to decide on the type of curve to be fitted. For a normal curve it is necessary that the skewness and excess should be so near zero that the difference may reasonably be attributed to sampling errors. For a Poisson curve all the cumulants must be equal. For a Pearson Type III curve $2\gamma_2 = 3\gamma_1^2$. If none of these conditions is reasonably well fulfilled, we can try a more general Pearson type, using the diagram referred to in § 5.5 to determine which type is appropriate. Alternatively, we can try an Edgeworth series.

In order to judge whether such relations are satisfied with reasonable probability, we need to know the standard errors of the statistics concerned. The *standard error* of any statistic is an approximation for large N to the square root of the true variance, any population parameters which occur in the expression for the variance being replaced by the sample estimates. The standard errors of $\bar{X}$ and s are $s/N^{1/2}$ and $(m_4 - s^4)/N^{1/2}$ respectively. Those of g_1 and g_2 are about $(6/N)^{1/2}$ and $(24/N)^{1/2}$ respectively (see § 6.10), if the population is normal, but may be quite different from these values for other types of population.

5.9 An Example of Curve-fitting. Consider the data in Table 2 giving weights of 1000 Glasgow school children to the nearest pound.

TABLE 2. WEIGHTS OF GLASGOW SCHOOL CHILDREN (NEAREST POUND)

X(lb)	X_{ei}	f	F	*Probit*
28–31	31.5	1	1	1.91
32–35	35.5	14	15	2.83
36–39	39.5	56	71	3.53
40–43	43.5	172	243	4.30
44–47	47.5	245	488	4.97
48–51	51.5	263	751	5.68
52–55	55.5	156	907	6.32
56–59	59.5	67	974	6.94
60–63	63.5	23	997	7.75
64–67	67.5	3	1000	—

The class-interval is here 4 lb and the true values of X at the ends of the intervals, X_{ei}, are as given in column 2. By the usual methods the values of the k-statistics, with Sheppard's corrections, are found to be

Sec. 10 Approximate Tests of Normality

(5.70)
$$\begin{cases} k_1 = 47.712 \text{ lb} \\ k_2 = 33.342 \text{ lb}^2 \\ k_3 = 22.074 \text{ lb}^3 \\ k_4 = -115.95 \text{ lb}^4 \end{cases}$$

whence

(5.71)
$$\begin{cases} g_1 = 0.114 \\ g_2 = -0.104 \end{cases}$$

The standard errors of g_1 and g_2 are about 0.077 and 0.154 respectively, so that g_1 differs from zero by about 1.5 times its standard error and g_2 by about $\tfrac{2}{3}$ of its standard error. The probabilities of differences as large as this, assuming the distribution to be normal, are about 0.14 and 0.50 respectively. Hence we can regard the true skewness and the true kurtosis as both zero.

We take the curve as

(5.72) $$y = N(2\pi\sigma^2)^{-1/2} e^{-(X-\mu)^2/2\sigma^2}$$

where $N = 1000$, $\mu = 47.712$ lb, $\sigma = 5.774$ lb. (The symbols μ and σ^2 will frequently be used for the population mean and variance, respectively, instead of ν_1 and μ_2.)

In order to plot the curve with frequencies per 4-lb interval as ordinates it is convenient to write

(5.73) $$y = 4N\phi(t)/\sigma = 692.8\phi(t)$$

where

(5.74) $$t = (X - \mu)/\sigma = (X - 47.712)/5.774$$

For selected values of t, $\phi(t)$ is found immediately from Table I in the Appendix, and the corresponding values of X are calculated from (5.74).

5.10 Approximate Tests of Normality. A rough test of the normality of the distribution may be made by plotting the percentage cumulative frequency $100F/N$ against X on special "probability paper." In Table 2, column 4, the values of F are given corresponding to X_{ei}. These are to be divided by 10 to give percentages, since N is here 1000.

On ordinary graph paper a smooth curve drawn between the plotted points will approximate in shape, if the distribution is nearly normal, the ogive curve of $\Phi(x)$, the distribution function of the normal law. On probability paper the scale of percentage cumulative frequency is so drawn out at both ends and compressed in the middle that the curve of $\Phi(x)$, or rather $100\Phi(x)$, becomes a straight line. Hence if the graph of $100F/N$ is nearly straight, the distribution is approximately normal.

Instead of using probability paper, we may achieve the same result by plotting "probits" corresponding to F on ordinary paper. A convenient table of probits may be found in *Statistical Tables* by Fisher and Yates (Table IX). In Table 2 above, the probits corresponding to the values of $F/10$ are given, and when these are plotted against X the points lie reasonably well on a straight line (Fig. 15). It may be noted that the graph gives rough estimates of the mean and standard deviation of the parent distribution, since probit 5 corresponds to μ and probit 6 to $\mu + \sigma$.

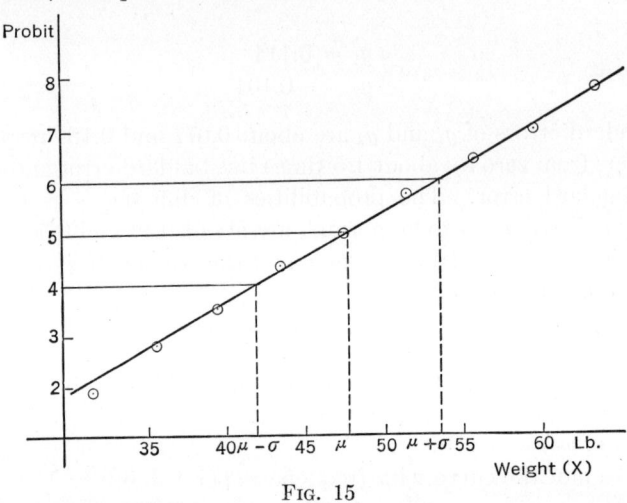

FIG. 15

The customary method with *ungrouped* data, when these are not too numerous, is to arrange the items in ascending order of X and to suppose that the percentage cumulative frequency corresponding to the kth item out of a total of n is $100(k - \frac{1}{2})/n$. The kth item is, as it were, split in two, half going with the preceding $k - 1$ items to make a total cumulated frequency of $k - \frac{1}{2}$.

5.11 The Multinomial Distribution. We consider a sample of N individuals grouped in k classes, the respective class frequencies being $f_1, f_2, \cdots f_k$, where $\sum_{i=1}^{k} f_i = N$. Following Karl Pearson, we regard this sample as a random sample of a hypothetical parent population in which the probability of belonging to the ith class is p_i, $i = 1, 2, \cdots k$. The joint distribution of the class frequencies is then the multinomial distribution.

Consider an event that is characterized by a variable v which can take on one of k values, $v_1, v_2, \cdots v_k$. Let the probability that v_i occurs be p_i, where $\sum_{1}^{k} p_i = 1$. Then in N independent trials, the probability that v_1 occurs m_1 times, v_2 occurs m_2 times, and so on, in a *specified order* (whatever it may be) is

$$p_1^{m_1} p_2^{m_2} \cdots p_k^{m_k}$$

where $\sum_{1}^{k} m_i = N$, the m's being positive integers or zero. The number of ways in which the order can be specified is the number of permutations possible

Sec. 11 The Multinomial Distribution

among N objects of which m_1 are of type T_1, m_2 of type T_2, $\cdots$ m_k of type T_k. Let this number be denoted by $p[m_i]$. Then we have

$$p[m_i] = \frac{N!}{m_1!\, m_2! \cdots m_k!}$$

Therefore, the probability that m_1 of the variates take the value v_1, m_2 the value v_2, and so on, *regardless of order* is

(5.75) $\qquad f(m_1, m_2, \cdots m_k) = p[m_i] p_1^{m_1} p_2^{m_2} \cdots p_k^{m_k}$

which is the general term of the expansion of the multinomial

$$(p_1 + p_2 + \cdots + p_k)^N$$

The binomial law, for a simple dichotomy, given in Chapter II, is a special case of this law. Thus if $k = 2$, the right member of (5.75) reduces to

(5.76) $\qquad \binom{N}{r} p^r q^{N-r}$

where

$r = m_1$, $\quad N - r = m_2$, $\quad p = p_1$, $\quad q = 1 - p_1 = p_2$, $\quad \binom{N}{r} = N!/m_1!\, m_2!$

If v is the number of spots appearing on the top face in a throw of a die, then v will take on one of the values 1, 2, 3, 4, 5, 6, and the probability of throwing exactly r aces (say) in N throws of the die is

$$\binom{N}{r}\left(\frac{1}{6}\right)^r\left(\frac{5}{6}\right)^{N-r}$$

We recall that (5.76) is the general term of the expansion of the binomial $(q + p)^N$. By using Stirling's approximation for factorials, we can derive an approximation for (5.75) which will bear to the multinomial law a relation analogous to that which the normal curve bears to the binomial. With this objective in mind, assume that every m_i is sufficiently large for $m_i!$ to be replaced by its Stirling approximation. Making these replacements (5.75) becomes, after some algebraic rearrangement,

(5.77) $\qquad f(m_1, m_2, \cdots m_k) = \dfrac{\prod\limits_{i=1}^{k}(Np_i/m_i)^{m_i+1/2}}{(2\pi N)^{(k-1)/2}(p_1 p_2 \cdots p_k)^{1/2}}$

Next introduce the transformation

(5.78) $\qquad t_i = \dfrac{m_i - Np_i}{\sigma_i}$

σ_i^2 being $Np_i(1 - p_i)$. Under this transformation (5.77) becomes

$$(2\pi N)^{(k-1)/2}(p_1 p_2 \cdots p_k)^{1/2} f = \prod_{i=1}^{k}\left(1 + \frac{\sigma_i t_i}{Np_i}\right)^{-Np_i - \sigma_i t_i - 1/2}$$

Then

$$\log \text{L.M.} = \sum_{1}^{k}(-Np_i - \sigma_i t_i - \tfrac{1}{2})\log\left(1 + \frac{\sigma_i t_i}{Np_i}\right)$$

where L.M. denotes the left-hand member of the preceding equation. Upon expanding the logarithm in a power series and collecting the results according to descending powers of N, we obtain

$$\log \text{L.M.} = -\sum_{1}^{k}\left(\sigma_i t_i + \frac{\sigma_i^2 t_i^2}{2Np_i} + \frac{\sigma_i t_i}{2Np_i} + \text{terms of lower order}\right)$$

From (5.78), $\sum \sigma_i t_i = \sum m_i - N\sum p_i = 0$, since $\sum m_i = N$ and $\sum p_i = 1$. Therefore, on substituting for σ_i^2, we have

$$f(m_1, m_2, \cdots m_k) = (2\pi N)^{(1-k)/2}(p_1 p_2 \cdots p_k)^{-1/2} e^{-K}$$

where

$$K \to \frac{1}{2}\sum\left\{t_i^2(1-p_i) + t_i\left(\frac{1-p_i}{Np_i}\right)^{1/2}\right\}$$

For large N the second term in K is negligible, and moreover, since some of the t_i will be positive and some negative, it will tend to cancel out on summation. Hence $K \to \tfrac{1}{2}\sum t_i^2(1-p_i)$ as N increases. The form of K suggests the substitution of a new variable $x_i = t_i(1-p_i)^{1/2}$ in place of t_i. This gives

(5.79) $$f(m_1, m_2 \cdots m_k) \to C e^{-\tfrac{1}{2}\Sigma x_i^2}$$

where $x_i = (m_i - Np_i)(Np_i)^{-1/2}$ and Np_i is the expected value of m_i. The multinomial distribution, therefore, tends to a joint normal distribution. The x_i are not independent, however, since $\sum x_i p_i^{1/2} = 0$, but we prove in the next section that $\sum x_i^2$ has, in the limit as $N \to \infty$, the χ^2 distribution of § 5.3 with $k-1$ degrees of freedom.

5.12 Chi-square as a Measure of Sample Deviation. On the hypothesis that the probabilities corresponding to the various classes in a distribution are $p_1, p_2 \cdots p_k$, the expected frequencies in a sample of N are $Np_1, Np_2 \cdots Np_k$. Hence the deviations of the sample frequencies from expectation are $m_1 - Np_1$, $\cdots m_k - Np_k$. The quantity

(5.80) $$\chi_s^2 = \sum_{i=1}^{k}(m_i - Np_i)^2/Np_i = \sum x_i^2$$

is, therefore, a measure of the total deviation of the sample from expectation, and was so chosen by Karl Pearson, who proved that the limiting distribution of χ_s^2 is the ordinary χ^2 distribution.

The moment-generating function of the binomial distribution is, as shown in § 4.7, $(q + pe^h)^N$. For the multinomial distribution one can show, as a generalization of this, that the mgf of the joint distribution of the variables $m_1, m_2, \cdots m_k$ is

Sec. 12   Chi-square as a Measure of Sample Deviation

(5.81) $M(u_1, u_2, \cdots u_k) = (p_1 e^{u_1} + p_2 e^{u_2} + \cdots + p_k e^{u_k})^N$

The mgf of the variables $x_1, x_2, \cdots x_k$ is therefore, by § 4.8,

(5.82) $M_1(u_1, u_2, \cdots u_k) = e^{-\Sigma u_i(Np_i)^{1/2}} [p_1 e^{u_1(Np_1)^{-1/2}} + \cdots + p_k e^{u_k(Np_k)^{-1/2}}]^N$

The cumulant generating function is

$$\begin{aligned}
(5.83)\quad K(u_1, u_2, \cdots u_k) &= \log M_1(u_1, u_2, \cdots u_k) \\
&= -\sum u_i (Np_i)^{1/2} + N \log \sum p_i e^{u_i(Np_i)^{-1/2}} \\
&= -\sum u_i (Np_i)^{1/2} + N \log \left[\sum p_i + \sum u_i \left(\frac{p_i}{N}\right)^{1/2} \right. \\
&\quad \left. + \frac{1}{2} \sum \frac{u_i^2}{N} + O(N^{-3/2}) \right]^* \\
&= -\sum u_i (Np_i)^{1/2} + N \log \left[1 + \sum u_i \left(\frac{p_i}{N}\right)^{1/2} \right. \\
&\quad \left. + \frac{1}{2N} \sum u_i^2 + O(N^{-3/2}) \right] \\
&= \tfrac{1}{2} \sum u_i^2 - \tfrac{1}{2} (\sum u_i p_i^{1/2})^2 + O(N^{-1/2}) \\
&= \tfrac{1}{2} Q(u_1, u_2, \cdots u_k) + O(N^{-1/2})
\end{aligned}$$

where

(5.84) $Q(u_1, u_2, \cdots u_k) = \sum u_i^2 - (\sum u_i p_i^{1/2})^2$

This is a quadratic function of the variables $u_1, u_2, \cdots u_k$.

From (5.83) we can prove that for any value of N

(5.85) $E(x_i) = [\partial K / \partial u_i]_{u_1 = \cdots = u_k = 0} = 0$
(5.86) $E(x_i^2) = \text{Var}(x_i) = [\partial^2 K / \partial u_i^2] = 1 - p_i$
(5.87) $E(x_i x_j) = \text{Cov}(x_i, x_j) = [\partial^2 K / \partial u_i \, \partial u_j]_{u_1 = \cdots = u_k = 0}$
         $= -p_i^{1/2} p_j^{1/2}$

so that, since

$$\chi_s^2 = \sum_{i=1}^{k} x_i^2$$

(5.88) $E(\chi_s^2) = \sum_i (1 - p_i) = k - 1$

Moreover in the limit as $N \to \infty$,

(5.89) $K(u_1, u_2, \cdots u_k) \to \tfrac{1}{2} Q(u_1, u_2, \cdots u_k)$

so that all cumulants of order higher than the second vanish.

Hence the variables x_i are in the limit normally distributed about zero with variance $1 - p_i$. They are not, however, independent, since

(5.90) $\sum_i x_i p_i^{1/2} = 0$

Let us now make an *orthogonal transformation* of the variables from $x_1, x_2, \cdots x_k$ to $y_1, y_2, \cdots y_k$, defined by

*$O(N^{-3/2})$ means terms of the order of $N^{-3/2}$.

(5.91) $$\begin{cases} y_1 = c_{11}x_1 + c_{12}x_2 + \cdots + c_{1k}x_k \\ \cdots \cdots \cdots \cdots \cdots \cdots \cdots \cdots \\ y_k = c_{k1}x_1 + c_{k2}x_2 + \cdots + c_{kk}x_k \end{cases}$$

where we choose $c_{ki} = p_i^{1/2}$, so that $y_k = 0$.

This transformation (see § 4.13) is such that

(5.92) $$\sum_{l=1}^{k} c_{il} c_{jl} = \begin{cases} 1, & \text{if } i = j \\ 0, & \text{if } i \neq j \end{cases}$$

Then $y_1^2 + \cdots + y_k^2 = x_1^2 + \cdots + x_k^2$ or, since $y_k = 0$,

(5.93) $$\sum_{i=1}^{k} x_i^2 = \sum_{j=1}^{k-1} y_j^2$$

The mgf of the joint distribution of the y's is given by

(5.94) $$M(t_1, t_2, \cdots t_k) = \int e^{y_1 t_1 + \cdots + y_k t_k} \, dF(y_1, \cdots y_k)$$

Using (5.91) and the fact that the Jacobian of this transformation is 1, we find

(5.95) $$M(t_1, t_2, \cdots t_k) = \int e^{x_1 u_1 + \cdots + x_k u_k} \, dG(x_1, x_2, \cdots x_k)$$

where

(5.96) $$\begin{cases} u_1 = c_{11} t_1 + \cdots + c_{k1} t_k \\ u_2 = c_{12} t_1 + \cdots + c_{k2} t_k \\ \cdots \cdots \cdots \cdots \cdots \cdots \\ u_k = c_{1k} t_1 + \cdots + c_{kk} t_k \end{cases}$$

The right-hand side of (5.95) is the joint mgf for the variables $x_1, x_2, \cdots x_k$, considered as a function of $u_1, u_2, \cdots u_k$. Hence in the limit when $N \to \infty$,

$$M(t_1, t_2, \cdots t_k) = e^{\frac{1}{2} Q(u_1, u_2 \cdots u_k)}$$

Now

(5.97) $$\begin{aligned} Q(u_1, u_2, \cdots u_k) &= \sum u_i^2 - \left(\sum u_i p_i^{1/2}\right)^2 \\ &= \sum t_i^2 - \left(\sum u_i c_{ki}\right)^2 \\ &= \sum t_i^2 - t_k^2 \end{aligned}$$

as is seen by multiplying the rows of (5.96) by $c_{k1}, c_{k2}, \cdots c_{kk}$ respectively, adding, and using (5.92). Therefore

(5.98) $$M(t_1, t_2, \cdots t_k) = e^{\frac{1}{2} \sum_{1}^{k-1} t_j^2}$$

which shows that the variables $y_1, y_2, \cdots y_{k-1}$ are independently and normally distributed with zero means and unit variances, while $y_k = 0$.

Hence, since χ_s^2 is a sum of squares of these variables, χ_s^2 as defined by (5.80) has in the limit as $N \to \infty$ the chi-square distribution described in § 5.3, with $k - 1$ degrees of freedom.

5.13 The Chi-square Test of Hypotheses. Let H stand for the hypothesis that a sample of N individuals forms a random sample from a population with a *given* probability distribution; that is, the parameters of the distribution are known or assumed and are not estimated from the sample itself. We calculate χ_s^2 from (5.80) and determine the probability of obtaining, on the hypothesis H, a value of χ_s^2 at least as great as this. This probability, on the assumption of the limiting chi-square distribution, is given by

(5.99) $$\Pr[\chi^2 \geq \chi_s^2] = \int_{\chi_s^2}^{\infty} f(\chi^2)\, d(\chi^2)$$

where, by (5.24),

(5.100) $$f(\chi^2) = \frac{1}{2}\left[\Gamma\left(\frac{k-1}{2}\right)\right]^{-1}\left(\frac{\chi^2}{2}\right)^{(k-3)/2} e^{-\chi^2/2}$$

The integral in (5.99) is readily expressed as an incomplete Gamma function, by the substitution $\frac{1}{2}\chi^2 = u$. In fact,

(5.101) $$\Pr[\chi^2 \geq \chi_s^2] = 1 - \Gamma_{(\chi_s^2)/2}\left(\frac{k-1}{2}\right)\bigg/\Gamma\left(\frac{k-1}{2}\right)$$
$$= 1 - I\left(\frac{\chi_s^2}{\sqrt{2(k-1)}}, \frac{k-3}{2}\right)$$

so that the probability can be calculated from tables of the incomplete Gamma function for given values of $k - 1 = n$. Separate tables of χ^2 have been calculated and may be found in Part I of Pearson's *Tables for Statisticians and Biometricians*, particularly Table XII. The n' of this table is our k, which is one more than the number of degrees of freedom. Tables of χ^2 for one degree of freedom (not given in Pearson's tables) are found in the Appendix to Yule and Kendall's *Theory of Statistics*, Tables 4A, 4B.

It is often convenient to arrange a table of χ^2 as was done by R. A. Fisher (see Table III of the Appendix to this book) with values of χ^2 corresponding to selected values of the probability. A more complete table of this type is given by Thompson in *Biometrika*, **32**, 1941, p. 187. Thus for a probability of 5% with 10 degrees of freedom, the tabular value of χ^2 is 18.31.

If the sample value χ_s^2 exceeds this when $k = 11$, and if the sample number N is so large that the distribution of χ_s^2 is practically identical with that of χ^2, the chance is less than 5% that if hypothesis H were true a *random* sample would give a value of χ_s^2 as great as or greater than the one actually obtained. In other words, if we agree to work on the 5% level of significance, we shall reject the hypothesis. To be still safer, of course, we could work on the 1% level, and then we should reject H only if $\chi_s^2 > 23.21$ for $k = 11$.

If, on the other hand, χ_s^2 is less than the tabular value corresponding to the appropriate k and the assigned level of significance, we can say that our sample is consistent with hypothesis H. This does not mean that H is true; merely that the sample supplies no evidence against it.

There is, of course, a possibility that we shall reject H when it is really true. The probability of doing this is the same as that of getting by chance a value of $\chi_s^2 > \chi_p^2$, where χ_p^2 is the tabular value corresponding to $p\%$, and hence this probability is equal to $p/100$. We shall, therefore, commit this kind of error (known as the *first kind*) in about $p\%$ of all cases in which we apply the criterion. This is why we speak of working on the $p\%$ level of significance.

It occasionally happens that the value of χ_s^2 from the sample is unexpectedly small, corresponding to a probability of nearly 1. In such a case the fit is too good, and it is highly likely that even if the hypothesis H were true we should get discrepancies greater than those actually observed. We may well suspect that our sample is not a truly random sample from the hypothetical population.

With regard to levels of significance, Fisher [7] says:

In preparing this table we have borne in mind that in practice we do not want to know the exact value of P for any observed χ^2, but, in the first place, whether or not the observed value is open to suspicion. If P is between .1 and .9 there is certainly no reason to suspect the hypothesis tested. If it is below .02 it is strongly indicated that the hypothesis fails to account for the whole of the facts. We shall not often be astray if we draw a conventional line at .05, and consider that higher values of χ^2 indicate a real discrepancy.

Just as the binomial distribution tends much more slowly to the normal distribution when p is very small than when it is around 0.5, so we may expect that the distribution of χ_s^2 will deviate appreciably from the limiting chi-square distribution if the expected numbers in some of the classes are small. This will often happen at the tails of the distribution, so that it is the usual practice to pool small adjacent classes until no class has fewer than five individuals in it.

Cramér [8] recommends pooling until the expected number in any class is at least 10. On the other hand, Cochran [9] has shown that, in some cases at least, numbers as small as 1 may be permitted without seriously affecting the validity of the test. It seems that pooling tends to increase the calculated probability, and hence to diminish the chance of rejecting the hypothesis (see Problem 7 below).

A convenient chart of χ^2 and P for various values of n is given in the Appendix to Yule and Kendall's textbook. Another useful chart has been prepared by C. I. Bliss.[10]

5.14 The Chi-square Test Applied to Curve Fitting. In most cases arising in practice, the hypothesis that we wish to test is that our sample has been drawn from a parent population of a certain *type* (e.g., a normal distribution), but with parameters that are not specified. In fact, we use the sample itself to estimate these parameters.

Sec. 14   Chi-square Test Applied to Curve Fitting

Let us suppose, for convenience, that there are two such parameters, θ_1 and θ_2 (the argument works equally well for any number). The probability p_i that a single item in the sample falls in the ith class is a function of θ_1 and θ_2, say $p_i(\theta_1, \theta_2)$. If we knew the true values of θ_1 and θ_2, we could calculate

(5.102) $$\chi_s^2 = \sum_{i=1}^{k} \frac{[m_i - Np_i(\theta_1, \theta_2)]^2}{Np_i(\theta_1, \theta_2)}$$

and apply the ordinary test. Actually, we replace θ_1 and θ_2 by their estimates $\hat{\theta}_1$ and $\hat{\theta}_2$, but this means that the p_i depend on the sample values, and we cannot assume that the limiting distribution of χ_s^2 is still the χ^2 distribution. It may be shown, however (as, for example, by Cramér[11]), that for an important class of estimates known as *most-efficient estimates* (see § 12.3) the limiting distribution as $N \to \infty$ is the same as that obtainable by making χ_s^2 a minimum with respect to θ_1 and θ_2, and in fact is the χ^2 distribution with $k - 3$ degrees of freedom ($k - s - 1$ if there are s parameters to be estimated from the sample). This seems reasonable, since each additional parameter introduces a further restriction on the x_i analogous to (5.90), and so reduces by one the number of degrees of freedom. The analogy is not exact, however, and the foregoing statement does not constitute a proof.

As mentioned in § 5.8 the estimates given by the method of moments are not, in general, most-efficient (see § 12.5). The χ^2 test for curves fitted by moments may, therefore, be unreliable except in special cases.

In fitting a continuous curve to a grouped distribution it is necessary to calculate the area under the curve corresponding to each class interval. This area is equal, in the standardized curve, to the difference of the values of the distribution function at the beginning and end of the interval, and is multiplied by the total frequency N to get the calculated frequency Np_i in the interval.

Since the *signs* of the differences $m_i - Np_i$ are ignored in the calculation of χ_s^2, it may happen that a very improbable distribution of signs may still give a value of χ_s^2 too small to reject the hypothesis H. Runs of one sign are more likely to occur near the tails of the distribution and may be hidden by pooling.

It is recommended that the student read "The χ^2-Test of Significance" by T. C. Fry, *Jour. Amer. Stat. Assoc.*, **33**, 1938, pp. 513–525. The three papers following Fry's exposition are also worth reading.

For the application of χ^2 to contingency tables, see Chapter VIII.

Example 1. Twelve dice were thrown 4096 times; only a throw of six was counted a success. The expected frequencies are given by $4096(\frac{1}{6} + \frac{5}{6})$.[12] How improbable, taken as a whole, is the observed distribution shown in Table 3? The symbol $\tilde{m}$ is used for the expected frequencies Np_i.

Table 3

Number of Successes	Observed Frequency	Theoretical Frequency	$(m - \tilde{m})^2$	$\dfrac{(m - \tilde{m})^2}{m}$
0	447	459	144	.3137
1	1145	1103	1764	1.5993
2	1181	1213	1024	.8442
3	796	809	169	.2089
4	380	364	256	.7033
5	115	116	1	.0086
6	24	27	9	.3333
7 and over	8	5	9	1.8000
Totals	4096	4096		$\chi^2 = 5.8113$

Entering Table III (see Appendix) with $n = 8 - 1 = 7$, and extrapolating for the value of P corresponding to the observed value of $\chi^2 = 5.8113$, we find $P = .56$. Hence there is no reason to reject the hypothesis that the underlying chance of a "success" is $p = \frac{1}{6}$. That is, there is no reason to suspect that the dice were biased.

Example 2. In § 5.9 we fitted a normal curve to the data of Table 2 on weights of Glasgow school children. We will now test the goodness of fit.

We first calculate standard t values corresponding to each value of X_{ei} and find from a table of the normal law the respective values of $\Phi(t)$. Differences of successive entries give the area under the standard normal curve for each class interval, and these areas are multiplied by 1000 to give the calculated frequencies f_c, with results shown in Table 4. The column headed f_0 gives the observed frequencies previously denoted by m_i.

Table 4. Weights of 1000 Glasgow School Children

X_{ei}(lb)	t	$\Phi(t)$	$\Delta\Phi(t)$	f_c	f_0	$f_0 - f_c$	$\dfrac{(f_0 - f_c)^2}{f_c}$
31.5	-2.808	.0025	.0025	2.5	1	-1.5 ⎫ -2.2	0.3
35.5	-2.115	.0172	.0147	14.7	14	-0.7 ⎭	
39.5	-1.422	.0775	.0603	60.3	56	-4.3	0.3
43.5	-0.729	.2330	.1555	155.5	172	16.5	1.8
47.5	-0.037	.4852	.2522	252.2	245	-7.2	0.2
51.5	0.656	.7441	.2589	258.9	263	4.1	0.1
55.5	1.349	.9113	.1672	167.2	156	-11.2	0.8
59.5	2.042	.9794	.0681	68.1	67	-1.1	0.0
63.5	2.734	.9969	.0175	17.5	23	5.5 ⎫ 5.4	1.4
∞	∞	1.0000	.0031	3.1	3	-0.1 ⎭	
							4.9

From the last column we see that χ_s^2 is 4.9, after pooling two classes at the tails of the distribution. The number of classes is thereby reduced to 8, and the number of degrees of freedom to 5, since two parameters, estimated from the sample, have been used in calculating t. The value of P is 0.44, so that there is no evidence, *as far as this test goes*, that the weights of Glasgow children are *not* normally distributed.

Sec. 14   Chi-square Test Applied to Curve Fitting

Example 3. The data in Table 5 refer to reaction-time differences to a light stimulus, with and without warning, in units of 1 millisecond. (X = reaction time without warning − reaction time with warning.)

TABLE 5. REACTION-TIME DIFFERENCES TO LIGHT STIMULUS

X_{ei}	t	$F(t)$	$\Delta F(t)$	f_c	f_0	$f_0 - f_c$	$\dfrac{(f_0 - f_c)^2}{f_c}$
−175	−2.754	.00027	.00027	.08	1	−.92	
−125	−2.391	.00208	.00181	.56	0	−0.56	
−75	−2.028	.01005	.00797	2.48	1	−1.48 } 1.50	0.21
−25	−1.665	.03377	.02372	7.38	7	−0.38	
25	−1.302	.08570	.05193	16.15	16	−0.15	0.00
75	−0.938	.17458	.08888	27.64	29	1.36	.07
125	−0.575	.29762	.12304	38.26	40	1.74	.08
175	−0.212	.44113	.14351	44.63	47	2.37	.13
225	0.151	.58553	.14440	44.91	42	−2.91	.19
275	0.514	.71347	.12794	39.79	41	1.21	.04
325	0.878	.81517	.10170	31.63	26	−5.63	1.00
375	1.241	.88810	.07293	22.68	25	2.32	.24
425	1.604	.93623	.04813	14.97	16	1.03	.07
475	1.967	.96504	.02881	8.96	8	−0.96	.10
525	2.331	.98249	.01745	5.42	5	−0.42	.03
575	2.694	.99148	.00899	2.80	5	2.20	
625	3.057	.99604	.00456	1.42	2	0.58 } 1.55	.44
∞	∞	1.0000	.00396	1.23	0	−1.23	
					311		2.60

The first four moments of the distribution of observed frequencies (with Sheppard's corrections, although the total frequency is rather small for these) give

$$k_1 = 204.2 \text{ msec}$$
$$k_2 = 18{,}951 \text{ msec}^2$$
$$g_1 = 0.372$$
$$g_2 = 0.009$$

Hence the estimated parameters of the parent population are

$$\mu = 204.2 \text{ msec}$$
$$\sigma = 137.7 \text{ msec}$$
$$\gamma_1 = 0.372$$
$$\gamma_2 = 0.009$$
$$\beta_1 = 0.139$$
$$\beta_2 = 3.009$$

The standard errors of g_1 and g_2 are roughly 0.15 and 0.36. (See Problem 19, Chapter VII.) For a Pearson Type III curve, we should have $2\gamma_2 - 3\gamma_1^2 = 0$, and this is sufficiently nearly fulfilled. On the Pearson diagram of Types the point corresponding to (β_1, β_2) lies near the beginning of the line corresponding to Type III.

The skewness may be taken as 0.4 approximately, and the values of $F(t)$ in Table 5 are read from Salvosa's tables for $\gamma_1 = 0.4$. As before, $f_0 = 311\Delta F(t)$. The value of χ_s^2 turns out to be 2.60 after pooling a few classes at the ends of the distribution. The number of degrees of freedom is $13 - 4 = 9$, since 3 parameters were estimated from the sample. The value of P is about 0.98, so that the fit is very good, almost suspiciously good.

5.15 The Log-normal Distribution. It sometimes happens that if a variable X is markedly skew in its distribution, $\log X$ is approximately normal. This is so, for instance, if X is affected by many random causes, each of which produces a small effect proportional to X itself. For, if $\Delta X = cX$, $\Delta \log X = (1/X) \Delta X = c$, and the resultant of many random causes, each producing a small constant effect, is a normal distribution.

A rough test of whether a distribution is log-normal may be made by plotting the distribution on *logarithmic probability paper* or by plotting $\log X$ against the probit corresponding to X. Either natural or common logarithms may be used. In either case the curve should be nearly straight.

Let $Y = \log_e X$ and suppose the distribution of Y is normal. The frequency function for Y is $p(Y) = (1/S\sqrt{2\pi})e^{-(Y-M)^2/2S^2}$, where M and S are the mean and standard deviation of the Y distribution. If m and s are the mean and standard deviation of the X distribution,*

$$(5.103) \qquad m = \int_0^\infty p(X) X \, dX$$

$$= \int_{-\infty}^\infty p(Y) e^Y \, dY$$

$$= \frac{1}{\sqrt{2\pi}S} \int_{-\infty}^\infty e^{Y-(Y-M)^2/2S^2} \, dY$$

$$= e^{M+\frac{1}{2}S^2} \frac{1}{\sqrt{2\pi}S} \int_{-\infty}^\infty e^{-(Y-M-S^2)^2/2S^2} \, dY$$

whence

$$m = e^{M+\frac{1}{2}S^2}$$

or

$$(5.104) \qquad \log m = M + \tfrac{1}{2}S^2$$

If we use common logarithms, M and S are replaced by M_1/c and S_1/c respectively, where M_1 and S_1 refer to the distribution of $\log_{10} X$ and $c = 0.4343 \cdots$, so that

$$(5.105) \qquad \log_{10} m = c \log m = M_1 + \frac{S_1^2}{2c}$$

Again,

$$m^2 + s^2 = \int_0^\infty p(X) X^2 \, dX$$

$$= \int_{-\infty}^\infty p(Y) e^{2Y} \, dY$$

$$= e^{2M+2S^2}$$

---

*m and s, as well as M and S, are here population parameters, not sample statistics. See § 6.1.

Therefore
$$1 + \frac{s^2}{m^2} = e^{S^2}$$
so that

(5.106) $$S^2 = \log\left(1 + \frac{s^2}{m^2}\right)$$

If common logarithms are used,
$$S_1^2 = c \log_{10}\left(1 + \frac{s^2}{m^2}\right)$$

Hence, from (5.104),

(5.107) $\quad M = \log\{m(1 + s^2/m^2)^{-1/2}\} \quad$ or $\quad M_1 = \log_{10}\{m_1(1 + s_1^2/m_1^2)^{-1/2}\}$

In an article in *Nature*, October 20, 1945, J. H. Gaddum has given many examples of distributions which are approximately log-normal. These include size of silver particles in photographic emulsion, survival time of bacteria in disinfectants, number of plankton organisms caught in a net, weight and blood pressure of human beings, and number of words in a sentence written by G. B. Shaw.

A *modified logarithmic transformation* $Y = \log(X + X_0)$ may be useful if the curve of probits against $\log X$ shows a more or less constant curvature. If the curve is convex upward, X_0 is negative; if concave upward, X_0 is positive. A rough estimate of X_0 may be made from the graph. If X_1, X_2, X_3 are values of X corresponding to three equidistant points on the probit scale, say 4, 5, and 6, then $X_2 + X_0$ is the geometric mean of $X_1 + X_0$ and $X_3 + X_0$, so that
$$X_0 = \frac{X_2^2 - X_1 X_3}{X_1 + X_3 - 2X_2}$$

The value so obtained can be tested by plotting $\log(X + X_0)$ against the probits and adjusting if necessary. It is claimed that various empirical distributions can be fitted better in this way than by any curves of the Pearson system.

Problems

1. The naturalist Buffon (1708–1788) tossed a coin 4040 times and obtained 2048 heads and 1992 tails. Use the table of χ^2 to test whether this result is reasonable, on the hypothesis that the true probability of a head with the coin Buffon used was $\frac{1}{2}$. *Ans.* The probability of a discrepancy at least as great is 0.366.

2. In one of his experiments with peas, the Abbé Mendel observed the shape and color of peas from a number of plants, and found the following distribution:

Round, yellow	315
Round, green	108
Angular, yellow	101
Angular, green	32

According to Mendel's theory of heredity, the expected numbers should be in the ratio 9:3:3:1. Calculate these expected numbers, and determine by the χ^2 test whether the agreement with theory can be regarded as satisfactory.

124 The Gamma, Beta, and Chi-square Distributions V

3. Toss seven coins 128 times and record the frequencies of heads. Apply the χ^2 test to the resulting distribution.

4. 1000 discs were put in a goldfish bowl, each disc bearing a number ranging from 0 to 24. A single disc was drawn 1000 times, the number being noted and the disc put back and mixed with the others after each drawing. The actual frequencies f_c of the discs in the bowl and the observed frequencies f_0 in 1000 drawings are shown in the table. Are the results consistent with the hypothesis that the method of drawing was really random?

X	0	1	2	3	4	5	6	7	8	9	10	11	12
f_0	0	27	57	87	105	109	94	89	78	78	46	55	35
f_c	1	23	61	92	106	100	94	87	78	69	59	49	40

X	13	14	15	16	17	18	19	20	21	22	23	24
f_0	19	37	18	18	6	11	15	7	6	2	1	0
f_c	32	26	20	16	13	10	8	6	4	3	2	1

5. In 500 throws with a die, 6 has turned up 98 times. Is this number large enough to cast suspicion on the die?

Hint. Prove that the probability of 98 or more sixes with a good die is about 0.04. This particular event is, therefore, rare enough to appear significant. The probability of a deviation from the expected number at least as great as that observed, *in either direction* and *for any face* of the die, is, of course, much greater and is not significant. The occurrence of this unexpectedly large number of sixes cannot, therefore, *by itself*, be regarded as good evidence of bias. A sounder opinion could be formed by examining the whole distribution (if available) of observed numbers of spots for the 500 throws of this die, and using the χ^2 test.

6. Suppose that the whole distribution referred to in the hint following Problem 5 is that given below, where X is the number of spots on the upper face of the die.

X	1	2	3	4	5	6
f	71	78	85	82	86	98

What opinion would you form of the accuracy of the die? *Ans.* The probability of a value of χ^2 at least as great as that observed is about 0.42. The observed result is, therefore, quite reasonable with a good die.

7. In a study of plant disease (spotted wilt of tomatoes), the numbers of diseased plants were counted in each of 160 groups of plants. Each group contained 9 plants evenly spaced, so that the number X of diseased plants could take integral values from 0 to 9. The distribution was as follows:

X	0	1	2	3	4	5	6	7	8	9
f	36	48	38	23	10	3	1	1	0	0

Assuming that the probability of being diseased, p, is constant, fit this distribution with the binomial $160(q + p)^9$, estimating p from the sample. Test the agreement by the χ^2 test by (*a*) pooling the last four frequencies, (*b*) pooling the last five, (*c*) pooling the last six, and noting in each case the value of $\Pr\{\chi^2 \geq \chi_s^2\}$. *Ans.* (*a*) .004. (*b*) .037. (*c*) .047.

The usual pooling procedure leads here to an over-estimate of the probability. It also disguises the fact that the differences between observed and calculated frequencies corresponding to $X = 4, 5, 6, 7$, are all of the same sign. The fit is really poorer than procedure (c) would suggest.

8. Prove that if $t = (\chi^2 - k + 1)/(2k - 2)^{1/2}$, the distribution of t is Pearson Type III, with skewness $2[2/(k - 1)]^{1/2}$. Hence Salvosa's tables of the Type III distribution may be used to calculate $\Pr\{\chi^2 \geq \chi_s^2\}$. Check by taking one or two values of χ^2 and k, calculating the corresponding t, and entering Salvosa's tables.

9. In a certain experiment involving counting yeast cells with a haemacytometer, the count in each of 400 squares varied between 1 and 12, with the distribution of frequencies shown in the attached table, where X represents the cell count.

X	1	2	3	4	5	6	7	8	9	10	11	12
f_0	20	43	53	86	70	54	37	18	10	5	2	2

Show that this distribution is fitted very well with a Poisson curve. Note that in the parent population X may take any integral value from 0 to ∞. All theoretical frequencies, from $X = 11$ on, may be pooled, however.

10. It has been observed by some hydrographic engineers [12] that the distribution of the maximum 24-hour run-off during a year, over a long series of years, follows for many rivers a Pearson Type III distribution, with a skewness of approximately 0.6. Test this hypothesis on the following data for the Merrimack River, where X is in thousand cu ft/sec and the class intervals run 20 to 30, 30 to 40, etc.

X	20–	30–	40–	50–	60–	70–	80–	90–
f	12	24	17	12	9	5	2	1

11. The following observations on maximum 24-hour run-off for the North Saskatchewan River form too short a series for the skewness to be estimated with much reliability. Assuming, however, that the skewness is really 0.6 (see Problem 10), test approximately whether the distribution is Pearson Type III by forming a cumulative frequency distribution in the way described in section 5.10 for ungrouped data, plotting on probability paper, and comparing with the theoretical Type III curve on the same sheet. It may be noted that if we use *logarithmic probability paper*, or if log X is plotted against the probit, the curves are much more nearly straight than if arithmetic probability paper is used. In the table X has been expressed as a percentage of the mean, so that the estimated expectation of X is 100.

Year	X	Year	X
1911–12	123.4	1920–21	75.3
1912–13	102.5	1921–22	73.2
1913–14	83.8	1922–23	105.0
1914–15	138.8	1923–24	85.6
1915–16	117.8	1924–25	113.7
1916–17	116.8	1925–26	99.2
1917–18	88.1	1926–27	124.0
1918–19	67.0	1927–28	120.6
1919–20	98.4	1928–29	66.1

12. Fit the following data, on weights of college freshmen (to the nearest pound), with three terms of an Edgeworth series. The values of X_{ei} refer to the true ends of the class intervals, the interval being 11 lb.

X_{ei}	f_0
110.5	15
121.5	43
132.5	138
143.5	162
154.5	129
165.5	82
176.5	35
187.5	16
198.5	5
209.5	3
220.5	1

The first four (corrected) moments for this sample may be taken to be

$m = 142.25$ lb
$m_2 = 309.46$ lb^2
$m_3 = 3,431.2$ lb^3
$m_4 = 353,980$ lb^4

The m's are defined in § 5.8.

13. If N observations are distributed among four classes, with a, b, c, d in the respective classes $(a + b + c + d = N)$ and if the probability that an observation falls in the ith class is $p_i (i = 1, 2, 3, 4)$, show that (a) the expected value of a linear function of the observed frequencies, $x = k_1 a + k_2 b + k_3 c + k_4 d$, is given by $E(x) = N \sum k_i p_i$, (b) the variance of x is given by Var $(x) = N\{\sum k_i^2 p_i - (\sum k_i p_i)^2\}$, (c) the covariance of two linear functions x and y, where $y = h_1 a + h_2 b + h_3 c + h_4 d$, is given by

$$\text{Cov}(x, y) = N\{\sum k_i h_i p_i - (\sum k_i p_i)(\sum h_i p_i)\}$$

Hint. The joint probability of a, b, c, d is the multinomial term

$$\frac{N!}{a!\,b!\,c!\,d!} p_1^a p_2^b p_3^c p_4^d$$

References

1. C. E. Weatherburn, *A First Course in Mathematical Statistics*, Chap. VIII.
2. E. B. Wilson & M. M. Hilferty, *Proc. Nat. Acad. Sci.*, **17**, 1931, p. 684. The approximation to the exact values calculated by C. M. Thompson (*Biometrika*, **32**, 1941, 187) is remarkably good.
3. W. G. Cochran, "The Distribution of Quadratic Forms in a Normal System," *Proc. Camb. Phil. Soc.*, **30**, 1933–4, p. 178. See also M. G. Kendall, *Advanced Theory of Statistics*, Vol. II, p. 177.
4. W. P. Elderton, *Frequency Curves and Correlation*, 3rd Edition, Chap. IV. This book is a compendium of information on the Pearson types.
5. C. C. Craig, "A New Exposition and Chart for the Pearson System of Frequency Curves," *Ann. Math. Stat.*, **7**, 1936, p. 16.
6. See H. Cramér, *Mathematical Methods of Statistics*, pp. 223–224, for a discussion with references.
7. R. A. Fisher, *Statistical Methods for Research Workers*, 10th Edition, p. 80.
8. H. Cramér, *loc. cit.*, p. 420.
9. W. G. Cochran, "The Chi-square Distribution for the Binomial and Poisson Series, with Small Expectations," *Ann. of Eugenics*, **7**, 1936, p. 207.
10. C. I. Bliss, "A Chart of the Chi-square Distribution," *Jour. Amer. Stat. Assoc.*, **39**, 1944, p. 246.
11. H. Cramér, *loc. cit.*, pp. 425–441 and p. 506.
12. See, *e.g.*, L. S. Hall, *Trans. Amer. Soc. Civil Engineers*, **84**, 1921, p. 191. Also discussion on pp. 241–257.
13. Types IX to XII are described in Karl Pearson's "Second Supplement to a Memoir on Skew Variation," *Phil. Trans. A*, **216**, 1916, pp. 429–457. This paper is reprinted in Pearson's *Early Statistical Papers*, Cambridge Univ. Press, 1948.

CHAPTER VI

FUNDAMENTALS OF SAMPLING THEORY WITH SPECIAL REFERENCE TO THE MEAN

6.1 Introduction. In many statistical problems the data at hand are regarded as a *random sample* drawn from a *parent population* or *universe of discourse* and we are interested in drawing inferences about the universe from the sample. The phase "random sample" implies that each individual from the universe has an equal and independent chance to be included in the sample. From such samples we attempt to draw inferences concerning the universe. In order to deal with this inductive argument we first consider a deductive argument; that is, we first consider an infinite (or finite) universe and investigate the behavior of samples according to the laws of probability. The methodology dealing with this class of problems is known as sampling theory. The center of interest in sampling theory is the development of criteria for assisting common sense or educated judgment concerning the magnitude of chance fluctuations in statistical ratios, averages, and coefficients.

The Bernoulli theory deals with sampling fluctuations in relative frequencies. In the words of Rietz,[1]

But it is fairly obvious that the interest of the statistician in the effects of sampling fluctuations extends far beyond the fluctuations in relative frequencies. To illustrate, suppose we calculate any statistical measure such as an arithmetic mean, median, standard deviation, correlation coefficient, or parameter of a frequency function from the actual frequencies given by a sample of data. If we need then either to form a judgement as to the stability of such results from sample to sample or to use the results in drawing inferences about the sampled population, the common-sense process of induction involved is much aided by a knowledge of the general order of magnitude of the sampling discrepancies which may reasonably be expected because of the limited size of the sample from which we have calculated our statistical measures.

A statistical measure calculated from the actual frequencies given by a sample has been called a *statistic* by R. A. Fisher.[2] This is to avoid a verbal confusion with the corresponding *parameter* in the universe which we should like to know but can generally only estimate. It is a matter of common experience that a statistic will vary from sample to sample. To characterize the variation that may be tolerated on the basis of chance is one of the fundamental problems of sampling theory.

In discussing such sampling fluctuations, Fisher[3] introduces the subject as follows:

The idea of an infinite population distributed in a frequency distribution in respect of one or more characters is fundamental to all statistical work. From a limited experience, for example, of individuals of a species, or of the weather of a locality, we may obtain some idea of the infinite hypothetical population from which our sample is drawn, and so of the probable nature of future samples to which our conclusions are to be applied. If a second sample belies this expectation we infer that it is, in the language of statistics, drawn from a different population; that the treatment to which the second sample of organisms had been exposed did in fact make a material difference, or that the climate (or methods of measuring it) had materially altered. Critical tests of this kind may be called tests of significance, and when such tests are available we may discover whether a second sample is or is not significantly different from the first.

6.2 Method of Attack. The whole theory of sampling is based on frequency distributions and probability. In order to explain the tests of significance that have been developed, it is desirable to outline briefly the philosophy underlying the method of attack.

Sampling theory deals with specific questions like the following: Given the mean and standard deviation of a sample of N variates, how reliable are these as estimates of the population mean and standard deviation, respectively? Given two samples, do their respective means or other statistics differ significantly? Can the differences be accounted for on the basis of chance or do the samples come from different populations? The answers require in general that we conceive the universe as one distribution, the values of the statistic calculated from all possible samples of size N from that universe as another distribution, and that there are mathematical expressions capable of representing both distributions. This is the chief reason for studying frequency curves and probability distributions.

Suppose, for example, that we have computed a statistic — say the mean of 100 observations or measurements. What we get is not an absolutely fixed quantity which may be exactly reproduced again by taking 100 similar measurements. Indeed, if such an experiment were repeated many times we would get values for the arithmetic mean which would form a frequency distribution. This distribution would have its own mean (mean of means) standard deviation, and higher moments. The law describing the frequency distribution of all possible means of samples of size N from a specified universe is called a frequency function when it can be expressed mathematically. What has been said of the mean holds for any other statistic.

Formulation of statistical judgment about a sample involves the specification of the universe and the determination of the frequency function of a given statistic in samples of a given size drawn from this universe. The problem of determining the frequency functions for the various statistics from specified universes is one which has challenged modern mathematical research. In most cases it has been necessary to assume that the parent universe is of the

Sec. 3 Point Estimation and Interval Estimation

normal form in order to obtain analytically the sampling distribution of the statistic. Many of the tests of significance are based upon this assumption. However, considerable information about sampling distributions from arbitrary universes is known in terms of their moments.

6.3 Point Estimation and Interval Estimation. Problems of estimating the actual values of population parameters are said to belong to "point estimation." It is equally important to know within what limits we can confidently expect the parameter values to lie, with any specified degree of confidence, and such problems belong to "interval estimation." They can be solved if we know the distribution of the statistic t used for estimating the parameter θ; the distribution function will, in general, depend on θ as well as possibly on other parameters.

It was formerly the custom to attach to the definitions of common statistics, such as the arithmetic mean or coefficient of correlation, a formula giving the so-called probable error of the statistic. The following concise exposition of the various usages of the term "probable error" is due to Professor A. T. Craig.

There are in the literature three conceptions of the probable error. If, purely for convenience of language, we refer to the probable error of the mean, these conceptions can be stated as follows: (i) The probable error of the mean is that deviation, extended on both sides of the mean of the *population*, such that $\frac{1}{2}$ is the probability that the mean of a *sample* will fall in this interval; (ii) The probable error of a mean is that deviation, extended on both sides of the mean of a *sample*, such that $\frac{1}{2}$ is the probability that the mean of the *population* lies in this interval; (iii) The probable error of the mean is that deviation, extended on both sides of the mean of a *sample*, such that $\frac{1}{2}$ is the probability that the mean of another *sample* will fall in this interval. Conception (i) leads without difficulty to the usual formula $.6745(\sigma/\sqrt{N})$ for the probable error of the mean. This formula is rigorously correct for samples of any size drawn from a normal population and is valid for large samples drawn from any population with finite variance. On the other hand, the formula cannot be established under conception (ii) without further assumptions. If, before the sample is drawn, it is assumed, in the absence of any knowledge concerning the distribution of possible values of the mean of the population, that the probability is constant, then the formula admits mathematical proof. But this assumption is essentially the same assumption as that made in applying Bayes' Theorem to problems of probability *a posteriori*.

The modern method of expressing the reliability of a statistical estimate of a population parameter in terms of confidence intervals seems likely to replace the traditional but often misleading mode of expression involving probable error. Conception (i) is seldom useful in practice, as the true population parameters are usually unknown. Conception (ii) seems to depend on a rather artificial probability scheme. If a sample is drawn from a *fixed* population, and an interval is calculated centering on the sample mean, the true population mean either does or does not lie in this interval. The probability that it does so is either 0 or 1. The population mean is not, in fact, a random variable at all. It is the sample mean that is the random variable. If we take many samples from the same population we can, however, calculate for each an interval, which will vary from sample to sample, but which will be such that if, on each occasion, we assert that the population mean lies inside it, we shall be right in a definite percentage, say 90%, of such occasions. An interval thus calculated is, in the language of J. Neyman and E. S. Pearson,[4] called a 90% *confidence interval*. It has a definite probability, 0.9, of *covering* the true value, whatever the true value may be.

On the other hand, conception (ii) depends on regarding the parent population not as fixed but as itself a random sample from a hypothetical family of parent populations with all possible values of the parameter θ. The *a posteriori* probability of θ, given the sample value t of the statistic used to estimate θ, can then be calculated by Bayes' Theorem, provided some assumption is made about the *a priori* distribution of θ. This assumption is usually the one made by Bayes himself, and strongly attacked by Fisher (see § 1.10), that before the sample is drawn all values of θ are equally likely.

The invalidity of this assumption in many applied problems of statistical interest may be seen clearly in cases of a continuous frequency function with a derivative. Suppose that our initial assumptions relating to a parameter θ were such that θ would initially be distributed in accord with a continuous frequency function, $g(\theta)$, which has a derivative at each point within its possible range on θ, say from $\theta = \alpha$ to $\theta = \beta$. Next, suppose $g(\theta)$ were restricted to be constant throughout the range of θ. Then it is well known that the distribution of a simple non-linear function of θ would not be constant. For example, the distribution of $z = \theta^n (n \neq 1, \theta$ real and non-negative) would not be constant, but would be distributed in accord with a frequency function $(1/n)z^{(1-n)/n}$. But if θ is a population parameter, it seems fairly obvious that the logical character of our theory should usually, if not always, be such as to enable us to use a power of θ as a parameter if we found it convenient to do so.

The preceding introduction is designed to lead up to the important fact that, although in the usual statistical inquiry by sample, the true value of the population parameter θ is unknown and remains unknown, there are cases in which precise statements can be made in terms of probabilities about the bounds within which a parameter θ lies without making an assumption about the initial distribution of the possible values of θ.

6.4 Confidence Belts and Limits. For simplicity, consider a case of a single parameter, θ, in which we know the frequency function of the statistic, t, to be given by an integrable function

(6.1) $$y_t = f(t, \theta)$$

Sec. 4   Confidence Belts and Limits   131

where the values of t obtained from observation may be assumed to be reasonable estimates of θ. Suppose we know (6.1) in such form that it is possible to calculate a table of values of the probabilities that the statistic, t, will fall into an assigned interval selected on a possible range (a, b) for any assigned value of θ within the possible range (α, β) of θ.

Next, for illustration, select a positive number ϵ, say $\epsilon = .005$, on which to base a certain level of confidence about values of θ to be expressed in terms of probabilities.

As our main problem may be clarified by a geometrical representation, conceive of corresponding values of t and θ obtained in an extensive statistical experiment as represented by rectangular coordinates within the rectangle bounded by lines $t = a$, $t = b$, $\theta = \alpha$, $\theta = \beta$ (Fig. 16).

Consider an arbitrary assignment for θ, say that $\theta = \theta'$ is the true value of θ. This gives the line AB (Fig. 16). Since the distribution of the statistic t is assumed to be known for each assigned value of θ, we may locate on the line AB two points, t_1 and t_2 ($t_1 \leq t_2$) such that ϵ is equal to the probability that a random sample will yield a value of t less than or equal to t_1, and similarly ϵ is the probability that such a sample will yield a value greater than or equal to t_2. Then we have an interval on AB from t_1 to t_2 such that $1 - 2\epsilon$ is the probability that the random sample will yield a value within this interval.

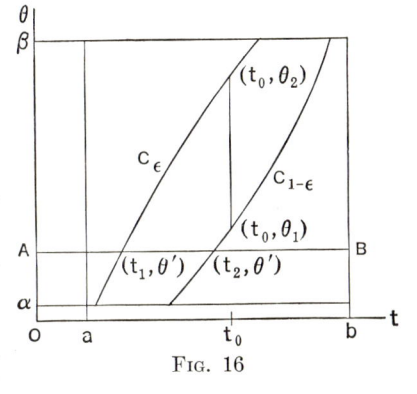

More formally stated, we may introduce a function $F(t, \theta)$ defined as the definite integral of $f(t, \theta)$ in (6.1) from $t = a$ to t. That is,

$$F(t, \theta) = \int_a^t f(t, \theta)\, dt$$

for any arbitrarily assigned real value of θ on its range from α to β. Then

$$F(a, \theta) = 0, \quad F(b, \theta) = 1, \quad F(t_1, \theta') = \epsilon, \quad F(t_2, \theta') = 1 - \epsilon,$$
$$(0 < \epsilon < \tfrac{1}{2})$$

By considering all possible assignments of θ, in its possible range (α, β), the locus of our set of lower values of t, illustrated by t_1 on the line AB, will give a continuous curve which we mark with C_ϵ in Figure 16, the subscript ϵ being used to remind us that ϵ is the probability that a random value of t for $\theta = \theta'$ will fall below or at t_1. Similarly, our set of upper values of t, illustrated by t_2 on AB, give a curve which we mark with $C_{1-\epsilon}$.

If t is a good estimate of θ, its value usually, if not always, increases with θ

for all possible values. Thus, we shall restrict our further considerations to cases in which we may assume that t increases as θ increases and vice versa. More precisely we are concerned with one-valued monotone increasing functions represented by the two curves marked C_ϵ and $C_{1-\epsilon}$. The region bounded by these two curves and the lines $\theta = \alpha$ and $\theta = \beta$ has been called by Neyman the *confidence belt* with *confidence coefficient* equal to $1 - 2\epsilon$.

Now suppose that for one particular random sample, of the size assumed in setting up the confidence belt, we obtain the value $t = t_0$. Regardless of the actual (but unknown) value of θ, the probability that the point (t_0, θ) will fall within the confidence belt is $1 - 2\epsilon$, as is clear from the way in which the belt has been constructed. Consider the line $t = t_0$ in relation to the belt. This line (parallel to the θ-axis) will, as a rule, intersect the belt in two points, (t_0, θ_1) and (t_0, θ_2), $\theta_1 < \theta_2$. The probability that it will fail to do so is less than 2ϵ. The point (t_0, θ) is outside the belt for any $\theta < \theta_1$ and for any $\theta > \theta_2$. In fact, θ_1 is the lower bound of values of θ for which the probability that $t > t_0$ is at least equal to ϵ, and similarly θ_2 is the upper bound of values of θ for which the probability that $t < t_0$ is at least ϵ. These boundary values of θ are called the *confidence limits* of θ corresponding to $t = t_0$, and the interval θ_1 to θ_2 is called the *confidence interval* for $t = t_0$, with the confidence coefficient $1 - 2\epsilon$.

There is no guarantee that for one particular random sample we shall be right in claiming that the true value of θ lies within the confidence interval, but the *probability* of our being right (in the sense of the relative frequency of true statements in repeated sampling) is equal to $1 - 2\epsilon$. If ϵ is small, we shall be right nearly all the time, but, of course, the width of the belt increases as ϵ diminishes. The surer we are of the statement, the vaguer is the statement itself.

6.5 Standard Error of the Mean. By the *standard error* of a statistic we mean an estimate of the standard deviation of the sampling distribution of that statistic. Since the sampling distribution usually depends on one or more unknown parameters which have to be estimated from the sample itself, these estimates must be substituted for the parameters in the formula for the standard error. It is desirable that such estimates should be unbiased and also "most-efficient" in the sense of having as small a sampling variance as possible, at least for large samples (see § 12.3). If the sampling distribution is such that, when the size N of the sample tends to infinity, the distribution function tends to that of the normal law, it is said to be *asymptotically normal*. The use of standard errors is usually restricted to distributions which are asymptotically normal, since then we may, as a rule, approximate to the percentage points of the distribution of the statistic with those of a normal distribution whose standard deviation is equal to the standard error. This gives an intuitive approximate interpretation of the standard error. It is not, however, necessarily true that, because a distribution tends to a normal distribution with variance σ^2, the variance of the distribution tends itself to the value σ^2, as the following example shows.*

Let the frequency function be

$$f = N^{1/2} \frac{N-2}{N-1} \phi(N^{1/2}t) + \frac{1}{N-1} \phi(t)$$

where as usual $\phi(t) = (2\pi)^{-1/2} \exp(-t^2/2)$. Then it is easily verified that $E(t) = 0$ and $E(t^2) = 2N^{-1}$, so that the variance of this distribution is $2N^{-1}$ for any finite N. However, for a fixed value of t, the function f tends, as $N \to \infty$, to $N^{1/2}\phi(N^{1/2}t)$, which is a normal distribution with variance N^{-1}. The variance of the limiting distribution is not therefore the same as the limit of the variance. The reason is that, as N increases with fixed t, the second term in f tends to zero. The function $N^{1/2}\phi(N^{1/2}t)$ tends itself, however, so rapidly to zero for large N and for non-zero values of t that the contributions of both terms in f to the variance are of the same order of magnitude.

If a random sample of N is taken from a population with known distribution function, the N values $X_1, X_2, \cdots X_N$ may be considered as independent variates having the same distribution. If the mean of the sample is

(6.2) $$\bar{X} = \frac{1}{N} \sum_{i=1}^{N} X_i$$

then by Theorems 4.4 and 4.9

(6.3) $$E(\bar{X}) = \mu$$
(6.4) $$\text{Var}(\bar{X}) = \sigma^2/N$$

where μ and σ^2 are the expectation and variance of the known distribution of the X_i.

By the Central Limit Theorem the distribution of $\bar{X}$ tends to normality as $N \to \infty$ (and it is normal for any N by Theor. 4.11 if the parent population is normal). Hence the standard error of $\bar{X}$ is $\sigma/N^{1/2}$.

If σ is not known it must be estimated from the sample. In large samples the sample standard deviation s may be substituted for σ.

It is not obvious how large N should be before we can regard the distribution of a statistic as practically normal, even when we know that it is asymptotically normal. For some statistics, including the arithmetic mean, a sample of 30 can usually be considered large; for others, such as the coefficient of correlation, a sample of 500 may not be sufficient to ensure a good approximation to normality.

It is customary to distinguish between parameters and sample statistics by using Greek letters for the former and Latin letters for the latter. We shall adopt this useful convention. Thus $m (= \bar{x})$, m_2, $\cdots$ will be used for sample moments corresponding to the population parameters μ, μ_2, $\cdots$.

* The authors are indebted for this illustration to a critic who read the book in manuscript.

6.6 Confidence Limits for the Mean. We know that m is (or tends to be) normally distributed about μ with standard deviation $\sigma_{\bar{x}} = \sigma/\sqrt{N}$. If the distribution of m be reduced to standard units by the transformation

$$(6.5) \qquad t = \frac{\bar{x} - \mu}{\dfrac{\sigma}{\sqrt{N}}}$$

then we know that t is approximately normally distributed about zero with standard deviation unity. Hence we can refer to a normal probability scale for the probability that one would obtain a random sample for which m differs from μ by as much as $|\delta|$, where δ is expressed in the $\sigma_{\bar{x}}$ unit. So we have the following theorem.

Theorem 6.1. *The probability Q_δ that a random sample from an infinite universe will have a mean, m, which will be within a distance $|\delta|$ of the mean, μ, of the universe is approximately*

$$Q_\delta = 2 \int_0^{|\delta|} \phi(t)\, dt$$

where δ is the observed value of t given by (6.5) and $\phi(t)$ is the normal curve. Then $P_\delta = 1 - Q_\delta$ is the approximate probability that m will not be within $|\delta|$ of μ. If the universe is normal, P_δ gives the exact probability.

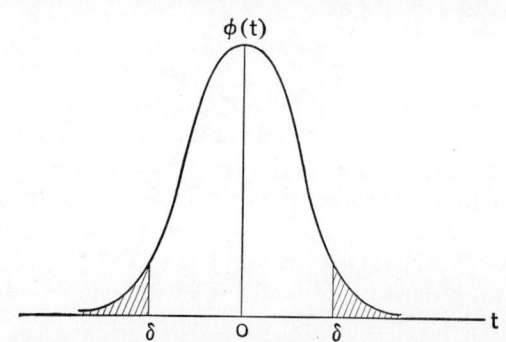

Fig. 17. $P_\delta =$ ▨. Q_δ is the Probability for a Deviation Equal to or Less than $|\delta|$, and P_δ is the Probability for a Deviation Greater than $|\delta|$

On the assumption of a normal distribution we may, in large samples, define the *probable error* of a statistic as 0.6745 times the standard error. This depends on the fact that if $\delta = 0.6745$, $Q_\delta = 0.5$, very nearly. The probability of a deviation from the true population value numerically at least as great as the probable error is therefore $\frac{1}{2}$. The term *probable error* is still in fairly common use in some branches of astronomy and physics.

We can also define confidence limits, based on the normal distribution, corresponding to any desired degree of confidence. Thus the probability that a sample mean will lie within an interval of 1.96 times the standard error

Sec. 7   Null Hypothesis and Significance Tests

on either side of the true mean is about 0.95, the probability that it will lie within 2.58 times the standard error on either side is about 0.99, and so on.

When the true mean is unknown and the sample mean is used as an estimate of it, we may form a confidence belt, as illustrated in Figure 18. If we assume

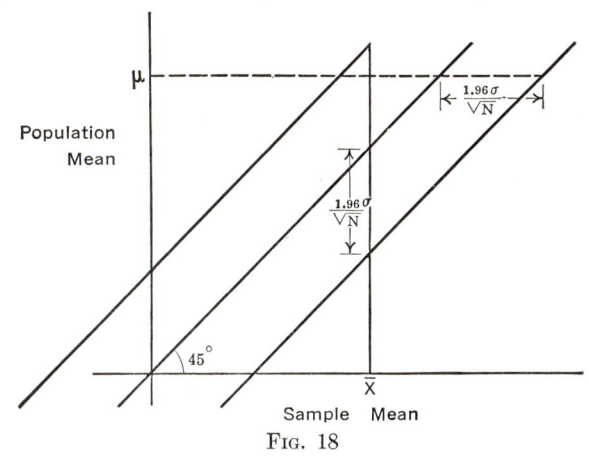

Fig. 18

that the variance σ^2 is fixed, but that different values of μ are possible in the parent population, we see from the figure that the 95% confidence limits for any given value of $\bar{X}$ are $\bar{X} \pm 1.96\sigma/\sqrt{N}$, or approximately $\bar{X} \pm 1.96s/\sqrt{N}$ for large N. In this example the belt is straight and of constant width, so that even if we assume that all our samples are from one and the same parent population, it is still true that the confidence interval calculated as above will cover the true population mean in 95% of random samples from this population.

6.7 Null Hypothesis and Significance Tests. The rationale underlying sampling theory has been summarized by E. S. Pearson[5] as follows:

In applying the methods of statistical analysis it is generally our aim to discriminate between two or more alternative hypotheses regarding the factors which have controlled certain observed events, which form what we term a sample or samples. If the process is examined in a little detail it will be found that the procedure may be described as follows:

(a) We define a hypothesis to be tested.
(b) We choose the criterion (or criteria) whose numerical value, derivable from the observations, is most suitable for testing the hypothesis. In doing this we recognize that the criterion is not a single-valued expression even if the hypothesis be true, but will vary from one sample of observations to another.
(c) We therefore refer the observed value of the criterion to this sampling distribution — e.g., to a normal probability scale, etc. — and so obtain a measure of the likelihood of the hypothesis.
(d) Finally, if judged on this probability scale the observed criterion is not exceptional, we conclude that upon the information available there are no grounds

for discarding the hypothesis; or if the value prove exceptional we consider the possibility of alternative hypotheses.

A hypothesis which is tested for possible rejection under the assumption that it is true has been called by Fisher [6] a *null hypothesis*. Commonly such a hypothesis assumes that the difference between the true value of a parameter and some assigned number is zero. In other words, null hypothesis refers to a particular form of population distribution which is assumed in considering whether or not a sample could reasonably have arisen from this population. If the sample could not reasonably have arisen from the population proposed, as measured by a significance test, we say that the null hypothesis is refuted for the level of significance adopted. If the significance test yields a verdict of "not significant" for the probability level adopted, we say that the null hypothesis is not refuted or contradicted at that level.

It is open to the investigator to be more or less exacting concerning the smallness of the probability he would require before he would be willing to admit that his test has demonstrated a significant result. However, it is conventional among certain workers to adopt the following *rule:*

If $P_\delta \geq 0.05$, δ is not significant; if $0.05 > P_\delta \geq 0.01$, δ is significant; if $P_\delta < 0.01$, δ is highly significant.

This is the rule we shall usually adopt (see § 2.11).

Other statisticians prefer to describe δ as definitely significant only when $P_\delta < 0.01$, and to regard a value between 0.01 and 0.05 as merely suggesting some doubt as to whether δ is significant or not and calling for additional information. Occasionally a still more conservative attitude may be justified.

Example 1. Suppose the mean span of 100 persons is found to be $m = 70.56$ inches. Does this differ significantly from the mean $\mu = 69.943$ of the "universe" with standard deviation $\sigma = 3.115$? Calculating the above test we find $\delta = \dfrac{70.56 - 69.943}{3.115/\sqrt{100}} = 1.99$. Referring to the normal probability scale we find the chance of a difference between the observed and hypothetical means as large as that noted to be $P_\delta = 0.0466$. Our conclusion is that the given statistic $m = 70.56$ is rather exceptional, and the sample quite possibly came from a different universe, that is, in this case a different race of men.

Example 2. Twelve dice were thrown 26,306 times (Weldon's data), and a throw of 5 or 6 points was reckoned a success. The mean of the observed distribution was found to be 4.0524. In tossing a true die the chance of scoring 5 or 6 is $\frac{1}{3}$ so the number of dice scoring 5 or 6 should be distributed with frequencies proportional to the terms in the expansion $(\frac{2}{3} + \frac{1}{3})^{12}$. Therefore, the expected mean, on the hypothesis that the dice were true, is $sp = 12(\frac{1}{3}) = 4$. Test this hypothesis using the difference between the observed and theoretical means as a criterion of judgment.

Solution.
$$\sigma = (spq)^{1/2} = \{(12)(\tfrac{1}{3})(\tfrac{2}{3})\}^{1/2} = 1.633$$
$$N = 26{,}306$$
$$\frac{\sigma}{N^{1/2}} = 0.010$$
$$\delta = \frac{0.0524}{0.010} = 5.2$$

The probability that a deviation outside $\delta = \pm 5$ would happen by chance is extremely small so we conclude that the dice were biased.

Example 3. For 868,445 U. S. Army recruits in World War I, the mean weight was 141.54 lb, with a standard deviation of 17.36 lb. The standard error of the mean is $17.36/(868,445)^{1/2} = .0186$ lb. Regarding these men as a random sample of men of military age in the United States in 1917–18, we can say that there is a 95% probability that an interval from 141.50 to 141.58 lb would cover the true mean weight of the parent population.

Samples are seldom as large as this and confidence limits as narrow. The above calculation does not take into account errors of weighing arising from various causes. The statistician, as such, accepts the data given. The effect of such errors would be to increase somewhat the estimate of the standard error.

6.8 The Distribution of the Mean. We have already calculated in § 4.16 the first four cumulants of the distribution of the mean of a random sample of N observations from an infinite parent population, the cumulants of which are given. If we denote the moments of the *population of means* of all possible samples of N from the parent population by $N_1, N_2, \cdots, M_1, M_2, \cdots$, we have in the new notation*

(6.6) $\qquad N_1 = \nu_1$
(6.7) $\qquad M_2 = \mu_2/N$
(6.8) $\qquad M_3 = \mu_3/N^2$
(6.9) $\qquad M_4 = \mu_4/N^3 + 3(N-1)\mu_2^2/N^3$

Hence the skewness of the population of means is given by

(6.10) $\qquad G_1 = M_3/M_2^{3/2} = \gamma_1/N^{1/2}$

and the excess of kurtosis by

(6.11) $\qquad G_2 = M_4/M_2^2 - 3 = \gamma_2/N$

The skewness and excess both tend to zero as N increases, and in fact for moderately large N the distribution of the mean is approximately normal even for parent populations which depart very widely indeed from the normal form.

6.9 An Experiment. We will now describe an exercise in experimental sampling which will help make the theory more meaningful. It was performed by a class of thirty students who took the distribution of Table 6 as a "universe."

In a box were placed 2000 discs † each bearing a number from the set $1, 2, 3, \cdots, 25$. The numbers on the discs were coded to the span values in

---

* Strictly, these should be Greek letters, since they refer to a theoretical distribution, but it is convenient to use ordinary capitals, and the notation will not often be used in later chapters. The corresponding notation for sample moments is n_r, m_r, but we usually write m or $\bar{x}$ for n_1 (and μ for ν_1).

† Small metal rimmed price tags were used. Ideally, each individual disc should be returned to the box before the next is drawn. However, this was not insisted upon and an entire sample may have been drawn before replacement.

TABLE 6. SPAN AMONG ADULT MALES. (See Table 29, Part I)

x	f
58.5	1
59.5	2
60.5	1
61.5	6
62.5	7
63.5	22
64.5	55
65.5	111
66.5	146
67.5	182
68.5	229
69.5	265
70.5	263
71.5	217
72.5	176
73.5	132
74.5	82
75.5	48
76.5	20
77.5	16
78.5	12
79.5	3
80.5	1
81.5	2
82.5	1

accordance with the scheme shown in Table 6A, and the frequency of the variously numbered discs equaled the frequency of the corresponding x's. Each member of the class drew samples from the box according to the following directions.

Directions

1. Intermix the discs thoroughly and withdraw four random samples of ten discs each.
2. Record the numbers in each sample of ten on the sampling record sheet; replace the discs in the box.
3. For each sample of ten: find (*a*) mean span, (*b*) variance, (*c*) standard deviation.
4. Combine the four samples into a single sample of forty and find the statistics named in 3.

The results of 3(*a*) will be reproduced here. There were, of course, 120 means from samples of $N = 10$. These were then grouped into a frequency distribution. The resulting distribution and its moments, together with the

Sec. 9   An Experiment   139

TABLE 6A. SAMPLING RECORD SHEET

Span	Number on Disc	First Sample	Second Sample	Third Sample	Fourth Sample	Total
58.5	1					
59.5	2					
60.5	3					
61.5	4					
62.5	5					
63.5	6					
64.5	7					
65.5	8					
66.5	9					
67.5	10					
68.5	11					
69.5	12					
70.5	13					
71.5	14					
72.5	15					
73.5	16					
74.5	17					
75.5	18					
76.5	19					
77.5	20					
78.5	21					
79.5	22					
80.5	23					
81.5	24					
82.5	25					
Mean *						
Standard Deviation						

* In computing the statistics let x denote span and u the number on a disc. Then $u = x - 57.5$, $\bar{x} = \bar{u} + 57.5$, and $s_x = s_u$. Note that in this book x and X are both frequently used for variates. The context should prevent any ambiguity.

moments of the universe, are given in Table 7. (The computations were made according to the definitions given in Part I for the moments of an observed distribution.)

Although the chief purpose of the experiment is an appreciation of the theory, it is of interest to compare the experimental and theoretical results. According to (6.6) the mean should be 69.943; we obtained 69.785. According to (6.7) the standard deviation should be $3.115/(10)^{1/2} = .985$; we obtained .894.

TABLE 7. DISTRIBUTION OF THE MEANS OF 120 SAMPLES OF $N = 10$ DRAWN FROM THE UNIVERSE OF SPAN

Interval	Mid $\bar{x}$	Frequency	Moments
67.0–67.3	67.15	1	Mean $\bar{x}$ = 69.785
67.4–67.7	67.55	1	
67.8–68.1	67.95	4	$s_{\bar{x}}$ = 0.8941
68.2–68.5	68.35	4	$g_1 : \bar{x}$ = 0.052
68.6–68.9	68.75	5	
69.0–69.3	69.15	19	$g_2 : \bar{x}$ = 0.030
69.4–69.7	69.55	27	
69.8–70.1	69.95	20	
70.2–70.5	70.35	20	μ = 69.943
70.6–70.9	70.75	7	σ = 3.115
71.0–71.3	71.15	6	
71.4–71.7	71.55	3	γ_1 = 0.161
71.8–72.1	71.95	3	γ_2 = 0.296

6.10 Standard Errors of Moments. By definition,

(6.12) $$n_r = \frac{1}{N} \sum_{i=1}^{N} x_i^r$$

(6.13) $$m_r = \frac{1}{N} \sum_{i=1}^{N} (x_i - n_1)^r$$

If the population rth moment exists,

(6.14) $$E(n_r) = E(x_i^r) = \nu_r$$

Also the variance of n_r is given by

$$\text{Var}(n_r) = E(n_r - \nu_r)^2$$
$$= \frac{1}{N^2} E\{\sum x_i^r - N\nu_r\}^2$$
$$= \frac{1}{N^2} E\{\sum_i x_i^{2r} + \sum_{i \neq j} x_i^r x_j^r - 2N\nu_r \sum_i x_i^r + N^2 \nu_r^2\}$$
$$= \frac{1}{N} \nu_{2r} - \nu_r^2 + \frac{1}{N^2} \sum_{i \neq j} E(x_i^r x_j^r)$$

Since x_i and x_j are assumed to be independent,

$$E(x_i^r x_j^r) = E(x_i^r) E(x_j^r) = \nu_r^2$$

The number of terms in the sum is $N(N - 1)$. Therefore

(6.15) $$\text{Var}(n_r) = \frac{1}{N} \nu_{2r} - \nu_r^2 + \frac{N-1}{N} \nu_r^2$$
$$= (\nu_{2r} - \nu_r^2)/N$$

Sec. 10 Standard Errors of Moments

Thus the variance of n_2 is given by

(6.16) $$\text{Var}(n_2) = (\nu_4 - \nu_2^2)/N$$

The calculation of the variance of the sample moments about the *mean* is more complicated. The standard error of n_1 is $(\mu_2/N)^{1/2}$, and since for moderately large values of N the distribution is nearly normal, almost all the actual values of n_1 will lie within a distance of ν_1 of order $N^{-1/2}$. Hence if we take the origin at the true mean of the parent population, so that $\nu_1 = 0$,

$$E(m_r) = \frac{1}{N} \sum_{i=1}^{N} E(x_i - n_1)^r$$

where n_1 is small of order $N^{-1/2}$ and powers of n_1 higher than the first can be neglected. Therefore

$$E(m_r) \approx \frac{1}{N} \sum_{i=1}^{N} E(x_i^r - r n_1 x_i^{r-1})$$

$$= \frac{1}{N} E \left\{ \sum x_i^r - \frac{r}{N} \sum x_i \sum x_i^{r-1} \right\}$$

$$= \frac{1}{N} E \left\{ \left(1 - \frac{r}{N}\right) \sum x_i^r - \frac{r}{N} \sum_{i \neq j} x_i x_j^{r-1} \right\}$$

Now $E(x_i x_j^{r-1}) = E(x_i) E(x_j^{r-1}) = 0$, since $E(x_i) = 0$. Hence, neglecting terms of order N^{-1},

(6.17) $$E(m_r) \approx \mu_r$$

It may be proved in the same way that for large N

(6.18) $$\text{Var}(m_r) \approx \frac{1}{N} [\mu_{2r} - \mu_r^2 + r^2 \mu_2 \mu_{r-1}^2 - 2r \mu_{r-1} \mu_{r+1}]$$

(6.19) $$\text{Cov}(m_r, m_s) \approx \frac{1}{N} [\mu_{r+s} - \mu_r \mu_s + rs \mu_2 \mu_{r-1} \mu_{s-1} - r \mu_{r-1} \mu_{s+1} - s \mu_{s-1} \mu_{r+1}]$$

Thus, for m_2,

(6.20) $$\text{Var}(m_2) \approx \frac{1}{N} (\mu_4 - \mu_2^2)$$

and, if the parent population is normal,

(6.21) $$\text{Var}(m_2) \approx 2\sigma^4/N$$

Similarly, if the parent population is normal, we find from (6.18) that

(6.22) $$\text{Var}(m_3) \approx 6\sigma^6/N$$
(6.23) $$\text{Var}(m_4) \approx 96\sigma^8/N$$

noting that $\mu_4 = 3\sigma^4$, $\mu_6 = 15\sigma^6$, and $\mu_8 = 105\sigma^8$, while all the μ's of odd order vanish.

Approximate standard errors of functions of these moments, such as $\sqrt{b_1} = m_3/m_2^{3/2}$ and $b_2 = m_4/m_2^2$, may be calculated by taking differentials of these functions, and noting that, since the fluctuations of any moment are of order $N^{-1/2}$, squares and higher powers of the differentials of the moments can be neglected. Thus,

$$\tfrac{1}{2} \delta b_1/b_1 \approx \delta m_3/m_3 - \tfrac{3}{2} \delta m_2/m_2$$

Squaring and taking expectations we find, for a normal population,

$$\frac{1}{4b_1^2} \operatorname{Var}(b_1) \approx \frac{1}{m_3^2} \operatorname{Var}(m_3) + \frac{9}{4m_2^2} \operatorname{Var}(m_2) - \frac{3}{m_2 m_3} \operatorname{Cov}(m_2, m_3)$$

$$\approx \frac{1}{N}\left[\frac{6\sigma^6}{m_3^2} + \frac{9}{4m_2^2} 2\sigma^4\right]$$

Hence

$$\operatorname{Var}(b_1) \approx \frac{4}{N}\left[\frac{6\sigma^6}{m_2^3} + \frac{9\sigma^4 m_3^2}{2m_2^5}\right] b_1$$

so that to terms of order N^{-1},

(6.24) $$\operatorname{Var}(\sqrt{b_1}) \approx 6/N$$

since to this first approximation we can put $m_3 = 0$, $m_2 = \sigma^2$.

Similarly,

$$\delta b_2/b_2 \approx \delta m_4/m_4 - 2\, \delta m_2/m_2$$

whence

$$\frac{1}{b_2^2} \operatorname{Var}(b_2) \approx \frac{1}{m_4^2} \operatorname{Var}(m_4) + \frac{4}{m_2^2} \operatorname{Var}(m_2) - \frac{4}{m_2 m_4} \operatorname{Cov}(m_4, m_2)$$

By (6.18) and (6.19) we find for a normal parent population

(6.25) $$\operatorname{Var}(b_2) \approx 24/N$$

6.11 Sampling from a Finite Parent Population. Suppose that the parent population is of size M and that a random sample of N is drawn. The probability of drawing an individual from a given class is affected each time that one is drawn from that class. The number of possible different samples is $\binom{M}{N}$. In our notation the population mean is given by

$$M\mu = \sum_{i=1}^{M} x_i$$

the sample mean by

$$Nm = \sum_{j=1}^{N} x_j$$

and the mean value of m for all possible samples by

$$\bar{m} = \frac{1}{\binom{M}{N}} \sum_{k=1}^{\binom{M}{N}} m^{(k)}$$

Sec. 11   Sampling from a Finite Parent Population

where $m^{(k)}$ is the mean of the kth sample. Writing

$$\bar{m} = \frac{1}{N\binom{M}{N}} \sum_{k=1}^{\binom{M}{N}} \sum_{j=1}^{N} x_j^{(k)}$$

we note that in this double sum all possible values of x_j occur with the same frequency, since the sum includes all possible different samples. Since there are only M possible values of x_j, each value must be repeated $\frac{N}{M}\binom{M}{N}$ times. We have

$$\sum_{k=1}^{\binom{M}{N}} \sum_{j=1}^{N} x_j = \frac{N}{M}\binom{M}{N} \sum_{i=1}^{M} x_i$$

so that

(6.26) $$\bar{m} = \frac{1}{M} \sum_{i=1}^{M} x_i = \mu$$

The mean of all possible different samples is thus equal to the mean of the parent population, or in other words the mean of one sample is an unbiased estimate of the mean of the parent population.

By similar algebraic methods it is possible to show[7] that the variance of the population of means is

(6.27) $$M_2 = \frac{M-N}{N(M-1)} \mu_2$$

the skewness is

(6.28) $$G_1 = \frac{M-2N}{M-2} \left[\frac{M-1}{N(M-N)} \right]^{1/2} \gamma_1$$

and the kurtosis is

(6.29) $$G_2 = \frac{(M-1)(M^2 - 6MN + M + 6N^2)\gamma_2 - 6M(MN + M - N^2 - 1)}{N(M-2)(M-3)(M-N)}$$

When $M \to \infty$ these last three equations become identical with (6.7), (6.10), and (6.11) respectively. The moments of the parent population must then be defined in terms of probabilities, and it is assumed that these moments exist.

The conclusion of investigators is that the distribution of means from nearly any finite universe is practically normal. In this connection the following striking example is given by Carver.[7]

A group of students chose arbitrarily the following most unusual distribution for a parent universe:

TABLE 8

x	f
3	2
15	9
29	43
405	189
1710	37
Total	280

and found the distribution of $\sum_{1}^{N} x_i = N\bar{x}$ of 1000 samples of twenty-five variates each shown in Table 9. It was obtained as follows.

TABLE 9

Class	f
5,000–	2
7,000–	54
9,000–	203
11,000–	310
13,000–	254
15,000–	130
17,000–	36
19,000–	9
21,000–	2
Total	1000

Two hundred and eighty Hollerith cards were punched with numbers corresponding to the two hundred and eighty variates of the parent population. The cards were thoroughly shuffled and then placed in a tabulating machine. After twenty-five cards had run through the electric tabulator their total was recorded. By repeating this procedure one thousand samples were readily obtained. It is thus possible to obtain experimentally some appreciation of the sensitivity of the sampling distribution of means to changes in population form. Carver concludes that if the sample N is fifty or larger and the population is at least ten times N, the parent population has relatively little control over the shape of the distribution of $\bar{x}$.

Another set of experiments was conducted by Shewhart[8] who comes to the following conclusion:

Such evidence, supported by more rigorous analytical methods beyond the scope of the present discussion, leads us to believe that in almost all cases in practice we may establish sampling limits for averages of samples of four or more upon the basis of normal law theory.

Sec. 13 Standard Error of an Observed Proportion 145

Example 4. Of the 868,445 U. S. Army recruits referred to in Example 3, 27,341 were from Minnesota. For these men the mean weight was 146.41 lb. Show that, considered as a random sample from the population of recruits, this one is extremely improbable.
Taking $M = 868{,}445$, $N = 27{,}341$, $\mu_2 = (17.36)^2$, we find from (6.27) that $M_2 = 0.01068$. The deviation of the sample mean from the population mean, in standard units, is therefore $(146.41 - 141.54)/(0.01068)^{1/2} = 47.1$. On the hypothesis of a normal distribution the probability of a deviation as high as this is practically zero, so that the Minnesota recruits certainly did not form a random sample, as regards weight, of the U. S. Army. The large proportion of men of Scandinavian descent in Minnesota is probably the reason for this.

6.12 Size of Sample to Have a Given Reliability. From § 6.6 we may determine the size N of a sample such that its mean, $\bar{x}$, will not differ from μ by more than a specified error $|\delta|$, with a degree of certainty equal to a specified probability.

Example 5. The American Rolling Mill Company investigated [9] the life of iron alloys under different corrosive conditions. Data obtained from a certain kind of sheet material immersed in Washington tap water showed that the average time of failure of such samples was 874.89 days and the standard deviation of the time of failure was 85.3 days. There arose the following question of practical interest to the research engineer of this company: What sample size N must be used in order that for similar test conditions, the probability shall be 0.90 that the average time for failure determined from the N tests will be in error by not more than 5 per cent of the average of the universe?
Assuming that $874.89 = \mu$ and that means of samples of N are distributed normally, we may answer this question as follows: The allowable error is 5 per cent of 874.89 days or 43.74 days, and this must correspond to a probability of 0.90. From Theorem 6.1 we have

$$Q\delta = 2\int_0^\delta \phi(t)\,dt = .90$$

that is

$$\int_0^\delta \phi(t)\,dt = .45$$

whence from the tables we find $\delta = 1.645$. Hence N is found by solving the equation

$$1.645\,\frac{\sigma}{\sqrt{N}} = 43.74$$

where $\sigma = 85.3$. We find $N = 10$.

6.13 Standard Error of an Observed Proportion. If we take samples of N from a binomial population with parameter θ the probability of Np successes is $\binom{N}{Np}\theta^{Np}(1-\theta)^{Nq}$ where $q = 1 - p$. As $N \to \infty$ the binomial distribution tends to a normal distribution with mean $N\theta$ and variance $N\theta(1-\theta)$. Hence the standard error of Np is $[N\theta(1-\theta)]^{1/2}$ if θ is known.

If θ is not known, we must use an estimate of it. The natural estimate to take is p, which is the relative frequency of success in the sample, so that the standard error of Np is approximately $(Npq)^{1/2}$ for large N. The standard error of the proportion p is, therefore, $(pq/N)^{1/2}$.

This estimate is unbiased since the expectation of p is the parameter value θ. Thus

$$E(p) = \sum_{Np=0}^{N} p \binom{N}{Np} \theta^{Np}(1-\theta)^{Nq}$$
$$= \theta \sum_{Np=1}^{N} \binom{N-1}{Np-1} \theta^{Np-1}(1-\theta)^{Nq}$$
$$= \theta[\theta + (1-\theta)]^{N-1} = \theta$$

This estimate is also the one obtained if we inquire what value of θ is most likely to give the observed sample, that is, what value of θ, for given p, will make $f = \binom{N}{Np} \theta^{Np}(1-\theta)^{Nq}$ a maximum. Upon setting $df/d\theta = 0$ we get $Np(1-\theta) - \theta Nq = 0$ whence $\theta = p$.

The method of estimation just used is known as the *method of maximum likelihood*. (See further in § 12.4.)

6.14 Standard Error of a Difference of Proportions. In the analysis of data obtained by sampling, certain problems occur which relate to the significance of apparent differences in proportions. Suppose we have two random samples of size n_1 and n_2, respectively, with x_1 individuals of the n_1 items and x_2 of the n_2 items which have a certain character or attribute. The question arises as to whether the observed difference is merely an accident of sampling or whether a similar difference exists in the universe. The following theorem may be used to test the null hypothesis that x_1/n_1 and x_2/n_2 are random and independent samples from the same universe.

Theorem 6.2. *If x_1/n_1 and x_2/n_2 are the observed proportions in random and independent samples from infinite populations in which the same proportion θ of individuals have the character in question, the probability that the difference in these observed proportions will be numerically as great as the observed difference $(w = x_1/n_1 - x_2/n_2)$ is approximately P_δ, where P_δ is defined in Theorem 6.1 and*
$$\delta = w/\sigma_w, \qquad \sigma_w = \left\{\theta(1-\theta)\left(\frac{1}{n_1} + \frac{1}{n_2}\right)\right\}^{1/2}$$

Proof: The expectation of x_1/n_1 is θ and its variance is $\theta(1-\theta)/n_1$. Similarly, the expectation and variance of x_2/n_2 are θ and $\theta(1-\theta)/n_2$. Hence the expectation of w is zero, and by Theorem 4.11 its variance is

$$(6.30) \qquad \sigma_w^2 = \theta(1-\theta)\left(\frac{1}{n_1} + \frac{1}{n_2}\right)$$

The ratio w/σ_w, therefore, varies about zero with unit standard deviation. Information about the form of this distribution may be obtained from its higher moments. It is not difficult to show (see Problem 11) that

$$(6.31) \qquad \gamma_1^2 = \frac{(n_1 - n_2)^2}{n_1 n_2 (n_1 + n_2)} \cdot \frac{1 - 4\theta(1-\theta)}{\theta(1-\theta)}$$

$$(6.32) \qquad \gamma_2 = \frac{n_1^2 - n_1 n_2 + n_2^2}{n_1 n_2 (n_1 + n_2)} \cdot \frac{1 - 6\theta(1-\theta)}{\theta(1-\theta)}$$

Sec. 15   Confidence Limits for a Binomial Distribution   147

For fixed θ it is clear that γ_1 and $\gamma_2 \to 0$ as the samples are taken indefinitely large. Even for moderately small samples the distribution of w/σ_w does not differ greatly from the normal form. The following empirical rule, suggested by E. S. Pearson, is useful.

Rule. Suppose $n_1 < n_2$ (we are at liberty to call either n_1). If $n_1\theta > 5$ the use of the normal probability scale is justified. If $n_1\theta \leq 5$, examine γ_1^2. If $\gamma_1^2 < 0.04$ the normal law is still sufficiently accurate, but if $\gamma_1^2 \geq 0.04$ no great confidence can be placed in the test.

In order to apply this rule, or Theorem 6.2, an estimate of θ is required. It is usual to take

$$\hat{\theta} = \frac{x_1 + x_2}{n_1 + n_2} \tag{6.33}$$

and it is easy to show that this estimate is unbiased, its expectation being θ.

Example 6. Suppose that in a survey conducted for a company selling a certain brand of tires, "XX," 750 persons polled in district A said they planned to purchase tires shortly and 300 of them said they intended to get "XX" brand. In district B, out of 600 persons planning on purchasing tires, 210 intended to get "XX" brand. Could this difference in the proportion of prospective "XX" purchasers be attributed to sampling fluctuations or should the company look for some other explanation?

Our null hypothesis is that the proportion θ of prospective "XX" purchasers is the same in A and B. As an estimate of θ we take $\hat{\theta} = 510/1350 = 0.3778$.

The difference of proportions is $0.40 - 0.35 = 0.05$, and the variance of the difference is $0.3778 \times 0.6222 \times (\frac{1}{600} + \frac{1}{750}) = 0.000705$. Hence $w/\sigma_w = 0.05/0.0266 = 1.88$, and the probability of a deviation numerically as great as 0.05 is about 0.060. The difference can, therefore, be attributed to sampling fluctuations, although it is rather close to the borderline of significance.

6.15 Confidence Limits for the Parameter of a Binomial Distribution. If in N trials of an event with probability θ the number of successes is Np,

$$E(p) = \theta$$
$$\text{Var}(p) = \theta(1 - \theta)/N$$

Since for large values of N and for θ not very near to 0 or 1 the binomial distribution is approximately normal, we have

$$\Pr\{p - \theta \leq t[\theta(1 - \theta)/N]^{1/2}\} \approx \Phi(t)$$

or

$$\Pr\{\theta - t_\alpha[\theta(1-\theta)/N]^{1/2} \leq p \leq \theta + t_\alpha[\theta(1-\theta)/N]^{1/2}\} \approx 1 - \alpha \tag{6.34}$$

where t_α is the value of t for which $\Phi(t_\alpha) = 1 - \alpha/2$, so that $100(1 - \alpha)\%$ is the confidence coefficient corresponding to t_α.

In practice, however, θ is unknown. From (6.34), we have

$$\Pr\left\{-t_\alpha \leq \frac{\theta - p}{[\theta(1 - \theta)/N]^{1/2}} \leq t_\alpha\right\} \approx 1 - \alpha \tag{6.35}$$

At the end-point of this interval

$$(\theta - p)^2 = \theta(1 - \theta)t_\alpha{}^2/N$$

so that

$$N(\theta - p)^2 = \theta(1 - \theta)t_\alpha{}^2$$

This is a quadratic in θ, which may be written

$$\theta^2(N + t_\alpha{}^2) - \theta(2pN + t_\alpha{}^2) + Np^2 = 0$$

Solving for θ, we get

(6.36) $$\theta = \frac{Np + \frac{1}{2}t_\alpha{}^2 \pm t_\alpha[Npq + \frac{1}{4}t_\alpha{}^2]^{1/2}}{N + t_\alpha{}^2}$$

If these two extreme values are written as $p_{u\alpha}, p_{l\alpha}$, corresponding respectively to the $+$ and $-$ signs in (6.36), (6.35) may be written in the form

(6.37) $$\Pr\{p_{l\alpha} \leq \theta \leq p_{u\alpha}\} \approx 1 - \alpha$$

In this form the equation gives confidence limits $p_{l\alpha}$ and $p_{u\alpha}$ for θ. If we assert that θ lies between these limits on a large number of occasions (the limits, of course, varying from sample to sample), we shall be right in a fraction $1 - \alpha$ of these assertions.

Thus if in 400 trials of an event with constant probability θ of success, we find 280 successes, our estimate of θ is $280/400 = 0.7$. If we take $t_\alpha = 1.96$, so that $\alpha = 0.05$, the values of $p_{l\alpha}$ and $p_{u\alpha}$ are $0.698 - 0.045$ and $0.698 + 0.045$ respectively, so that the 95% confidence limits for θ are 0.653 and 0.743.

For small values of N, the normal approximation is not justified. However, it is possible to determine the parameter θ_1 of a binomial such that the observed value of $x = Np$ cuts off the upper $2\frac{1}{2}\%$ tail of the distribution, that is,

$$\sum_{x=Np}^{N} \binom{N}{x} \theta_1{}^x (1 - \theta_1)^{N-x} = 0.025$$

This can be done by a rather tedious method of successive approximations.* The value of θ_1 then provides a 95% lower confidence limit for θ. In the same way, θ_2 can be found so that in the corresponding binomial distribution the observed Np cuts off the lower $2\frac{1}{2}\%$ tail. Then θ_2 provides the 95% upper confidence limit for θ.

Useful charts have been prepared by Clopper and Pearson,[11] by means of which the 95% and 99% limits for any observed value of p may be read off approximately. These charts are drawn for several different values of N between 10 and 1000. The 95% chart is reproduced in S. S. Wilks' *Elementary Statistical Analysis* (1948), p. 201.

* More conveniently, we can use the new *Tables of the Binomial Probability Distribution* (National Bureau of Standards, Washington, 1950) which give individual terms and cumulative sums of terms for values of N from 2 to 49.

6.16 Sampling from a Finite Binomial Population. For a finite parent population of size M and a sample of size N, the expectation and variance of the sample proportion p are given by

(6.38)
$$\begin{cases} E(p) = \theta, \\ \text{Var}(p) = \frac{M-N}{M-1} \frac{\theta(1-\theta)}{N} \end{cases}$$

For large N and still larger M, p may be regarded as normally distributed about θ, so that $(p-\theta)[\theta(1-\theta)/N \times (M-N)/(M-1)]^{1/2}$ is approximately a standard normal variate. Confidence limits may then be determined as in § 6.15.

6.17 Confidence Limits for the Difference of Parameters in Two Binomial Distributions. Suppose that independent samples of sizes N_1 and N_2 are taken from two binomial populations in which the proportions of individuals having a certain characteristic are θ_1 and θ_2. If the observed proportions are p_1 and p_2, $(p_1 > p_2)$, we have

(6.39)
$$\begin{cases} E(p_1 - p_2) = \theta_1 - \theta_2 \\ \text{Var}(p_1 - p_2) = \frac{\theta_1(1-\theta_1)}{N_1} + \frac{\theta_2(1-\theta_2)}{N_2} \end{cases}$$

Assuming as before a normal distribution, we have approximately

$$\Pr\{p_1 - p_2 - t_\alpha[\theta_1(1-\theta_1)/N_1 + \theta_2(1-\theta_2)/N_2]^{1/2} < (\theta_1 - \theta_2) \\ < p_1 - p_2 + t_\alpha[\theta_1(1-\theta_1)/N_1 + \theta_2(1-\theta_2)/N_2]^{1/2}\} = 1 - \alpha$$

where, as previously noted, the probability refers to the variables p_1 and p_2 in repeated pairs of samples from the same two parent populations.

In this inequality the limits depend on the unknown parameters θ_1 and θ_2. If we replace these by their estimates p_1 and p_2, respectively, we have approximate confidence limits,

(6.40)
$$\begin{aligned} p_{l\alpha} &= p_1 - p_2 - t_\alpha(p_1q_1/N_1 + p_2q_2/N_2)^{1/2} \\ p_{u\alpha} &= p_1 - p_2 + t_\alpha(p_1q_1/N_1 + p_2q_2/N_2)^{1/2} \end{aligned}$$

where $q_1 = 1 - p_1$, $q_2 = 1 - p_2$.

Example 7. Out of 400 voters polled in constituency A, 160 stated that they intended to vote Liberal in a forthcoming election. Out of 500 polled in constituency B, 250 stated that they would vote Liberal.

Here $p_1 = 0.5$, $p_2 = 0.4$, $N_1 = 500$, $N_2 = 400$, and

$$\left(\frac{p_1q_1}{N_1} + \frac{p_2q_2}{N_2}\right)^{1/2} = 0.0333$$

Taking $t_\alpha = 1.96$ we have, as 95% confidence limits, $p_{l\alpha} = .035$, $p_{u\alpha} = .165$. The *difference* of the proportion of Liberal voters in the two constituencies may be expected to lie between these limits, assuming that the voters polled form random samples of their respective constituencies, and that they really vote as they say they will.

6.18 Confidence Limits for the Poisson Distribution. Variables distributed according to the Poisson law arise in several physical and biological problems. Thus, if organisms of a certain species are distributed at random over the bottom of a lake, the numbers found in a series of trial dredgings from separate small areas of the same size will follow this law. The frequency function of the Poisson distribution contains a single parameter m which is the expectation of the variable X. For any given m, values X_1 and X_2 can be calculated such that the probability that X lies below X_2 or above X_1 is, say, 0.025, and upper and lower confidence curves can be constructed.[12] Since the Poisson distribution is discrete, these curves are stepped curves. Thus, for any given m, there will, in general, be one value of X_1 such that $\sum_{X_1}^{\infty} e^{-m} m^X / X! < 0.025$ and $\sum_{X_1-1}^{\infty} e^{-m} m^X / X! > 0.025$, but as m increases through a value such that $\sum_{X_1}^{\infty} e^{-m} m^X / X! = 0.025$, the corresponding X_1 increases by one unit. The curves in Figure 19 are drawn just inside the calculated step curves. We see

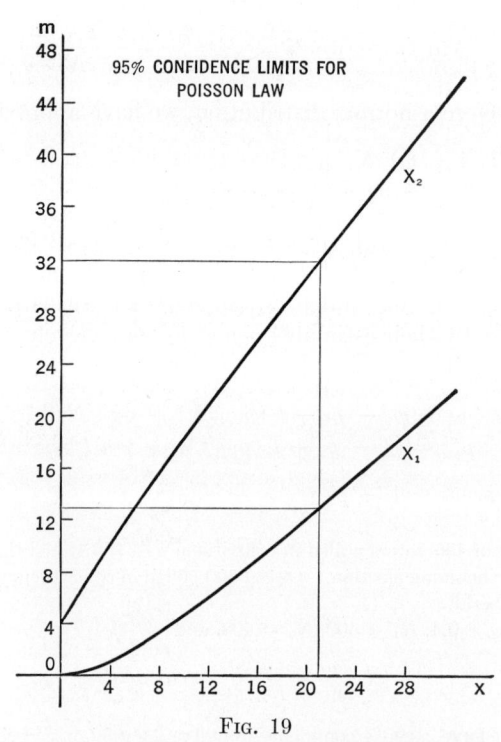

95% CONFIDENCE LIMITS FOR POISSON LAW

FIG. 19

from these curves that if $X = 21$, m lies between 13 and 32, so that if, for example, we count 21 organisms in a square yard of a lake bottom, we can state with 95% confidence that the average number of organisms per square yard lies between 13 and 32.

6.19 Picking a Random Sample. A random sample was defined in § 6.1 as a sub-set of a set of variates in which each individual variate from the parent population has an equal chance to be included. This is, however, more of an abstract than a practical definition and gives no indication of how to obtain a random sample or to test a given sample for randomness. These matters are of very great importance for experimental statisticians, and, although this book is primarily concerned with mathematical statistics, some remarks on the subject may be worth while.

In the first place, we note that the use of the theory of probability to make inferences about a parent population from observations on a sample (for example, to test some hypothesis about the population or to calculate confidence limits for a parameter) is based on the essential assumption that the sample is random. A *purposive sample*, which is one selected according to one or more definite criteria in the mind of the experimenter and which depends on his skill and judgment in making the selection, may be thought to be more "typical" of the parent population than a random sample, but the reliability of inferences about the parent population cannot be assessed from such a sample.

If the parent population is finite, the individuals may be numbered and arranged in order, and a sample taken by choosing, say, every kth individual starting with the ith, i being some positive number from 1 to k chosen at random. This is called *systematic sampling*. If the attribute under discussion is clearly independent of the ordering (as, for instance, if a group of students are arranged in alphabetical order of their surnames and a sample is wanted of their performance on an intelligence test), the sample is practically equivalent to a random sample. Care must be taken that there is no natural periodicity of period k in the parent population. Thus if every tenth house along a street is selected, and if there are ten houses to a block, it may happen that every selected house is a corner house. Such a sample of households would probably not be representative of the population in respect of any attribute depending on economic status. If there is some serial correlation between the individuals of the population (as arranged in order), that is, a correlation between, say, the ith and the $(i + j)$th individuals, the variance of a systematic sample may be greater than, equal to, or less than the variance of a random sample, depending on the extent of this correlation (see § 6.22).

Various mechanical devices may be used to obtain random samples from a finite population, ranging from "drawing numbers out of a hat" to the elaborate revolving drums filled with metal cylinders each containing a number, as used in large lotteries. A simple method is to write the numbers on cards which are then thoroughly shuffled. A selection of some of these cards will give an approximately random sample of the numbers. All such devices are subject to possible mechanical imperfections which may introduce a bias. Even the best-made roulette wheels will show a slight tendency to favor some compartments above others. Cards will differ slightly in their tendency to stick together, and shuffling by the customary procedures is notoriously imperfect.

Large tables of numbers, such as telephone directories for big cities or sets of statistical tables, may be used to get random numbers. The table is opened haphazardly and the right-hand digits, or pairs of right-hand digits, are written down in order, any numbers of less than four digits being ignored. It has been found in practice, however, that this method is not satisfactory — the frequencies of the different digits often differ from their expected values by larger amounts than can reasonably be attributed to sampling fluctuations. Mathematical tables, such as seven-figure logarithms, should not be used in this way because of the obvious relationship between successive entries — the first differences tend to be constant over many entries. The 15th to the 19th digits in A. J. Thompson's 20-figure tables of logarithms (*Logarithmetica Britannica*) have been used, however, by Fisher and Yates in obtaining random numbers. Since the first differences are themselves 15-digit numbers, very little systematic effect is to be expected. Moreover, additional randomness was introduced by selecting pages of the table, choosing a particular column (between the 15th and 19th), and choosing the position of the first digit in a block, all these choices being made by the use of two packs of playing cards. Even so, Fisher and Yates found an undue preponderance of 6's, which they corrected by picking out some of the 6's at random and replacing them by other digits, also chosen at random.[13]

There are now available several sets of numbers which have been carefully compiled and tested in various ways for randomness, and one of these sets is commonly used when it is necessary to take a random sample from a finite population. There are: (*a*) Tippett's Random Sampling Numbers,[14] consisting of 41,600 digits taken from census reports and combined into fours to make 10,400 four-figure numbers; (*b*) Kendall and Babington Smith's more extensive set,[15] consisting of 100,000 digits grouped in 2's and 4's, and in separate thousands: these were obtained by means of a specially constructed machine; (*c*) Fisher and Yates's numbers, 15,000 digits arranged in 2's given in their *Statistical Tables* (Table XXXIII) and obtained in the way described above.

Example 8. To draw a sample of 30 from the 1000 children of Table 2 (§ 5.9).

The individuals are supposed numbered in order of increasing weight, number 1 in the group 28–31 lb, numbers 2 to 15 in the group 32–35 lb, and so on. Since 1000 goes into 10,000 ten times, it is convenient to multiply the frequencies by 10 and allot numbers 0000 to 0009 to the first group, 0010 to 0149 to the second group, and so on, numbers 9970 to 9999 belonging to the tenth group. Opening a table of random numbers (say Fisher and Yates) and starting anywhere, we read off consecutive digits in groups of four, thus: 0564, 1270, 8880, 5835, 0688, 7348, · · · until 30 numbers have been accumulated. The number 0564 belongs to group 3, 1270 to group 4, 8880 to group 7, and so on. For a sample obtained in this way, the mean was 47.63 lb, as compared with 47.712 lb for the population.

If the total frequency in a distribution is, say, 759 instead of 1000, we can multiply class frequencies by 12 and neglect any random numbers equal to or greater than 9108.

Example 9. To arrange 16 numbered objects (such as plots of land in a block) in random order.

A method of doing this is to take the random two-figure numbers as they occur, starting anywhere, divide each by 16 and use the remainders (counting 0 as 16). It is rather easier to divide by 20 and reject 0, 17, 18, and 19. Whenever a number is repeated in the sequence, it must be rejected. This, however, means that toward the end of the process most numbers will have to be rejected. Alternatively, after choosing the first 7 numbers as above, we can divide the next two-figure random numbers that occur by 9, 8, 7, $\cdots$ and use the remainders to indicate which of the numbers from 1 to 16 *still remaining unchosen* is to be selected. Thus, the random numbers may be

$$53, 81, 29, 13, 39, 35, 01, 20, 71, 34, 62, \cdots$$

These give as remainders

$$13, 1, 9, \cancel{13}, \cancel{19}, 15, \cancel{1}, \cancel{0}, 11, 14, 2$$

so that our first 7 numbers are 13, 1, 9, 15, 11, 14, 2.
The next 8 random numbers are

$$33, 74, 82, 14, 53, 73, 19, 09$$

which give as remainders on dividing by 9, 8, 7, $\cdots$ 2,

$$6, 2, 5, 2, 3, 1, 1, 1$$

The nine unchosen numbers in order are

$$3, 4, 5, 6, 7, 8, 10, 12, 16$$

of which the 6th is 8, the 2nd of those remaining is 4, the 5th is 10, and so on. The last 9 numbers are therefore

$$8, 4, 10, 5, 7, 3, 6, 12, 16$$

Example 10. To draw a random sample from a normal population with mean 20 and standard deviation 4.

Here the parent population is infinite, but the proportion of individuals occurring in any specified interval can be found from a table of the normal law. We may choose intervals 4–, 6–, 8–, 10–, 12–, $\cdots$ which correspond to intervals for the standard normal curve beginning at –4.0, –3.5, –3, –2.5, –2, $\cdots$. The areas of the normal curve up to these points, rounded off to four figures, are 0.0000, 0.0002, 0.0013, 0.0062, 0.0228, 0.0668, 0.1587, 0.3085, 0.5000, 0.6915, 0.8413, 0.9332, 0.9772, 0.9938, 0.9987, 0.9998. Hence in a table of four-digit random numbers, we can allot the numbers 0000–0001 to the first interval (with center 5), the numbers 0002–0012 to the second interval (with center 7), and so on.

6.20 Tests for Randomness. Any finite set of numbers, however improbable, *could* arise by random sampling in a sufficiently prolonged series of trials, but a very improbable set would be unsatisfactory, *by itself*, as a basis for a randomizing experiment. In the table of Kendall and Babington Smith referred to above, there are 100 groups of 1000 single-digit numbers each, and 5 of these groups are starred to indicate that they did not satisfy certain tests of randomness. These groups should not be used for sampling experiments involving less than 1000 digits, but can safely be used in conjunction with at least four neighboring groups.

Four tests of randomness were used:

1. *Frequency test.* The frequency of occurrence of each digit 0 to 9 was compared with the expected value (one-tenth of the number of digits in the group).

2. *Serial test.* The frequencies of all pairs 00–99 were compared with the expected values.

3. *Poker test.* The numbers were grouped in fours, and the frequencies of various combinations of digits (four of the same kind, three of one kind and one different, two pairs, one pair, and all different) were compared with expectation.

4. *Gap test.* The lengths of gaps between successive zeros were counted and a frequency distribution formed for comparison with expectation.

In all cases the comparison was made by the χ^2 test, with rejection levels at 1% and 99%. The gap test was not suitable for groups as small as 1000, but was used for blocks of 5000, 25,000, and the whole 100,000 digits.

6.21 Stratified Sampling. Suppose the population, of size N, is divided into sub-populations (strata) of sizes $N_1, N_2, \cdots N_k$. Let $n_1, n_2, \cdots n_k$ be the sizes of random samples from the respective strata and let $n = \sum n_i$. Then if, for any variable x, the sample weighted mean and the population mean are $\bar{x}_n$ and $\bar{x}_p$ respectively, we shall show that, with weights N_i

(6.41) $$E(\bar{x}_n) = \bar{x}_p$$

and

(6.42) $$\text{Var}(\bar{x}_n) = \frac{1}{N^2} \sum_i \frac{N_i^2(N_i - n_i)}{N_i - 1} \frac{\sigma_i^2}{n_i}$$

where σ_i^2 is the population variance in the ith stratum. If a heterogeneous population is divided into relatively homogeneous strata, the variance of the mean may be reduced by sampling in this way. Also there may be compelling administrative reasons for stratification, as, for instance, by counties within a state or province.

If $\bar{x}_{ni}$ and $\bar{x}_{pi}$ represent sample and population means within the ith stratum, we have

$$\bar{x}_n = \frac{1}{N} \sum N_i \bar{x}_{ni}, \qquad \bar{x}_p = \frac{1}{N} \sum N_i \bar{x}_{pi}$$

and since $E(\bar{x}_{ni}) = \bar{x}_{pi}$ by (6.26), the truth of (6.41) is established. Moreover,

$$\text{Var}(\bar{x}_n) = E(\bar{x}_n - \bar{x}_p)^2$$
$$= \frac{1}{N^2} \sum N_i^2 [E(\bar{x}_{ni} - \bar{x}_{pi})^2 + E\text{ (cross-product terms)}]$$

The expectation of the cross-product terms will be zero, since the sample from one stratum is independent of the sample from another stratum. By (6.27) the variance in the ith stratum is given by

$$E(\bar{x}_{ni} - \bar{x}_{pi})^2 = \frac{N_i - n_i}{N_i - 1} \frac{\sigma_i^2}{n_i}$$

so that

$$\text{Var}(\bar{x}_n) = \frac{1}{N^2} \sum_i \frac{N_i^2(N_i - n_i)}{N_i - 1} \frac{\sigma_i^2}{n_i}$$

which is (6.42).

It will be proved in the next chapter (§ 7.2) that an unbiased estimate of σ_i^2, based on the sample of n_i, is $n_i/(n_i - 1) \cdot s_i^2$, where s_i^2 is the observed variance for this sample. Hence

(6.43) $$\text{Var}(\bar{x}_n) = \frac{1}{N^2} \sum \frac{N_i^2(N_i - n_i)}{N_i - 1} \frac{s_i^2}{n_i - 1}$$

It has been shown by J. Neyman[16] that in stratified sampling the variance of the mean is least (and therefore the mean is most accurately estimated) if, for a fixed total sample size, the n_i are proportional to $N_i \sigma_i$. If this condition is satisfied, and if the cost of taking the sample is proportional to the sample size, the sampling is *optimum*, in the sense that the greatest possible accuracy is obtained for a fixed cost.

To prove this, we have to minimize Var $(\bar{x}_n)$, as given by (6.42), with the added condition $\sum n_i = $ constant. Using the Lagrange multiplier[18] λ, we have to minimize, without restriction, the quantity

$$\frac{1}{N^2} \sum \frac{N_i^2(N_i - n_i)}{N_i - 1} \frac{\sigma_i^2}{n_i} + \lambda \sum n_i$$

Differentiating with respect to n_i, we obtain

$$-\frac{N_i^3 \sigma_i^2}{N^2(N_i - 1)n_i^2} + \lambda = 0$$

so that

$$n_i = \frac{\sigma_i}{N\lambda^{1/2}} \left(\frac{N_i^3}{N_i - 1}\right)^{1/2} = \frac{N_i \sigma_i}{N\lambda^{1/2}}, \qquad \text{approx.}$$

if we ignore the difference between N_i and $N_i - 1$. Since $\sum n_i = n$, we have

$$n = \frac{1}{N\lambda^{1/2}} \sum N_i \sigma_i$$

so that

(6.44) $$n_i = n \frac{N_i \sigma_i}{\sum N_i \sigma_i}$$

The application of this result requires a knowledge of σ_i which is not usually available before the sample is taken. However, it is often possible to obtain a useful estimate from general knowledge of the population, from a preliminary survey, or from previous experience.

If the σ_i are all equal, $n_i = nN_i/N$, so that the n_i are proportional to the corresponding N_i. The sampling is then said to be *proportional*. In this case,

$$\bar{x}_n = \frac{1}{n}\sum n_i \bar{x}_{ni}$$

and so is equal to the sample total divided by the sample size. The sample is *self-weighting*.

6.22 Systematic Sampling. If there are $N = nk$ units in the population, all numbered consecutively, and if we take a unit at random from the first k units and every kth unit subsequently, we shall obtain a systematic sample of n. Thus if $k = 20$, and the first unit drawn is the 7th, the subsequent units in the sample are the 27th, 47th, etc.

This method of sampling is convenient and rapid. If the individual data are on cards, all of the same size, arranged in a file drawer, a ruler may be laid alongside and a card drawn out at, say, each inch without the cards being numbered. This is not perhaps strictly "every kth" sampling but is very speedy.

In effect, systematic sampling divides the population into strata, each consisting of k successive units, and chooses one sampling unit per stratum. This unit is not, however, chosen at random but occupies the same relative position in each stratum. Since the systematic sample is spread evenly over the population, it often gives a very accurate estimate of the mean. The theory was worked out by W. G. and L. H. Madow.[17]

Let i be a random number between 1 and k inclusive. The sample mean is

$$m_i = \{x_i + x_{i+k} + \cdots + x_{i+(n-1)k}\}/n$$

Since there are k values of i, all equally likely,

(6.45) $\qquad E(m_i) = (m_1 + m_2 + \cdots + m_k)/k = \bar{x}_p$

where $\bar{x}_p$ is the mean value of x for the whole population. The sample mean is, therefore, an unbiased estimate of the population mean. The variance is given by

$$\text{Var}(m_i) = E(m_i - \bar{x}_p)^2 = \frac{1}{k}\sum_i (m_i - \bar{x}_p)^2$$

$$= \frac{1}{n^2 k}\sum (nm_i - n\bar{x}_p)^2$$

where

$$nm_i - n\bar{x}_p = (x_i - \bar{x}_p) + (x_{i+k} - \bar{x}_p) + \cdots + (x_{i+(n-1)k} - x_p)$$

On squaring and adding, the squared terms sum to $\sum_{i=1}^{N}(x_i - \bar{x}_p)^2 = N\sigma^2$. As for the cross-product terms, there are $k(n-1)$ terms like $2(x_i - \bar{x}_p)(x_{i+k} - \bar{x}_p)$ which come from observations k units apart; $k(n-2)$ terms like $2(x_i - \bar{x}_p)(x_{i+2k} - \bar{x}_p)$ which come from observations $2k$ units apart, and so on. Hence

(6.46) $$\text{Var}(m_i) = \frac{1}{n^2 k}\left[N\sigma^2 + 2\sum_{i=1}^{k(n-j)}\sum_{j=1}^{n-1}(x_i - \bar{x}_p)(x_{i+jk} - \bar{x}_p)\right]$$

Now let ρ_{jk} be the non-circular *serial correlation coefficient* for a lag of jk defined by

(6.47) $$k(n-j)\sigma^2 \rho_{jk} = \sum_{i=1}^{k(n-j)}(x_i - \bar{x}_p)(x_{i+jk} - \bar{x}_p)$$

Then, from (6.46),

(6.48) $$\text{Var}(m_i) = \sigma^2\left[N + 2k\sum_{j=1}^{n-1}(n-j)\rho_{jk}\right]\Big/n^2 k$$
$$= \sigma^2\left[1 + \frac{2}{n}\sum(n-j)\rho_{jk}\right]\Big/n$$

This may be compared with the result for a random sample,

$$\text{Var}(\bar{x}_n) = \frac{\sigma^2}{n}\frac{N-n}{N-1} = \frac{k-1}{nk-1}\sigma^2$$
$$= \frac{\sigma^2}{n}\left[1 - \frac{1}{k}\right], \quad \text{very nearly}$$

if N is large compared with 1. It follows that systematic sampling will be more accurate than random sampling if the serial correlation coefficients are negative and sufficiently large. If the serial correlation coefficients are all zero, random sampling is the more accurate.

Problems

1. Suppose a variable w is normally distributed and a value is selected at random. Show that the odds are about 369 to 1 against the value differing from $E(w)$ by more than $3\sigma_w$'s.

2. (a) Consider a finite universe of 5 variates: x_1, x_2, x_3, x_4, x_5. The number of distinct samples of 3 variates each that may be drawn is $\binom{5}{3} = 10$. Write these down.

(b) Let $\bar{x}_i$ represent the ith sample mean and write down the 10 distinct sample means. For example,
$$\bar{x}_1 = \frac{x_1 + x_2 + x_3}{3}$$

(c) Show that the mean of the 10 values of $\bar{x}_i$ is the mean of the 5 values of x_i. Thus,
$$\frac{1}{10}\sum \bar{x}_i = \frac{1}{5}\sum x_i = \bar{x}$$

What formula does this example illustrate?

3. Show that the expected value of w^2 is greater than the square of the expected value of w.

4. From a box containing 2000 discs representing the distribution of span, draw a sample of 25 and compute its mean and standard deviation. Test the significance of the difference between your mean and the mean of the universe $\mu = 69.943$ inches.

5. Suppose the weights of a sample of 1000 men of the same age are obtained yielding $\bar{x} = 140$ lb. Assuming that $\sigma = 20.0$ lb, what is the standard error of the mean of this sample? What is the probability that this mean does not differ from the mean of the universe at this age by more than five pounds?

Fundamentals of Sampling Theory

6. (*Camp*) [10] The mean age of death of men who are alive at age 20 is, in the United States, 59.13. For the city of Chicago it is 58.98, and in 1910 the male population of age 20 was 24,000. Can the difference between the United States and Chicago be explained on the hypothesis of chance? Assume $\sigma = 10$ years, and that the distribution of the universe is approximately normal.

7. (*Camp*) [10] A fraternal organization wishes to be very sure that the average age of death in its group of men now aged 20 will not differ from the expected 59.13 years by more than one year. By "very sure" it means that Q_δ must equal .999 or more. How large should the group be? (Assume as before that $\sigma = 10$.)

8. Given that

$$w = \sum_1^k (f_i + x_i)$$

If the x's are independent and $\sum_1^k f_i$ is a constant, show that $\sigma_w^2 = \sum_1^k \sigma_i^2$

where σ_i^2 represents the variance of x_i.

9. Find the mean value of all positive ordinates of the first quadrant of $x^2 + y^2 = r^2$,
(a) when equally spaced along the x-axis,
(b) when equally spaced along the circle.

Answers

(a) $\dfrac{1}{r} \int_0^r y\, dx = \dfrac{1}{r} \int_0^r \sqrt{r^2 - x^2}\, dx = \dfrac{\pi r}{4}$

(b) $\dfrac{2}{\pi r} \int_0^r y\, ds = \dfrac{2}{\pi r} \int_0^r \sqrt{r^2 - x^2} \sqrt{1 + \left(\dfrac{dy}{dx}\right)^2}\, dx = \dfrac{2r}{\pi}$

10. Find the mean value of all the ordinates of the curve $y = a + b^x$ from 0 to x, when equally spaced along the x-axis.

11. Derive (6.31) and (6.32). *Hint.* $\mu_r = E(w/\sigma_w)^r = E(w^r)/\sigma_w^r$.

12. Show that the moment relations (6.27), (6.28), (6.29) reduce to the corresponding relations (6.7), (6.10), (6.11) if $M \to \infty$.

13. Suppose 300 mice having cancer of about the same degree of malignancy were divided at random into two groups of $n_1 = 100$ and $n_2 = 200$, respectively. The first group was given a certain serum treatment which was withheld from the second group but otherwise the two groups were treated alike. Among the serum-treated there were $x_1 = 8$ deaths, and among the other group there were $x_2 = 25$ deaths. Test the significance of the difference between the mortality of 8% and $12\frac{1}{2}$% in the two groups.

14. An instructor had two classes of 20 and 30 students in the same subject. Four in the smaller class and 8 in the larger made grades of B or better. Should one seek a further explanation of this difference beyond variation due to sampling?

15. For a sample of 345 eleven-year-old boys, the mean weight was found to be 74.71 lb and the standard deviation 10.65 lb. Calculate 98% confidence limits for the mean weight. *Ans.* 73.37 lb and 76.05 lb.

16. In certain states of the United States in a certain year the number of white males dying between the ages of 30 and 31 was 1609 out of a total of 253,445 white males in this age-group. For Negro males of the same age the number dying was 115 out of 6975. Does there seem to be a significant racial difference in the death rates?

17. A railway company has experimented with two processes A and B for creosoting its ties. Of 50 ties preserved by process A, 22 are still in service after 23 years. Of 50 preserved by process B, 18 are still in service. Both sets were subjected to practically identical conditions. Is the difference significant?

18. An aquarium contains a culture of a certain organism suspended in water. The water is well stirred and 0.1 ml is examined on a slide. The number of organisms counted

References

is 13. Estimate from Figure 19 the 95% confidence limits for the number of organisms per milliliter of the water.

19. Use a table of random numbers to draw four random samples of 10 from the population specified in Table 6. Calculate the mean for each sample and compare with the distribution given in Table 7.

20. If the cost per unit of sampling in a stratified sample varies from stratum to stratum, so that the total cost is $c = \sum c_i n_i$, prove that for fixed c the minimum variance of the mean is given when n_i is proportional to $N_i \sigma_i / c_i^{1/2}$. That is, more sampling units should be picked from a given stratum if it is (a) larger, (b) more variable, (c) cheaper to sample.

References

1. H. L. Rietz, *Mathematical Statistics*, 1927, p. 114.

2. R. A. Fisher, "On the Mathematical Foundations of Theoretical Statistics," *Phil. Trans. Roy. Soc.* (A), **222**, 1921, p. 309.

3. R. A. Fisher, *Statistical Methods for Research Workers*, 10th edition, 1947, p. 41.

4. J. Neyman and E. S. Pearson, "On the use and interpretation of certain test criteria for purposes of statistical inference," *Biometrika*, **20 A**, 1928, pp. 175 and 263.

See also J. Neyman, *Lectures and Conferences on Mathematical Statistics*, 1938, for a good discussion of the problem of statistical estimation.

5. E. S. Pearson, "The Test of Significance for the Correlation Coefficient," *J. Amer. Stat. Assoc.*, **26**, 1931, p. 128.

6. R. A. Fisher, *The Design of Experiments*, 4th Edition, p. 18.

7. See an article by H. C. Carver, "Fundamentals of the Theory of Sampling," *Ann. Math. Stat.*, **1**, 1930, p. 101. According to A. E. R. Church (*Biometrika*, **18**, 1926, p. 357), it is not known who first developed these formulas. See also Irwin and Kendall, *Ann. Eugenics*, London, **12**, 1944, p. 138, where the formulas for a finite population are derived in a simple way from the formulas for an infinite population.

8. W. A. Shewhart, *Economic Control of the Quality of Manufactured Products*, 1931, p. 183.

9. W. A. Shewhart, *loc. cit.*, p. 391.

10. B. H. Camp, *Mathematical Statistics*, 1931, p. 251.

11. C. J. Clopper and E. S. Pearson, "The Use of Confidence or Fiducial Limits," *Biometrika*, **26**, 1934, p. 404. These charts (and additional ones for 80% and 90% confidence limits) are reproduced in *Introduction to Statistical Analysis* by W. J. Dixon and F. J. Massey (McGraw-Hill, 1950).

12. W. E. Ricker, "The Concept of Confidence or Fiducial Limits Applied to the Poisson Frequency Distribution," *J. Amer. Stat. Assoc.*, **32**, 1937, p. 349.

13. Fisher and Yates, *Statistical Tables* (1st Edition, 1938), pp. 18–20.

14. L. H. C. Tippett, *Random Sampling Numbers* (Tracts for Computers, No. 15), Cambridge Univ. Press.

15. M. G. Kendall and B. Babington Smith, *Tables of Random Sampling Numbers* (Tracts for Computers, No. 24), Cambridge Univ. Press.

16. J. Neyman, *J. Roy. Stat. Soc.*, **97**, 1939, pp. 558–606.

17. W. G. Madow and L. H. Madow, "On the Theory of Systematic Sampling," *Ann. Math. Stat.*, **15**, 1944, pp. 1–24.

18. See, *e.g.*, A. R. Forsyth, *Calculus of Variations*, § 15.

CHAPTER VII

SMALL OR EXACT SAMPLING THEORY

7.1 Introduction. A theory of sampling which assumes that N is large is inadequate for many practical problems. In recent years a theory has been developed to give more exact methods in dealing with small samples. In the practical field, the call for the solution of problems based on comparatively few observations was first realized in 1908 by a young man,[*] then unknown, who published his results under the now celebrated pseudonym of "Student." Since then, many important contributions have been made toward the development and extension of this theory. Its applications are widespread. In the opinion of the present writers, continuity between large and small sample theory is an essential part of the newer attitude. In general, the methods of small sample theory are applicable to large samples, although the reverse is not true. It is our purpose in this chapter to facilitate an appreciation of some of the simpler aspects of this theory. The treatment centers around significance tests for means, variances, and other statistics.

7.2 Expected Value of s^2. By definition, the variance of a sample is given by

(7.1) $$s^2 = \frac{x_1^2 + x_2^2 + \cdots + x_N^2}{N} - \bar{x}^2$$

Then the expected value of s^2 from repeated samples is

(7.2) $$E(s^2) = E\left\{\frac{1}{N}(x_1^2 + x_2^2 + \cdots + x_N^2)\right\} - E(\bar{x}^2)$$

Since the x's constitute a sample we may write

(7.3) $$E(x_1^2 + x_2^2 + \cdots + x_N^2) = NE(x^2)$$

It will do no harm, and simplify the algebra considerably, if we assume that the origin is so chosen that the mean of the parent population is zero. Then $\nu_1 = 0$, and all the μ_i are identical with the corresponding ν_i. We have, therefore,

(7.4) $$E(x_i) = 0$$

Moreover, since any two observations x_i and x_j may be regarded as independent random variates with the same distribution (that of the parent population),

(7.5) $$E(x_i x_j) = E(x_i)E(x_j) = 0$$

---

[*] William Sealy Gosset (1876–1937). See reference 9.

Sec. 2   Expected Value of s^2

and similarly for any expression which contains as a factor any of the x_i raised to the first power.

From (7.4),

(7.6) $$E(\bar{x}) = \sum E(x_i)/N = 0$$

Also, $E(\bar{x}^2) = E(\sum x_i)^2/N^2$. Now $(\sum x_i)^2$ contains N terms like x_i^2 and $N(N-1)$ terms like $x_i x_j$, where $i \neq j$. Therefore

$$E(\bar{x}^2) = [NE(x_i^2) + N(N-1)E(x_i x_j)]/N^2$$

But $E(x_i^2) = \mu_2$, and hence by (7.5),

(7.7) $$E(\bar{x}^2) = \mu_2/N$$

We have, therefore,

(7.8) $$\begin{aligned} E(s^2) &= E(x_i^2) - E(\bar{x}^2) \\ &= \mu_2 - \mu_2/N \\ &= \frac{N-1}{N}\mu_2 \end{aligned}$$

This result is sometimes stated as in the following theorem.

Theorem 7.1 *The mean of the sampling distribution of s^2 from an arbitrary universe equals the variance of the universe multiplied by the factor* * $(N-1)/N$.

It is to be anticipated that the expected value of s^2 is less than σ^2, as the following analysis will show. The variance σ^2 refers to deviations from ν_1, whereas any s^2 refers to deviations from an $\bar{x}$. For any sample, then, we may regard ν_1 as an arbitrary origin. Since, in the case of any sample, the sum of the squares of deviations from its mean, $\bar{x}$, is less than the sum of the squares of deviations of the same variates from an arbitrary point ν_1 (unless the sample is one whose mean falls at ν_1), it is to be expected that the mean of all the values of s^2 will be less than σ^2. Relation (7.8) measures the extent of this inequality.

It follows from (7.8) that $E\{Ns^2/(N-1)\} = \sigma^2$, so that $Ns^2/(N-1)$ is an unbiased estimate of σ^2, based on a single sample. Since s^2 is defined as $\sum(x_i - \bar{x})^2/N$, the unbiased estimate is $\sum(x_i - \bar{x})^2/(N-1)$. This latter quantity is, in fact, frequently used (*e.g.*, by R. A. Fisher and by S. S. Wilks[1]) as a *definition* of the sample variance and denoted by the same symbol s^2. With this definition, of course, s^2 is an unbiased estimate of σ^2. In consulting references the student should note which definition of s^2 the author uses. It is conventional to take

(7.9) $$\hat{\sigma} = \left\{\frac{N}{N-1}\right\}^{1/2} s$$

as an estimate of σ. If N is large the difference between unity and the

---

* This factor is sometimes called "Bessel's correction." Perhaps it should be attributed more appropriately to Gauss who made use of it, in this connection, as early as 1823.

coefficient of s is negligible in numerical problems. With N large it would not be invalid, to any appreciable extent, to use s as an estimate of σ.

If two independent samples are available from the same universe, an unbiased estimate based on the two samples is given by

(7.10) $$\hat{\sigma}^2 = \frac{q}{N-2}$$

where

$$q = N_1 s_1^2 + N_2 s_2^2, \quad N = N_1 + N_2$$

s_1^2 and s_2^2 being the variances of samples consisting of N_1 and N_2 variates, respectively. It is left as an exercise for the student to verify that the expected value of $q/(N-2)$ is σ^2.

In case k independent samples are available from the same universe, we may generalize (7.10) and write

(7.11) $$\hat{\sigma}^2 = \frac{Q}{U-k}$$

where

$$Q = N_1 s_1^2 + N_2 s_2^2 + \cdots + N_k s_k^2$$
$$U = N_1 + N_2 + \cdots + N_k$$

and s_i^2 is the variance in the ith sample consisting of N_i variates. When $\hat{\sigma}^2$ is used in future discussions it will be clear from the context whether this estimate is based on 1, 2, or k samples.

If $N_i = N$ is the same for every sample, (7.11) reduces to

(7.12) $$\hat{\sigma}^2 = \frac{N(s_1^2 + s_2^2 + s_3^2 + \cdots + s_k^2)}{U-k}$$

where $U = Nk$. Clearly, (7.12) may be written in the form

(7.13) $$\frac{N-1}{N}\hat{\sigma}^2 = \frac{1}{k}(s_1^2 + s_2^2 + s_3^2 + \cdots + s_k^2)$$

7.3 Degrees of Freedom. In § 7.2 we have proved, essentially, that the expected value of $\sum(x_i - \bar{x})^2$ is $(N-1)\sigma^2$, where the N values of x in the sample are subject to the linear restriction $\sum x_i = N\bar{x}$. This is equivalent to proving that the expected value of $\sum x_i^2$ is $(N-1)\sigma^2$ when the x's are subject to the linear restriction $\sum x_i = 0$. Suppose, however, that there are $k < N$ linear restrictions on the x's. What, then, is the expected value of $\sum x_i^2$? A. T. Craig[2] has proved analytically that if $x_1, x_2, \cdots x_N$ are N independent values of a variable which is normally distributed about zero with variance σ^2 and if the N values of x are subject to $k < N$ homogeneous linear restrictions, then the expected value of $\sum x_i^2$ is $(N-k)\sigma^2$. The number $n = N - k$ is frequently called the number of *degrees of freedom*.

The concept of degrees of freedom was introduced in § 5.3, in connection with the chi-square distribution, and will recur frequently in this and later chapters. It is important to get a clear idea of its meaning.

A point constrained to move along a fixed curve has one degree of freedom of movement — it can move backward and forward only. If it is free to move anywhere in a plane or on a fixed surface, such as the surface of a sphere, it has two degrees of freedom, and if it is free to move anywhere in ordinary space it has three degrees of freedom. We cannot visualize more than three dimensions of space, but it is often convenient to use the geometrical language of N dimensions. As will be described more fully in § 7.7, we can represent a sample of N observations of a variable x by the sample point S in N-dimensional space, with coördinates $x_1, x_2, \cdots x_N$. Different samples of N will correspond to different points S, and if no restrictions are imposed, S has N degrees of freedom. This is the case, for instance, when the sample is from an infinite normal population with known mean and variance.

All samples with the same mean $\bar{x}$ satisfy the condition $\sum x_i = N\bar{x}$, which is the equation of a hyperplane in N-dimensional space. The hyperplane itself is a space of $N - 1$ dimensions. If we do not know the population mean but have to estimate it from one sample, we take $\bar{x}$ as this estimate, and then we are, in effect, considering our sample as belonging to the particular class of samples whose representative points S lie in the hyperplane $\sum x_i = N\bar{x}$. In other words, the sample has only $N - 1$ degrees of freedom for the estimation of σ^2.

If σ^2 is estimated from the sample as $Ns^2/(N-1) = \sum(x_i - \bar{x})^2/(N-1)$, the sample point is taken as lying on the surface of a sphere, $\sum(x_i - \bar{x})^2 = Ns^2$, of center $(\bar{x}, \bar{x}, \cdots \bar{x})$ and radius $sN^{1/2}$. This sphere intersects the hyperplane in a sphere of dimensionality less by one, so that S has now only $N - 2$ degrees of freedom.

In Chapter V, χ^2 was used to test the goodness of fit of a normal curve to a given distribution, and the number of degrees of freedom was taken as $k - 3$, k being the number of classes in the distribution. There the degrees of freedom refer to the different ways in which a sample might be spread over a fixed set of class-intervals. The total size of the sample is fixed, so that only $k - 1$ of the k classes can be filled arbitrarily. Moreover, the mean and variance of the parent population are estimated from the sample, so that the degrees of freedom are further reduced by 2.

Various other uses of the "degrees of freedom" concept will appear later. A good elementary discussion may be found in an article by Helen Walker in *Journal of Educational Psychology*, **31**, 1940, pp. 253–269.

7.4 Standard Error of the Variance. By the method of § 7.2 we can find the exact variance and other moments of s^2, although the algebra becomes heavy for the higher moments.

Thus,

(7.14) $$\text{Var}(s^2) = E(s^4) - \{E(s^2)\}^2$$

where $E(s^2)$ is given by (7.8). Also

(7.15) $$s^4 = \{\sum x_i^2/N - (\sum x_i/N)^2\}^2$$
$$= (\sum x_i^2)^2/N^2 - 2\sum x_i^2 (\sum x_i)^2/N^3 + (\sum x_i)^4/N^4$$

Now
$$(\sum x_i^2)^2 = \sum x_i^4 + \sum_{i \neq j} x_i^2 x_j^2$$

where the first sum contains N terms and the second $N(N-1)$. Since $E(x_i^4) = \mu_4$, and x_i and x_j are independent, we get

(7.16) $$E(\sum x_i^2)^2 = N\mu_4 + N(N-1)\mu_2^2$$

Again,
$$\sum x_i^2 (\sum x_i)^2 = \sum x_i^4 + \sum x_i^3 x_j + \sum x_i^2 x_j^2 + \sum x_i^2 x_j x_k$$

The expectations of the second and fourth sums on the right-hand side vanish. The first sum contains N terms and the third contains $N(N-1)$ terms. Therefore

(7.17) $$E\{\sum x_i^2 (\sum x_i)^2\} = N\mu_4 + N(N-1)\mu_2^2$$

Finally,
$$(\sum x_i)^4 = \sum x_i^4 + \sum x_i^3 x_j + \sum x_i^2 x_j^2 + \sum x_i^2 x_j x_k + \sum x_i x_j x_k x_l$$

The expectations of the second, fourth, and fifth sums vanish. The first contains N terms and the third $3N(N-1)$ terms. (There are $N(N-1)/2$ ways of picking out i and j, and the multinomial coefficient of $x_i^2 x_j^2$ is $4!/2!\,2! = 6$.) Hence

(7.18) $$E(\sum x_i)^4 = N\mu_4 + 3N(N-1)\mu_2^2$$

and, from (7.15), on collecting terms,

(7.19) $$E(s^4) = \mu_4(N-1)^2/N^3 + \mu_2^2(N-1)(N^2 - 2N + 3)/N^3$$

Then, from (7.14) and (7.8),

(7.20) $$\text{Var}(s^2) = \mu_4(N-1)^2/N^3 - \mu_2^2(N-1)(N-3)/N^3$$
$$= \frac{N-1}{N^3}[(N-1)\mu_4 - (N-3)\mu_2^2]$$

This is an exact result, true for any parent population for which the fourth moment exists. If the parent population is *normal*,

(7.21) $$\text{Var}(s^2) = 2\mu_2^2(N-1)/N^2 = 2\sigma^4(N-1)/N^2$$

Hence the standard error (s.e.) of the variance is
$$2^{1/2}(N-1)^{1/2}\sigma^2/N$$

Sec. 6   The Analytical Approach   165

or, if σ^2 is estimated by $Ns^2/(N-1)$,

(7.22) $\qquad$ s.e. of $s^2 = s^2[2/(N-1)]^{1/2}$

7.5 The Distribution of s^2 in Samples from a Normal Population. By similar methods to those used in § 7.4, "Student"[9] calculated higher moments of the distribution of s^2 and found that the skewness and kurtosis were given respectively by

(7.23) $\qquad \gamma_1 = [8/(N-1)]^{1/2}, \qquad \gamma_2 = 12/(N-1)$

so that $3\gamma_1^2 - 2\gamma_2 = 0$. This relationship is characteristic of a Pearson Type III distribution, and "Student" conjectured that the true frequency function of the distribution of s^2 is

(7.24) $\qquad f(s^2) = C(s^2)^{(N-3)/2} e^{-Ns^2/2\sigma^2}$

This was later proved by R. A. Fisher.* We shall now derive the sampling distributions of both the mean and the variance in samples of any size N from a normal population of variance σ^2. As before, we will assume that $\nu_1 = 0$.

The joint frequency function for a sample consisting of the N independent normal random variates $x_1, x_2, \cdots x_N$ is

(7.25) $\qquad f(x_1, x_2, \cdots x_N) = (2\pi\sigma^2)^{-N/2} e^{-V^2/2\sigma^2}$

where

$$V^2 = \sum x_i^2 = \sum(x_i - \bar{x} + \bar{x})^2 = Ns^2 + N\bar{x}^2$$

since $\sum(x_i - \bar{x}) = 0$. Hence $f(x_1, x_2, \cdots x_N)$ is a function of the sample mean $\bar{x}$ and the sample variance s^2. In order to find the distributions of $\bar{x}$ and s^2 separately, we require to change the variables from $x_1, x_2, \cdots x_N$ to a new set, of which two may be taken as $\bar{x}$ and s. This can be done either analytically or geometrically. Both methods are typical of many proofs in mathematical statistics, and therefore both will be presented here.

7.6 The Analytical Approach. This method is direct, but involves considerable algebra. It depends on an extension to N variables of the theorem on change of variables given in § 3.2.

We change from the set $x_1, x_2, \cdots x_N$ to the set $\bar{x}, s, w_1, w_2, \cdots w_{N-2}$, the $w_1, w_2, \cdots w_{N-2}$ being chosen in any convenient way which ensures that $\sum(x_i - \bar{x}) = 0$ and $\sum(x_i - \bar{x})^2 = Ns^2$. We then have

(7.26) $\qquad dx_1 \, dx_2 \cdots dx_N = |J| \, d\bar{x} \, ds \, dw_1 \cdots dw_{N-2}$

where

(7.27) $\qquad J = J\left(\dfrac{x_1, x_2, x_3, \cdots x_N}{\bar{x}, s, w_1, \cdots w_{N-2}}\right)$

---

* The distribution of s^2 was actually obtained by Helmert in 1876, but this work was for a long time overlooked (see ref. 9).

a determinant of N rows and columns. The frequency function in the new variables is then

(7.28) $$f_1(\bar{x}, s, w_1, \cdots w_{N-2}) = |J| f(\bar{x}, s)$$

where $f(\bar{x}, s)$ is the right-hand side of (7.25), which is a function of the variables $\bar{x}$ and s alone. By integrating (7.28) over the whole range of values of $w_1, w_2, \cdots w_{N-2}$ we obtain the joint distribution of $\bar{x}$ and s. By integrating once more over one of these variables we obtain the frequency function of the other. The relations between the two sets of variables may be taken as

(7.29) $$\begin{cases} x_1 = \bar{x} + sN^{1/2}w_0 w_1 w_2 \cdots w_{N-3} w_{N-2} \\ x_2 = \bar{x} + sN^{1/2}w_0 w_1 w_2 \cdots w_{N-3}(1 - w_{N-2}^2)^{1/2} \\ x_3 = \bar{x} + sN^{1/2}w_0 w_1 w_2 \cdots (1 - w_{N-3}^2)^{1/2} \\ \cdots \cdots \cdots \cdots \cdots \cdots \cdots \cdots \cdots \cdots \\ x_{N-1} = \bar{x} + sN^{1/2}w_0(1 - w_1^2)^{1/2} \\ x_N = \bar{x} + sN^{1/2}(1 - w_0^2)^{1/2} \end{cases}$$

where we have temporarily introduced a new variable w_0 which can be expressed in terms of the remaining w's.

From the first two equations of (7.29), we obtain

$$(x_1 - \bar{x})^2 + (x_2 - \bar{x})^2 = s^2 N w_0^2 w_1^2 \cdots w_{N-3}^2$$

Adding $(x_3 - \bar{x})^2$, we get $s^2 N w_0^2 w_1^2 \cdots w_{N-4}^2$, and so on. Finally we obtain

$$\sum (x_i - \bar{x})^2 = Ns^2$$

thus satisfying the second condition mentioned above.

To satisfy the other condition, $\sum (x_i - \bar{x}) = 0$, we must obviously have

(7.30) $$w_0[w_1 w_2 \cdots w_{N-2} + w_1 w_2 \cdots (1 - w_{N-2}^2)^{1/2} \\ + \cdots + (1 - w_1^2)^{1/2}] + (1 - w_0^2)^{1/2} = 0$$

which expresses w_0 in terms of the other w's.

By differentiating each of the equations in (7.29) partially with respect to $\bar{x}, s, w_1, w_2, \cdots w_{N-2}$ in turn, we see that the first column of the Jacobian J consists of all 1's, the second column has a common factor $N^{1/2}$, and all the remaining columns have a common factor $sN^{1/2}$. Taking out these factors we get

(7.31) $$J = N^{(N-1)|2} s^{N-2} D$$

where D is a determinant depending only on the w's. The frequency function is, therefore, from (7.28) and (7.25),

(7.32) $$f_1(\bar{x}, s, w_1, \cdots w_{N-2}) = C_1 |D| s^{N-2} e^{-N(\bar{x}^2 + s^2)/2\sigma^2}$$

where C_1 is a constant depending on N and σ. Integrating over $w_1, w_2, \cdots w_{N-2}$, we get

(7.33) $$f_2(\bar{x}, s) = C_2 e^{-N\bar{x}^2/2\sigma^2} s^{N-2} e^{-Ns^2/2\sigma^2}$$

Sec. 7   Derivation of Distribution of Variance

Note that in obtaining (7.33) we do not need actually to carry out the integration. The integral of D is a constant and is absorbed in the constant C_2, the numerical value of C_2 remaining for the present undetermined.

Since $f_2(\bar{x}, s)$ can be split into two parts, one depending only on $\bar{x}$ and the other only on s, it is clear that the distributions of $\bar{x}$ and of s are independent. The distribution of $\bar{x}$ is given by

(7.34) $$f_3(\bar{x}) = C_3 e^{-N\bar{x}^2/2\sigma^2}$$

which is a normal distribution with variance σ^2/N. The constant C_3 is determined by $\int_{-\infty}^{\infty} f_3(\bar{x}) \, d\bar{x} = 1$, whence $C_3 = (N/2\pi\sigma^2)^{1/2}$.

The distribution of s is given by

(7.35) $$f_4(s) = C_4 s^{N-2} e^{-Ns^2/2\sigma}$$

Since

$$f_5(s^2) \, d(s^2) = f_4(s) \, ds$$

where $f_5(s^2)$ is the frequency function for s^2, we have

(7.36) $$f_5(s^2) = f_4(s)/2s = C_5(s^2)^{(N-3)/2} e^{-Ns^2/2\sigma^2}$$

This represents a curve belonging to Pearson Type III. The constant C_5 is determined from $\int_0^{\infty} f_5(s^2) d(s^2) = 1$, and is found to be (see Example 2, § 3.5)

(7.37) $$C_5 = \left(\frac{N}{2\sigma^2}\right)^{(N-1)/2} \bigg/ \Gamma\left(\frac{N-1}{2}\right)$$

It may be noted that the distribution of Ns^2/σ^2 is precisely that of χ^2 with $N-1$ degrees of freedom. Putting $\chi^2 = Ns^2/\sigma^2$ in (7.36) we obtain

(7.38) $$f(\chi^2) \, d(\chi^2) = \left(\frac{\chi^2}{2}\right)^{(N-3)/2} e^{-\chi^2/2} d\left(\frac{\chi^2}{2}\right) \bigg/ \Gamma\left(\frac{N-1}{2}\right)$$

The sum of squares of N independent normal variates measured from a *fixed* origin is distributed as $\chi^2\sigma^2$ with N degrees of freedom, whereas if the variates are measured from the sample mean the sum of squares is distributed as $\chi^2\sigma^2$ with $N-1$ degrees of freedom. As noted in § 7.3, the variates when measured from their mean are subject to a single linear constraint.

7.7 The Geometrical Derivation of the Sampling Distribution of Variance. This method (the one used by Fisher) is concise and illuminating.[3] The chief drawback is that geometrical relations, in space of more than three dimensions, are not easily apprehended.

We think of an N-dimensional *sample space*, in which an actual sample is represented by a point of coördinates $(x_1, x_2, \cdots x_N)$. The probability of a sample with values of the variates respectively in the ranges $x_1 \pm \frac{1}{2} dx_1, \cdots x_N \pm \frac{1}{2} dx_N$, is $f(x_1, x_2, \cdots x_N) \, dv$, where $dv (= dx_1 \, dx_2 \cdots dx_N)$ is an element of volume of the sample space located at the point $(x_1, x_2, \cdots x_N)$. The density of the probability distribution at this point is $f(x_1, x_2, \cdots x_N)$.

It is convenient to take a new origin at the point $(\nu_1, \nu_2, \cdots \nu_N)$, and axes $Ou_1, Ou_2, \cdots Ou_N$ through this point. Therefore, we may represent the sample by the point $P(u_1, u_2, \cdots u_N)$ where $u_i = x_i - \nu_1$. Although it is impossible to visualize a space of N dimensions for $N > 3$, we will carry through the argument for the general case by analogy with the case of $N = 3$. So we consider the latter case first.

When $N = 3$, the sample is represented by the point $P(u_1, u_2, u_3)$ and we have the mean $\bar{u}$ and variance s^2 defined by

(a) $$u_1 + u_2 + u_3 = 3\bar{u}$$

and

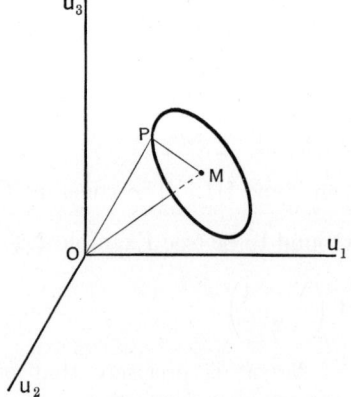

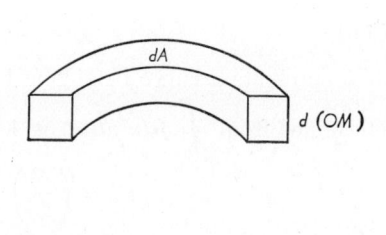

(b) $$(u_1 - \bar{u})^2 + (u_2 - \bar{u})^2 + (u_3 - \bar{u})^2 = 3s^2$$

For an assigned $\bar{u}$, (a) represents a plane; and, for an assigned pair of values of $(\bar{u}, s)$, (b) represents a sphere with center at the point $M(\bar{u}, \bar{u}, \bar{u})$. The line

(c) $$u_1 = u_2 = u_3$$

has direction cosines each equal to $1/(3)^{1/2}$ and is normal to the plane (a). The perpendicular distance of P from this line is

$$MP = s(3)^{1/2}$$

as can be seen from (b). We require the probability, to within infinitesimals of order higher than $d\bar{u}\,ds$, of getting a sample of $N = 3$ independent values of u which will simultaneously yield values of $\bar{u}$ and s which lie within the region bounded by $\bar{u}, \bar{u} + d\bar{u}$ and $s, s + ds$. If we assume the normal law, an element of the joint distribution function is given by

$$dF = (2\pi\sigma^2)^{-3/2} e^{-(u_1^2 + u_2^2 + u_3^2)/2\sigma^2}\,dv$$
$$= (2\pi\sigma^2)^{-3/2} e^{-3(s^2 + \bar{u}^2)/2\sigma^2}\,dv$$

where

$$dv = du_1\,du_2\,du_3$$

Sec. 7   Derivation of Distribution of Variance

As the sample point $P(u_1, u_2, u_3)$ varies, $\bar{u}$ and s also vary. Corresponding to different values of s we have a set of concentric spheres defined by (b). Since the plane (a) passes through the common center of the spheres, the region dv is a shell between concentric spheres of radii $\sqrt{3}s$ and $\sqrt{3}(s + ds)$ and parallel planes corresponding to $\bar{u}$ and $\bar{u} + d\bar{u}$. These are the planes (in the figure) at a distance apart $d(OM)$. To use a homely illustration, dv corresponds to one of the successive layers in a thin slice of an onion. Our problem is to express dv in terms of $\bar{u}$, s, $d\bar{u}$, and ds. Now the line (c) meets the plane (a) at M and the distance OM is

$$OM = \bar{u}(3)^{1/2}$$

so we have the differential element

$$d(OM) = (3)^{1/2}\, d\bar{u}$$

Since the plane (a) passes through M, the intersection of the plane and sphere is a great circle with center at M and radius equal to $s(3)^{1/2}$. The area of this circle is

$$A = 3\pi s^2$$

and the differential element dA is

$$dA = 6\pi s\, ds$$

Therefore, within infinitesimals of higher order,

$$\begin{aligned} dv &= dA\, d(OM) \\ &= C_1 s\, ds\, d\bar{u} \end{aligned}$$

where here and hereafter, in this section, the C's are constants. Hence, the required probability is

$$dF = C_2 e^{-3(s^2+\bar{u}^2)/2\sigma^2} s\, ds\, d\bar{u}$$

Passing now to the general case involving N-space, let P be the point representing the sample $(u_1, u_2, \cdots u_N)$. Then PM is the perpendicular from P upon the line

(d) $$u_1 = u_2 = \cdots = u_N$$

and we have

$$OM = (N)^{1/2}\bar{u}, \quad \overline{OP}^2 = \sum u^2$$
$$\overline{MP}^2 = \overline{OP}^2 - \overline{OM}^2 = \sum u^2 - N\bar{u}^2 = Ns^2$$

In N-space, the plane (a) generalizes into the hyperplane

(e) $$\sum u_i = N\bar{u}$$

and the sphere (b) generalizes into the hypersphere

(f) $$\sum (u_i - \bar{u})^2 = Ns^2$$

with radius $MP = (N)^{1/2}s$ and center at $(\bar{u}, \bar{u}, \cdots \bar{u})$. Now, the hyperplane

(e) will intersect the hypersphere (f) in an $(N-1)$-dimensional hypersphere to correspond to the circle for the case $N = 3$. Consequently, for a given pair of values of $\bar{u}$ and s, the point P will lie on an $(N-1)$-dimensional hypersphere orthogonal to the line OM. The volume of this $(N-1)$-hypersphere is given by

$$A = C_3(\sqrt{N}s)^{N-1}$$

and so

$$dA = C_4 s^{N-2}\, ds$$

Therefore, the volume $dv = du_1\, du_2 \cdots du_N$ between two concentric spheres of radius $\sqrt{N}s$ and $\sqrt{N}(s + ds)$ and two hyperplanes corresponding to $\bar{u}$ and $\bar{u} + d\bar{u}$ is approximately

$$dv = dA\, d(OM)$$
$$= C s^{N-2}\, ds\, d\bar{u}$$

Since $du_i = dx_i$ and $d\bar{u} = d\bar{x}$, we arrive at (7.33). It has been proved by Geary [4] that a necessary and sufficient condition that $\bar{x}$ and s^2 from samples of N values of x be independent in the probability sense is that the x's be normally distributed in the parent universe.

In § 7.2, the mean of the sampling distribution of s^2 from an arbitrary universe was obtained. It is interesting to verify that result in the present case where the universe is specialized. The mean of the distribution of variances of samples of N from a normal universe is given by

$$E(s^2) = \int_0^\infty f_5(s^2) s^2\, d(s^2)$$

where $f_5(s^2)$ is given by (7.36) and (7.37). Consequently, we have

$$E(s^2) = C_5 \int_0^\infty e^{-Ns^2/2\sigma^2}(s^2)^{(N-1)/2}\, d(s^2)$$
$$= C_5 \left(\frac{2\sigma^2}{N}\right)^{(N+1)/2} \Gamma\left(\frac{N+1}{2}\right)$$
$$= \frac{N-1}{N}\sigma^2$$

7.8 The Distribution of the Standard Deviation. The frequency function of the standard deviations of samples of N from a normal universe is, from (7.36),

(7.39) $$f_4(s) = 2C_5 e^{-Ns^2/2\sigma^2} s^{N-2}$$

so its mean value is given by

$$E(s) = \int_0^\infty f_4(s) s\, ds = C_5 \left(\frac{2\sigma^2}{N}\right)^{N/2} \Gamma\left(\frac{N}{2}\right)$$

Sec. 9 Estimate of the Population Standard Deviation

Upon substituting the value of C_5 given in (7.37), we get

$$(7.40) \qquad E(s) = \frac{\left(\dfrac{2}{N}\right)^{1/2} \Gamma\left(\dfrac{N}{2}\right)}{\Gamma\left(\dfrac{N-1}{2}\right)} \sigma$$

If we denote this coefficient of σ by $b(N)$ we have

$$\sigma = \frac{E(s)}{b(N)}$$

Romanovsky[5] showed that asymptotically $b(N) = 1 - 3/4N - 7/32N^2 - \cdots$. Table 10 gives values of the reciprocal of $b(N)$ for a few values of N.[6] An unbiased estimate of σ is $s/b(N)$.

The rth moment of the distribution of s is given by

$$(7.41) \qquad \nu_r = 2C_5 \int_0^\infty s^{N-2+r} e^{-Ns^2/2\sigma^2}\, ds$$

$$= \left(\frac{2}{N}\right)^{r/2} \frac{\Gamma\left(\dfrac{N-1+r}{2}\right)}{\Gamma\left(\dfrac{N-1}{2}\right)} \sigma^r$$

Hence the variance of s is given by

$$(7.42) \qquad \text{Var}(s) = \nu_2 - \nu_1^2$$

$$= \frac{N-1}{N}\sigma^2 - \{b(N)\sigma\}^2$$

$$= k(N)\sigma^2$$

where

$$k(N) = N^{-1}\left[N - 1 - \frac{2\Gamma^2(N/2)}{\Gamma^2\{(N-1)/2\}}\right]$$

$$= \frac{1}{2N} - \frac{1}{8N^2} - \frac{3}{16N^3} - \cdots$$

TABLE 10

N	$1/b(N)$
2	1.772
3	1.382
4	1.253
5	1.189
6	1.151
7	1.126
8	1.108
9	1.094
10	1.084
20	1.040
30	1.026
50	1.015
100	1.008

The approximate value

$$(7.43) \qquad \sigma_s \approx \left(\frac{1}{2N}\right)^{1/2} \sigma$$

is frequently used in practice and this is the basis for the common statement that *the standard error of a standard deviation is $1/(2)^{1/2}$ that of a mean.*

7.9 The "Best" Estimate of the Population Standard Deviation. We have seen that an *unbiased* estimate of σ for a normal parent population is given by

$$\frac{s}{b(N)} = s\left(1 + \frac{3}{4N} + \frac{25}{32N^2} + \cdots\right)$$

There are, however, several other estimates which have desirable properties and which differ somewhat from the unbiased estimate for small samples. Thus, the *modal value* of s, say $\check{s}$, is found by differentiating $f_4(s)$ and putting the derivative equal to zero. We find

$$(N-2)/\check{s} - N\check{s}/\sigma^2 = 0$$

so that

(7.44) $$\check{s} = \sigma(N-2)^{1/2}/N^{1/2}$$

The *modal estimate* of σ may, therefore, be taken as

$$\frac{sN^{1/2}}{(N-2)^{1/2}} = s\left(1 + \frac{1}{N} + \frac{3}{2N^2} + \cdots\right)$$

It is that value of σ which would give, with maximum frequency in all possible samples, that sample value of s which is actually observed. In practice the observed values of the variate will be rounded off, so that the estimate of σ is subject to a small uncertainty.

Again, we may enquire what value of σ, say $\check{\sigma}$, would make $f_4(s)$ a maximum for a given value of s. Putting

$$\frac{d}{d\sigma}[\sigma^{-(N-1)}e^{-Ns^2/2\sigma^2}] = 0$$

the other factors in $f_4(s)$ being independent of σ, we have

$$-\frac{N-1}{\check{\sigma}} + \frac{Ns^2}{\check{\sigma}^3} = 0$$

or

(7.45) $$\check{\sigma} = \frac{sN^{1/2}}{(N-1)^{1/2}} = s\left(1 + \frac{1}{2N} + \frac{3}{8N^2} + \cdots\right)$$

This may be called the *maximum probability* estimate of σ. It is that value of σ, among all possible population values, for which the observed value of s is also the most probable value.

At least two other estimates have certain claims to be called the "best." The *least squares* estimate may be defined as that for which the expectation of the square of the difference from the true population value is a minimum. That is, $E\{(\tilde{s} - \sigma)^2\}$ is a minimum.

If we suppose that $\tilde{s} = \alpha s$, where α is a function of N to be determined, we find on equating to zero the derivative of $E(\alpha s - \sigma)^2$ with respect to α that $\alpha = \sigma E(s)/E(s^2) = Nb(N)/(N-1)$. Therefore

(7.46) $$\tilde{s} = \frac{sNb(N)}{N-1} = s\left[1 + \frac{1}{4N} + \frac{1}{32N^2} + \cdots\right]$$

The *maximum likelihood* estimate is that value of σ for which the whole sample actually found is the most probable sample. The probability of a given sample is proportional to $\sigma^{-N} \exp\{-\sum(x_i - \mu)^2/2\sigma^2\}$. The logarithm of the probability is

(7.47) $$L = -N \log \sigma - \sum(x_i - \mu)^2/2\sigma^2$$

There is no value of σ for which L is a maximum regardless of the value of μ, but if we want simultaneous maximum likelihood estimates of σ and μ we may put $\partial L/\partial \sigma = 0$ and $\partial L/\partial \mu = 0$, and so obtain estimates $\hat{\sigma}$ and $\hat{\mu}$ given by

$$-N/\hat{\sigma} + \sum(x_i - \hat{\mu})^2/\hat{\sigma}^3 = 0, \qquad \sum(x_i - \hat{\mu}) = 0$$

Hence

(7.48) $$\hat{\mu} = \sum x_i/N = \bar{x}$$
(7.49) $$\hat{\sigma}^2 = \sum(x_i - \bar{x})^2/N = s^2$$

The maximum likelihood estimates of μ and σ are, therefore, $\bar{x}$ and s respectively.

We see, therefore, that there is no single best estimate.[7] What is the best estimate from one point of view may not be the best from another. By convention, however, the estimate usually selected is the maximum probability one, $\check{\sigma} = sN^{1/2}/(N-1)^{1/2}$. It is not unbiased, but it is the square root of an unbiased estimate of σ^2.

7.10 The $(\bar{x}, s)$-Frequency Surface. We may regard $f_2(\bar{x}, s)$ in (7.33) as describing a frequency surface if the volume under the surface represents the expected relative frequency of the means and standard deviations of all possible samples of size N. In depicting this surface it is convenient to let $\bar{u} = \bar{x} - \nu_1$ so that the origin of $\bar{u}$ is at $\bar{x} = \nu_1$.

Since

$$\int_0^\infty \int_{-\infty}^\infty f(\bar{x}, s)\, d\bar{x}\, ds = 1$$

then the volume under the surface over a closed contour in the $\bar{u}s$-plane represents the proportion or percentage of samples whose means and standard

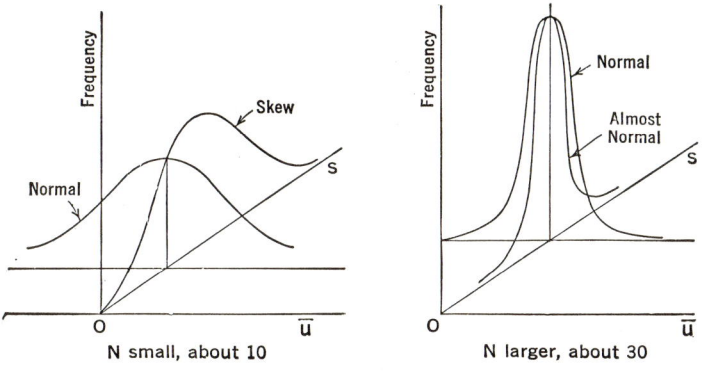

FIG. 20. THE SURFACE $f(\bar{x}, s)$ ILLUSTRATED BY SECTIONS

deviations fall simultaneously within the ranges defined by the boundary of the given contour. In an illuminating paper [8] by Deming and Birge two such frequency surfaces are represented. These are reproduced in Figure 20, one for a small value of N and the other for a comparatively large value of N.

As the authors point out, the highest point of the surface has the coördinates $\bar{u} = 0$, $s = \sigma\{(N - 2)/N\}^{1/2}$. Because of the independence of $\bar{x}$ and s, all plane sections $s = $ constant will be normal curves with standard deviations equal to $\sigma/(N)^{1/2}$. The $\bar{u} = $ constant sections will be skew curves whose equations are given by $f_4(s)$. They will all have the same mean and mode. As N increases, their mean and mode approach coincidence with the value σ while the curves lose their skewness and become normal with center at $s = \sigma$ and standard deviations equal to $\sigma/(2N)^{1/2}$. As N increases, the surface becomes more and more concentrated about the point $\bar{u} = 0$, $s = \sigma$.

7.11 "Student's" z-Distribution. The formula used in testing a null hypothesis that a given sample comes from a universe with a proposed mean is

$$(7.50) \qquad t = \frac{(\bar{x} - \mu)(N)^{1/2}}{\sigma}$$

As stated in Chapter VI, (7.50) is normally distributed if the universe is normal. In practice, σ is seldom available and usually must be estimated from the data available. If we substitute into (7.50) the estimate of σ given in (7.45) and calculate

$$(7.51) \qquad t = \frac{(\bar{x} - \mu)(N - 1)^{1/2}}{s}$$

we are not justified in asserting that t is normally distributed unless N is large. And so, in testing the significance of the mean of a small sample we are not justified in referring t to a normal probability scale. The variability of s from sample to sample invalidates that procedure.

While Helmert obtained the distribution of s^2 as early as 1876 it seems that "Student"[9] was the first to recognize the importance, for the theory of small samples, of taking account of the variability of s in (7.51). "Student" actually found the distribution of a slightly different variable, namely

$$(7.52) \qquad z = \frac{\bar{x} - \mu}{s}$$

Obviously, z is functionally related to t by

$$(7.53) \qquad z = t(N - 1)^{-1/2}$$

so the distribution of t can easily be obtained from that of z. From (7.52) we obtain $d\bar{x} = s\,dz$ for a fixed value of s. Substituting in (7.33), for which μ is supposed zero, we obtain, for the joint distribution of s and z,

$$(7.54) \qquad ke^{-Ns^2(1+z^2)/2\sigma^2} s^{N-1}\, ds\, dz$$

This expression is defined for $s \geq 0$, since s is taken as the positive square root of s^2. If s is integrated out of (7.54), the distribution of the single variable z is obtained. To perform this integration, let

$$y = s(1 + z^2)^{1/2}, \qquad ds = (1 + z^2)^{-1/2}\, dy$$

Integrating with respect to y from 0 to ∞, we have

$$k\left\{\int_0^\infty y^{N-1} e^{-Ny^2/2\sigma^2}\, dy\right\} (1 + z^2)^{-N/2}\, dz$$

which reduces to

$$K(1 + z^2)^{-N/2}\, dz$$

where, as shown in Example 3, § 3.5,

(7.55) $$K = \frac{k}{2}\left(\frac{2\sigma^2}{N}\right)^{N/2} \Gamma\left(\frac{N}{2}\right) = \frac{\Gamma\left(\dfrac{N}{2}\right)}{(\pi)^{1/2}\Gamma\left(\dfrac{N-1}{2}\right)}$$

Therefore, the frequency function for "Student's" z is

(7.56) $$f(z) = \frac{\Gamma\left(\dfrac{N}{2}\right)}{(\pi)^{1/2}\Gamma\left(\dfrac{N-1}{2}\right)} (1 + z^2)^{-N/2}$$

The curve is symmetrical with mean zero and infinite range. It is quite different, however, in mathematical character from the normal curve although it approaches this form as $N \to \infty$. From the viewpoint of sampling theory the important property of (7.56) is its independence of σ. The revolutionary character of this property is revealed in certain applications that involve drawing probable inferences from small samples, say from a sample of $N = 10$.

7.12 "Student's" t-Distribution. Substituting (7.53) into (7.56) and replacing $N - 1$ by n we obtain

(7.57) $$f_n(t) = K_n\left(1 + \frac{t^2}{n}\right)^{-(n+1)/2}$$

where $1/K_n = n^{1/2} B(n/2, 1/2)$, B being the Beta function.

Inasmuch as (7.57) is independent of σ, it can be used in situations in which the value of σ is unknown. The quantity t involves no hypothetical quantities except μ, being otherwise completely expressible in terms of the observations.

In 1925, "Student" published in *Metron*[10] an extensive table of the probability integral $\int_{-\infty}^t f_n(t)\, dt$. More recently, Fisher[11] has given a short table of the probability P of occurrence of deviations outside $\pm t$, for values of t and n commonly met in applications of small sample theory. Let

$$P_n(t) = 2\int_0^t f_n(t)\, dt$$

Then the probability P tabulated by Fisher is
$$P = 1 - P_n(t)$$
Several "t-tables" are available.* The one in *Statistical Tables* by Fisher and Yates, shows for n between 1 and 120 the values of t for which P takes the values given at the head of the columns. The number n, with which to enter the table, is determined by the number of degrees of freedom involved in the available estimate of σ^2. In testing a null hypothesis H, if a computed value of (7.51) is larger than the tabular value for the level of P selected, then H is rejected at that level of significance. Or, if one prefers, he may note the tabular value of P for the computed value of (7.51) and use the rule in § 6.7, where now, of course, P_δ is to be replaced by P.

The distribution of t (as well as that of z) approaches the normal form as $n \to \infty$. This may be established as follows. Using Stirling's approximation on the coefficient K_n in (7.57) we obtain, after some algebraic simplification, the following expression:

$$K_n = e^{-1/2}(n\pi)^{-1/2}\left(\frac{n-1}{n-2}\right)^{(n-2)/2}\left(\frac{n-1}{n-2}\right)^{1/2}\left(\frac{n-1}{2}\right)^{1/2}$$

From this it is easy to show that
$$\lim_{n \to \infty} K_n = (2\pi)^{-1/2}$$

The rest of the t function may be written as
$$\left(1 + \frac{t^2}{n}\right)^{-1/2}\left(1 + \frac{t^2}{n}\right)^{-n/2}$$
which, when $n = \infty$, becomes $e^{-t^2/2}$. Therefore,
$$\lim_{n \to \infty} f_n(t) = (2\pi)^{-1/2} e^{-t^2/2}$$

The entries in the last line of Fisher's table, corresponding to $n = \infty$, are the deviations from the mean of a normal curve with unit standard deviation.

The variance of t is given by
$$\int_{-\infty}^{\infty} f_n(t) t^2 \, dt = n/(n-2)$$

Hence $t[(n-2)/n]^{1/2}$ is a standard variate, and, as shown above, is approximately normally distributed when n is large. In applications, therefore, it is frequently satisfactory to refer

* Table IV in our Appendix is an abridged version giving $\frac{1}{2}P$ for $n = 1$ to 30. Obviously, $\frac{1}{2}P = \int_t^{\infty} f_n(t) \, dt = 1 - F_n(t)$ where $F_n(t)$ is the distribution function of t. Another table is given by M. Merrington in *Biometrika*, **32**, 1941–42, p. 300. This gives values of t for values of P (0.005, 0.025, 0.25) not included in *Statistical Tables*.

(7.58) $$t' = t\left[\frac{n-2}{n}\right]^{1/2} = \frac{(\bar{x} - \mu)(N-3)^{1/2}}{s}$$

to a normal probability scale when $N > 30$.

Example 1. For a random sample of 10 the mean is 12.1 and the standard deviation 3.2. Is it reasonable to suppose that this sample came from a normal parent population with mean 10?

Solution. Here
$$t = \frac{(12.1 - 10.0)\sqrt{9}}{3.2} = 1.97$$

with 9 degrees of freedom. The probability of getting a value of t *numerically* as great as this, on the assumed hypothesis, is about 0.08.

The probability of getting a value *as great as* 1.97 is one half of this, 0.04. Hence although the hypothesis is not definitely unreasonable, it is rather doubtful if the sample could have come from a population with a mean as low as 10.

It may be noted that, if t were a standard normal variate, the probability of obtaining a value as large as 1.97 would be only 0.024.

The distribution of the "Student" t statistic is also obtainable quite readily from the remark in § 7.6 that Ns^2/σ^2 is distributed as χ^2 with $N - 1$ degrees of freedom. For, since
$$t = (N-1)^{1/2}(\bar{x} - \mu)/s$$
$$\frac{t^2}{N-1} = \frac{(\bar{x}-\mu)^2}{s^2} = \frac{[N^{1/2}(\bar{x}-\mu)/\sigma]^2}{Ns^2/\sigma^2}$$

which is the quotient of the square of a standard normal variate and a χ_{N-1}^2 variate. Now, by Theorems 5.2 and 5.5 the numerator is a $\gamma(\frac{1}{2})$ variate and the denominator is a $\gamma[(N-1)/2]$ variate. Hence by Theorem 5.4, the quotient is a $\beta'[\frac{1}{2}, (N-1)/2]$ variate.

The frequency function of t^2 is therefore given by

(7.59) $$f(t^2)\, d(t^2) = \left(\frac{t^2}{n}\right)^{-1/2}\left(1 + \frac{t^2}{n}\right)^{-\frac{1}{2}(n+1)} \frac{1}{n} d(t^2) \bigg/ B\left(\frac{1}{2}, \frac{n}{2}\right)$$

where $n = N - 1$.

Hence the frequency function of t is

(7.60) $$f(t) = \left[n^{1/2} B\left(\frac{1}{2}, \frac{n}{2}\right)\left(1 + \frac{t^2}{n}\right)^{\frac{1}{2}(n+1)}\right]^{-1}$$

The factor 2 does not appear, because t goes from $-\infty$ to ∞, whereas t^2 goes from 0 to ∞, and the constant is so adjusted that

$$\int_{-\infty}^{\infty} f(t)\, dt = 1$$

From the above argument we obtain

Theorem 7.2. *Any statistic t has the "Student" t-distribution for n degrees of freedom if t^2/n is the ratio of two independent variates distributed respectively as χ^2 with 1 and n degrees of freedom.*

7.13 Difference Between Two Means.

Fisher [12] demonstrated that (7.57) has a much wider range of application than the problem for which it was designed. He showed that the t-distribution is applicable whenever we are dealing with a normally distributed variate whose standard deviation is not known exactly but is independently estimated from observations amounting to n degrees of freedom. The scheme by which the "Student" idea is made available to other problems consists in constructing a variable t in the nature of a fraction whose numerator is any statistic normally distributed and whose denominator is the square root of an independently distributed and unbiased estimate of the variance of the numerator involving n degrees of freedom.*
Thus the t-distribution has been found useful in such problems as testing the significance of the difference between two means and testing hypotheses regarding regression coefficients.

Let $\bar{x}_1$, $\bar{x}_2$ be the means and s_1, s_2 the standard deviations of two independent samples of N_1 and N_2 variates, respectively, from a normal universe with mean μ and variance σ^2. According to Theorem 4.11 the variance of the difference between the two means is $\sigma^2(N_1 + N_2)/N_1 N_2$. Then it follows [13] that the variable

$$t = \frac{\bar{x}_1 - \bar{x}_2}{\sigma} \left\{ \frac{N_1 N_2}{N_1 + N_2} \right\}^{1/2}$$

is normally distributed with unit standard deviation. However, in most practical problems σ is unavailable and must be estimated from the samples. Using the unbiased estimate of σ^2 defined in (7.10), the above formula becomes

(7.61)
$$t = \frac{\bar{x}_1 - \bar{x}_2}{\hat{\sigma}} \left\{ \frac{N_1 N_2}{N_1 + N_2} \right\}^{1/2}$$

Fisher showed that (7.61) is distributed in accord with (7.57) for $n = N_1 + N_2 - 2$, and we can find from Fisher's table of P the probability of a greater difference between the means than that observed.

As N_1 and N_2 become large, $(N_1 + N_2)/(N_1 + N_2 - 2)$ tends toward unity and (7.61) tends toward the value

(7.62)
$$t' = \frac{\bar{x}_1 - \bar{x}_2}{\left\{ \dfrac{s_1^2}{N_2} + \dfrac{s_2^2}{N_1} \right\}^{1/2}}$$

Since (7.61) is asymptotically normally distributed, the older procedure of referring (7.62) to a normal probability scale in testing a null hypothesis that two samples are from the same universe would not be invalid to any appreciable extent for large values of N_1 and N_2. Kenney [14] has called attention to a formula which is commonly used in place of (7.62). This formula has $\{s_1^2/N_1 + s_2^2/N_2\}^{1/2}$ in the denominator. It is approximately valid if we

---
* A statistic so treated is often said to be "studentized."

Sec. 13   Difference Between Two Means

have reason to believe that the two samples come from populations with *different* σ_1 and σ_2.   (See § 9.8.)

If one of the samples, say N_2, is so much larger than the other that it tends toward the universe, then $\bar{x}_2$ tends toward μ and s_2 tends toward σ.   So, under these conditions, (7.62) tends toward

$$t'' = \frac{(\bar{x}_1 - \mu)\sqrt{N_1}}{\sigma}$$

which, if the subscripts are dropped, is the formula used in testing a null hypothesis that a given sample comes from a normal universe with a proposed mean.   When $N_1 = N_2 = N$, (7.61) reduces to

(7.63) $\qquad t = (\bar{x}_1 - \bar{x}_2)\left\{\dfrac{N-1}{s_1{}^2 + s_2{}^2}\right\}^{1/2}, \qquad n = 2(N-1)$

Inasmuch as we do not ordinarily know whether a sample is drawn from a normal universe or some other type of universe, a question quite naturally arises as to whether the procedure inaugurated by "Student" and extended by Fisher is applicable to small samples from non-normal universes. The question may be considered partially answered by Bartlett[15] and others who have shown that it gives a good approximation for considerable departures from normality in the sampled universe. However, a word of caution seems to be in order lest the procedure be oversold in the applications by completely neglecting the underlying assumptions of normality in the universe and randomness of the samples.

The following example, cited by Rietz,[16] illustrates the "Student" theory.

Example 2. The following data represent the yields in bushels of Indian corn on ten subdivisions of equal areas of two agricultural plots in which Plot 1 was a control plot treated the same as Plot 2, except for the amount of phosphorus applied as a fertilizer.

Plot 1	Plot 2
6.2	5.6
5.7	5.9
6.5	5.6
6.0	5.7
6.3	5.8
5.8	5.7
5.7	6.0
6.0	5.5
6.0	5.7
5.8	5.5
10)60.0	10)57.0
$\bar{x}_1 = 6.0$	$\bar{x}_2 = 5.7$

Is there a significant difference between the yields on the two plots, using the difference between their means as a criterion of judgment?

Solution.

$$s_1^2 = \frac{0.64}{10} = .064$$

$$s_2^2 = \frac{0.24}{10} = .024$$

Substitution in (7.63) gives

$$t = (6.0 - 5.7)\left\{\frac{9}{.088}\right\}^{1/2}$$

$$= (.3)(10.113) = 3.034$$

Entering "Student's" tables in *Metron* (loc. cit.) at $n = 18$, we find $P = .0072$ for the probability that t will fall outside the range -3.034 and $+3.034$. Hence a null hypothesis that the samples are from the same universe would be refuted by the test for both the .05 and .01 levels of significance. In other words, our conclusion is that, on the levels of significance adopted, there is a significant difference between the yields on the plots.

7.14 Fisher's z-Distribution. Suppose u^2 and v^2 are two independent and unbiased estimates of the variance σ^2 of a variable x which is normally distributed. If these estimates are based upon samples of N_1 and N_2, respectively, or upon n_1 and n_2 degrees of freedom, then we have

$$u^2 = \frac{1}{N_1 - 1}\sum_1^{N_1}(x_{1i} - \bar{x}_1)^2 = \frac{1}{n_1}\sum_1^{n_1+1}(x_{1i} - \bar{x}_1)^2$$

$$v^2 = \frac{1}{N_2 - 1}\sum_1^{N_2}(x_{2i} - \bar{x}_2)^2 = \frac{1}{n_2}\sum_1^{n_2+1}(x_{2i} - \bar{x}_2)^2$$

in which $\bar{x}_1$ and $\bar{x}_2$ are the means of the two samples. In previous notation u^2 and v^2 would be denoted by $\hat{\sigma}_1^2$ and $\hat{\sigma}_2^2$, but these symbols are too unwieldy in the present discussion.

In constructing a test of significance for the difference between two sample variances it might seem logical to form the difference $w = u^2 - v^2$ and seek the frequency function of w. However, such a procedure is impractical because of the mathematical difficulty involved in determining this function. Fisher circumvented this difficulty by building a statistic, z, defined by

(7.64) $$z = \tfrac{1}{2}(\log_e u^2 - \log_e v^2) = \log_e \frac{u}{v}$$

whose frequency function, $g(z)$, he obtained and which proved to have extremely wide application. To derive $g(z)$ we make use of the distribution of $f_5(s^2)$ given in (7.36), replacing $N - 1$ by n and s^2 by $(n/\overline{n+1})u^2$. After this modification, (7.36) becomes

(7.65) $$f(u^2)\,d(u^2) = \frac{\left\{\dfrac{n}{2\sigma^2}\right\}^{n/2}}{\Gamma\left(\dfrac{n}{2}\right)}(u^2)^{(n-2)/2}e^{-nu^2/2\sigma^2}\,d(u^2)$$

Since u^2 and v^2 are independent their joint distribution is

(7.66) $$K(u^2)^{(n_1-2)/2}(v^2)^{(n_2-2)/2}e^{-(n_1u^2+n_2v^2)/2\sigma^2}\,d(u^2)\,d(v^2)$$

Sec. 15 Significance of Difference Between Variances

where
$$K = \frac{(n_1)^{n_1/2}(n_2)^{n_2/2}}{2^{(n_1+n_2)/2}\sigma^{(n_1+n_2)}\Gamma\left(\frac{n_1}{2}\right)\Gamma\left(\frac{n_2}{2}\right)}$$

From (7.64) we have

(7.67) $$u^2 = v^2 e^{2z}$$

and for a fixed value of v^2,

(7.68) $$d(u^2) = 2v^2 e^{2z}\, dz$$

Using (7.67) and (7.68) in (7.66) we obtain

(7.69) $$2Ke^{n_1 z}e^{-(n_1 e^{2z}+n_2)v^2/2\sigma^2}(v^2)^{(n_1+n_2-2)/2}\,d(v^2)\,dz$$

for the joint distribution of v^2 and z. Integrating with respect to v^2 between the limits 0 and ∞ and making use of the Gamma function we obtain the distribution of z,

(7.70) $$g(z)\,dz = \frac{2n_1^{n_1/2} n_2^{n_2/2}}{B\left(\frac{n_1}{2},\frac{n_2}{2}\right)} \cdot \frac{e^{n_1 z}\,dz}{(n_1 e^{2z}+n_2)^{(n_1+n_2)/2}}$$

The function $g(z)$ has the important property that it depends solely upon n_1 and n_2, not at all upon the variance of the sampled universe. Fisher's z should not be confused with the z-distribution of "Student."

The z-distribution is extremely general, including as special cases the χ^2-distribution, the t-distribution of "Student" and Fisher, and the normal distribution. Rider [17] has made easily available the transformations and substitutions by which these special cases can be obtained from (7.70).

The positive part of the curve for $z = \log_e(u/v)$ is the same as the negative part for $z = \log_e(v/u)$. Since it is optional which estimate is considered as u^2 it is usual, in tabulating the probability integral of $g(z)$, to consider only positive values of z by making u^2 the larger variance estimate (based on n_1 degrees of freedom).

Let $Q = \int_{-\infty}^{z_0} g(z)\,dz$ and let $P = 1 - Q$. Thus P is the probability that $z > z_0$. In his book, Fisher [18] has given values of z_0 corresponding to the probabilities $P = .05, .01,$ and $.001$, for various combinations of n_1 and n_2. These values, z_0, are called the "5%, 1%, and 0.1% points" and are used as critical values in judging significance. In practice, however, tables constructed from the F-distribution (see §§ 7.15 and 7.16) instead of the z-distribution are commonly used.

7.15 Significance of Difference Between Variances. The usual hypothesis tested by the z-test is that u^2 and v^2 are estimates of one and the same population variance and therefore that $z = 0$. The significance of the divergence of the observed value of z from zero is the crux of the test. Small values of z

mean a tenable hypothesis whereas values of z larger than z_0 refute the hypothesis. If for $P = .05$ (or $.01$) the observed value of z, as computed from the samples in accordance with (7.64), is larger than z_0, the hypothesis is to be rejected and the conclusion is that the samples come from universes with different variances.

The z-test may well be applied before testing the difference between two means since the latter test depends on the equality of the population variances.

To avoid the troublesome logarithmic computation involved in (7.64) Snedecor[19] has published tables which give 5% and 1% points for the ratio u^2/v^2, where $e^{2z} = u^2/v^2$. Snedecor calls this ratio F in honor of Fisher.* Therefore,

$$F = \frac{u^2}{v^2}$$

where u^2 is to be chosen the larger of the two given variance estimates. This table is reproduced in the Appendix. (See Table II.)

Example 3. In Example 2 suppose we wish to test the assumption, which was made there, that the two samples come from universes with equal variance. We have

$$u^2 = \frac{n_1 + 1}{n_1} s_1^2 = \frac{.64}{9} = .0711$$

$$v^2 = \frac{n_2 + 1}{n_2} s_2^2 = \frac{.24}{9} = .0267$$

$$F = \frac{.0711}{.0267} = 2.663$$

$$z = .5 \log_e F$$

$$= 1.1513 \log_{10} F = .49$$

Entering Fisher's table (*loc. cit.*) for $n_1 = n_2 = 9$ we find $z_0 = .58$ for $P = .05$ and $z_0 = .84$ for $P = .01$. This means that, if the true value of z were zero, random sampling fluctuations would be expected to give a value of z as great as .84, or greater, once in 100 trials, and a value of z as great as .58, or greater, five times in 100 trials. The observed value of z is .49 and so this value might be accounted for by chance, at either the .05 or .01 points of significance. Using Snedecor's table we find $F = 3.18$ for $P = .05$ and $F = 5.35$ for $P = .01$. Since the observed value of F is only 2.663, the hypothesis that the variances are equal is not rejected.

7.16 The Distribution of F. Since $F = N_1 s_1^2/n_1 \div N_2 s_2^2/n_2$, it follows that $n_1 F/n_2$ is the ratio of two variates distributed as χ^2 with n_1 and n_2 degrees of freedom, respectively. It is therefore the ratio of a $\gamma(n_1/2)$ variate to a $\gamma(n_2/2)$ variate, and so is a $\beta'(n_1/2, n_2/2)$ variate, with frequency function

(7.71)
$$f(F) = \left(\frac{n_1 F}{n_2}\right)^{(n_1/2)-1} \left(1 + \frac{n_1 F}{n_2}\right)^{-\frac{1}{2}(n_1+n_2)} \frac{n_1}{n_2} \bigg/ B\left(\frac{n_1}{2}, \frac{n_2}{2}\right)$$

$$= K F^{\frac{1}{2}n_1 - 1} \left(1 + \frac{n_1 F}{n_2}\right)^{-\frac{1}{2}(n_1+n_2)}, \quad 0 \leq F < \infty$$

* In *Statistical Tables* by Fisher and Yates it is called the variance ratio. The 3rd edition (1948) gives tables for 0.1%, 1%, 5%, 10%, and 20% points. More extensive tables by M. Merrington and C. M. Thompson are available in *Biometrika*, **33**, 1943, pp. 73–88.

Sec. 16   The Distribution of F

where

(7.72) $$K = (n_1/n_2)^{n_1/2}/\mathrm{B}(n_1/2, n_2/2)$$

The expectation of $n_1 F/n_2$ is, by (5.14), $(n_1/2)/[(n_2/2) - 1]$, so that the expectation of F is $n_2/(n_2 - 2)$, provided, of course, that $n_2 > 2$. This is always greater than unity and is independent of n_1. The modal value of F, given by differentiating (7.71), is $[n_2/(n_2 + 2)][(n_1 - 2)/n_1]$, which is always less than unity.

When $n_1 = 1$, the distribution of F is the same as that of t^2 with n_2 degrees of freedom.

When $n_2 = \infty$, $s_2^2 = \sigma^2$, so that $n_1 F$ is distributed as χ^2 with n_1 degrees of freedom.

When $n_1 = \infty$, n_2/F is distributed as χ^2 with n_2 degrees of freedom. When $n_2 = \infty$ and $n_1 = 1$, the distribution of $\sqrt{F}$ is normal.

The table of F given in the Appendix gives only the upper tail. For testing values of $F < 1$, we may take the reciprocal of F and interchange the degrees of freedom n_1 and n_2, although this is seldom necessary.

It should be observed that the 5% and 1% points of the F-table (and also of the z-table), when used to test the equality of two estimates of variance, refer to 10% and 2% levels of significance. The reason for this will be clear on considering the hypothesis that is being tested.

Suppose we have two samples of sizes $n_1 + 1$ and $n_2 + 1$ from normal populations with means $\mu_{(1)}$, $\mu_{(2)}$ and variances σ_1^2, σ_2^2, respectively. Let $\theta = \sigma_1^2/\sigma_2^2$, and let the hypothesis H_0 be that $\theta = 1$, regardless of the actual values of σ_2^2, $\mu_{(1)}$, and $\mu_{(2)}$. Let A_{12} and B_{12} be two numbers, depending on n_1 and n_2, chosen so that for any given n_1 and n_2

$$\int_{A_{12}}^{B_{12}} f(F) \, dF = 1 - \alpha, \qquad 0 < \alpha < 1$$

If then we agree to reject H_0 when either $F < A_{12}$ or $F > B_{12}$, the probability of rejecting H_0 when it is true will be $1 - \Pr\{A_{12} \leq F \leq B_{12}\} = \alpha$, so that α is our level of significance.

Moreover, a confidence interval for θ, corresponding to confidence coefficient $1 - \alpha$, will be given by $F/B_{12} \leq \theta \leq F/A_{12}$, since the probability that the true value of θ is covered by this interval when H_0 is true is

$$\Pr\left\{\frac{F}{B_{12}} \leq \theta \leq \frac{F}{A_{12}} \Big| \theta = 1\right\} = \Pr\{A_{12} \leq F \leq B_{12}\} = 1 - \alpha$$

Now A_{12} and B_{12} may be chosen in different ways. If we wish for a test that is equally sensitive for $\theta < 1$ and $\theta > 1$, it will be natural to use both tails of the F-distribution and to put

$$\int_0^{A_{12}} f(F) \, dF = \int_{B_{12}}^{\infty} f(F) \, dF = \tfrac{1}{2}\alpha$$

This implies that $A_{12} = 1/B_{21}$, where B_{21} is the number obtained from B_{12} by interchanging n_1 and n_2, since if we put $u = 1/F$, we obtain

$$\int_0^{A_{12}} f(F)\, dF = \frac{(n_2/n_1)^{n_2/2}}{B(\tfrac{1}{2}n_1, \tfrac{1}{2}n_2)} \int_{1/A_{12}}^\infty \left(1 + \frac{un_2}{n_1}\right)^{-(n_1+n_2)/2} u^{\frac{1}{2}n_2 - 1}\, du$$

and the right-hand side is the F integral with n_1 and n_2 interchanged.

Because of the relation between A_{12} and B_{12}, it does not matter which sample we take as number 1 and which as number 2. With one arrangement we shall reject H_0 unless $A_{12} \leq F \leq B_{12}$ and with the other arrangement we shall reject it unless $A_{21} \leq 1/F \leq B_{21}$. But it is easily seen that if $A_{12} = 1/B_{21}$ (and hence $A_{21} = 1/B_{12}$) the conditions of rejection are identical. We can, therefore, agree to use only values of $F > 1$, and so are interested only in the upper tail of the F-distribution.

The values of B_{12} are given by Snedecor's tables for $\tfrac{1}{2}\alpha = 0.05$ and 0.01, and hence correspond to $\alpha = 0.1$ and 0.02. That is, the 5% point corresponds to a 10% level of significance.

If, on the other hand, we want to reject H_0 if $\theta > 1$ but do not mind accepting it if $\theta < 1$ (a situation which is common in the analysis of variance, Chapter IX), we shall want to use a *one-tailed test*. We choose B_{12} so that

$$\int_{B_{12}}^\infty f(F)\, dF = \alpha,$$

and reject H_0 if $F > B_{12}$. The values of B_{12} are still given by Snedecor's tables, but they now correspond to significance levels of $\alpha = 0.05$ and 0.01. The confidence interval for θ is from F/B_{12} to ∞.

It may be proved that if

$$F = \frac{n_2}{n_1}\frac{1-x}{x}$$

then x is a Beta-variate with distribution function equal to the incomplete Beta-function $I_x(\tfrac{1}{2}n_1, \tfrac{1}{2}n_2)$. Tables have been computed by Miss C. M. Thompson (*Biometrika*, **32**, 1941, pp. 151–181) giving values of x corresponding to $I_x = 0.005, 0.01, 0.025, 0.05, 0.10, 0.25$, and 0.50. From these values the extensive F tables cited in the footnote to § 7.15 were calculated.

7.17 Confidence Limits. (a) *For the mean.* Let $\bar{x}$ and s be the mean and standard deviation of a sample of $N = n + 1$ items drawn from a normal universe with unknown mean μ. The problem is to determine an interval surrounding $\bar{x}$ in which we may assume, with a certain degree of confidence, that μ is contained. We have seen that the variable

$$t = \frac{\sqrt{n}(\bar{x} - \mu)}{s}$$

is distributed in accord with the $f_n(t)$ curve and that $P = 1 - P_n(t)$ has been tabulated for various values of t and n, where

$$P_n(t) = 2\int_0^t f_n(t)\, dt$$

Sec. 17 Confidence Limits

Therefore, for an assigned ϵ and for an assigned value of n, $(n \leq 30)$, we may obtain from the tables upper and lower critical values of t by solving the equation $P = 2\epsilon$. With these critical values we can determine the required interval surrounding $\bar{x}$ for the given value of ϵ. It is conventional to take $\epsilon = 0.005$ (or 0.025) since we wish to determine confidence limits dividing hypotheses that will be rejected from those acceptable at the 1% (or 5%) level of significance.

Suppose, then, that we make the claim

$$\bar{x} - t_\epsilon \frac{s}{\sqrt{n}} < \mu < \bar{x} + t_\epsilon \frac{s}{\sqrt{n}} \tag{7.73}$$

and we desire the probability of an error in this statement to be not more than $2\epsilon = 0.01$. Taking $n = 15$, for example, we find from Table IV, that $t = \pm 2.947$ when $P = 0.01$. Then we have

$$(\bar{x} - \mu) = \frac{\pm 2.947 s}{\sqrt{15}}$$
$$= \pm 0.76 s$$

and the claim

$$\bar{x} - 0.76s < \mu < \bar{x} + 0.76s$$

will be correct 99% of the time.

It is clear from the above procedure that our confidence in the limits $\bar{x} \pm t_\epsilon s/\sqrt{n}$ is measured by the area under the $f_n(t)$ curve inside $t = \pm t_\epsilon$, that is, by $P_n(t_\epsilon)$. This means that, if we could observe all possible samples, the proportion represented by $P_n(t_\epsilon)$ would yield values of $\bar{x}$ and s for which the claim (7.73) is true, while the remaining proportion, $P = 1 - P_n(t_\epsilon)$, would yield values of $\bar{x}$ and s for which the claim is false.

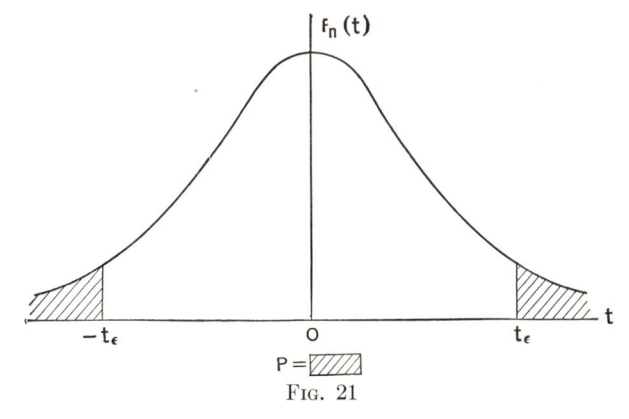

FIG. 21

If we were testing a hypothetical value of μ we would say that $\bar{x}$ is not significantly different at the 1% level of significance if μ has any value in the $\bar{x} \pm t_\epsilon s/\sqrt{n}$ interval, $\epsilon = 0.005$. If μ does not lie in this interval we say that $\bar{x}$ is significantly different at this level.

Obviously, values of t satisfying the equation $P = 0.01$, that is, $P_n(t) = 0.99$, vary with n. To avoid the trouble of entering a table we give an *alternate method* which is valid when the sample is not small. Recall that the variable

$$t' = \frac{(\bar{x} - \mu)(N - 3)^{1/2}}{s}$$

is approximately normally distributed when $N > 30$. The area under the normal curve outside $t' = \pm 2.576$ is 0.01. Therefore, the 99% confidence interval of μ is then

$$\bar{x} \pm \frac{2.576 s}{\sqrt{N - 3}}$$

and the interval gets smaller as N increases.

(b) *For the difference between two means.* Let $\bar{x}_1$ and s_1^2 be the observed mean and variance of a sample of N_1 drawn from a normal universe with unknown mean $\mu_{(1)}$ and let $\bar{x}_2$ and s_2^2 be the observed mean and variance of a sample of N_2 drawn from a normal universe with unknown mean $\mu_{(2)}$. It is assumed that the two universes have a common variance σ^2. For brevity, let

$$\bar{w} = \bar{x}_1 - \bar{x}_2, \qquad \omega = \mu_{(1)} - \mu_{(2)}, \qquad N = N_1 + N_2$$

$$\hat{\sigma}_{\bar{w}} = \left[\left\{\frac{N_1 s_1^2 + N_2 s_2^2}{N - 2}\right\}\left\{\frac{N_1 + N_2}{N_1 N_2}\right\}\right]^{1/2}$$

Then

(7.74) $$t = \frac{\bar{w} - \omega}{\hat{\sigma}_{\bar{w}}}$$

is distributed in accord with $f_n(t)$ for $n = N - 2$. From (7.74), upper and lower confidence values of ω can be found by assigning to t the solutions of $P_n(t) = 0.99$, that is, of $P = 0.01$. If the value $\omega = 0$ falls outside the confidence interval thus established, the conclusion is that the difference between the means is significant at the 1% level. That is, $\omega \neq 0$ and hence $\mu_{(1)} \neq \mu_{(2)}$.

If the two samples are equal in number and if the variates are paired in some manner we may compute (7.74) by a different method. Let $N = N_1 = N_2$, $w = x_1 - x_2$, and compute $\bar{w}$ and $\sum_{1}^{N}(w_i - \bar{w})^2$. Then

(7.75) $$t = \frac{\bar{w} - \omega}{\sigma_w / \sqrt{N}} = \frac{\bar{w} - \omega}{\frac{s_w}{\sqrt{N - 1}}}$$
$$= \frac{\bar{w} - \omega}{\left[\frac{\sum_{1}^{N}(w_i - \bar{w})^2}{N(N - 1)}\right]^{1/2}}$$

The last expression is sometimes called *Bessel's Formula.*

Example 4 (Snedecor [19]). Imagine a newly discovered apple, attractive in appearance, delicious in flavor, having apparently all the qualifications of success. It has been christened "King." Only its yielding capacities in various localities are yet to be tested. The following procedure is decided upon. King is planted adjacent to Standard in 15 orchards scattered about the region suitable for production. Years later, when the trees have matured, the yields are measured and recorded in the following table where x_1 refers to King, x_2 to Standard, and $w = x_1 - x_2$. The yields are in bushels.

x_1	x_2	w	$(w - \bar{w})^2$
13	11	2	16
12	6	6	0
10	3	7	1
6	1	5	1
13	7	6	0
15	10	5	1
19	9	10	16
10	4	6	0
11	3	8	4
11	6	5	1
13	8	5	1
9	5	4	4
14	7	7	1
12	6	6	0
12	4	8	4
Totals		90	50

Substituting in (7.75) we get

$$t = \frac{6 - \omega}{\left[\dfrac{50}{(15)(14)}\right]^{1/2}} = \frac{6 - \omega}{0.488}$$

Entering Table IV for $n = 14$ we find that $P = .01$ when $t = 2.977$. Then solving the equation

$$\frac{6 - \omega}{0.488} = \pm 2.977$$

we obtain $\omega = 4.55$ and $\omega = 7.45$. Since $\omega = 0$ is outside the interval from 4.55 to 7.45, the observed value of $\bar{w}$ differs significantly from zero. In other words, we would reject (at the 1% level of significance) the null hypothesis that there is no significant difference between the yields of the two varieties.

It is important to note that the circumstances in which (7.74) and (7.75) apply are quite different. In using (7.74) we are assuming that we have two completely independent samples from two normal populations with the same variance. We make the null hypothesis that the means are also the same, and construct the confidence interval on this assumption. If the observed difference of means is too great we reject the null hypothesis. The number of degrees of freedom is $N_1 + N_2 - 2$.

In using (7.75), however, the two samples are not assumed to be independent. They consist of N pairs, the members of each pair differing perhaps in their values of x, but otherwise as identical as possible. In Example 4, the two varieties of apple are planted adjacent to each other, so as to minimize any differential effects of moisture, soil fertility, etc., on the yields. The degrees of freedom are here only $N - 1$.

(c) *For the variance.* As noted in § 7.6, Ns^2/σ^2 has the χ^2 distribution with $n = N - 1$ degrees of freedom.

To determine the confidence limits of σ^2 we first observe that $Ns^2 = n\hat{\sigma}^2 = \sum_1^N (x_i - \bar{x})^2$, and therefore we may write $\chi^2 = n\hat{\sigma}^2/\sigma^2$. If now we make the claim

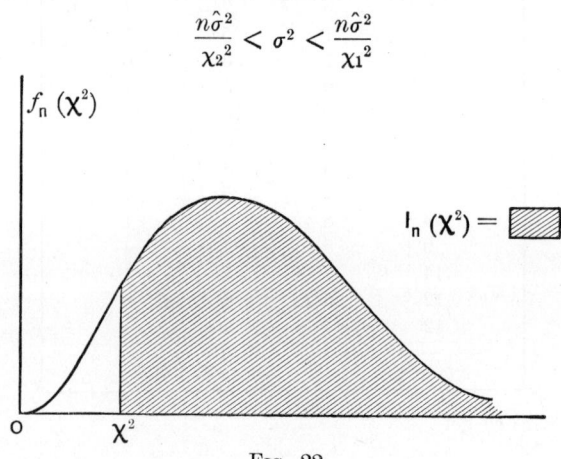

$$\frac{n\hat{\sigma}^2}{\chi_2^2} < \sigma^2 < \frac{n\hat{\sigma}^2}{\chi_1^2}$$

Fig. 22

where χ_1^2 and χ_2^2 are arbitrarily chosen constants ($\chi_1^2 < \chi_2^2$), then our confidence in this claim is measured by $I_n(\chi_1^2) - I_n(\chi_2^2)$, where

$$I_n(\chi^2) = \int_{\chi^2}^{\infty} f_n(\chi^2)\, d\chi^2$$

Values of $I_n(\chi^2)$ can be obtained from Pearson's *Tables,*[20] or from Appendix, Table III.

More extensive tables have been calculated by C. M. Thompson, *Biometrika,* **32,** 1941–42, pp. 187–191. These give χ^2 for $P = I_n(\chi^2) = 0.005, 0.01, 0.025, 0.05, 0.10, 0.25, 0.50, 0.75, 0.90, 0.95, 0.975, 0.99, 0.995$ and for $n = 1(1)\ 30,$* 40, 50, 60, 70, 80, 90, 100.

(d) *For the standard deviation.* The frequency function of s is given in (7.39).

An unbiased estimate of σ from a sample value s is $s/b(N)$, where $1/b(N)$ is given by Table 10. Values of s/σ at selected probability points are given in a table compiled by Croxton and Cowden [21] and reprinted as Appendix G_2 in their textbook *Practical Business Statistics,* from which several sets of con-

*i.e., for all n between 1 and 30 at intervals of 1.

Sec. 18   Standard Errors of the k-Statistics

fidence limits may be calculated. Alternatively we may find limits for s^2 and take the square root.

7.18 Standard Errors of the k-Statistics and of g_1 and g_2. The k-statistics were defined in § 5.8 as follows:

$$k_1 = n_1 = m$$
$$k_2 = Nm_2/(N-1)$$
$$k_3 = N^2 m_3/(N-1)(N-2)$$
$$k_4 = N^2[(N+1)m_4 - 3(N-1)m_2^2]/(N-1)(N-2)(N-3)$$

We have already proved that, for any parent population for which the moments up to the fourth exist (see (6.14), (7.8), (7.19)),

$$E(n_1) = \nu_1$$
$$E(m_2) = (N-1)\mu_2/N$$
$$E(m_2^2) = (N-1)[(N-1)\mu_4 + (N^2-2N+3)\mu_2^2]/N^3$$

By similar algebraic calculations it may be shown that

$$E(m_3) = (N-1)(N-2)\mu_3/N^2$$
$$E(m_4) = (N-1)[(N^2-3N+3)\mu_4 + 3(2N-3)\mu_2^2]/N^3$$

Hence, bearing in mind the definition of the cumulants κ_r given in (4.65), we see that

(7.76) $$\begin{cases} E(k_1) = \kappa_1 \\ E(k_2) = \kappa_2 \\ E(k_3) = \kappa_3 \\ E(k_4) = \kappa_4 \end{cases}$$

From (5.64) and (7.20) it follows that

(7.77) $$\operatorname{Var}(k_2) = N^2(N-1)^{-2} \operatorname{Var}(m_2)$$
$$= N^{-1}\kappa_4 + 2(N-1)^{-1}\kappa_2^2$$

From (7.19) and (7.76), we can show that

$$E[2k_2^2(N+1)^{-1} + k_4(N-1)N^{-1}(N+1)^{-1}] = \kappa_4 N^{-1} + 2\kappa_2^2(N-1)^{-1}$$

Therefore an unbiased estimate of $\operatorname{Var}(k_2)$ is

(7.78) $$[2k_2^2 + (N-1)k_4/N]/(N+1),$$

and the square root of this is the standard error of k_2.

If the parent population is known to be *normal*,

(7.79) $$\operatorname{Var}(k_2) = 2(N-1)^{-1}\kappa_2^2$$

and

(7.80) $$E(s^4) = (N^2-1)N^{-2}\kappa_2^2$$

Hence an estimate of the variance of k_2 is

(7.81) $$2s^4 N^2(N-1)^{-1}(N^2-1)^{-1} = 2(N+1)^{-1}k_2^2$$

and the square root of this is the standard error of k_2. The result (7.81) is obtained by putting $k_4 = 0$ in (7.78).

It may similarly be proved that for any parent population

(7.82) $\quad$ Var $(k_3) = \kappa_6 N^{-1} + 9\kappa_4\kappa_2(N-1)^{-1} + 9\kappa_3{}^2(N-1)^{-1}$
$\quad\quad\quad\quad + 6\kappa_2{}^3 N(N-1)^{-1}(N-2)^{-1}$

For a normal parent population this reduces to

(7.83) $\quad$ Var $(k_3) = 6\kappa_2{}^3 N(N-1)^{-1}(N-2)^{-1}$

Since, from (7.41) with $r = 6$,

$$E(s^6) = N^{-3}(N-1)(N+1)(N+3)\kappa_2{}^3$$

an unbiased estimate of Var (k_3) is

$6s^6 N^4(N-2)^{-1}(N-1)^{-2}(N+1)^{-1}(N+3)^{-1} =$
$\quad\quad\quad\quad 6k_2{}^3 N(N-1)(N-2)^{-1}(N+1)^{-1}(N+3)^{-1}$

and the square root of this is the standard error of k_3.

A similar argument shows that an unbiased estimate of the variance of k_4 for a sample from a normal parent population is

(7.84) $\quad$ Var $(k_4) = 24k_2{}^4 N(N-1)^2(N-3)^{-1}(N-2)^{-1}(N+3)^{-1}(N+5)^{-1}$

The variances of $g_1 = k_3/k_2{}^{3/2}$ and of $g_2 = k_4/k_2{}^2$, for samples from a normal parent population, were worked out by Fisher [25] who found that

(7.85) $\quad$ Var $(g_1) = 6N(N-1)(N-2)^{-1}(N+1)^{-1}(N+3)^{-1}$

and

(7.86) $\quad$ Var $(g_2) = 24N(N-1)^2(N-3)^{-1}(N-2)^{-1}(N+3)^{-1}(N+5)^{-1}$

For large N these approximate to the values $6/N$ and $24/N$ given in Chapter VI.

7.19 The Distribution of Extreme Values and of the Range. Let $x_1, x_2, \cdots x_N$ be a set of sample values, arranged in ascending order, from a parent population with distribution function $F(x)$. The probability that all N individuals in the sample lie between $-\infty$ and x is $[F(x)]^N$, since by definition $F(x)$ is equal to the corresponding probability for any member of the population. But if all the x_i lie between $-\infty$ and x, so does x_N. Hence the distribution function for x_N is

$$G(x) = \Pr\{x_N \leq x\} = [F(x)]^N$$

If $F(x)$ is known, $G(x)$ can be found. For a normal parent population $F(x) = \Phi(x)$, and L. H. C. Tippett has calculated a table for selected values of N between 3 and 1000. This is reproduced in *Tables for Statisticians and Biometricians*, Part II (Table XXI). Since the normal distribution is symmetrical, the table serves equally well for the least value, x_1. Thus

$$\Pr\{x_N \leq x\} = \Pr\{x_1 \geq -x\}$$

Sec. 19 Distribution of Extreme Values and of Range

In this table the unit is the standard deviation of the parent population and the x's are measured from the population mean.

The table may be used to determine whether an outlying sample value should be rejected as being too large (or too small) to be reasonably regarded as a random fluctuation. For this purpose, Tippett and Egon Pearson have calculated a table (*loc. cit.*, Table XXI *bis*) from which Table 11 is a brief extract, giving for various sample sizes the deviations which are exceeded by the extreme variate in the stated percentage of cases.

TABLE 11

N	5%	1%
1	1.645	2.326
5	2.319	2.877
10	2.568	3.089
15	2.705	3.207
20	2.799	3.289
30	2.928	3.402
50	3.082	3.539
100	3.283	3.718
1000	3.884	4.264

Example 5. Suppose that in the mass production of a certain article the manufacturer aims at an average breaking strength of 180 lb with a standard deviation not exceeding 12 lb. In a sample of 10 items the lowest breaking strength would be below $180 - 12 \times 3.089 = 142.9$ lb only once in 100 times, on the hypothesis that the sample is a random one from a normal population with mean 180 lb and standard deviation 12 lb. Hence the occurrence of such a sample might well warrant investigation of the process.

The chance that in a sample of N there will be one individual at x_1, one at x_N, and $N - 2$ in between, is given by

$$N(N - 1)(F_N - F_1)^{N-2} \, dF_1 \, dF_N$$

where F_1 stands for $F(x_1)$ and F_N for $F(x_N)$, and where $dF_1 = f(x_1) \, dx_1$. This is because there are $N(N - 1)$ ways of fixing the order of appearance of the greatest and least individuals within a random sample of N. The greatest member might be the first, second, or any one up to the Nth, and the smallest could appear in any of the remaining $N - 1$ positions. For this sample, the range is given by

$$w = x_N - x_1$$

Putting $x_N = x_1 + w$, and noting that for a fixed value of x_1, $dx_N = dw$, we have as the joint frequency function of x_1 and w

$$N(N - 1)[F(x_1 + w) - F(x_1)]^{N-2} f(x_1 + w) f(x_1)$$

Integrating over all values of x_1 we obtain for the frequency function of the range $(0 \leq w < \infty)$

(7.87) $\quad g(w) = N(N - 1) \displaystyle\int_{-\infty}^{\infty} [F(x_1 + w) - F(x_1)]^{N-2} f(x_1 + w) f(x_1) \, dx_1$

The distribution function for the range is

(7.88) $$G(w) = \int_0^w g(w)\, dw$$

Since the order of integration may be reversed, and since
$$f(x_1 + w)\, dw = d[F(x_1 + w) - F(x_1)]$$
we find

(7.89) $$G(w) = N(N-1) \int_{-\infty}^{\infty} f(x_1)\, dx_1 \int_0^w [F(x_1 + w) - F(x_1)]^{N-2} \times d[F(x_1 + w) - F(x_1)]$$
$$= N \int_{-\infty}^{\infty} [F(x_1 + w) - F(x_1)]^{N-1} f(x_1)\, dx_1$$

This formula, although apparently simple, is not in general of much use, because of the difficulty of expressing $F(x + w)$ in terms of $F(x)$. Tippett[22] has calculated the expectation of w as

(7.90) $$E(w) = \int_{-\infty}^{\infty} [1 - F^N - (1 - F)^N]\, dx$$

and has evaluated this expression by numerical integration for values of N from 2 to 1000 when the parent population is normal [that is, when $F = \Phi(x)$]. His results are reproduced as Table XXII of Pearson's *Tables for Statisticians and Biometricians*, Part II.

If the parent population is *rectangular*, so that $f(x) = 1$, $0 \leq x \leq 1$, we have $F(x) = x (0 \leq x \leq 1)$ and $F(x) = 1 (x > 1)$. Therefore

(7.91) $$G(w) = N \int_0^{1-w} w^{N-1}\, dx + N \int_{1-w}^1 (1-x)^{N-1}\, dx$$
$$= Nw^{N-1}(1-w) + w^N$$

If the parent population is *normal*, $f(x) = \phi(x)$, $F(x) = \Phi(x)$, and

$$G(w) = N \int_{-\infty}^{\infty} \phi(x)[\Phi(x + w) - \Phi(x)]^{N-1}\, dx$$

Now, putting $x = -y - w$, we have

$$\int_{-\infty}^{-w/2} \phi(x)[\Phi(x+w) - \Phi(x)]^{N-1}\, dx$$
$$= -\int_{\infty}^{-w/2} \phi(y+w)[\Phi(-y) - \Phi(-y-w)]^{N-1}\, dy$$

because $\phi(x) = \phi(-x)$. Also,

$$\Phi(-y) - \Phi(-y-w) = \Phi(y+w) - \Phi(y)$$

so that on replacing the variable of integration y by x we obtain

Sec. 20   Limits for Binomial and Poisson Distributions   193

$$\int_{-\infty}^{-w/2} \phi(x)[\Phi(x+w) - \Phi(x)]^{N-1}\,dx = \int_{-w/2}^{\infty} \phi(x+w)[\Phi(x+w) - \Phi(x)]^{N-1}\,dx$$

Consequently

(7.92) $$G(w) = N \int_{-w/2}^{\infty} [\phi(x) + \phi(x+w)][\Phi(x+w) - \Phi(x)]^{N-1}\,dx$$

$$= -N \int_{-w/2}^{\infty} [\phi(x+w) - \phi(x)][\Phi(x+w) - \Phi(x)]^{N-1}\,dx$$

$$+ 2N \int_{-w/2}^{\infty} \phi(x+w)[\Phi(x+w) - \Phi(x)]^{N-1}\,dx$$

The first integral is equal to

$$\left[\Phi\left(\frac{w}{2}\right) - \Phi\left(-\frac{w}{2}\right)\right]^N = \left[2 \int_0^{w/2} \phi(x)\,dx\right]^N$$

The second is equal to

$$2N \int_{w/2}^{\infty} \phi(u)[\Phi(u) - \Phi(u-w)]^{N-1}\,du$$

where $u = x + w$. Values of $G(w)$ may be calculated by numerical methods. H. O. Hartley [23] has given an accurate 4-place table of $G(w)$ for all values of N from 2 up to 20. For sample sizes larger than 20 the range is of little value in practice and the distribution is so sensitive to slight variations from normality in the parent population that the tabulated values cease to be trustworthy.

The principal use of the range as a measure of variability is in the construction of charts for quality control in the process of manufacturing certain articles, and sample sizes of 5 or so are quite common in such use. (See Ref. 6.)

7.20 Confidence Limits for the Binomial and Poisson Distributions. The usual method of obtaining confidence limits for the proportion of individuals in a population having a certain characteristic is to assume that the sample is large enough to justify the normal approximation to the binomial. This method was described in § 6.15. It assumes also that the sample proportion p is an adequate estimate of the true proportion θ, and this may not be true for sample sizes less than, say, 100.

A more accurate procedure is to use Table VIII 1, in *Statistical Tables* by Fisher and Yates. If an event is observed to occur a times in N trials, the observed proportion is $p = a/N$. If θ_l is the lower $100(1 - \alpha)\%$ confidence limit for the true proportion θ, then if θ were really equal to θ_l an observed number of successes at least as *great* as a would occur by chance with probability $P = \alpha/2$. Similarly if θ_u is the upper $100(1 - \alpha)\%$ confidence limit, then if θ were really equal to θ_u an observed number of successes at least as *small* as a would occur by chance with the same probability P. The corresponding limits of expectation for a are $a_l = \theta_l N$ and $a_u = \theta_u N$. These are tabulated for three values of P (0.005, 0.025, and 0.1), corresponding to $\alpha = 0.01, 0.05, 0.2$ respectively, and for values of a from 0 to 10, and of p from 0 to 0.5. The values for $p = 0$ give the limits of expectation for the Poisson distribution.

Thus suppose $a = 2$ and $N = 5$, so that $p = 0.4$. The standard error of p by the usual formula is $[(0.4 \times 0.6)/5]^{1/2} = 0.2191$, and the 95% limits obtained by (6.35), with $t_\alpha = 1.96$ are 0.922 and -0.035.

The limits obtained by the still simpler formula $0.4 \pm 1.96 \times 0.2191$ are 0.829 and -0.029. The correct limits as given by Table VIII 1 are 0.853 and 0.053. (The table gives values of a_l and a_u, which must be divided by N to give θ_l and θ_u.)

A more extensive set of tables for the same purpose has been prepared by D. Mainland.[24] For all values of N from $2a$ up to 30 and by increasing steps up to 1000, three sets of confidence limits are given. If $a > N/2$, we use $a' = N - a$, instead of a. Less complete tables are given for $a > 20$. With the help of these tables it is an easy matter to determine confidence limits corresponding to any sample proportion likely to occur in practice.

Problems

1. In a certain observed distribution, $N = 20$, $\bar{x} = 42$, $s = 5$. Test the hypothesis that this distribution is a random sample from a normal universe with mean of 50.

2. In a certain test, one section of 20 students had an average score of 40 with a standard deviation of 5. Another section of 25 had an average of 46 with standard deviation of 4. Does this indicate a significant difference in the two groups? What assumptions do you make in applying the test?

3. In an experiment in industrial psychology a job was performed by one group of 30 workmen according to Method I and by a second group of 40 according to Method II. (The groups were independent and equally efficient.) Are the following distributions of the time (in seconds) taken such as to justify the conclusion that Method I is the speedier of the two? Use the difference between the means as a criterion of judgment.

Time	I	II
50	1	0
51	3	1
52	5	2
53	4	5
54	7	8
55	5	9
56	3	6
57	1	3
58	1	3
59	0	1
60	0	2
Totals	30	40

Problems

4. From the separate distribution functions of $\bar{x}$ and s derive the distribution of "Student's" z, and from that obtain the function $f_n(t)$.

Hint. Let $z = \bar{x}/s$, $u = \bar{x}^2 + s^2$, and find the joint distribution of z and u. Then integrate out u.

5. Prove that $f_n(t)$ is asymptotically normally distributed.

6. Write out in full the derivation of Fisher's z function, $g(z)$ of (7.70), as outlined in § 7.14.

7. Verify the Romanovsky expansions of $b(N)$ and $k(N)$ in series, as quoted in § 7.8.

Hint. Prove that $\Gamma\left(\dfrac{N}{2}\right)\Gamma\left(\dfrac{N-1}{2}\right) = \dfrac{(N-2)!}{2^{N-2}}\sqrt{\pi}$ (see Chapter III). Then

$$b(N) = \left(\frac{2}{N}\right)^{1/2} \frac{\left[\Gamma\left(\dfrac{N}{2}\right)\right]^2 2^{N-2}}{(N-2)!\sqrt{\pi}}$$

Put $\Gamma\left(\dfrac{N}{2}\right) = \dfrac{2}{N}\left(\dfrac{N}{2}\right)!$, $(N-2)! = \dfrac{N!}{N(N-1)}$, and expand the factorials by means of Stirling's approximation, using three terms of the series. $k(N)$ can be verified only as far as the second term, unless four terms are used in the Stirling series. (The fourth term is $-139/51840N^3$.)

8. Show that by the change of variable $x = \dfrac{n_1 F}{n_2}\left(1 + \dfrac{n_1 F}{n_2}\right)^{-1}$, the F-distribution of (7.71) becomes a Pearson Type I distribution.

9. The breaking strengths of 10 specimens of 0.104-in. diameter hard-drawn copper wire are found to be 578, 572, 570, 568, 572, 570, 570, 572, 596, 584 lb. Calculate the 95% confidence limits for the breaking strength of this kind of wire. *Ans.* 569 and 581 lb.

10. In the course of archaeological investigations conducted at a certain site, 16 lower first molars were found with mean length 13.57 mm and standard deviation 0.72 mm. From a near-by site, 9 lower first molars were taken with a mean of 13.06 mm and a standard deviation of 0.62 mm. Is the difference in mean length compatible with the hypothesis that the two finds are samples of the same population?

11. Calculate 98% confidence limits for the variance and for the standard deviation of the breaking strength in samples of 10 of the pieces of copper wire mentioned in Problem 9.

12. Suppose that a number of measurements are made in duplicate. Prove that the standard deviation of a sample of 2 is given by $s = \tfrac{1}{2}|X_1 - X_2|$, where X_1 and X_2 are the duplicate measurements. Hence show that an unbiased estimate of the standard deviation of the population of such samples is $\hat{\sigma} = 0.8862$ times the mean value of $|X_1 - X_2|$ for the samples measured.

Hint. Use (7.40).

13. In a series of 6 duplicate plate counts of molds on butter, the following results were obtained:

Sample No.	Count (1)	Count (2)
1	1400	1600
2	4100	2700
3	900	1100
4	6800	7400
5	3800	4200
6	7100	6000

Estimate the standard deviation of the population of duplicates, by the method of Problem 12. Compare this with the actual standard deviation of the differences between duplicates.

Use the t test to determine whether there is any significant difference between duplicate counts.

14. Two chemists A and B repeat a protein analysis 20 times. If X_i and Y_i are the values obtained by A and B respectively, and if $\sum X_i = 196.40$, $\sum X_i^2 = 1928.6560$, $\sum Y_i = 205.16$, $\sum Y_i^2 = 2104.7152$, determine whether there is a significant difference in precision between the two sets of analyses, the precision being measured by the inverse of the variance.

15. In two series of hauls to determine the number of plankton organisms inhabiting the waters of a lake, the following results were found:

Series I: 80, 96, 102, 77, 97, 110, 99, 88, 103, 108
Series II: 74, 122, 92, 81, 104, 92, 90

In series I the 10 hauls were made in succession at the same point. In series II the 7 hauls were made at points scattered over the lake. Do the observations suggest any greater variability between different places than exists at the same place?

16. Twelve hogs were fed on diet A; 15 on diet B. The gains in weight for the individual hogs (in pounds) were as shown:

A: 25, 30, 28, 34, 24, 25, 13, 32, 24, 30, 31, 35
B: 44, 34, 22, 8, 47, 31, 40, 30, 32, 35, 18, 21, 35, 29, 22

What conclusions may be drawn from this experiment?

17. An observer made the following observations on the vertical diameter of the planet Venus (in seconds of arc): 42.70, 42.56, 43.01, 43.48, 42.76, 43.06, 43.63, 42.87, 41.60, 42.78, 42.95, 43.20, 43.18, 43.39, 43.10.

Assuming that the population of readings is normally distributed about a true value which is estimated by the arithmetic mean, calculate 95% confidence limits for the vertical diameter of Venus.

From Table 11 show that the probability that in a sample of 15 the smallest value would be at least as small as 41.60 is nearly 0.05. Show that the probability of a *single reading* being as low as this is about 0.007. (Use the t-distribution.)

Weight (pounds) Class Marks	Frequency Boys	Frequency Girls
42.5	1	0
48.5	3	1
54.5	9	7
60.5	33	37
66.5	65	41
72.5	80	59
78.5	72	58
84.5	41	48
90.5	27	23
96.5	7	26
102.5	4	16
108.5	2	5
114.5	1	3
120.5	0	2
Totals	345	326

18. A question arose in a physical education class as to whether eleven-year-old girls weigh, as a rule, more than eleven-year-old boys. Suppose you wished to make a thorough analysis of the data in the table on page 196 concerning weights of boys and girls aged eleven. Describe the tests you might apply, the reasoning and assumptions underlying these, and the interpretation that might be placed on the results.

The following points are suggested for discussion:

(a) Is there a clear difference between the two distributions? How would you test this: from the means, from the variances, from the samples as a whole?

(b) 32.3% of the boys and 26.4% of the girls have weights less than 69.5 pounds. Is this difference significant?

(c) Within what limits would you say that the mean and standard deviation in the population of eleven-year-old boys (from which you have the sample of 345) is almost certain to lie in each case?

(d) Summarize your results.

19. Use the method for obtaining approximate standard errors (commonly known as the *delta method*) of § 6.10 to find the standard errors, to terms of order $1/N$, for g_1 and g_2 for samples of N from a parent population having a Gamma (Pearson Type III) distribution with frequency function $f(x) = e^{-x} x^{\lambda-1}/\Gamma(\lambda)$. Show that to this approximation

$$\text{Var }(g_1) = 6\, N^{-1}(1 + 6/\lambda + 5/\lambda^2)$$
$$\text{Var }(g_2) = 24\, N^{-1}(1 + 42/\lambda + 167/\lambda^2 + 126/\lambda^3)$$

The skewness of this distribution is $2\lambda^{-1/2}$.

Hint. To terms of order N^{-1}, $g_1 = \sqrt{b_1}$, $g_2 = b_2 - 3$. Use (6.18) and (6.19).

References

1. S. S. Wilks, *Elementary Statistical Analysis*, 1948, page 36.

2. A. T. Craig, "A Certain Mean-Value Problem in Statistics," *Bull. Amer. Math. Soc.*, **42**, pp. 670–674.

3. See an article "The Geometrical Method in Mathematical Statistics," by D. D. Kosambi, *Amer. Math. Monthly*, **51**, 1944, pp. 382–389.

4. R. C. Geary, "The Distribution of 'Student's' Ratio for Non-Normal Samples," *Jour. Royal Stat. Soc. Supplement*, **3**, 1936, pp. 178–184.

A proof by the method of characteristic functions is given by E. Lukacs, *Ann. Math. Stat.*, **13**, 1942, pp. 91–93.

5. V. Romanovsky, "On the Moments of the Standard Deviation and of the Correlation Coefficient in Samples from Normal," *Metron*, **5**, 1925, pp. 3–46.

6. A fuller table may be found in Egon Pearson, *The Application of Statistical Methods to Industrial Standardization and Quality Control*, 1935.

7. See E. S. Keeping, "Note on a Point in the Theory of Sampling," *Amer. Math. Monthly*, **42**, 19, p. 161.

E. S. Keeping, "Estimation and Confidence," *Canadian Math. Congress*, 1945, p. 36.

E. G. Olds, "A Note on the Problem of Estimation," *Amer. Math. Monthly*, **44**, 19, p. 92.

8. W. E. Deming and R. T. Birge, "On the Statistical Theory of Errors," *Reviews of Modern Physics*, **6**, pp. 119–161.

9. "Student," "Probable Error of the Mean," *Biometrika*, **6**, 1908, p. 1. Interesting biographical sketches of Mr. Gosset will be found in the *Jour. Amer. Stat. Assoc.*, **33**, No. 201, March, 1938, pp. 226–228, and *Jour. Roy. Stat. Soc.*, **101**, Part I, pp. 248–251.

For an account of the earlier contributions by Helmert (1876) and Czuber (1891) see "Some Topics in Sampling Theory," H. L. Rietz, *Bull. Amer. Math. Soc.*, April, 1937.

10. *Metron*, **5**, 1925, pp. 114–120. This table is more readily available in Yule and Kendall, *Introduction to the Theory of Statistics*, Appendix, Table 5.

11. R. A. Fisher, *Statistical Methods for Research Workers*, Table IV, p. 174 (10th Edition, 1946).

12. R. A. Fisher, "Applications of 'Student's' Distribution," *Metron*, **5**, 1925, pp. 90–93.

13. Dunham Jackson, "The Theory of Small Samples," *Amer. Math. Monthly*, **42**, 1935, pp. 344–364.

14. J. F. Kenney, "A Note on Certain Formulas Used in Sampling Theory," *Amer. Math. Monthly*, **45**, pp. 456–458.

15. M. S. Bartlett, "The Effect of Non-Normality on the t-distribution," *Proc. Camb. Phil. Soc.*, **31**, 1935, pp. 223–231.

16. H. L. Rietz, "Comments on Applications of the Recently Developed Theory of Small Samples," *Jour. Amer. Stat. Assoc.*, **26**, 1931, pp. 150–158.

17. P. R. Rider, "A Note on Small Sample Theory," *Jour. Amer. Stat. Assoc.*, **26**, 1931, pp. 172–174.

18. Table VI in ref. (11).

19. G. W. Snedecor, *Statistical Methods*.

20. *Tables for Statisticians and Biometricians*, Part I, Table XII.

21. F. E. Croxton and D. J. Cowden, "Tables to Facilitate Computation of Sampling Limits of s and Fiducial Limits of σ," *Industrial Quality Control*, July, 1946.

22. L. H. C. Tippett, "The Distribution of the Range," *Biometrika*, **17**, 1925, p. 364.

23. H. G. Hartley, "The Range in Random Samples," *Biometrika*, **32**, 1942, p. 309. These tables are also given in A. Hald's *Methods of Statistical Analysis* (Wiley).

24. D. Mainland, "Statistical Methods in Medical Research, I Qualitative Statistics," *Canadian Journal of Research*, **E. 26** (1948), pp. 1–166.

25. R. A. Fisher, "The Moments of the Distribution for Normal Samples of Measures of Departure from Normality," *Proc. Roy. Soc., A*, **130**, 1930, p. 16.

CHAPTER VIII

LINEAR REGRESSION, SIMPLE CORRELATION, AND CONTINGENCY

8.1 Linear Regression. Let x and y be two variables with the joint probability density function $f(x, y)$ and the marginal density functions $g(x)$ and $h(y)$ respectively. If y is fixed between y and $y + dy$, the probability that x lies in the interval x to $x + dx$ is $\dfrac{f(x, y)}{h(y)} dx$, since $\int_{-\infty}^{\infty} f(x, y) \, dx = h(y)$. The ratio $\dfrac{f(x, y)}{h(y)}$ is called the *conditional probability density* of x, given y. It is the probability density for an array of x's all having the same value of y.

In the same way, the conditional probability density of y, given x, is $\dfrac{f(x, y)}{g(x)}$, since $\int_{-\infty}^{\infty} f(x, y) \, dy = g(x)$. It is the probability density of an array of y's all having the same value of x.

The notion of arrays may be made more concrete by thinking of a joint distribution of the heights and weights of men. If x refers to weight and y to height, then an example of an x array of y's is the distribution of the heights of all men who weigh 150 pounds, and the weights of all men who are six feet tall is an example of a y array of x's.

The expectation of an x array of y's is

$$(8.1) \qquad \eta_x = \int y f(x, y)/g(x) \, dy$$

integrated over all values of y in the array defined by x. The variance is given by

$$(8.2) \qquad \sigma_{y|x}^2 = \int (y - \eta_x)^2 f(x, y)/g(x) \, dy$$

The locus of η_x as a function of x is called the *true regression curve* of y on x.

If the equation of the regression curve is of the form

$$(8.3) \qquad \eta_x = \alpha + \beta x$$

the regression of y on x is said to be linear. Similarly, if the equation of the true regression curve of x on y is

$$(8.4) \qquad \xi_y = \alpha' + \beta' y$$

the regression of x on y is linear. If one regression is linear it does not follow that the other is linear also.

From (8.1) and (8.3),

(8.5) $$\int_{-\infty}^{\infty} yf(x, y)\, dy = \alpha g(x) + \beta x g(x)$$

and on integrating both sides with respect to x, we have by (4.6) and (4.7)

(8.6) $$\nu_{01} = \alpha + \beta \nu_{10}$$

Multiplying each side of (8.5) by x and integrating, we have similarly

(8.7) $$\nu_{11} = \alpha \nu_{10} + \beta \nu_{20}$$

Solving (8.6) and (8.7) together for α and β, we obtain

(8.8) $$\beta = \frac{\nu_{11} - \nu_{10}\nu_{01}}{\nu_{20} - \nu_{10}^2} = \frac{\mu_{11}}{\mu_{20}} = \frac{\rho \sigma_y}{\sigma_x}$$

and

(8.9) $$\alpha = \nu_{01} - \nu_{10}\rho\sigma_y/\sigma_x$$

The equation of linear regression can, therefore, be written

(8.10) $$\eta_x - \nu_{01} = \rho \frac{\sigma_y}{\sigma_x}(x - \nu_{10})$$

In the same way, from (8.4),

(8.11) $$\xi_y - \nu_{10} = \rho \frac{\sigma_x}{\sigma_y}(y - \nu_{01})$$

The quantities β and β' are called the *regression coefficients*. Their product is ρ^2.

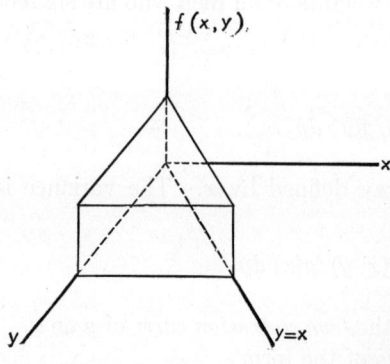

Example 1. Given

$$f(x, y) = \frac{2}{a^2}, \quad \begin{array}{l} 0 \leq x \leq y \\ 0 \leq y \leq a \end{array}$$

as the joint probability function of two variables x and y. Find (i) the marginal totals $g(x)$ and $h(y)$; (ii) the mean and variance of each of the marginal totals, i.e., ν_{10} and $\sigma_x^2 = \mu_{20}$ for $g(x)$, ν_{01} and $\sigma_y^2 = \mu_{02}$ for $h(y)$; (iii) the equations of the regression curves of y on x and of x on y, η_x and ξ_y; (iv) the correlation coefficient ρ.

Solutions. The volume under the surface represented by the given function is unity. Thus

$$\int_0^a \int_0^y \frac{2}{a^2}\, dx\, dy = \frac{2}{a^2}\int_0^a y\, dy = 1$$

The surface is shown above.

(i) The marginal totals are

$$g(x) = \int_x^a \frac{2}{a^2}\, dy = \frac{2}{a^2}(a - x)$$

$$h(y) = \int_0^y \frac{2}{a^2}\, dx = \frac{2y}{a^2}$$

(ii) The means are

$$\nu_{10} = \int_0^a x \frac{2}{a^2}(a-x)\,dx = \frac{a}{3}$$

$$\nu_{01} = \int_0^a y \frac{2y}{a^2}\,dy = \frac{2a}{3}$$

Since

$$\nu_{20} = \int_0^a x^2 \frac{2}{a^2}(a-x)\,dx = \frac{a^2}{6}$$

$$\nu_{02} = \int_0^a y^2 \frac{2}{a^2} y\,dy = \frac{a^2}{2}$$

the variances are

$$\mu_{20} = \sigma_x^2 = \frac{a^2}{6} - \frac{a^2}{9} = \frac{a^2}{18}$$

$$\mu_{02} = \sigma_y^2 = \frac{a^2}{2} - \frac{4a^2}{9} = \frac{a^2}{18}$$

(iii) The regression lines are

$$\eta_x = \int_x^a y \frac{2/a^2}{2(a-x)/a^2}\,dy = \frac{a+x}{2}$$

$$\xi_y = \int_0^y x \frac{2/a^2}{2y/a^2}\,dx = \frac{y}{2}$$

(iv) From the equations of the regression lines it follows that $\rho^2 = \frac{1}{4}$ and $\rho = \frac{1}{2}$ since $\rho(\sigma_y/\sigma_x)$ is positive.

8.2 The Standard Error of Estimate. The expectation, over all x arrays, of the variance $\sigma_{y|x}^2$, weighted with the marginal distribution of x, is usually called the "variance of estimate" and will be denoted here by σ_{ey}^2. It is not a squared standard error in the ordinary sense,* being a population parameter instead of an estimate based on a sample. By definition,

$$\sigma_{ey}^2 = \int g(x)\sigma_{y|x}^2\,dx$$

$$= \int_{-\infty}^{\infty}\int_{-\infty}^{\infty}(y-\eta_x)^2 f(x,y)\,dy\,dx$$

By (8.10), if the regression is linear,

$$(y-\eta_x)^2 = (y-\nu_{01})^2 - 2\rho\frac{\sigma_y}{\sigma_x}(y-\nu_{01})(x-\nu_{10}) + \rho^2\frac{\sigma_y^2}{\sigma_x^2}(x-\nu_{10})^2$$

so that on integrating term by term we get

(8.12) $$\sigma_{ey}^2 = \sigma_y^2 - 2\rho\frac{\sigma_y}{\sigma_x}\mu_{11} + \rho^2\sigma_y^2$$

$$= \sigma_y^2(1-\rho^2)$$

It is evident from this result that

$$-1 \leq \rho \leq 1$$

---

* See § 8.7 and § 8.9 for a definition of the real standard error of estimate.

8.3 The Normal Correlation Surface. We shall now consider a joint probability function of special interest. The normal correlation surface is defined by the following function

(8.13) $$f(x, y) = Ke^{-P}$$

where

$$P = \frac{1}{2(1 - \rho^2)} \left\{ \frac{x^2}{\sigma_x^2} - \frac{2\rho xy}{\sigma_x \sigma_y} + \frac{y^2}{\sigma_y^2} \right\}$$

$$\frac{1}{K} = 2\pi \sigma_x \sigma_y (1 - \rho^2)^{1/2}$$

$$-\infty \leq x \leq \infty, \quad -\infty \leq y \leq \infty$$

and the variables x and y have the origin of their reference system at their respective means, that is,

(8.14) $$\begin{cases} \nu_{10} = \displaystyle\int_{-\infty}^{\infty} xg(x)\, dx = 0 \\ \nu_{01} = \displaystyle\int_{-\infty}^{\infty} yh(y)\, dy = 0 \end{cases}$$

The conditions (8.14) may be imposed without essential loss of generality and will simplify the algebraic discussion.

The marginal distribution of x is given by

$$g(x) = \int_{-\infty}^{\infty} f(x, y)\, dy$$

$$= Ke^{-x^2/2\sigma_x^2} \int_{-\infty}^{\infty} e^{-[y/\sigma_y - \rho x/\sigma_x]^2/2(1-\rho^2)}\, dy$$

$$= Ke^{-x^2/2\sigma_x^2} \int_{-\infty}^{\infty} e^{-y'^2/2(1-\rho^2)} \sigma_y\, dy'$$

$$= Ke^{-x^2/2\sigma_x^2} \{2\pi(1 - \rho^2)\}^{1/2} \sigma_y$$

$$= \frac{1}{\sigma_x \sqrt{2\pi}} e^{-x^2/2\sigma_x^2}$$

Similarly, the marginal distribution of y is

$$h(y) = \int_{-\infty}^{\infty} f(x, y)\, dx$$

$$= \frac{1}{\sigma_y \sqrt{2\pi}} e^{-y^2/2\sigma_y^2}$$

Hence we may state

Theorem 8.1. *If two variables are normally correlated, each variable is normally distributed in its marginal totals.*

Sec. 3   The Normal Correlation Surface

That the converse is not necessarily true is shown by the following illustration. Consider a clay model of a normal correlation surface such that its marginal totals are necessarily normal distributions by the above theorem. Quantities of the clay can be redistributed by piling up in certain spots the clay that is scooped out in other spots in such a way that the marginal totals are not disturbed. It is obvious that the resulting surface is not one that is defined by (8.13).

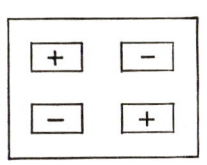

Other interesting properties of normally correlated variables are described by the following theorems.

Theorem 8.2. *The regression systems of a normal correlation surface are linear.*

The proof is a matter of integration. Let us find the probability function of an x array of y's. By definition, this is given by $f(x, y)/g(x)$. To get the mean of such an array we must multiply its probability distribution by y and integrate over all values of y in the array. Thus we have

$$\eta_x = \int_{-\infty}^{\infty} \frac{yf(x, y)\, dy}{g(x)}$$

$$= \int_{-\infty}^{\infty} \frac{1}{\sigma_y\{2\pi(1 - \rho^2)\}^{1/2}} e^{-[y/\sigma_y - \rho(x/\sigma_x)]^2/2(1-\rho^2)} y\, dy$$

$$= \frac{x\rho\sigma_y}{\sigma_x}$$

If x is allowed to vary over the arrays, it is evident that the locus of the means of the x arrays of y's is the line

(8.15) $$\eta_x = \frac{x\rho\sigma_y}{\sigma_x}$$

In a similar way the mean of a y array of x's is given by

$$\xi_y = \int_{-\infty}^{\infty} \frac{xf(x, y)\, dx}{h(y)}$$

$$= \frac{y\sigma_x\rho}{\sigma_y}$$

and this lies on the regression line

(8.16) $$\xi_y = \frac{y\rho\sigma_x}{\sigma_y}$$

While it is an intrinsic property of a normal correlation surface that both regressions are linear, one should not infer that this is characteristic of joint probability functions in general. One or both or neither of the regression systems of a joint probability function may be linear. The student will observe that the definition of the correlation coefficient did not involve the condition that $f(x, y)$ was normal nor that regression was linear. Although the *definition* of a correlation coefficient does not require linear regression, nevertheless the correlation coefficient may not be a good measure of relationship if the regression is definitely non-linear.

Theorem 8.3. *If x and y are normally correlated, then each array is a normal distribution, each x-array of y's has the same variance σ_{ey}^2 and each y-array of x's has the same variance σ_{ex}^2.*

The proof consists in exhibiting the frequency function for an x array of y's and for a y array of x's. Thus, for the first case we have

$$\frac{f(x, y)}{g(x)} = \frac{1}{\sqrt{2\pi}\sigma_{ey}} \exp\left[-\{y - \rho x(\sigma_y/\sigma_x)\}^2/2\sigma_{ey}^2\right]$$

where $\sigma_{ey}^2 = \sigma_y^2(1 - \rho^2)$. Evidently, this is a normal distribution with variance σ_{ey}^2 which is independent of x and therefore is constant over all x arrays. It is left as an exercise for the student to give the companion proof for the arrays in the y direction.

When the variance is constant over the arrays in the x direction the regression system of y on x is said to be *homoscedastic* (equally scattered). Similarly for the y direction. A geometrical representation of a normal correlation surface is given in Part I, § 18 of Chapter VIII.

8.4 Limiting Forms. Suppose a plane is passed through the surface defined by (8.13) parallel to the xy-plane. Analytically, this means that we let $f(x, y) = c$ where c is some constant less than the maximum value of the function, that is, we take $0 < c < K$ to insure a real intersection. We obtain

$$(8.17) \qquad \frac{x^2}{\sigma_x^2} - \frac{2\rho xy}{\sigma_x \sigma_y} + \frac{y^2}{\sigma_y^2} = \lambda^2$$

where

$$(8.18) \qquad \lambda^2 = 2(1 - \rho^2) \log_e \frac{K}{c}$$

which is obviously not negative. Thus the points (x, y) for which the probability density is constant lie on an ellipse.

It is easier to study (8.17) if we transform the variables to standard units by letting $t_x = x/\sigma_x$ and $t_y = y/\sigma_y$. Then (8.17) becomes

$$(8.19) \qquad t_x^2 - 2\rho t_x t_y + t_y^2 = \lambda^2$$

The cross-product term will vanish under the transformations

$$t_x = u \cos \theta - v \sin \theta$$
$$t_y = u \sin \theta + v \cos \theta$$

when $\theta = \pi/4$. So the required rotation formulas are

$$(8.20) \qquad t_x = \frac{u - v}{(2)^{1/2}} \quad \text{and} \quad t_y = \frac{u + v}{(2)^{1/2}}$$

Applying these to (8.19) we obtain

(8.21) $$u^2(1 - \rho) + v^2(1 + \rho) = \lambda^2$$

which may be written in the standard form of an ellipse

(8.22) $$\frac{u^2}{a^2} + \frac{v^2}{b^2} = 1$$

with semi-axes a and b, where

$$a^2 = \frac{\lambda^2}{1 - \rho} \quad \text{and} \quad b^2 = \frac{\lambda^2}{1 + \rho}$$

The eccentricity of the ellipse (8.22) is $(1 - b^2/a^2)^{1/2} = [2\rho/(1 + \rho)]^{1/2}$. We see that $b \to a$ as $\rho \to 0$. When $\rho = 0$, $b = a = \lambda$. Then (8.22) would be a circle, and (8.13) would be a surface of revolution if the variables were expressed in standard units. When $\rho = 1$, it follows from (8.21) and (8.18) that $v = 0$. From (8.20) it is seen that the line $v = 0$ is the same as $t_y = t_x$, and the ellipse has degenerated into a straight line. The surface then shrinks into a normal curve in the plane $t_y = t_x$.

8.5 Tetrachoric Correlation. The word *tetrachoric* refers to a 2 × 2 fold table. Suppose N objects are classified according as they possess one or both or neither of two qualitative traits or attributes which may, for convenience, be denoted by I and II. Such a classification will yield a four-fold table as shown in Table 12,

TABLE 12

	Not II	II	Total
Not I	a	b	$a + b$
I	c	d	$c + d$
Total	$a + c$	$b + d$	N

where $a + b + c + d = N$, the four classes being mutually exclusive but not necessarily exhaustive. The attributes may sometimes admit also of quantitative measurement, but we are considering only the case where they are classified dichotomously (that is, in two classes), such as "tall" and "not tall" "male" and "female," "alive" and "dead," "good" and "bad," "dull" and "not dull," etc. An example is the following classification of 26,287 children where attribute I is dullness and attribute II is developmental defects.

The problem in such classifications is to measure the intensity of association between the two attributes in the set. Let us suppose that our data had been given initially so that a fine division into many cells was possible and that the

TABLE 13. (K. Pearson, *Tables*, p. li)

	Without Defects	With Defects	Totals
Not Dull	22,793	1,420	24,213
Dull	1,186	888	2,074
Totals	23,979	2,308	26,287

result would have presented a normal correlation surface. If this surface were then divided into four cells by planes $x = h$ and $y = k$ to yield the relative frequencies observed, then the correlation coefficient that characterizes this normal correlation surface is called *tetrachoric r*. It will be denoted by r_t. It is the correlation coefficient for the normal surface that reproduces the data.

Karl Pearson and Alice Lee have given tables for determining r_t. (See *Tables for Statisticians and Biometricians*, Part I, Table XXX. Also fuller tables in Part II, Tables VIII and IX.)

Suppose the 2 × 2 table is arranged (as it always can be) so that $a + c > b + d$ and $a + b > c + d$. We now find h and k so that

$$\frac{b+d}{N} = \int_h^\infty \phi(t)\, dt, \qquad \frac{c+d}{N} = \int_k^\infty \phi(t)\, dt$$

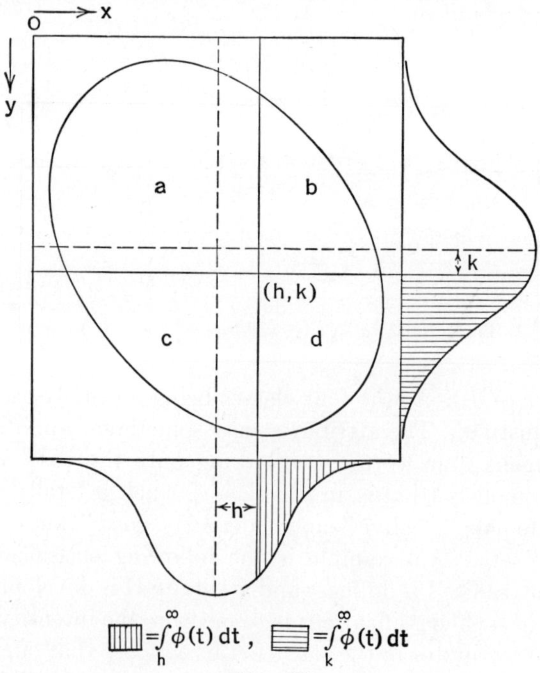

FIG. 23

Sec. 6 Linear Regression as Estimated from a Sample

h and k being, therefore, positive numbers (Figure 23). We then calculate d/N and interpolate in the tables to find r_t corresponding to the given h, k, and d/N. The procedure involves a double interpolation to find d/N for each of two near values of r_t and a final interpolation between these two values. Thus for Table 13 we find $h = 1.354$, $k = 1.413$, $d/N = 0.03378$. For $r_t = 0.65$, $d/N = 0.0337$ approximately; for $r_t = 0.70$, $d/N = 0.0371$ approximately; so that finally $r_t = 0.650$.

An approximate simple method of finding r_t, useful when $|r_t| < 0.8$, has been given by Camp.[1] This avoids most of the labor in interpolation.

8.6 Linear Regression as Estimated from a Sample. Let (x_i, y_i) be corresponding sets of values of x and y, where $i = 1, 2, \cdots N$. We will assume that the x_i are fixed numbers, whereas the y_i are random variables. We assume also that the true regression is linear, given by equation (8.3), and that the y_i are independently and normally distributed about the regression values with variance σ_{ey}^2, the same for all values of x. Hence, if

(8.23) $$\eta_i = \alpha + \beta x_i$$

we have

(8.24) $$y_i = \eta_i + e_i$$

and the e_i are independent normal variates with expectation zero and variance σ_{ey}^2.

The method of least squares determines a straight line

(8.25) $$Y = a + bx$$

such that the sum of squares of the distances of the points (x_i, y_i) from this line, measured perpendicular to the x-axis, is a minimum. The a and b so determined are estimates of the α and β of the true regression line.

Writing

$$S = \sum (y_i - Y_i)^2 = \sum (y_i - a - bx_i)^2$$

and putting

$$\frac{\partial S}{\partial a} = 0, \quad \frac{\partial S}{\partial b} = 0$$

we have as the conditions for a minimum of S

(8.26) $$\begin{cases} \sum (y_i - a - bx_i) = 0 \\ \sum x_i(y_i - a - bx_i) = 0 \end{cases}$$

or

(8.27) $$\begin{cases} Na + \sum x_i b = \sum y_i \\ \sum x_i a + \sum x_i^2 b = \sum x_i y_i \end{cases}$$

From these two equations (known as *normal equations*), a and b may be determined. We find, on writing

Linear Regression and Contingency VIII

$$\sum x_i = N\bar{x}, \qquad \sum y_i = N\bar{y}$$
$$\sum x_i^2 = N(s_x^2 + \bar{x}^2), \qquad \sum y_i^2 = N(s_y^2 + \bar{y}^2)$$
$$\sum x_i y_i = N\overline{xy}$$

that
(8.28) $$b = (\overline{xy} - \bar{x}\bar{y})/s_x^2 = rs_y/s_x$$

where r is Pearson's coefficient of correlation for the sample, and that

(8.29) $$a = \bar{y} - b\bar{x}$$

The equation of the "best-fitting" straight line, in the sense described before, is, therefore,

(8.30) $$Y - \bar{y} = b(x - \bar{x})$$

and so passes through the point $(\bar{x}, \bar{y})$. This line is called the *sample regression line* of y on x, or the *trend line* of y on x. It is used to estimate y for a given value of x.

The minimum value of S is given by

(8.31) $$\begin{aligned} S_{\min} &= \sum [(y_i - \bar{y}) - b(x_i - \bar{x})]^2 \\ &= N(s_y^2 + b^2 s_x^2 - 2rbs_x s_y) \\ &= N s_y^2 (1 - r^2) \end{aligned}$$

so that $S_{\min}/N$ is an estimate of σ_{ey}^2 as given by (8.12). It is not, however, unbiased. We shall now prove that an unbiased estimate is provided by $S_{\min}/(N-2)$.

8.7 The Sample Standard Error of Estimate. From (8.23), (8.24), and (8.25),

(8.32) $$y_i - Y_i = e_i - (a - \alpha) - (b - \beta)x_i$$

Also, from (8.29), (8.23) and (8.24),

$$a + b\bar{x} = \bar{y} = \alpha + \beta\bar{x} + \bar{e}$$

where $\bar{e}$ is the sample mean of the e_i, so that

(8.33) $$a - \alpha + (b - \beta)\bar{x} = \bar{e} = \frac{1}{N}\sum e_i$$

From (8.28),

$$\begin{aligned} b &= \sum(y_i - \bar{y})(x_i - \bar{x})/Ns_x^2 \\ &= \sum y_i(x_i - \bar{x})/Ns_x^2 \\ &= \sum(x_i - \bar{x})(\alpha + \beta x_i + e_i)/Ns_x^2 \\ &= \sum(x_i - \bar{x})[\alpha + \beta(x_i - \bar{x}) + \beta\bar{x} + e_i]/Ns_x^2 \end{aligned}$$

(8.34) $$= \beta + \sum e_i(x_i - \bar{x})/Ns_x^2$$

since $\sum(x_i - \bar{x}) = 0$ and $\sum(x_i - \bar{x})^2 = Ns_x^2$. Hence b is normally dis-

Sec. 8 Confidence Limits for the Regression Line

tributed about β with variance σ_{ey}^2/Ns_x^2. It follows similarly from (8.33) and (8.34) that a is normally distributed about α with variance $\sigma_{ey}^2(s_x^2 + \bar{x}^2)/Ns_x^2$.

We have, therefore,

$$
\begin{aligned}
y_i - Y_i &= e_i - \bar{e} - (b - \beta)(x_i - \bar{x}) \\
&= e_i - \bar{e} - (x_i - \bar{x})\sum e_i(x_i - \bar{x})/Ns_x^2 \\
&= e_i - \bar{e} - e_b(x_i - \bar{x})
\end{aligned}
$$

(8.35)

where

$$e_b = \sum e_i(x_i - \bar{x})/Ns_x^2 = b - \beta$$

and so

$$
\begin{aligned}
\sum (y_i - Y_i)^2 &= \sum e_i^2 - N\bar{e}^2 + Ne_b^2 s_x^2 - 2e_b\sum e_i(x_i - \bar{x}) \\
&= \sum e_i^2 - N\bar{e}^2 + Ne_b^2 s_x^2 - 2Ne_b^2 s_x^2 \\
&= \sum e_i^2 - \frac{1}{N}(\sum e_i)^2 - Ns_x^2 e_b^2
\end{aligned}
$$

Now $\sum (e_i/\sigma_{ey})^2$ is a sum of N squares of normal standard variates, and $N^{-1/2}\sum (e_i/\sigma_{ey})$ is a linear function of these variates. Also $N^{1/2}s_x e_b/\sigma_{ey} = N^{-1/2}\sum (x_i - \bar{x})(e_i/\sigma_{ey}s_x)$ is an independent linear function of the same variates since it is easily verified that these two functions are orthogonal. Hence by Theorem 5.10 $\sum (y_i - Y_i)^2/\sigma_{ey}^2$ is independently distributed as χ^2 with $N - 2$ degrees of freedom.

Since the expectation of χ^2 is equal to the number of degrees of freedom, it follows that

$$E\{\sum (y_i - Y_i)^2\} = (N - 2)\sigma_{ey}^2$$

Hence $\sum (y_i - Y_i)^2/(N - 2)$ is an unbiased estimate of σ_{ey}^2. Denoting this estimate by $\hat{\sigma}_{ey}^2$ we have from (8.31)

(8.36) $$\hat{\sigma}_{ey}^2 = Ns_y^2(1 - r^2)/(N - 2)$$

$\hat{\sigma}_{ey}$ is an *estimate*, from the sample, of the quantity called in § 8.2 the "standard error of estimate." The loss of two degrees of freedom is suggested by the fact that two constants a and b of the regression line have been calculated from the sample.

When a and b have been determined from the normal equations, the value of $\sum (y_i - Y_i)^2$ may be estimated from the following equation:

(8.37) $$
\begin{aligned}
\sum (y_i - Y_i)^2 &= \sum (y_i - a - bx_i)^2 \\
&= \sum y_i(y_i - a - bx_i), \quad \text{by (8.26)} \\
&= \sum y_i^2 - a\sum y_i - b\sum x_i y_i
\end{aligned}
$$

8.8 Confidence Limits for the Constants of the Regression Line. The variance of b is σ_{ey}^2/Ns_x^2, so that an independent and unbiased estimate of the variance is, from (8.36), given by

(8.38) $$\text{Var}(b) = \frac{s_y^2}{s_x^2}\frac{1-r^2}{N-2} = \frac{b^2}{N-2}\frac{1-r^2}{r^2}$$

Hence the ratio

(8.39) $$t = \frac{r(b-\beta)}{b}\left(\frac{N-2}{1-r^2}\right)^{1/2}$$

has the Student distribution with $N-2$ degrees of freedom. For the important case $\beta = 0$, $t = r[(N-2)/(1-r^2)]^{1/2}$, and thus is independent of the population parameters.

By choosing suitable values of t in (8.39), limits of β corresponding to certain assigned degrees of confidence may be calculated.

The variance of a is $\sigma_{ey}^2(s_x^2 + \bar{x}^2)/Ns_x^2$, which is estimated by

$$s_y^2\left(1 + \frac{\bar{x}^2}{s_x^2}\right)\frac{1-r^2}{N-2} = (s_x^2 + \bar{x}^2)\frac{b^2(1-r^2)}{(N-2)r^2}$$

Therefore

$$t = \frac{r(a-\alpha)}{b}\left\{\frac{N-2}{(1-r^2)(s_x^2+\bar{x}^2)}\right\}^{1/2}$$

has also the t distribution with $N-2$ degrees of freedom. and this fact may be used in calculating confidence limits for α.

Example 2. For 29 families living in Edmonton, Alberta, x represents the dollar income per adult unit per week in 1936 and y the calories in food purchased per adult unit per week (the size of family was expressed in terms of equivalent "adult units"). From the data obtained, $\sum x = 201.9$, $\sum x^2 = 1658.6$, $\sum y = 6.7060 \times 10^5$, $\sum y^2 = 1.6357 \times 10^{10}$, and $\sum xy = 4.9861 \times 10^6$. The calculated regression line is $Y = a + bx$, where a and b, from equations (8.27), are 14,387 and 1255 respectively. $\sum(y_i - Y_i)^2$, from (8.37), is 4.517×10^8, so that $\hat{\sigma}_{ey} = 4090$. Also $Ns_x^2 = 252.9$, so that the standard error of b is $4090/(252.9)^{1/2} = 257.2$. Taking $t = 2.052$, we have, as the 95% confidence limits for β,

$$\beta = b \pm 2.052 \times 257.2$$
$$= 1255 \pm 528$$

Hence the slope of the true regression line may be taken with 95% confidence as lying between 727 and 1783 calories per dollar. Since $N(s_x^2 + \bar{x}^2) = \sum x^2 = 1658.6$, the standard error of a is $4090[1658.6/(29 \times 252.9)]^{1/2} = 1945$, so that $\alpha = 14,387 \pm 3991$. The true value α may, therefore, be regarded, with 95% confidence, as lying between about 10,400 and 18,380.

The assumption made in Ex. 2 that the true variance of y is the same for all x is probably not realistic. One might well expect the variance to increase with increasing x. The alternative assumption that $\sigma_{y|x}/y$ is constant would mean calculating the regression of $\log y$ instead of y on x (since $\delta \log y \approx \delta y/y$). (See § 9.6.)

It may be observed that if the values of x are at our disposal, as is sometimes the case in planned experiments, they may be chosen so as to minimize

Sec. 9   Confidence Limits for the True Regression

the variance of b. This variance varies inversely as s_x^2. If, for example, we have $2N$ observations covering the range from $x = -a$ to $x = +a$ at equally spaced intervals, the value of s_x^2 is $[(2N+1)/(2N-1)](a^2/3)$, but if we make N observations at $-a$, N at $+a$, and none in between, $s_x^2 = a^2$. The ratio of the variance of b in the second case to that in the first is $(2N+1)/(6N-3)$, which for $N > 1$ is always less than 1, and for large N approaches $\frac{1}{3}$. It is assumed, of course, that the regression is definitely known to be linear. If we want to test the linearity, we must space out our observations.

8.9 Confidence Limits for the True Regression and for an Estimated y Corresponding to any Given x. From (8.24) and (8.35),

(8.40) $\quad Y - \eta = \bar{e} + e_b(x - \bar{x})$

$\qquad = N^{-1} \sum_i e_i [1 + (x_i - \bar{x})(x - \bar{x})/s_x^2]$

Hence Y is normally distributed about η with variance

$$\sigma_{ey}^2 N^{-1}[1 + (x - \bar{x})^2/s_x^2]$$

Replacing σ_{ey}^2 by its estimate $\hat{\sigma}_{ey}^2$, we have

(8.41) $\quad$ s.e. $(Y) = \hat{\sigma}_{ey} N^{-1/2}[1 + (x - \bar{x})^2/s_x^2]^{1/2}$

This is the real standard error of estimate.

Since $Y - \eta$ divided by this standard error has the t-distribution with $N - 2$ degrees of freedom, confidence limits for η may be calculated in the usual way. It should be observed that the standard error of Y increases as $(x - \bar{x})^2$ increases, so that the curves bounding the confidence intervals for different values of x are hyperbolas. (See Figure 24.)

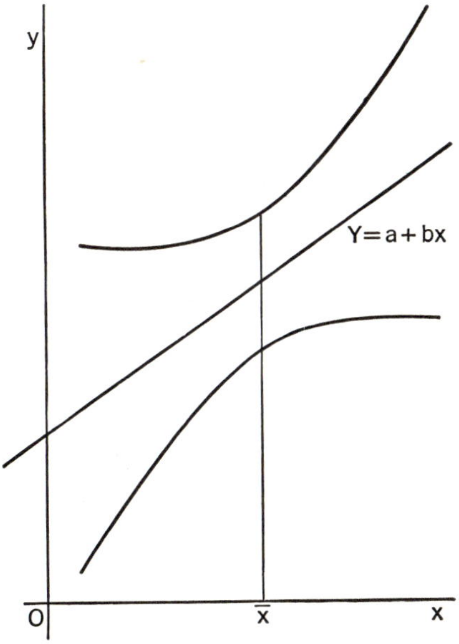

If, however, we are interested not so much in Y itself as in the *difference* between an actual y corresponding to a given x and the predicted Y for the same x, we must take into account also the variation of y. Since y is normally distributed about η with variance σ_{ey}^2, independently of Y, we have

(8.42) $\quad$ Var $(Y - y) = $ Var $Y + $ Var y

$\qquad = \sigma_{ey}^2 \left[1 + \dfrac{1}{N} + \dfrac{(x - \bar{x})^2}{N s_x^2} \right]$

Fig. 24

Since the expectation of $Y - y$ is zero, it follows that the ratio of $Y - y$ to $\hat{\sigma}_{ey}[1 + N^{-1} + (x - \bar{x})^2/Ns_x^2]^{1/2}$ is distributed as Student's t with $N - 2$ degrees of freedom. Hence confidence limits for y may be determined. They are given by

$$a + bx \pm t_\alpha \hat{\sigma}_{ey}[1 + N^{-1} + (x - \bar{x})^2/Ns_x^2]^{1/2}$$

Example 3. For the data of Example 2, $\hat{\sigma}_{ey} = 4090$. At $x = \bar{x} = 6.962$, the standard error of Y is 760, while at $x = 15$ it is 2203. The 95% confidence limits for y at $x = \bar{x}$ are $23{,}124 \pm 8536$ calories while at $x = 15$ they are $33{,}211 \pm 9534$ calories.

8.10 Confidence Limits for x, Given y, When the Regression Is Calculated for Fixed x. It sometimes happens that we desire to estimate x for a given y, even though we have calculated the regression for fixed values of x. We may, for example, wish to estimate the median lethal dose of a drug (that is, the dose that will kill 50% of the time) from observations on the proportions killed with various known doses.

Writing $y' = y - \bar{y}$, $x' = x - \bar{x}$, $\lambda = 1 + 1/N$, we know from § 8.9 that

(8.43) $$t = (y' - bx')[\hat{\sigma}_{ey}(\lambda + x'^2/Ns_x^2)]^{-1/2}$$

has the Student t-distribution with $N - 2$ degrees of freedom. This equation may be regarded as a quadratic in x', namely,

$$x'^2(1 - B^2) - 2x'y'/b + y'^2/b^2 = \lambda B^2 Ns_x^2$$

where $B^2 = \hat{\sigma}_{ey}^2 t^2/(Nb^2 s_x^2)$.

The estimated x' for a given y' is y'/b, so that, on denoting this estimate by X', we have

(8.44) $$f(x') = x'^2(1 - B^2) - 2X'x' + X'^2 - \lambda B^2 Ns_x^2 = 0$$

For a given value of t, say t_α, the roots of this equation supply confidence limits for x'. Since, for values of x' between the $\alpha\%$ confidence limits, $|t|$ is

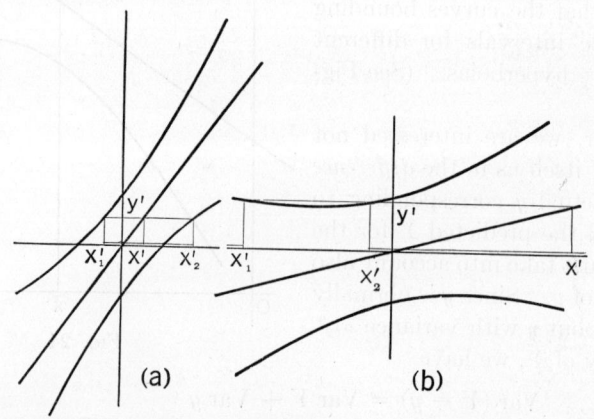

Fig. 25. (a) $B^2 < 1$, (b) $B^2 > 1$. The Confidence Intervals Are Indicated by Double Lines.

Sec. 11   Linear Regression with the x's and y's

less than t_α, it follows that $y' - bx' \leq t_\alpha \hat{\sigma}_{ey}(\lambda + x'^2/Ns_x^2)^{1/2}$, and hence that $f(x') \leq 0$ when x' lies between the confidence limits.

The practically important case is that when $B^2 < 1$. In this case the two roots are real and the confidence interval lies between them. Note that $B^2 < 1$ implies that b is greater than t_α times the standard error of b, which means that b is different from zero at the level of significance represented by α.

If $B^2 > 1$, the roots of (8.44) may be either real or complex. If they are complex, no confidence limits exist, except $-\infty$ to ∞, and if they are real, say x_1' and x_2', $(x_1' < x_2')$, the confidence limits are from $-\infty$ to x_1' and from x_2' to $+\infty$, since these are the regions in which $f(x') \leq 0$. The two cases are illustrated in Figure 25.

8.11 Linear Regression with the x's and y's Both Subject to Error. An appropriate mathematical model for this case is the set of equations

(8.45) $$x_i = \xi_i + d_i$$
(8.46) $$y_i = \eta_i + e_i$$
(8.47) $$\eta_i = \alpha + \beta \xi_i$$

where d_i and e_i are normally and independently distributed about zero with variances σ_d^2 and σ_e^2 respectively.

If the ξ_i are considered as *fixed values*, x and y have a joint bivariate normal distribution given by

$$f(x, y) = (2\pi\sigma_d\sigma_e)^{-1} \exp\left[-\frac{(x-\xi)^2}{2\sigma_d^2} - \frac{(y-\eta)^2}{2\sigma_e^2}\right]$$

For a sample of N pairs of observations, the likelihood (defined as the logarithm of the probability function for the actual sample) is given, apart from a constant, by

$$L = -N \log \sigma_d - N \log \sigma_e - \frac{1}{2\sigma_d^2} \sum (x_i - \xi_i)^2 - \frac{1}{2\sigma_e^2} \sum (y_i - \alpha - \beta \xi_i)^2$$

This expression contains $N + 2$ unknown parameters, namely, α and β and the N values of ξ_i. If L is to be a maximum relative to all these parameters, we must have $\partial L/\partial \alpha = 0$, $\partial L/\partial \beta = 0$, $\partial L/\partial \xi_i = 0$, $i = 1, 2, \cdots N$. These equations give

(8.48)
$$\sum (y_i - \alpha - \beta \xi_i) = 0$$
$$\sum \xi_i (y_i - \alpha - \beta \xi_i) = 0$$
$$(x_i - \xi_i)/\sigma_d^2 + \beta(y_i - \alpha - \beta \xi_i)/\sigma_e^2 = 0, \quad i = 1, 2, \cdots N$$

From the third equation of (8.48),

(8.49) $$\xi_i(1 + \beta^2 \sigma_d^2/\sigma_e^2) = x_i + \beta(y_i - \alpha)\sigma_d^2/\sigma_e^2$$

and by substituting (8.49) in the first and second equations of (8.48) we arrive after a little reduction at

(8.50) $$\begin{cases} N\alpha + \sum x_i \beta = \sum y_i \\ \sum x_i \alpha + (\sum x_i^2 - \lambda \sum y_i^2)\beta + \lambda \sum y_i \alpha \beta + \lambda \sum x_i y_i \beta^2 = \sum x_i y_i \end{cases}$$

where $\lambda = \sigma_d^2/\sigma_e^2$. If λ is known, α can be eliminated from the two equations of (8.50) and the resulting quadratic in β solved. This quadratic reduces to

(8.51) $$\lambda r s_x s_y \beta^2 + (s_x^2 - \lambda s_y^2)\beta - r s_x s_y = 0$$

which has two real roots, one positive and one negative. If r is positive, the positive root is to be chosen.

If the value of λ is not known, we can add two further equations to (8.48), given by $\partial L/\partial \sigma_d = 0$ and $\partial L/\partial \sigma_e = 0$, but the solution of the complete set is not practicable.

If the ξ_i are not fixed, but are considered as *random variables*, which we may take to be normally distributed about zero with variance σ_ξ^2 independently of the d_i and e_i, x and y are normally distributed and the joint distribution is bivariate normal, but they are not independent. The regression of y on x is, therefore, linear.

From (8.45), (8.46), and (8.47), we have

$$E(x_i) = 0, \qquad E(y_i) = \alpha$$
$$\text{Var}(x_i) = \sigma_\xi^2 + \sigma_d^2$$
$$\text{Var}(y_i) = \beta^2 \sigma_\xi^2 + \sigma_e^2$$
$$\text{Cov}(x_i, y_i) = E\{(\xi_i + d_i)(\alpha + \beta \xi_i + e_i)\} = \beta \sigma_\xi^2$$

Hence
$$\sigma_x^2 = \sigma_\xi^2 + \sigma_d^2, \qquad \sigma_y^2 = \beta^2 \sigma_\xi^2 + \sigma_e^2$$

and
$$\rho \sigma_x \sigma_y = \beta \sigma_\xi^2$$

The expected value of the slope of the regression line is, therefore, $\rho \sigma_y/\sigma_x = \beta \sigma_\xi^2/(\sigma_\xi^2 + \sigma_d^2)$ and so is not in general equal to β. The squared standard error of estimate is $\sigma_y^2(1 - \rho^2) = \sigma_e^2 + \beta^2 \sigma_d^2(1 + \sigma_d^2/\sigma_\xi^2)^{-1}$, and the actual variance of a prediction based on sample regression will agree with this to terms of order $1/n$, n being the number of degrees of freedom.

It is of interest to observe that the prediction made from the sample regression of y on x is better than we could make if we knew the true values of α and β. For suppose our estimate for a given x is $Y = \alpha + \beta x$. Then $Y - y = \beta(x - \xi) - e$, so that

$$E(Y - y) = 0$$

and
$$\text{Var}(Y - y) = \beta^2 \sigma_d^2 + \sigma_e^2$$

which is greater than the variance of estimate given above. Hence, at least when n is large, the best predicting equation to use is the ordinary regression of y on x.

8.12 The Distribution of r When $\rho = 0$.

We have already seen in § 8.8 that when $\beta = 0$ (which means that $\rho = 0$) the quantity $t = r[(N-2)/(1-r^2)]^{1/2}$ has the t-distribution with $N - 2$ degrees of freedom. This enables us to determine whether a calculated r is significantly different from zero.

Example 4. For a sample of 27, $r = 0.36$. The value of t is 1.929 with $n = 25$, giving $P = 0.07$ approximately. The observed r is, therefore, not significantly different from zero.
The significance of r may be judged directly from tables (Fisher and Yates, Table VI, or *Statistical Methods for Research Workers*, Table V A). Thus for $r = 0.36$ and $n = 25$, we see at once from these tables that P lies between 0.05 and 0.1 and is, therefore, non-significant at the usual level.

We proceed to find the frequency function for r when $\rho = 0$. We assume that we are dealing with a random sample of N pairs of independent observations, x_i, y_i, and for convenience we suppose that x and y are measured from their respective population means. Let the y_i be subject to a linear orthogonal transformation (see § 4.13) yielding N variates η_i, of which we take η_1 as $N^{-1/2} \sum y_i$. Then

$$\sum_{i=1}^{N} \eta_i^2 = \sum y_i^2$$
$$= \sum (y_i - \bar{y})^2 + N\bar{y}^2$$
$$= N s_y^2 + \eta_1^2$$

Therefore

$$\sum_{i=2}^{N} \eta_i^2 = N s_y^2$$

and since the η_i are normal and independent variates the sum, divided by σ_y^2, is distributed like χ^2 with $N - 1$ degrees of freedom.

Let us now take

$$\eta_2 = N^{1/2} r s_y = \sum (x_i - \bar{x})(y_i - \bar{y})/N^{1/2} s_x$$
$$= \sum (x_i - \bar{x}) y_i / N^{1/2} s_x$$

We can do this, since η_2 is orthogonal to η_1 and the sum of squares of coefficients of y_i in η_2 is equal to 1. Then

$$\sum_{i=3}^{N} \eta_i^2 = N s_y^2 (1 - r^2)$$

so that $N s_y^2 (1 - r^2)/\sigma_y^2$ is distributed like χ^2 with $N - 2$ df. Also η_2^2, or $N r^2 s_y^2$, is independently distributed as $\chi^2 \sigma_y^2$ with 1 df.

Now $r^2 = \eta_2^2/(\eta_2^2 + \sum_3^N \eta_i^2) = \chi_1^2/(\chi_1^2 + \chi_{N-2}^2)$, and since $\frac{1}{2}\chi_1^2$ is a $\gamma(\frac{1}{2})$ variate and $\frac{1}{2}\chi_{N-2}^2$ is a $\gamma[(N-2)/2]$ variate, it follows from Theorem 5.3 that r^2 is a $\beta[\frac{1}{2}, (N-2)/2]$ variate.

The frequency function of r^2 is, therefore, given by

$$(8.52) \quad f(r^2)\, d(r^2) = \frac{(r^2)^{-1/2}(1-r^2)^{(N-4)/2}\, d(r^2)}{\mathrm{B}(\tfrac{1}{2},\, (N-2)/2)}, \quad 0 \le r^2 \le 1$$

from which it follows that

$$(8.53) \quad E(r^2) = (N-1)^{-1}$$

so that the standard error of r is $(N-1)^{-1/2}$

Since $d(r^2) = 2r\, dr$, and since r^2 goes from 1 to 0 and back while r goes from -1 to 1, the frequency function of r is given by

$$(8.54) \quad f(r)\, dr = (1-r^2)^{(N-4)/2}\, dr / \mathrm{B}(\tfrac{1}{2},\, (N-2)/2), \quad -1 \le r \le 1$$

This distribution belongs to Pearson Type II, a symmetrical bell-shaped curve if $N \ge 5$. The kurtosis $(\gamma_2) = -6/(N+1)$ and so tends to zero as $N \to \infty$. As N becomes large the function is practically normal and consequently

$$(8.55) \quad t = r(N-1)^{1/2}$$

tends to be normally distributed with mean zero and unit standard deviation. Therefore, to test the significance of a value of r computed from a large sample (say 50 or more) it would not be invalid, to any appreciable extent, to refer (8.55) to a normal probability scale.

We may observe in passing that

$$(8.56) \quad N s_y^2 = N(1-r^2)s_y^2 + N r^2 s_y^2$$

that is,

$$\sum (y_i - \bar{y})^2 = \sum (y_i - Y_i)^2 + \sum (Y_i - \bar{y})^2$$

This means that the total sum of squares of deviations of y from the mean can be split up into a sum of squares of deviations from the regression line and a sum of squares of deviations of points on the regression line from the mean. These sums of squares, divided by σ_y^2, are (when $\rho = 0$) distributed as χ^2 with $N-1$, $N-2$, and 1 degrees of freedom respectively. Hence the mean squares, given by dividing the sums of squares by the df, are unbiased estimates of σ_y^2. Moreover, the second and third of these mean squares are independent. We could, therefore, apply the F test to the ratio $r^2(N-2)/(1-r^2)$, with $n_1 = 1$ and $n_2 = N-2$, in order to determine whether or not the correlation is significantly different from zero.

8.13 Confidence Limits for the Variance Ratio of Two Correlated Variates. If x and y are measured from their respective population means, their joint normal bivariate distribution is given by

$$(8.57) \quad f(x, y) = (2\pi \sigma_x \sigma_y)^{-1}(1-\rho^2)^{-1/2} \exp[-P/2(1-\rho^2)]$$

where

$$P = x^2/\sigma_x^2 - 2\rho xy/\sigma_x \sigma_y + y^2/\sigma_y^2$$

Sec. 14 The Distribution of r When ρ Is Not Zero

It was pointed out by Pitman[2] that if $u = x/\sigma_x + y/\sigma_y$ and $v = x/\sigma_x - y/\sigma_y$, then $P/[2(1 - \rho^2)]$ can be written as $\frac{1}{4}[u^2/(1 + \rho) + v^2/(1 - \rho)]$. Hence the joint probability function for u and v can be written as the product of a function of u and a function of v, so that u and v are *independent* normal variates with variances $2(1 + \rho)$ and $2(1 - \rho)$ respectively. If R is the observed correlation coefficient between u and v, $R[(N - 2)/(1 - R^2)]^{1/2}$ has the t-distribution with $N - 2$ df, or in other words, R^2 is a $\beta[\frac{1}{2}, (N - 2)/2]$ variate.

Now
$$R = \frac{\sum(u - \bar{u})(v - \bar{v})}{[\sum(u - \bar{u})^2 \sum(v - \bar{v})^2]^{1/2}}$$

and on substituting $u = x/\sigma_x + y/\sigma_y$, $v = x/\sigma_x - y/\sigma_y$, we obtain

(8.58) $\quad R = \dfrac{[s_x^2/\sigma_x^2 - s_y^2/\sigma_y^2]}{[(s_x^2/\sigma_x^2 + s_y^2/\sigma_y^2 + 2rs_x s_y/\sigma_x \sigma_y) \times (s_x^2/\sigma_x^2 + s_y^2/\sigma_y^2 - 2rs_x s_y/\sigma_x \sigma_y)]^{1/2}}$

where
$$Ns_x^2 = \sum(x - \bar{x})^2, \qquad Ns_y^2 = \sum(y - \bar{y})^2$$
and
$$Nrs_x s_y = \sum(x - \bar{x})(y - \bar{y})$$

If $w = s_x^2/s_y^2$, $\omega = \sigma_x^2/\sigma_y^2$, (8.58) becomes, on multiplying numerator and denominator by σ_x^2/s_y^2,

(8.59) $\quad R = (w - \omega)/[(w + \omega)^2 - 4r^2 w\omega]^{1/2}$

whence confidence limits for ω can be found (see Problem 5).

8.14 The Distribution of r When ρ Is Not Zero. The exact distribution of r for samples from a correlated parent population was found by Fisher,[3] using a geometrical method. The following analytical treatment is due to Sawkins.[4]

Writing $t = x/\sigma_x$, $u = y/\sigma_y$, the joint frequency distribution of t and u is, from (8.57),

(8.60) $\quad f(t, u) = (2\pi)^{-1}(1 - \rho^2)^{-1/2} \exp[-P/2(1 - \rho^2)]$

where
$$P = t^2 - 2\rho tu + u^2$$
$$= (u - \rho t)^2 + (1 - \rho^2)t^2$$

Hence, if $v = (u - \rho t)(1 - \rho^2)^{-1/2}$, the exponent in (8.60) can be written as $-v^2/2 - t^2/2$, and the joint distribution of t and v is given by

(8.61) $\quad f(t, v) = (2\pi)^{-1} e^{-v^2/2} e^{-t^2/2}$

t and v are therefore independent normal standard variates, and $\sum v^2$ is distributed as χ^2 with N degrees of freedom.

Let us now make an orthogonal linear transformation from the v_i to a new set of variates $\xi_1, \xi_2, \cdots \xi_N$, where we choose

$$\xi_1 = N^{-1/2} \sum v_i$$
$$= N^{1/2}(1 - \rho^2)^{-1/2}(\bar{u} - \rho \bar{t})$$

Then

$$\sum_1^N \xi_i^2 = \sum v^2$$
$$= (1-\rho^2)^{-1}[\sum u^2 - 2\rho \sum ut + \rho^2 \sum t^2]$$
$$= (1-\rho^2)^{-1}[\sum (u-\bar{u})^2 - 2\rho \sum (u-\bar{u})(t-\bar{t}) + \rho^2 \sum (t-\bar{t})^2$$
$$+ N(\bar{u}^2 - 2\rho\bar{u}\bar{t} + \rho^2\bar{t}^2)]$$
$$= (1-\rho^2)^{-1}[S_2^2 - 2\rho r S_2 S_1 + \rho^2 S_1^2] + \xi_1^2$$

where
$$S_1^2 = \sum (t-\bar{t})^2, \qquad S_2^2 = \sum (u-\bar{u})^2$$

Hence

(8.62) $$\sum_2^N \xi_i^2 = (1-\rho^2)^{-1}[S_2^2 - 2\rho r S_2 S_1 + \rho^2 S_1^2]$$

and this is distributed as χ^2 with $N-1$ df.

Now let us choose ξ_2 as

$$\xi_2 = S_1^{-1} \sum (t_i - \bar{t}) v_i$$

which is orthogonal to ξ_1 and is such that the sum of squares of coefficients is equal to unity. Then

$$\xi_2 = S_1^{-1}(1-\rho^2)^{-1/2} \sum (t_i - \bar{t})(u_i - \rho t_i)$$
$$= S_1^{-1}(1-\rho^2)^{-1/2} \sum (t_i - \bar{t})[u - \bar{u} - \rho(t_i - \bar{t})]$$
$$= (1-\rho^2)^{-1/2}(rS_2 - \rho S_1)$$

so that

(8.63) $$\xi_2^2 = (1-\rho^2)^{-1}(r^2 S_2^2 - 2r\rho S_2 S_1 + \rho^2 S_1^2)$$

From (8.62) and (8.63) we have

$$\sum_3^N \xi_i^2 = S_2^2(1-r^2)(1-\rho^2)^{-1}$$

and this is distributed as χ^2 with $N-2$ df.

Moreover $S_1^2 = \sum (t_i - \bar{t})^2$ is independently distributed as χ^2 with $N-1$ df. We have then three statistically independent variates, namely,

(8.64) $$\begin{cases} a = \xi_2 = (1-\rho^2)^{-1/2}(rS_2 - \rho S_1) \\ b = \tfrac{1}{2}\sum_3^N \xi_i^2 = \tfrac{1}{2}S_2^2(1-r^2)(1-\rho^2)^{-1} \\ c = \tfrac{1}{2}\sum (t_i - \bar{t})^2 = \tfrac{1}{2}S_1^2 \end{cases}$$

and these are respectively normal, $\gamma[(N-2)/2]$ and $\gamma[(N-1)/2]$ variates. Their joint frequency function is, therefore,

(8.65) $$f(a,b,c) = (2\pi)^{-1/2} e^{-a^2/2} b^{(N-4)/2} e^{-b} c^{(N-3)/2} e^{-c} \Big/ \Gamma\left(\frac{N-1}{2}\right) \Gamma\left(\frac{N-2}{2}\right)$$

Sec. 14 The Distribution of r When ρ Is Not Zero

We now change the variables to r, S_1, S_2. From (8.64) the Jacobian of the transformation is

$$J\begin{pmatrix} a, b, c \\ r, S_1, S_2 \end{pmatrix} = (1 - \rho^2)^{-3/2} \begin{vmatrix} S_2 & -\rho & r \\ -rS_2 & 0 & S_2(1-r^2) \\ 0 & S_1 & 0 \end{vmatrix}$$

$$= - (1 - \rho^2)^{-3/2} S_1 S_2{}^2$$

Also

$$\tfrac{1}{2}a^2 + b + c = \tfrac{1}{2}(1-\rho^2)^{-1}[(rS_2 - \rho S_1)^2 + (1-r^2)S_2{}^2 + (1-\rho^2)S_1{}^2]$$
$$= \tfrac{1}{2}(1-\rho^2)^{-1}(S_1{}^2 + S_2{}^2 - 2r\rho S_1 S_2)$$

The joint frequency function of r, S_1, S_2, is, therefore, from (8.65),

$$(8.66) \quad f(r, S_1, S_2) = \frac{(1-r^2)^{(N-4)/2} S_1{}^{N-2} S_2{}^{N-2} \exp\left[-\dfrac{S_1{}^2 + S_2{}^2 - 2r\rho S_1 S_2}{2(1-\rho^2)}\right]}{(1-\rho^2)^{(N-1)/2}(2\pi)^{1/2} 2^{N-7/2} \Gamma\left(\dfrac{N-1}{2}\right)\Gamma\left(\dfrac{N-2}{2}\right)}$$

and the frequency function for r is given by integrating with respect to S_1 and S_2 from 0 to ∞.

This integration is not straightforward. Fisher found an ingenious transformation from S_1 and S_2 to new variables α and β, such that

$$S_1 = \alpha^{1/2} e^{\beta/2}, \qquad S_2 = \alpha^{1/2} e^{-\beta/2}$$

The Jacobian $J(S_1, S_2/\alpha, \beta) = -\tfrac{1}{2}$, and the part of (8.66) depending on S_1 and S_2 becomes

$$\alpha^{N-2} \exp\left[-\alpha(\cosh \beta - \rho r)/(1-\rho^2)\right]$$

The limits of α are from 0 to ∞ and those of β from $-\infty$ to ∞. The integration with respect to α gives

$$\Gamma(N-1)(1-\rho^2)^{N-1}/(\cosh \beta - \rho r)^{N-1}$$

and on noting that

$$2^{N-3} \Gamma\left(\frac{N-1}{2}\right) \Gamma\left(\frac{N-2}{2}\right) = \pi^{1/2} \Gamma(N-2)$$

we obtain for the frequency function of r,

$$(8.67) \quad f(r) = \pi^{-1}(N-2)(1-r^2)^{(N-4)/2}(1-\rho^2)^{(N-1)/2} \int_0^\infty \frac{d\beta}{(\cosh \beta - \rho r)^{N-1}}$$

The integral can be expressed as a hypergeometric function

$$\left(\frac{\pi}{2}\right)^{1/2} \frac{\Gamma(N-1)}{\Gamma(N-\tfrac{1}{2})} (1-\rho r)^{-(N-3/2)} F\left(\tfrac{1}{2}, \tfrac{1}{2}, \frac{2N-1}{2}; \frac{\rho r + 1}{2}\right)$$

and we finally obtain $f(r)$ as a rapidly convergent series,[18]

$$(8.68) \quad f(r) = \frac{(N-2)\Gamma(N-1)(1-\rho^2)^{(N-1)/2}(1-r^2)^{(N-4)/2}}{(2\pi)^{1/2} \Gamma(N-\tfrac{1}{2})(1-\rho r)^{N-3/2}}$$

$$\times \left[1 + \frac{1}{4}\frac{\rho r + 1}{2N - 1} + \frac{9}{16}\frac{(\rho r + 1)^2}{(2N-1)(2N+1)} + \cdots \right]$$

When $\rho = 0$, the integral in (8.67) is readily evaluated as $2^{N-3}B[(N-1)/2, (N-1)/2]$, and (8.67) then reduces to the simple form given in (8.54).

Tables of $f(r)$ and $\int_{-1}^{r} f(r)\, dr$ have been prepared by Miss David[5] for the whole range of r and ρ and for all sample sizes from 2 up to 25. Values for a few larger sizes are also given, as well as charts from which the confidence limits for ρ can be determined for any given r and N.

The moments of the distribution of r can be expressed in the form of series. Thus

$$(8.69) \begin{cases} E(r) = \rho - \dfrac{\rho(1-\rho^2)}{2n} + \cdots \\ \mathrm{Var}\,(r) = \dfrac{(1-\rho^2)^2}{n}\left[1 + \dfrac{11\rho^2}{2n} + \cdots\right] \\ \gamma_1 = -\dfrac{6\rho}{n^{1/2}}\left[1 + \dfrac{77\rho^2 - 30}{12n} + \cdots\right] \\ \gamma_2 = \dfrac{6}{n}(12\rho^2 - 1) + \cdots \end{cases}$$

where n is written for $N-1$. It is apparent that the distribution is far from normal unless n is quite large. If the samples are large ($N > 400$) and if ρ is small or only moderately large ($|\rho| < .6$ perhaps) then it is true that r is approximately normally distributed about the value ρ with standard deviation

$$\sigma_r = (1 - \rho^2)(N-1)^{-1/2}$$

It is customary, under these conditions, to attach to an observed value of r a standard error

$$\sigma_r = (1 - r^2)(N-1)^{-1/2}$$

and, for a proposed ρ, to refer the computed value of

$$t = \frac{r - \rho}{\sigma_r}$$

to a normal probability scale.

This procedure is invalid, however, if N is small and ρ is large. The distribution of r from small samples is skew and the skewness increases with ρ. This may be understood intuitively by considering the distribution of r's from a universe in which ρ is .9. The range of possible variation of r above ρ is only .1. But the possible range below ρ is 1.9. Accordingly the sampling distribution of r (N small) from this universe will be sharply skew, as is evident from (8.69). (An extensive cooperative study of the distribution of r by Soper[6] et al. is now only of historical interest.)

The upper panel of Figure 26 (from Fisher's book) shows the r curves for two values of ρ with $N = 8$. They indicate the rapid departure from normality that may be expected from small samples as ρ approaches high values.

Sec. 15 Fisher's z'-Transformation 221

It may be observed from (8.69) that r is a biased estimate of ρ. An approximately unbiased estimate is given by putting

$$r = E(r) = \rho - \rho(1 - \rho^2)/2n$$

and solving this equation for ρ. We obtain, to terms of order $1/n$,

$$\check{\rho} = r[1 + (1 - r^2)/2n]$$

This result is, however, different from that obtained by maximizing $\log f(r)$ for variations in ρ, which gives a kind of maximum likelihood estimate. It

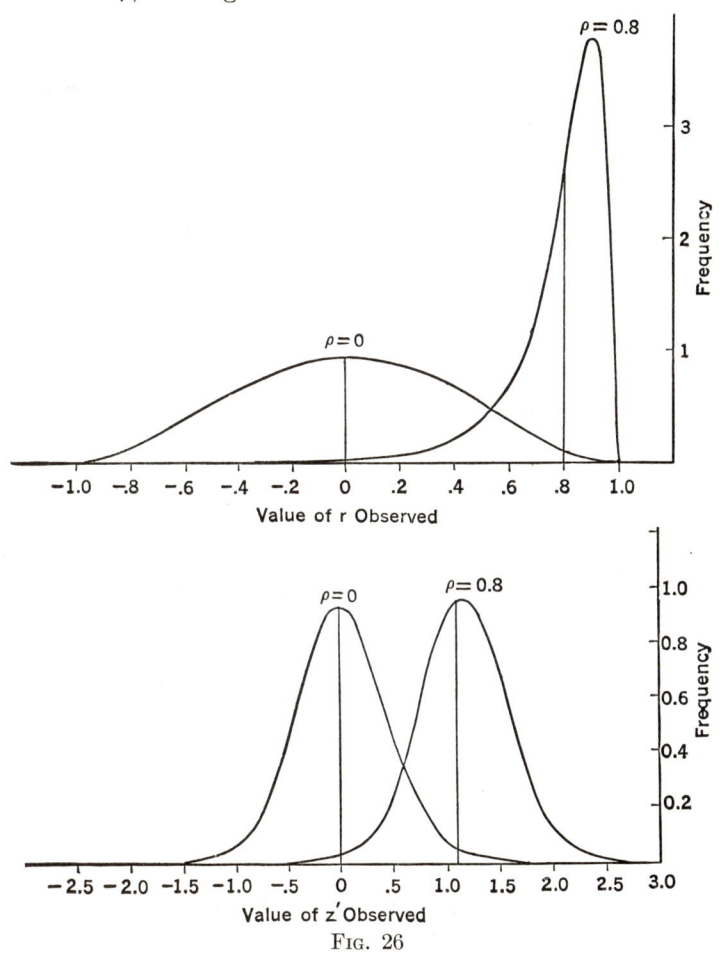

FIG. 26

is easily proved that, to terms of order $1/n$, $\hat{\rho} = r[1 - (1 - r^2)/2n]$. This estimate has minimum variance for large n among all nearly unbiased estimates (that is, estimates with a bias of order $1/n$).

8.15 Fisher's z'-Transformation. In his study of the sampling distribution of the correlation coefficient Fisher found that it was not desirable to use r

as the independent variable and he introduced a transformation which has distinctive merits. He showed that the quantity*

(8.70) $$z' = \tfrac{1}{2} \log_e \frac{1+r}{1-r} = \tanh^{-1} r$$

is approximately normally distributed and is nearly constant in form as ρ changes. The lower panel of Figure 26 shows the distribution curves for z' corresponding to the r curves in the upper panel. The standard deviation is approximately

(8.71) $$\sigma_{z'} = (N-3)^{-1/2}$$

and is practically independent of ρ.

If $\zeta = \tanh^{-1} \rho$, it may be proved from the known distribution of r that

(8.72) $$\begin{cases} E(z') = \zeta + \dfrac{\rho}{2n} + \cdots \\[4pt] \mathrm{Var}\,(z') = \dfrac{1}{n} + \dfrac{4-\rho^2}{2n^2} + \cdots \\[4pt] \gamma_1 = \dfrac{\rho^3}{n^{3/2}} + \cdots \\[4pt] \gamma_2 = \dfrac{2}{n} + \dfrac{4 + 2\rho^2 - 3\rho^4}{n^2} \end{cases}$$

For moderate values of n, therefore, the skewness is much less for the z'-distribution than it is for the r-distribution. If we write the variance as

$$\frac{1}{n-k} = \frac{1}{n}\left[1 + \frac{k}{n} + \cdots\right]$$

and choose an integral value of k to give approximate agreement with the value in (8.72) we must clearly put $k = 2$. The approximate variance of z' is, therefore, $(n-2)^{-1} = (N-3)^{-1}$.

Fisher's transformation is applicable in the following tests (among others):

(a) To test if an observed value of r differs significantly from a proposed theoretical value.

(b) To test if two observed values are significantly different.

The procedure for (a) is to calculate

$$t = (z' - \zeta)(N-3)^{1/2}$$

and refer the result to a normal probability scale. For (b) the procedure is to find, in accordance with (8.70), the two values of z', say z'_1 and z'_2, corresponding to the two observed values of r, say r_1 and r_2 from samples of N_1 and N_2, respectively. Then compute $d = z'_1 - z'_2$ and $\sigma_d = \{1/(N_1-3) + 1/(N_2-3)\}^{1/2}$ and refer

* This quantity is not quite the same as the z used for the ratio of two variances and so we use a prime here to distinguish between them. (See § 9.18.)

Sec. 15   Fisher's z'-Transformation

$$t = \frac{d}{\sigma_d}$$

to a normal probability scale. For exact work the bias indicated in the first equation of (8.72) may be allowed for.

Example 5. In a class of 20 students the correlation coefficient between the scores in two different tests is $r = 0.65$. Is it likely that the true coefficient of correlation is as high as 0.5? Here

$$z' = \frac{1}{2} \log \frac{1.65}{0.35} = 0.7753$$

$$\zeta = \frac{1}{2} \log \frac{1.5}{0.5} = 0.5493$$

and $(N - 3)^{-1/2} = 0.2425$. Hence $(z' - \zeta)(N - 3)^{1/2} = 0.932$, corresponding to a probability of 0.176 of obtaining a value of r as high as 0.65 when the true $\rho = 0.50$. To allow for the bias, we may put $\zeta + \rho/2n = 0.5493 + 0.5/38$ instead of ζ. This reduces the standard variate to 0.877, giving $P = 0.190$. In either case, the true coefficient of correlation may well be below 0.5.

We may establish approximate confidence limits for ρ by means of the z'-transformation. For ζ, 95% confidence limits will be given by $z' \pm 1.96(N - 3)^{-1/2}$, and the corresponding values of ρ may then be calculated. Thus, for the example above, the confidence limits for ζ are $0.7753 \pm 0.4753 = 0.3000$ and 1.2506. These correspond to $\rho = 0.29$ and $\rho = 0.85$. An approximate correction for the bias may be made by subtracting $r/2n = 0.65/38$ from z'. This changes the confidence limits for ζ to 0.2829 and 1.2335, corresponding to $\rho = 0.28$ and $\rho = 0.84$. The actual limits as given by David's chart are 0.28 and 0.83. It is evident that the normal approximation is satisfactory even in this case. (Correlation coefficients derived from samples as small as 20 are generally of little practical value.)

Fisher has given a table[7] for converting r to z', but a 4-place table[8] of $\tanh x$ is at least as convenient to use.

The z'-transformation is convenient in taking the average of correlations from a number of samples, supposedly from the same population. Thus, if $r_1, r_2, \cdots r_k$ are the sample coefficients obtained from samples of sizes $N_1, N_2, \cdots N_k$, the weighted mean of the z' will be

$$\bar{z}' = \sum z_i'(N_i - 3) / \sum (N_i - 3)$$

each z_i' being weighted inversely as its variance. The mean r is then given by $\bar{r} = \tanh \bar{z}'$.

E. J. G. Pitman[16] has given a *distribution-free* test of the significance of r when $\rho = 0$, that is, a test which is independent of any assumption about the distribution (normal or not) of the parent population. The test consists in comparing r for the sample, with r for all other samples consisting of *the same* set of X and Y values but paired in all possible ways, all such pairings being considered equally likely. With small numbers an exact test is possible, but with moderately large N and for a parent distribution with not too great γ_1 and γ_2 the distribution of r is approximately that of (8.54), so that r^2 is a $\beta[\tfrac{1}{2}, (N-2)/2]$ variate. A significant value of r^2 for any assigned level of significance can, therefore, be calculated from the tables of the *Incomplete Beta Function*.

8.16 Rank Correlation. It sometimes happens that, while two attributes X and Y cannot be accurately measured, individuals possessing these attributes can be ranked in some definite order. The product-moment coefficient, calculated by replacing the unknown actual values of X and Y by their ranks, is known as the *coefficient of rank correlation;* its use was proposed by Spearman[9] in 1904.

If X and Y now denote the ranks, and if for the present we ignore ties, the mean values of X and Y will be $\bar{X} = \bar{Y} = \tfrac{1}{2}(N+1)$. Putting $x = X - \bar{X}$, $y = Y - \bar{Y}$, we have for the rank coefficient

$$(8.73) \qquad r' = \sum xy / (\sum x^2 \sum y^2)^{1/2}$$

summed over the N sample values. Now the sum of the first N integers is $\tfrac{1}{2}N(N+1)$ and the sum of their squares is $N(N+1)(2N+1)/6$, so that

$$(8.74) \qquad \begin{aligned}\sum x^2 &= \sum X^2 - (\sum X)^2/N \\ &= N(N+1)(2N+1)/6 - N(N+1)^2/4 \\ &= N(N^2-1)/12\end{aligned}$$

$\sum y^2$ has the same value. Also if $d_i = X_i - Y_i = x_i - y_i$, we have

$$\begin{aligned}\sum d^2 &= \sum x^2 + \sum y^2 - 2\sum xy \\ &= N(N^2-1)/6 - 2\sum xy\end{aligned}$$

Therefore

$$(8.75) \qquad \begin{aligned}r' &= \frac{N(N^2-1)/12 - \sum d^2/2}{N(N^2-1)/12} \\ &= 1 - 6\sum d^2/N(N^2-1)\end{aligned}$$

which is the usual formula for computing r'. If the X's are arranged in a table in their natural order, and the Y's placed alongside, it is a simple matter to compute the d_i, and hence r'. For samples less than about 40, r' is easier to compute than r, and it is principally for such small samples that r' is used.

Example 6.

X	1	2	3	4	5	6	7	8	9	10
Y	1	2	5	3	8	4	9	6	7	10
d^2	0	0	4	1	9	4	4	4	4	0

Hence $\sum d^2 = 30$, $N = 10$, so that $r' = 1 - 180/990 = 81/99 = 0.82$.

It was shown by Hotelling and Pabst[10] that r' can be used as a test of the existence of correlation in populations of any type, not necessarily normal, and they obtained exact tests for small samples. For large samples the distribution of r' approximates a normal distribution.

If we assign the ranks $1, 2, \cdots N$ to the variates $X_1, X_2, \cdots X_N$, and if the Y's are independent of the X's, the actual set of ranks in any sample corresponding to $Y_1, Y_2, \cdots Y_n$ will be any one of the $N!$ equally likely permutations of the numbers 1 to N. The probability of any given value of r' is, therefore, proportional to the number of permutations giving rise to it. For small values of N, only a few values of r' are possible. For $N = 3$, for example, r' is either $-1, -\frac{1}{2}, \frac{1}{2}$ or 1, with probabilities $\frac{1}{6}, \frac{1}{3}, \frac{1}{3}, \frac{1}{6}$ respectively, as is easily seen by writing down all the permutations of 1, 2, 3 and computing r' for each. The two extreme values, $r' = \pm 1$, correspond respectively to the X and Y being in precisely the same order and in precisely reverse order, and both these values have probability $1/N!$.

From (8.73) and (8.74) we have

$$r' = \frac{12 \sum xy}{N(N^2 - 1)}$$

Since we are assuming independence,

$$E(r') = 0$$

and

$$\text{Var}(r') = E(r'^2) = 144 N^{-2}(N^2 - 1)^{-2} E(\sum xy)^2$$

Now the x_i take the same values in all samples, a set of N consecutive integers centered at zero (if N is odd) or numbers of the form $\cdots -2\frac{1}{2}, -1\frac{1}{2}, -\frac{1}{2}, \frac{1}{2}, 1\frac{1}{2}, 2\frac{1}{2}, \cdots$ (if N is even). In either case $\sum x_i = 0$ and $\sum x_i^2 = N(N^2 - 1)/12$. Also, if i is not equal to j, $\sum x_i x_j = (\sum x_i)^2 - \sum x_i^2 = -\sum x_i^2$. Since the y_i are the same numbers as the x_i, $E(y_i) = 0$, $E(y_i^2) = (N^2 - 1)/12$ and $E(y_i y_j) = -(N^2 - 1)/12(N - 1)$, there being $N(N - 1)$ terms of the form $y_i y_j$.

Also

$$(\sum xy)^2 = \sum_i x_i^2 y_i^2 + \sum_{i \neq j} x_i x_j y_i y_j$$

so that

$$E(\sum xy)^2 = \sum x_i^2 E(y_i^2) + \sum_{i \neq j} x_i x_j E(y_i y_j)$$

$$= \frac{N(N^2 - 1)^2}{144} + \frac{N(N^2 - 1)^2}{144(N - 1)}$$

Hence

(8.76) $$\text{Var}(r') = \frac{1}{N} + \frac{1}{N(N - 1)} = \frac{1}{N - 1}$$

This formula was originally obtained by "Student." The calculation of the higher moments of even order is long and complicated. The odd moments are all zero, from symmetry. It turns out that

(8.77) $$\gamma_2 = -\frac{114}{25N} - \frac{6}{5N^2} - \cdots$$

and so tends to zero for large N, and that in general the 2αth moment of $r'\sqrt{N-1}$ tends, as N increases, to the value $(2\alpha)!/\alpha!\,2^\alpha$ which is the 2αth moment of a standard normal variate.

8.17 Kendall's Method of Rank Correlation.[11] M. G. Kendall has suggested a different method of computing a rank correlation, which has certain definite advantages. If, as in Example 6, the X_i are arranged in a row in their natural order of increasing rank and the Y_i are placed as they come, underneath, we count for each number in the row of Y how many other numbers there are lying to the right of, and greater than, that number. If, for the nth number, the number counted is ϕ_n, we compute $K = \sum_{n=1}^{N} \phi_n$ and $\tau = 4K/[N(N-1)] - 1$. Then τ is a measure of the agreement of ranks in A and B.

It is easily verified in Example 6 that $K = 9 + 8 + 5 + 6 + 2 + 4 + 1 + 2 + 1 = 38$, whence $\tau = 0.69$. If the ranks of X and Y agree completely, $\tau = 1$, and if the ranks of Y are the exact reverse of those of X, $\tau = -1$.

A useful check on the calculation is provided by counting all greater numbers to the *left* of each number. If L is the sum of these counts, $K + L = \frac{1}{2}N(N-1)$.

The distribution of values of τ when a given ranking is correlated with each of the $N!$ possible permutations of the ranks may be found fairly readily. Like that of r', this distribution tends to normality as $N \to \infty$, but it does so much more rapidly. For $N \geq 10$, the normal approximation is quite close. The variance of τ is $2(2N+5)/9N(N-1)$, the skewness is zero, and the kurtosis (γ_2) is $-54/25N + O(1/N^2)$.

8.18 Ties in Rank Correlation. The customary procedure when there are ties in the ranking is to divide the corresponding rank numbers equally among the variates concerned, using fractions where necessary. Thus, if a group of 14 students were given letter grades as indicated below, and these grades were interpreted as ranks, we should have

Grade	A+	A	A−	B+	B	B	B	B−	C+	C	C	C−	D
Rank	1	2.5	2.5	4	5	7	7	7	9	10	11.5	11.5	13	14

When there are ties in one or both of two rankings, Spearman's rank order formula (8.75) does not give the same result as the product-moment correlation of ranks, since $\sum x^2$ is not equal to $N(N^2-1)/12$.

The presence of ties affects also the variance of the rank correlation. For example, if one ranking is untied and the other contains sets of $t_1, t_2, \cdots$ tied members, the variance of τ is reduced by the amount $\frac{2}{9}\sum t(t-1)(2t+5)/N^2(N-1)^2$. Thus, in the example given, if the ranking were correlated with another (untied) ranking, we should have $t_1 = 2$, $t_2 = 3$, $t_3 = 2$, so that $\sum t(t-1)(2t+5)$ would be 102 and the variance would be reduced from 0.0403 to 0.0396.

8.19 Contingency Tables. Very frequently in experimental work we deal with some characteristics or attributes that are not susceptible of accurate measurement, although it is possible to divide the population into two or more categories with reference to these attributes.

An example was given in § 8.5, where the division into two categories produced a 2 × 2 table (Tables 12 and 13). For other attributes, such as hair color, it may be desirable to have four or five categories. Such tables are called *contingency tables*. For the special case of a 2 × 2 table, the method of tetrachoric correlation described in § 8.5 gives a measure of the association between the two attributes, but for other sizes of table some other method of measuring the association is necessary, and even for 2 × 2 tables this other method is generally preferable.

Let us suppose that we have two attributes denoted by A and B and that our sample of N is divided into s and t classes with respect to these two attributes. The resulting frequency table will be of the form shown in Table 14 where $s = 5$ and $t = 3$.

TABLE 14

	B_1	B_2	B_3	
A_1	f_{11}	f_{12}	f_{13}	r_1
A_2	f_{21}	f_{22}	f_{23}	r_2
A_3	f_{31}	f_{32}	f_{33}	r_3
A_4	f_{41}	f_{42}	f_{43}	r_4
A_5	f_{51}	f_{52}	f_{53}	r_5
	c_1	c_2	c_3	N

The row marginal totals are denoted by $r_1, r_2, \cdots r_s$, and the column marginal totals by $c_1, c_2, \cdots c_t$.

If the attributes A and B are completely independent, the proportions in the different B-categories will, in the parent population, be the same, irrespective of the distribution of the A-categories. That is, if we select a sub-population consisting only of those individuals with attribute A_m, the proportions $p_{m1}, p_{m2}, \cdots p_{mt}$, in the various B-categories of this sub-population will be the same as in the corresponding categories of the whole population. The same thing, of course, holds also for the proportions in the various A-categories corresponding to a fixed B-category. Hence, if the observed frequencies in the sample reflected precisely the corresponding proportions in the parent population, we should have, in the case of complete independence, $f_{mn}/r_m =$

c_n/N or $f_{mn} = r_m c_n/N$. Deviations from these equalities in the observed sample are to be attributed, on our hypothesis of independence, to sampling fluctuations.

It is conventional to consider the probabilities of such deviations relative to the set of all possible cell-frequencies with the *same marginal totals*. That is, the r_m and c_n are treated as fixed, and the expected frequency in the mnth cell is then $\phi_{mn} = r_m c_n/N$. The value of χ^2 is $\sum_{m,n}(f_{mn} - \phi_{mn})^2/\phi_{mn}$ summed over all the st cells in the table. Since all the marginal totals are fixed, however, the number of degrees of freedom is reduced by $s + t - 1$ (not $s + t$, because the sum of the row marginal totals must be equal to the sum of the column marginal totals.) Hence the number of degrees of freedom for χ^2 is $(s-1)(t-1)$, and the significance of an observed χ^2 can be determined.

A measure of the degree of association between the two attributes considered is provided by Pearson's *coefficient of mean square contingency*. This is defined by

(8.78) $$C = [\chi^2/(\chi^2 + N)]^{1/2} = [\psi^2/(\psi^2 + 1)]^{1/2}$$

where $\psi^2 = \chi^2/N$. From the definition of χ^2 we have

$$\chi^2 = \sum [f_{mn}^2/\phi_{mn} - 2f_{mn} + \phi_{mn}]$$
$$= \sum f_{mn}^2/\phi_{mn} - N$$
$$= N[\sum (f_{mn}^2/r_m c_n) - 1]$$

since $\sum f_{mn} = \sum \phi_{mn} = N$. (This is, in fact, the simplest way of computing χ^2.) It follows that $\psi^2 + 1 = \sum (f_{mn}^2/r_m c_n) = S$, say, and that

(8.79) $$C = [(S-1)/S]^{1/2}$$

Even with perfect association between the two attributes, C is not equal to 1, although it tends to this value as the number of rows and columns increases. For a 2×2 table, C cannot exceed $1/\sqrt{2} = 0.707$. If the parent universe is assumed to have an underlying bivariate normal distribution, then C tends with finer and finer subdivisions to equality with the Pearson coefficient of correlation r.

Example[12] 7. The following results were obtained in an investigation of the association between "left-handedness" (determined by a balancing test) and "left-eyedness" (as measured by general astigmatism).

TABLE 15

	Left-eyed	Ambiocular	Right-eyed	Totals
Left-handed	34	62	28	124
Ambidextrous	27	28	20	75
Right-handed	57	105	52	214
Totals	118	195	100	413

Here
$$S = \frac{34^2}{124 \times 118} + \cdots + \frac{52^2}{100 \times 214} = 1.009734$$
$$\chi^2 = 413(S - 1) = 4.020, \quad \text{and} \quad C = 0.0096$$

The value of χ^2 is certainly not significant with 4 degrees of freedom, and the coefficient C is very small. There is very little evidence against the assumption of complete independence.

8.20 The $2 \times n$ and 2×2 Contingency Tables. For the special case of a $2 \times n$ or $n \times 2$ table, the calculation of χ^2 may be simplified. If the table is arranged as in Table 16, where A and B are the totals of the a_i and b_i respec-

TABLE 16

a_1	$a_2 \cdots a_n$	A
b_1	$b_2 \cdots b_n$	B
c_1	$c_2 \cdots c_n$	N

tively, the proportion of a's in the ith column is $p_i = a_i/c_i$, and the proportion of b's is $q_i = b_i/c_i$. The weighted mean values of p_i and q_i are $\bar{p} = A/N$ and $\bar{q} = B/N$ respectively. Then

$$\chi^2 = N \sum_i \left(\frac{a_i^2}{A c_i} + \frac{b_i^2}{B c_i} \right) - N$$

Now $b_i^2 = (c_i - a_i)^2 = c_i^2 - 2a_i c_i + a_i^2$, so that since $\sum c_i = N$ and $\sum a_i = A$, we have

$$\chi^2 = N \sum_i \frac{a_i^2}{c_i} \left(\frac{1}{A} + \frac{1}{B} \right) + \frac{N^2}{B} - \frac{2NA}{B} - N$$
$$= \frac{N^2}{AB} \sum \frac{a_i^2}{c_i} - \frac{NA}{B}$$
(8.80) $$= \frac{1}{\bar{p}\bar{q}} \left\{ \sum \frac{a_i^2}{c_i} - \frac{A^2}{N} \right\}$$

which is the formula attributed to Brandt and Snedecor.[13] Either the a's or the b's can, of course, be used in (8.80), the smaller frequencies being generally chosen.

For a 2×2 table, arranged as in Table 12 (§ 8.5), the contribution to χ^2 arising from the cell with observed frequency a is $(a - \alpha)^2/\alpha$, $\alpha = (a + b) \times (a + c)/N$. Now $a - \alpha = (ad - bc)/N$, and because of the assumed constancy of the marginal totals, this difference between observed and expected frequencies is numerically the same for each cell, differing only in sign. Hence $\chi^2 = (ad - bc)^2(1/\alpha + 1/\beta + 1/\gamma + 1/\delta)/N^2$. The second bracket on the right is easily seen to reduce to $N^2/(a + b)(a + c)(b + d)(c + d)$, on substituting for α, β, γ, δ, and remembering that $a + b + c + d = N$. (β, γ, δ are expressions like α for the other three cells.) We have then

$$\chi^2 = \frac{N(ad-bc)^2}{(a+b)(a+c)(b+d)(c+d)}$$
(8.81)
$$= \frac{N(ad-bc)^2}{r_1 r_2 c_1 c_2}$$

where r_1, r_2 are the two row totals and c_1, c_2 the two column totals.

The distribution in a contingency table is necessarily discontinuous, whereas the χ^2 distribution is continuous. The approximation to χ^2 is something like the approximation of the discontinuous binomial distribution to a normal one, where, as was noted in Chapter II, the calculated frequency between two values of x, say a and b inclusive, is given by the area under the corresponding normal curve, not between a and b but between $a - \frac{1}{2}$ and $b + \frac{1}{2}$. Similarly, as was suggested by Yates, the approximation to χ^2 is improved by replacing one cell frequency, say d, by $d \pm \frac{1}{2}$ according as $ad \lessgtr bc$, and adjusting the others to keep the marginal totals unaltered. The effect is to replace $ad - bc$ in (8.81) by $|ad - bc| - N/2$. This is known as *Yates's correction for continuity*. It undoubtedly improves the estimate of significance for a 2×2 table, and should always be applied unless the cell frequencies are all quite large, say 500 or more. In using the χ^2 test for tables with small values of N, it should be borne in mind that the quantity on the right-hand side of (8.81) actually has the χ^2 distribution only in the limit as N tends to infinity. Even with the Yates correction, it cannot be assumed that for small values of N the probabilities calculated from χ^2 will be accurate.

8.21 The Exact Distributions for 2×2 Tables. There has been some discussion [14] in the literature concerning the proper method of dealing with 2×2 tables. The situation has been clarified in two papers, one by G. A. Barnard and one by E. S. Pearson [15] in *Biometrika*, 1947, pointing out that there are really three distinct problems, each of which gives rise to a 2×2 table, although the underlying probability conceptions are different.

Problem I. This is the one usually considered, in which both sets of marginal totals are fixed. It is called by Barnard the *2×2 independence trial*. The mathematical model corresponding to Table 14, with a, b, c, d written for f_{11}, f_{12}, f_{21}, f_{22}, is that of N balls in an urn, of which r_1 are marked A_1 and r_2 are marked A_2. The balls are withdrawn in random order and put into a row of N boxes, one ball to a box, of which c_1 are marked B_1 and c_2 are marked B_2. The number of balls marked A_1 in the boxes marked B_1 will be f_{11} or a, and similarly for the three other cells in the table.

The probability of a A_1's and c A_2's in the c_1 boxes marked B_1 is given by the hypergeometric law [see (2.66)], since this is a problem of sampling without replacements. It is

$$\binom{r_1}{a}\binom{r_2}{c} \bigg/ \binom{N}{c_1} = \frac{r_1!\, r_2!\, c_1!\, c_2!}{a!\, b!\, c!\, d!\, N!}$$

When the distribution in the boxes marked B_1 is fixed, that in the boxes

Sec. 21   The Exact Distributions for 2 × 2 Tables

marked B_2 is also determined, so that the probability of the observed 2 × 2 table, in which we suppose that d is the smallest frequency, is

(8.82) $$p' = (r_1!\, r_2!\, c_1!\, c_2!)/(a!\, b!\, c!\, d!\, N!)$$

R. A. Fisher derived from this expression his "exact test." This consists in computing the total probability of the observed distribution and of all less likely ones in the same direction, that is, for all values of d from 0 up to the observed value (if $d < \delta$). This probability $P = p_0' + p_1' + p_2' + \cdots + p_d'$ corresponds to one tail of the distribution, and thus is comparable with *half* the probability calculated from χ^2, since the latter corresponds to both tails of the distribution. If $d > \delta$ the tail is from d up to c_2 inclusive.

Example 8. The data are intended to exhibit a relationship between inoculation and immunity from attack among a population exposed to a certain disease.

	Not inoculated	Inoculated	
Not attacked	3	5	8
Attacked	10	2	12
	13	7	20

For this table, $\chi^2 = (44^2 \times 20)/(8 \times 12 \times 13 \times 7) = 4.43$, corresponding to $P = 0.035$. With the Yates correction, χ^2 is reduced to 2.65, corresponding to $P = 0.103$, so that the correction changes a significant probability to a nonsignificant one, on the customary level. The probability of the observed distribution is $(8!\,12!\,13!\,7!)/(3!\,5!\,10!\,2!\,20!) = 0.0477$, and the probabilities of the two more extreme ones corresponding to $d = 1$ and $d = 0$ are 0.0043 and 0.0001, so that Fisher's $P = 0.052$, or, for both tails, 0.104. It is obvious that Yates's correction makes a great improvement.

The chief objection to Fisher's exact test is the large amount of computation involved when the cell frequencies are at all large. E. S. Pearson[15] has pointed out that a normal approximation, with a continuity correction equivalent to Yates's correction, gives, as a rule, a surprisingly good result. The method consists in calculating, for the cell frequency d, the expected value $\delta = r_2 c_2/N$, and the variance $\sigma_d^2 = r_1 r_2 c_1 c_2/N^2(N-1)$, as given by (2.77) and (2.80). Then the quantity

$$t = \{|d - \delta| - \tfrac{1}{2}\}/\sigma_d$$

is treated as a normal variate and $P = \int_t^\infty \phi(t)\, dt$.

For Example 8, $\delta = 84/20$, $\sigma_d^2 = 1.149$, $t = 1.7/1.072 = 1.586$ so that $P = 0.056$ which agrees fairly well with the exact value.*

---

* Mainland, see reference (17), has given extensive tables based on Fisher's method, for estimating the significance of observed 2 × 2 distributions without going through the labor of computation.

Problem II. This is the test of whether the proportion of individuals having the characteristic A_1 is the same in two different populations, distinguished by the characteristics B_1 and B_2, a random sample being drawn from each. Barnard calls this the *2 × 2 comparative trial.* The mathematical model is of two urns each containing a very large number of balls, these balls being all labeled either A_1 or A_2. In the first urn (B_1) the proportion of A_1's is p_1, while in the second urn (B_2) it is p_2. A random sample of c_1 is drawn from urn I and contains a A_1's and c A_2's. A random sample of c_2 from urn II contains b A_1's and d A_2's. The hypothesis H_0 to be tested is that $p_1 = p_2 = p$.

If this hypothesis is true, the probability of the observed result is

$$\frac{c_1!}{a!\,c!} p^a (1-p)^c \frac{c_2!}{b!\,d!} p^b (1-p)^d = \frac{c_1!\,c_2!}{a!\,b!\,c!\,d!} p^{r_1} (1-p)^{r_2}$$

which is equal to Fisher's expression p' (8.82) multiplied by a factor

$$p_{r_1} = \frac{N!}{r_1!\,r_2!} p^{r_1} (1-p)^{r_2}$$

Here, of course, the conditions are different, because we are no longer insisting on constant row totals. In various repetitions of the experiment the row totals can vary, although the column totals are still fixed.

In this problem the basic probability set, with reference to which probabilities are calculated, is two-dimensional, instead of one-dimensional. The set of possible values of a and b ($0 \leq a \leq c_1$, $0 \leq b \leq c_2$) is a lattice of points as represented in Figure 27. It is fairly clear that for points lying near the diagonal OD there will be little reason to reject the hypothesis that $p_1 = p_2$, whereas the argument for doing so gains force as the point (a, b) moves toward one of the corners A or B. We should like to be able to draw lines L_α, L_α' on this diagram, cutting off at each end of every diagonal, $r_1 = $ constant, a group of dots (shown in black) for which the total probability $\sum p'$ is equal to α. If this were done, and if the null hypothesis were rejected whenever (a, b) fell in the region of the black dots, the chance of committing an error of the first kind (that is, rejecting H_0 when it is true) would be

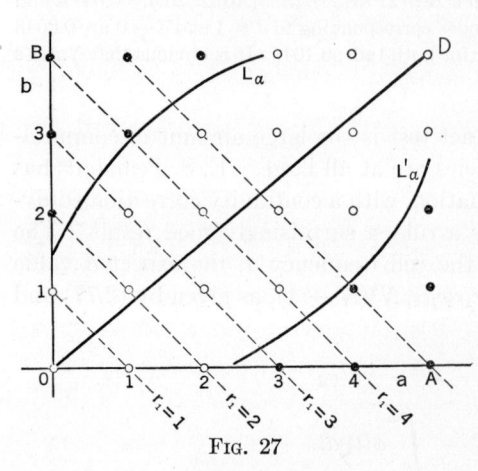

Fig. 27

$$\alpha \sum_{r_1=0}^{N} p_{r_1} = \alpha$$

Sec. 22 The Combination of Probabilities from Tables

and so would be independent of the unknown parameter p. Although this is not practicable, Barnard has given a systematic method of classifying the points in the lattice, and Pearson has suggested that, when all the marginal totals are fairly large, the quantity $u = (a - \bar{a})/\sigma_a$ may, on the null hypothesis, be treated as a standard normal variate. Here $\bar{a}$ and σ_a are given by the hypergeometric formulae

$$\bar{a} = r_1 c_1 / N$$
$$\sigma_a^2 = r_1 r_2 c_1 c_2 / N^2 (N - 1)$$

If, in Example 8, we think of the 13 not-inoculated and the 7 inoculated persons as independent random samples from two exposed populations (the not-inoculated and the inoculated), in which the numbers of persons actually attacked may vary from 0 to 13, or from 0 to 7, respectively, we have a problem of type II. For the observed a, $u = -2.05$, corresponding to $P = 0.020$, which suggests significance.

Problem III. This is the case of a *double dichotomy*. It is assumed that in the parent population there is a probability p_a that an individual selected at random will have the characteristic A_1 and an independent probability p_b that a random individual will have the characteristic B_1. The probabilities of the four possible combinations (A_1B_1, A_1B_2, A_2B_1, A_2B_2) are, therefore, $p_{11} = p_a p_b$, $p_{12} = p_a(1 - p_b)$, $p_{21} = (1 - p_a)p_b$ and $p_{22} = (1 - p_a)(1 - p_b)$ respectively. The probability of the observed sample is given by the multinomial law and is

$$\frac{N!}{a!\,b!\,c!\,d!} p_{11}{}^a p_{12}{}^b p_{21}{}^c p_{22}{}^d = \frac{N!}{a!\,b!\,c!\,d!} p_a{}^{r_1}(1 - p_a)^{r_2} p_b{}^{c_1}(1 - p_b)^{c_2}$$
$$= p' \cdot p_{r_1} \cdot p_{c_1}$$

where p' is Fisher's expression (8.82), and p_{r_1}, p_{c_1} are the binomial probabilities for the row totals and the column totals respectively. The basic probability set is now three-dimensional, since the column totals as well as the row totals may vary, and little has been done on the exact treatment. Unless some of the marginal totals are very small, it appears, however, that the usual χ^2 approximation is reasonably adequate.

8.22 The Combination of Probabilities from 2 × 2 Tables. Sometimes, in a group of related experiments, it is desired to estimate the over-all significance of the results. R. A. Fisher has given a method of combining probabilities which is useful in such cases. If a continuous variable x has the frequency function $f(x)$, and if P is the probability that x does not exceed the value x_1, then

$$P = \int_{-\infty}^{x_1} f(x)\,dx$$

and has a range from 0 to 1. Treating P as a random variable depending on x_1 with frequency function $g(P)$, we have

$$g(P)\,dP = f(x_1)\,dx_1$$

But $dP = f(x_1)\,dx_1$, so that $g(P) = 1$. This means that P has a rectangular distribution on the range 0 to 1.

If $u = -2\log_e P$, we have
$$\frac{du}{dP} = -\frac{2}{P}$$
so that, if the frequency function of u is $h(u)$,
$$h(u)\,|\,du\,| = dP$$
or
$$h(u) = \frac{P}{2} = \frac{1}{2}e^{-u/2}$$

The distribution of u is, therefore, the same as that of χ^2 with 2 df.

If now we combine k independent probabilities, the combined probability is the product of the k separate probabilities, or
$$u = -2\log_e P = -2\log_e(P_1 P_2 \cdots P_k)$$
$$= -2\sum \log_e P_i = \sum u_i$$
and so has the χ^2 distribution with $2k$ degrees of freedom.

Example 9. The one-tailed probabilities on the basis of the null hypothesis obtained from three related 2×2 tables are 0.0178, 0.0214, and 0.0052. What is the probability of the combined result?

Here $\sum \log_{10} P_i = -5.7032$, so that $u = 2 \times 2.3026 \times 5.7032 = 26.26$.

The corresponding P for 6 degrees of freedom is 0.0020, which also is a one-tailed probability. It may be doubled to give the customary two-tailed significance probability, but in any case is obviously highly significant.

In a 2×2 table, the distribution is actually discrete instead of continuous, so that the distribution of P is not really rectangular, but for moderately large frequencies, the approximation is satisfactory.

Problems

1. Establish the truth or falsity of the following proposition: A necessary and sufficient condition that two variables be normally correlated is that their regression systems be linear.

2. Prove that the regression systems of two normally correlated variables are linear and homoscedastic.

3. For (8.13) prove the following:
(a) the mean value of $\bar{y}_x$ taken over all values of x is zero, ($\bar{y}_x = \eta_x$ of (8.1))
(b) the variance of $\bar{y}_x$ is equal to $\rho^2 \sigma_y^2$,
(c) the correlation coefficient between $\bar{y}_x$ and y is equal to ρ.

Hints. (a) Evaluate $\int_{-\infty}^{\infty}\int_{-\infty}^{\infty} \bar{y}_x f(x,y)\,dy\,dx$

(b) $\sigma_{\bar{y}_x}^2 = \int_{-\infty}^{\infty}\int_{-\infty}^{\infty} \bar{y}_x^2 f(x,y)\,dy\,dx$

(c) Evaluate $\int_{-\infty}^{\infty}\int_{-\infty}^{\infty} \frac{\bar{y}_x}{\sigma_{\bar{y}_x}}\frac{y}{\sigma_y} f(x,y)\,dy\,dx$

Problems

4. Prove the statement in § 8.7 that a is normally distributed about α with variance $\sigma_{ey}^2(s_x^2 + \bar{x}^2)/Ns_x^2$.

5. Show that the $100(1 - \alpha)\%$ confidence limits for $\omega = \sigma_x^2/\sigma_y^2$ obtained from (8.59) are given by

$$\omega^2 - 2A w \omega + w^2 = 0$$

where

$$A = \frac{N - 2 + 2(1 - r^2)t_\alpha^2}{N - 2}$$

and therefore are equal to

$$Aw \pm w(A^2 - 1)^{1/2}$$

6. Obtain the maximum likelihood estimate of ρ from the sampling distribution of r, (8.68), by putting $d \log f(r)/d\rho = 0$ and solving the resulting quadratic equation for ρ as far as terms of order $1/n$. (Take only the first term of the series in (8.68).)

7. Prove that χ^2 for the table

$a + \tfrac{1}{2}$	$b - \tfrac{1}{2}$
$c - \tfrac{1}{2}$	$d + \tfrac{1}{2}$

is given by $\chi^2 = \dfrac{N\left(|ad - bc| - \dfrac{N}{2}\right)^2}{(a+b)(c+d)(a+c)(b+d)}$, if $ad < bc$.

8. One random sample of 28 from a certain bivariate population gave $r = 0.60$; another independent random sample of 23 gave $r = 0.40$. Is the difference significant? (Use a two-tailed test in estimating the probability, since we are interested here in the numerical value of the difference, and not in the sign.)

9. A correlation coefficient of 0.561 is said to be highly significant. Assuming that this refers to the 1% level of significance, what is the least number of pairs of observations that must have been made in order to warrant the statement? *Ans.* 20.

10. For the data of Example 2, § 8.8, plot the observed regression line and the band on either side of it contained between the upper and lower confidence limits for y. Note that this band is not of uniform width, although the width does not vary a great deal. For large values of N the edges of the band are practically parallel to the regression line.

The following three problems are from Fisher's book.

11. For the twenty years 1885–1904, the mean wheat yield of Eastern England was found to be correlated with the autumn rainfall; the correlation was found to be $-.629$. Is this value significant?

12. In a sample of $N = 25$ pairs of parent and child the correlation in a certain character was found to be $.60$. Is this value consistent with the view that the true correlation in that character was $.46$?

13. Of two samples the first, of 20 pairs, gives a correlation of $.6$, the second, of 25 pairs, gives a correlation $.8$. Are these values significantly different?

14. The following table gives average annual wheat yield (bushels/acre to the nearest bushel) and effective rainfall (to the nearest inch) for the Calgary district of Alberta, 1910–1937. Effective rainfall is defined as the rainfall during September and October of the previous year plus rainfall in May, June, July, and August of the specified year.

Year	Wheat Yield	Rainfall	Year	Wheat Yield	Rainfall
1910	13	5	1924	9	11
1911	21	17	1925	17	14
1912	18	19	1926	18	15
1913	20	14	1927	28	30
1914	15	13	1928	26	17
1915	31	17	1929	11	10
1916	27	12	1930	17	11
1917	19	9	1931	13	9
1918	8	7	1932	19	17
1919	12	7	1933	10	10
1920	21	15	1934	12	12
1921	11	8	1935	13	14
1922	11	9	1936	6	9
1923	28	21	1937	8	13

Calculate the regression coefficient of wheat yield on rainfall. Obtain 95% confidence limits for this coefficient. Calculate the coefficient of correlation, and find 95% confidence limits for it. If wheat yield y is estimated from rainfall x, obtain an expression for the 95% confidence limits of y as a function of x. *Ans.* $\beta = 0.95 \pm 0.38$, $r = 0.71$, $\rho = 0.45$ to 0.85, $y = 4.16 + 0.946x \pm 10.1[1.036 + (x - \bar{x})^2/717]^{1/2}$.

15. From the following 2×2 table can one conclude that the medical condition known as synostosis of the sternum is associated with tuberculosis?

	Without Synostosis	With Synostosis
Without T.B.	66	7
With T.B.	7	4

Hint. The smallest expected frequency is here so small that the χ^2 test is unreliable. Note that the frequency 4 is *above* expectation, so that the tail of the distribution of possible frequencies corresponds to values even greater than 4. There is a marked asymmetry in the distribution, the only possible values of d which are *less* than expectation being 1 and 0. Fisher and Yates (*Statistical Tables*, VIII) give a table for use whenever the smallest expectation in the 2×2 table is less than 10. The 2.5 and 0.5 per cent points of the corrected χ_c (the square root of χ_c^2) are calculated for the two tails separately. In the above example we would use the longer tail.

References

1. B. H. Camp, *Mathematical Part of Elementary Statistics*, pp. 307–309.
2. E. J. G. Pitman, "Note on Normal Correlation," *Biometrika*, **31,** 1939, p. 9.
3. R. A. Fisher, "Frequency Distribution of the Values of the Correlation Coefficient in Samples from an Indefinitely Large Population," *Biometrika*, **10,** 1915, p. 507.
4. D. T. Sawkins, "Simple Regression and Correlation," *J. and Proc. R. Soc. N.S.W.*, **77,** 1944, pp. 85–95.
5. F. N. David, *Tables of the Correlation Coefficient* (Biometrika Office, University College, London).

Table XXXII in Pearson's *Tables for Statisticians and Biometricians*, Part II, also contains tables of the ordinate $f(r)$. The ordinates are given at sufficiently small intervals to enable a fair approximation to be made to the area.

References

6. H. E. Soper et al., "On the Distribution of the Correlation Coefficient in Small Samples," *Biometrika*, **11,** 1917, pp. 328–413.

7. *Statistical Methods for Research Workers*, Table VB, p. 210. Also Fisher and Yates, *Statistical Tables*, Table VII.

8. Such a table is found in J. W. Campbell's *Numerical Tables of Hyperbolic and Other Functions*, Edmonton, Alberta.

9. C. Spearman, "The Proof and Measurement of Association between Two Things," *Amer. Jour. Psych.*, **15,** 1904.

10. Harold Hotelling and M. R. Pabst, "Rank Correlation and Tests of Significance Involving No Assumption of Normality," *Ann. Math. Stat.*, **7,** 1936, pp. 29–43.

11. M. G. Kendall, *Biometrika*, **30,** 1938, p. 81. See also Kendall's book *Rank Correlation Methods*, 1949 (Griffin).

12. T. L. Woo, *Biometrika*, **20 A,** 1928, pp. 79–148.

13. See Snedecor's *Statistical Methods*, 4th Edition, p. 206.

14. See, *e.g.*, *Nature*, **156,** 1945, pp. 177, 388, 783, and *Science*, **93,** 1941, p. 557; **94,** 1941, p. 210; and **96,** 1942, p. 13.

15. G. A. Barnard, "Significance Tests for 2 × 2 Tables," and E. S. Pearson, "Choice of Statistical Tests Illustrated on Interpretation of Data Classed in a 2 × 2 Table," *Biometrika*, **34,** 1947, pp. 123–169.

16. E. J. G. Pitman, "Significance Tests Which May Be Applied to Samples from Any Populations, II The Correlation Coefficient Test," *Supp. Jour. Roy. Stat. Soc.*, **4,** 1937, pp. 225–232.

17. A. B. D. Fortuyn, *China Med. J.*, **42,** 1928, pp. 757–762. This example is quoted by Mainland, "Statistical Methods in Medical Research," *Can. Jour. Research* (section E), **26,** 1948, pp. 1–166.

18. The expression of the integral in (8.67) as a hypergeometric function, and the series (8.68), are due to Harold Hotelling, and were given by him in lectures at the Institute of Statistics, North Carolina.

CHAPTER IX

ANALYSIS OF VARIANCE AND COVARIANCE

9.1 Analysis of Variance. One-way Classification. The test of significance between two independent estimates of a population variance may be applied in a great many types of experimental design. A general technique, known as the analysis of variance, was developed by R. A. Fisher for separating the experimentally observed variance into portions traceable to specific sources. The kind of procedure one attempts to follow in such an analysis can be illustrated by the following scheme.

Imagine a set of b families of which the kth family contains N_k individuals. These families are subjected to different treatments $T_1, T_2, \cdots T_b$, and a variable x is measured for each individual. The individuals may, for example, be plots of land, and the T's may be fertilizer treatments. The x's would then be yields of some specified crop grown on all the plots. Or the families may be batches of steel ingots containing slightly different amounts of some ingredient, and the x's the result of tests on the breaking strength of the metal. We have, then, $N = \sum N_k$ independent values of x, classified into b columns as in Table 17.

TABLE 17

T_1	T_2	$\cdots$	T_b
x_{11}	x_{12}	$\cdots$	x_{1b}
x_{21}	x_{22}	$\cdots$	x_{2b}
.	.		.
.	.		.
.	.		.
$x_{N_1,1}$	$x_{N_2,2}$		$x_{N_b,b}$

Let $\bar{x}_{\cdot k}$ denote the mean of the kth family and $\bar{x}$ the overall mean. Then

(9.1) $$N_k \bar{x}_{\cdot k} = \sum_{j=1}^{N_k} x_{jk}, \qquad k = 1, 2, \cdots b$$

and

(9.2) $$N\bar{x} = \sum_{j,k} x_{jk}$$

Now the variance of the whole set of x's in Table 17 is Q/N, where

(9.3) $$Q = \sum_{j,k}(x_{jk} - \bar{x})^2 = \sum_{j,k} x_{jk}^2 - N\bar{x}^2$$

and this can be split up into two sums of squares

(9.4) $$Q = q_1 + q_2$$

Sec. 1 Analysis of Variance. One-way Classification

where

(9.5)
$$\begin{cases} q_1 = \sum N_k(\bar{x}_{\cdot k} - \bar{x})^2 = \sum_k (\sum_j x_{jk})^2/N_k - N\bar{x}^2 \\ q_2 = \sum_{j,k}(x_{jk} - \bar{x}_{\cdot k})^2 = \sum x_{jk}^2 - \sum_k (\sum_j x_{jk})^2/N_k \end{cases}$$

To show that (9.4) is an identity, we write

$$\sum(x_{jk} - \bar{x})^2 = \sum(x_{jk} - \bar{x}_{\cdot k} + \bar{x}_{\cdot k} - \bar{x})^2$$
$$= \sum(x_{jk} - \bar{x}_{\cdot k})^2 + \sum(\bar{x}_{\cdot k} - \bar{x})^2 + 2\sum(x_{jk} - \bar{x}_{\cdot k})(\bar{x}_{\cdot k} - \bar{x})$$

The last term vanishes, since by (9.1)

$$\sum_j (x_{jk} - \bar{x}_{\cdot k}) = 0$$

Moreover,

$$\sum_{j,k}(\bar{x}_{\cdot k} - \bar{x})^2 = \sum_k N_k(\bar{x}_{\cdot k} - \bar{x})^2 = \sum N_k \bar{x}_{\cdot k}^2 - N\bar{x}^2$$
$$= \sum_k (\sum_j x_{jk})^2/N_k - (\sum x_{jk})^2/N$$

whence the required result follows.

The quantity q_1 measures the variability between families averaged over the individuals in each family, while q_2 measures the remaining part of the variability which cannot be explained by differences of treatment between families. This part of the variability is commonly attributed to "error."

If the families are all the same size, so that $N_k = a$, say,

(9.6)
$$q_1 = a \sum_k (\bar{x}_{\cdot k} - \bar{x})^2$$

The quadratic forms Q, q_1, q_2 are commonly called *sums of squares* (SS). The name "squariance," on the analogy of variance, has been proposed by Pitman and will often be used in this chapter. M. G. Kendall has suggested the term "deviance."

The mathematical model[1] underlying our treatment is as follows. The total response x_{jk} of the jth individual to the kth treatment is made up of an overall effect μ, a part β_k characteristic of the kth treatment, and a part ϵ_{jk} which can be regarded as error. These parts are supposed to be additive, so that

(9.7)
$$x_{jk} = \mu + \beta_k + \epsilon_{jk}$$

We can imagine μ adjusted so that $\sum \beta_k = 0$. We assume also that each ϵ_{jk} is an independent* random variate with expectation 0, independent not only of the other ϵ's but also of the β's. The hypothesis to be tested is that the β_k are all zero, or in other words that the treatments do not effectively differ from each other.

* It is sufficient for some purposes to assume that the ϵ_{jk} are *uncorrelated*, but if they are normally distributed zero covariances imply independence.

Often it is necessary to make special experimental arrangements to ensure approximate independence of the ϵ_{jk}. Thus the individual plots of land receiving the same treatment are not side by side but randomly arranged in blocks.

A further assumption we will make is that the ϵ_{jk} are normally distributed about zero with a common variance σ^2. If so and if our hypothesis is true, the x_{jk} are independent normal variates and (see § 7.6) $\sum_{jk}(x_{jk} - \bar{x})^2/\sigma^2$ is distributed as χ^2 with $\sum N_k - 1 = N - 1$ df. Moreover, for each value of k, $\sum_{j}(x_{jk} - \bar{x}_{\cdot k})^2/\sigma^2$ is distributed as χ^2 with $N_k - 1$ df, and since the various columns in Table 17 are independent, we can add the χ^2 for these columns. Hence $\sum_{jk}(x_{jk} - \bar{x}_{\cdot k})^2/\sigma^2$ is distributed as χ^2 with $\sum(N_k - 1) = N - b$ df.

Since, therefore, Q and q_2 in Equation (9.4) are distributed as $\chi^2\sigma^2$ with $N - 1$ and $N - b$ df respectively, it follows from Fisher's Theorem (§ 5.4) that q_1 is distributed as $\chi^2\sigma^2$ with $b - 1$ df, independently of q_2. Since the expectation of χ^2 with ν df is equal to ν, it follows that $E[q_1/(b - 1)] = \sigma^2$, $E[q_2/(N - b)] = \sigma^2$ and $E[Q/(N - 1)] = \sigma^2$, or in other words $q_1/(b - 1)$, $q_2/(N - b)$, and $Q/(N - 1)$ are all unbiased estimates of σ^2. The first two of these are independent. The ratio of these estimates is distributed as F with $b - 1$ and $N - b$ df, and hence we have a convenient test for the significance of any apparent treatment effects.

The results may be summarized in an analysis of variance table, such as Table 18.

TABLE 18

Sum of Squares (SS)	Degrees of Freedom (df)	Mean Square (MS)
Between families $q_1 = a\sum_{k}(\bar{x}_{\cdot k} - \bar{x})^2$	$b - 1$	$q_1/(b - 1)$
Within families $q_2 = \sum_{jk}(x_{jk} - \bar{x}_{\cdot k})^2$	$N - b$	$q_2/(N - b)$
Total $Q = \sum_{jk}(x_{jk} - \bar{x})^2$	$N - 1$	$Q/(N - 1)$

The first two columns are additive, but not the third. The name "mean square" is given to the squariance divided by the degrees of freedom. All these mean squares are estimates of the population variance.

Example 1. To test the effect of a small proportion of coal in the sand used for making concrete, several batches were mixed under practically identical conditions except for the variation in the percentage of coal. From each batch some cylinders were made and tested for breaking strength (lb/in^2). The results were

	\multicolumn{5}{c}{Percentage of Coal}
	0	0.05	0.1	0.5	1.0
	1690	1550	1625	1725	1530
	1580	1445	1450	1550	1545
	1745	1645	1510	1430	1565
	1685	1545		1445	1520
Mean	1675	1546.2	1528.3	1537.5	1540

One of the cylinders containing 0.1% was defective, so that there are only three individuals in this family. We find $Q = \sum x^2 - (\sum x)^2/19 = 165{,}918$, $q_1 = 59{,}257$, $q_2 = 106{,}661$.* The analysis of variance is, therefore,

	SS	df	MS
Between families	59,257	4	14,814
Within families	106,661	14	7,619
Total	165,918	18	9,218

$F = 14{,}814/7619 = 1.94$, with 4 and 14 df. The 5% point is 3.11 and the 1% point 5.03, so that this value of F is clearly not significant. The admixture of coal does not, as far as this experiment goes, affect the breaking strength.

There are three estimates of the variance of the parent population, given in the last column of the analysis of variance table. On the null hypothesis the third one is the most reliable, being based on the largest number of degrees of freedom, although we usually use the second, as it is valid even when the null hypothesis is not true.

The standard error of the mean of samples of n is, therefore, estimated as $(7619/n)^{1/2}$. The significance of the difference between two family means may be estimated by the t-test, but it must be remembered that even if we really have several groups drawn at random from the same population, the difference between the *largest* and *smallest* group means may well appear significant as judged by a test appropriate only to two random samples.

9.2 Two-way Classification, with One Individual in Each Sub-class. Instead of regarding the individuals in a column of Table 17 as mere replicates of one another, subject only to random variation, we may be interested in a possible significant variation between the individuals. We may have, for example, b varieties of sugar beet, to be tested for sugar yield, these varieties corresponding to the b treatments of the Table. If each variety is grown on a plots of land, we have the possibility of distinguishing experimentally be-

* The physical dimensions of q_1 and q_2 (lb^2 in^{-4}) are omitted for convenience. The quantity F, being a ratio of two variances, has of course no dimensions.

tween the variations in yield due to the difference between varieties and the variations in yield due to soil factors (fertility, moisture, etc.). In order to do so, we group the plots in *blocks*, in the simplest case b plots to a block, and arrange that each variety is grown on one and only one plot in each block. There may, and often will, be well-marked differences between blocks due to gradients of soil fertility in the field, but if the different varieties are assigned to plots within a block in a truly random manner the effect of block differences can be separated completely from the effect of variety differences. The $ab\ (= N)$ values of the variate x are now classified into a rows (representing blocks) and b columns (representing varieties).

Let x_{jk} be the value of x in the jth row and kth column. Let $\bar{x}_{j.}$ be the mean of the jth row and $\bar{x}_{.k}$ the mean of the kth column, and let Q be the total squariance. Now Q can be resolved into three quadratic forms as follows:

(9.8) $$Q = q_1 + q_2 + q_3$$

where

$$q_1 = b\sum_1^a (\bar{x}_{j.} - \bar{x})^2$$

$$q_2 = a\sum_1^b (\bar{x}_{.k} - \bar{x})^2$$

$$q_3 = \sum_1^a \sum_1^b (x_{jk} - \bar{x}_{j.} - \bar{x}_{.k} + \bar{x})^2$$

That (9.8) is an identity in the $N = ab$ values of x can be readily seen as follows:

$$\sum_1^a \sum_1^b (x_{jk} - \bar{x})^2 = \sum_1^a \sum_1^b \{(x_{jk} - \bar{x}_{j.} - \bar{x}_{.k} + \bar{x}) + (\bar{x}_{j.} - \bar{x}) + (\bar{x}_{.k} - \bar{x})\}^2$$

$$= \sum_1^a \sum_1^b (x_{jk} - \bar{x}_{j.} - \bar{x}_{.k} + \bar{x})^2 + \sum_1^a \sum_1^b (\bar{x}_{j.} - \bar{x})^2$$

$$+ \sum_1^a \sum_1^b (\bar{x}_{.k} - \bar{x})^2$$

To show that the cross-product terms vanish consider the term

$$\sum_1^a \sum_1^b (x_{jk} - \bar{x}_{j.} - \bar{x}_{.k} + \bar{x})(\bar{x}_{j.} - \bar{x})$$

This becomes

$$\sum_{j=1}^a (\bar{x}_{j.} - \bar{x}) \sum_{k=1}^b (x_{jk} - \bar{x}_{j.} - \bar{x}_{.k} + \bar{x})$$

$$= \sum_{j=1}^a (\bar{x}_{j.} - \bar{x})(b\bar{x}_{j.} - b\bar{x}_{j.} - b\bar{x} + b\bar{x}) = 0$$

A similar demonstration can be made for the other cross-product terms. This is left as an exercise for the student. Since

Sec. 2   Two-way Classification

$$\sum_{1}^{a}\sum_{1}^{b}(\bar{x}_{j\cdot} - \bar{x})^2 = b\sum_{1}^{a}(\bar{x}_{j\cdot} - \bar{x})^2$$

$$\sum_{1}^{a}\sum_{1}^{b}(\bar{x}_{\cdot k} - \bar{x})^2 = a\sum_{1}^{b}(\bar{x}_{\cdot k} - \bar{x})^2$$

(9.8) is established.

The variability *between rows* is measured by q_1 and *between columns* by q_2. The residual variability, freed from the influence of either rows or columns, is measured by q_3. On the assumption that the row effects and the column effects are independent of each other, q_3 measures the "experimental error" inherent in the experiment and over which no control is attempted. If blocks are distinguished by rows and treatments by columns and if there is a differential response of individuals in certain blocks to treatments, markedly different from the average differential response over all blocks to the same treatments, there is said to be *interaction* between blocks and treatments. Such interaction, if it exists, will be lumped with the experimental error, and the usual mathematical model ignores it.

The mathematical model is now

(9.9) $\qquad\qquad x_{jk} = \mu + \alpha_j + \beta_k + \epsilon_{jk}$

where the part α_j is characteristic of the jth individual and β_k of the kth treatment, and where

$$\sum \alpha_j = 0, \qquad \sum \beta_k = 0$$

If we suppose that the ϵ_{jk} are all normally and independently distributed about zero with the same variance σ^2, and if all the α_j and β_k are zero, then Q is distributed as $\chi^2\sigma^2$ with $N - 1$ df. Also $\bar{x}_{j\cdot}$ is normally distributed with variance σ^2/b so that q_1 is distributed as $\chi^2\sigma^2$ with $b - 1$ df, and similarly q_2 is so distributed, independently, with $a - 1$ df. It follows that q_3 is distributed as $\chi^2\sigma^2$ with $N - a - b + 1 = (a - 1)(b - 1)$ df, independently of q_1 and q_2. The analysis of variance is as shown in Table 19.

TABLE 19

Variance due to	df	SS	MS
Rows	$a - 1$	$q_1 = b\sum_{1}^{a}(\bar{x}_{j\cdot} - \bar{x})^2$	$q_1/(a - 1)$
Columns	$b - 1$	$q_2 = a\sum_{1}^{b}(\bar{x}_{\cdot k} - \bar{x})^2$	$q_2/(b - 1)$
Interaction	$(a - 1)(b - 1)$	$q_3 = Q - q_1 - q_2$	$q_3/(a - 1)(b - 1)$
Total	$ab - 1$	$Q = \sum_{1}^{a}\sum_{1}^{b}(x_{jk} - \bar{x})^2$	

The quantities in the 4th column are all independent unbiased estimates of σ^2. The quotient $Q/(ab - 1)$ is also an unbiased estimate but is not independent of the others. Under the null hypothesis that there is no significant variation between individuals, the quantity

(9.10) $$F = \frac{(b-1)q_1}{q_3}$$

has the F-distribution with $b - 1$ and $(a - 1)(b - 1)$ df. Under the null hypothesis that there is no significant variation between treatments,

(9.11) $$F = (a - 1)q_2/q_3$$

has the F-distribution with $a - 1$ and $(a - 1)(b - 1)$ df.

Example 2. On a feeding experiment a farmer has four types of hogs denoted by I, II, III, IV. These types are each divided into three groups which are fed varietal rations A, B, and C. The following results are obtained, the numbers in the table being the gains in weight in pounds in the various groups.

	I	II	III	IV	Totals
A	7.0	16.0	10.5	13.5	47.0
B	14.0	15.5	15.0	21.0	65.5
C	8.5	16.5	9.5	13.5	48.0
Totals	29.5	48.0	35.0	48.0	160.5

The computations yield the following results:

Sum of Squares		df	Unbiased Estimates
Rations	54.1250	2	27.06
Types	87.7292	3	29.24
Residual	28.2083	6	4.70

To test the significance of the variation in rations we refer $F = 27.06/4.70 = 5.76$ to Snedecor's table where, corresponding to (2, 6) degrees of freedom, we find 5.14 for the 5% point and 10.92 for the 1% point. Similarly, to test the significance of the variation between types we compute $F = 29.24/4.70 = 6.2$. The entries in the table for (3, 6) degrees of freedom are 4.76 for the 5% point and 9.78 for the 1% point. Our conclusion is that there is a significant difference between breeds and between varieties of rations at the 5% point, but that neither is significant at the 1% point.

9.3 Interpretation of the Mean Square. Suppose that in the one-way classification of § 9.1 the null hypothesis that the β_k are all zero is untenable. The true mean of the kth family is then $\mu + \beta_k$, with $\sum \beta_k = 0$. Even if the null hypothesis is *not* rejected at the chosen level of significance, we cannot be

Sec. 3   Interpretation of the Mean Square   245

sure that the β_k are really all zero. The expected values of q_1 and of Q then include terms depending on the β_k, although, as we shall see, the mean square *within* families still provides a valid estimate of σ^2.

$$E(q_1) = E\sum_k N_k\{\bar{x}_{\cdot k} - \mu - \beta_k - (\bar{x} - \mu) + \beta_k\}^2$$
$$= E\sum N_k\{\bar{x}_{\cdot k} - \mu - \beta_k - (\bar{x} - \mu)\}^2 + \sum N_k \beta_k^2$$

Since $\bar{x}_{\cdot k} - \mu - \beta_k$ has a mean $\bar{x} - \mu$ and variance σ^2/N_k, the expectation of $\sum N_k\{\bar{x}_{\cdot k} - \mu - \beta_k - (\bar{x} - \mu)\}^2$ is $(b-1)\sigma^2$. Hence

$$E(q_1) = (b-1)\sigma^2 + \sum N_k \beta_k^2$$

The expectation of the mean square *between* families is, therefore, always greater than σ^2 unless all the β_k vanish. In the same way

$$E(Q) = E\sum\{x_{jk} - \mu - \beta_k - (\bar{x} - \mu)\}^2 + \sum N_k \beta_k^2$$
$$= (N-1)\sigma^2 + \sum N_k \beta_k^2$$

It follows that

$$E(q_2) = (N-b)\sigma^2$$

The null hypothesis is tested by finding the value of $F = [E(q_1)/E(q_2)] \times [(N-b)/(b-1)]$, which should be equal to 1 if all the β_k vanish. Note that in using this F-test we are testing the null hypothesis that $F = 1$ against the alternative hypothesis that F is greater than 1. Hence, as already indicated in § 7.16, the 5% point, for example, really does provide in this case a 5% level of significance.

The assumption that the population variance is the same for all the families, even though their means differ, appears rather artificial. There are, however, many situations in which it may not be unreasonable. A fertilizer treatment, for example, may cause a marked change in the yield from each of a number of plots, without much affecting the variability from plot to plot.

In the two-way classification, given by

$$x_{jk} = \mu + \alpha_j + \beta_k + \epsilon_{jk}$$

where

$$\sum_j \alpha_j = 0, \qquad \sum_k \beta_k = 0$$

$$E(q_1) = bE\sum_j (\bar{x}_{j\cdot} - \bar{x})^2$$
$$= bE\sum_j \{\bar{x}_{j\cdot} - \mu - \alpha_j - (\bar{x} - \mu) + \alpha_j\}^2$$
$$= bE\sum_j \{\bar{x}_{j\cdot} - \mu - \alpha_j - (\bar{x} - \mu)\}^2 + b\sum_j \alpha_j^2$$
$$= (a-1)\sigma^2 + b\sum_j \alpha_j^2$$

In the same way

$$E(q_2) = (b-1)\sigma^2 + a\sum_k \beta_k^2$$

and

$$E(Q) = (N-1)\sigma^2 + a\sum_k \beta_k^2 + b\sum_j \alpha_j^2$$

so that $E(q_3) = (a-1)(b-1)\sigma^2$. Hence it is still true that the residual mean square provides an unbiased estimate of the population variance, although the other mean squares contain additional components, as set out in Table 20.

TABLE 20

	Mean Square	Expectation
Rows	$q_1/(a-1)$	$\sigma^2 + b\sum \alpha_j^2/(a-1)$
Columns	$q_2/(b-1)$	$\sigma^2 + a\sum \beta_k^2/(b-1)$
Interaction (Residual)	$q_3/(a-1)(b-1)$	σ^2
Total	$Q/(N-1)$	$\sigma^2 + (a\sum \beta_k^2 + b\sum \alpha_j^2)/(N-1)$

9.4 Three-way Classification (One Member in Each Sub-class). Let us suppose that our material is classified into A-, B-, and C-classes, in number a, b, c, respectively, and that the value of the observed variate corresponding to the sub-class $A_j B_k C_l$ is x_{jkl}. The mean value of x over the A-classes for fixed B_k and C_l is $\bar{x}_{.kl}$, the mean value over the A- and B-classes for fixed C_l is $\bar{x}_{..l}$, and the general mean is $\bar{x}$ (written for short instead of $\bar{x}...$). Then, on the hypothesis of homogeneity and normality, we can prove by a direct extension of the method already given for the simpler cases that the total sum of squares may be split into 7 components ($7 = 2^3 - 1$) with degrees of freedom as given in Table 21.

TABLE 21

Variance	SS	df
Between A-classes	$q_1 = bc\sum(\bar{x}_{j..} - \bar{x})^2$	$a-1$
Between B-classes	$q_2 = ca\sum(\bar{x}_{.k.} - \bar{x})^2$	$b-1$
Between C-classes	$q_3 = ab\sum(\bar{x}_{..l} - \bar{x})^2$	$c-1$
Interaction AB	$q_4 = c\sum(\bar{x}_{jk.} - \bar{x}_{j..} - \bar{x}_{.k.} + \bar{x})^2$	$(a-1)(b-1)$
Interaction BC	$q_5 = a\sum(\bar{x}_{.kl} - \bar{x}_{.k.} - \bar{x}_{..l} + \bar{x})^2$	$(b-1)(c-1)$
Interaction CA	$q_6 = b\sum(\bar{x}_{j.l} - \bar{x}_{..l} - \bar{x}_{j..} + \bar{x})^2$	$(c-1)(a-1)$
Interaction ABC (Residual)	$q_7 = \sum(x_{jkl} + \bar{x}_{j..} + \bar{x}_{.k.} + \bar{x}_{..l}$ $-\bar{x}_{jk.} - \bar{x}_{j.l} - \bar{x}_{.kl} - \bar{x})^2$	$(a-1)(b-1)(c-1)$
Total	$Q = \sum(x_{jkl} - \bar{x})^2$	$abc-1$

The mean squares, given by dividing the SS by the df, are all, on the null hypothesis, unbiased estimates of σ^2, and all except the last (for the total) are independent. If the null hypothesis is rejected, the residual mean square $q_7/\{(a-1)(b-1)(c-1)\}$ is an unbiased estimate of σ^2 and so are the mean squares $q_4/\{(a-1)(b-1)\}$, $q_5/\{(b-1)(c-1)\}$ and $q_6/\{(c-1)(a-1)\}$, provided that we assume the *additivity* of the A-, B- and C-effects, as represented by the equation

(9.12) $$x_{jkl} = \mu + \alpha_j + \beta_k + \gamma_l + \epsilon_{jkl}$$

where as usual ϵ_{jkl} is supposed normally distributed about zero with variance σ^2.

We can therefore use the F-test to see whether the ratios of these last three estimates to the residual mean square differ significantly from unity. If all the interactions are non-significant, the sums of squares and the degrees of freedom may be pooled and the joint estimate of error used for testing the main effects. If one or more of the interactions are significant the mathematical model (9.12) must be modified.

The general model involving interactions may be written

$$x_{jkl} = \mu + \alpha_j + \beta_k + \gamma_l + (\alpha\beta)_{jk} + (\alpha\gamma)_{jl} + (\beta\gamma)_{kl} + \epsilon_{jkl}$$

where, for example, the term $(\alpha\beta)_{jk}$ represents the effect of the AB interaction superimposed on the separate A and B effects, and where $\sum \alpha_j$, $\sum \beta_k$, $\sum \gamma_l$, $\sum_j (\alpha\beta)_{jk}$, $\sum_k (\alpha\beta)_{jk}$, etc., are all zero.

The expectation of $q_4/\{(a-1)(b-1)\}$ may be shown, as in § 9.3, to be $\sigma^2 + c \sum (\alpha\beta)_{jk}^2/\{(a-1)(b-1)\}$, and similarly for the other interaction terms. The expectation of $q_1/(a-1)$ is, however, $\sigma^2 + bc \sum \alpha_j^2/(a-1)$, so that the significance of the main effects may still be judged by comparison of the mean squares for these effects with the residual mean square. We shall see later that when the effects, including the interactions, are treated as independent random variables this procedure is no longer correct. (See § 9.9.)

When there is interaction the quantity q_4 is no longer strictly distributed as χ^2. Instead,

$$c \sum \{\bar{x}_{jk\cdot} - \bar{x}_{j\cdot\cdot} - \bar{x}_{\cdot k\cdot} + \bar{x} - (\alpha\beta)_{jk}\}^2$$

is so distributed. The comparison of, say, q_1 with q_4 by the F-test is not justified. However, this kind of test is commonly made, on the ground that, if there are interaction effects, the main effects must be large compared with these interaction effects if they are to have any practical importance.

Example 3. In an experiment at the Dominion Laboratory of Plant Pathology, Alberta, to determine the effect on the growth of wheat when the seeds are buried for a time in ground pitchblende (and so subjected to radiations) the variable measured was the average length of shoot in millimeters for 25 plants. The seeds were planted in four replicate blocks, 14 plots to a block, the time of exposure varied from 1 to 7 days, and there was a complete set of controls, treated in all respects like the experimental seeds except that they were not irradiated. The A-classes are irradiated (R) and non-irradiated (N). The B-classes are exposure times and the C-classes blocks. The results are shown in Table 22.

TABLE 22

Exposure (days)	Treatment	Blocks				Totals	
		I	II	III	IV		
1	R	136.7	106.1	110.0	135.0	487.8	905.4
	N	96.6	99.1	109.2	112.7	417.6	
2	R	140.9	131.4	142.7	154.3	569.3	1029.0
	N	117.8	142.1	92.1	107.7	459.7	
3	R	149.0	133.0	126.0	136.4	544.4	1048.9
	N	148.5	112.4	139.0	104.6	504.5	
4	R	165.2	152.3	167.0	145.7	630.2	1217.0
	N	131.7	160.8	145.6	148.7	586.8	
5	R	122.6	151.3	93.8	110.7	478.4	1009.6
	N	94.2	147.1	141.4	148.5	531.2	
6	R	161.2	147.0	158.7	150.2	617.1	1214.0
	N	137.9	149.7	145.8	163.5	596.9	
7	R	125.0	144.4	138.4	147.7	555.5	1034.5
	N	109.9	117.5	125.5	126.1	479.0	
Totals		1837.2	1894.2	1835.2	1891.8	7458.4	7458.4

The sum for all the R cells is 3882.7, and for all the N cells 3575.7. Here $a = 2$, $b = 7$, $c = 4$, so that the total number of df is 55. We find $Q = \sum x^2 - (\sum x)^2/N = 1{,}016{,}197 - C$, where $C = (7458.4)^2/56 = 993{,}352$, so that $Q = 22{,}845$.

Since $\bar{x}_1.. = 3882.7/28$ and $\bar{x}_2.. = 3575.7/28$,

$$q_1 = [(3882.7)^2 + (3575.7)^2]/28 - C = 1655$$

and similarly,

$$q_2 = [(905.4)^2 + \cdots + (1034.5)^2]/8 - C = 9541$$
$$q_3 = [(1837.2)^2 + \cdots + (1891.8)^2]/14 - C = 230.8$$

The calculations of the interaction terms are a little more complicated. Thus q_4 can be written

$$q_4 = c \sum_{jk} \bar{x}_{jk.}^2 - bc \sum_{j} \bar{x}_{j..}^2 - ac \sum_{k} \bar{x}_{.k.}^2 + abc\,\bar{x}^2$$
$$= c \sum_{jk} \bar{x}_{jk.}^2 - q_1 - q_2 - C$$
$$= \tfrac{1}{4}[(487.8)^2 + \cdots + (479.0)^2] - 11{,}196 - C$$
$$= 2029$$

Similarly, since $\bar{x}_{.11} = (136.7 + 96.6)/2 = 233.3/2$, etc.,

$$q_5 = a \sum \bar{x}_{.kl}^2 - q_2 - q_3 - C$$
$$= \tfrac{1}{2}[(233.3)^2 + \cdots + (273.8)^2] - C - 9772$$
$$= 4174$$

and, since $\bar{x}_{1.1} = (136.7 + 140.9 + \cdots + 125.0)/7 = 1000.6/7$,

Sec. 5   Assumptions Made in Analysis of Variance

$$q_6 = b \sum \bar{x}_{j.}^2 - q_3 - q_1 - C$$
$$= \tfrac{1}{7}[(1000.6)^2 + \cdots + (911.8)^2] - C - 1886$$
$$= 798$$

By subtraction, $q_7 = 4417$, so that the complete analysis of variance is as shown in Table 23.

Table 23

Variation due to	SS	df	MS
Treatments (A)	1,655	1	1655
Exposures (B)	9,541	6	1590
Blocks (C)	231	3	77
Interaction AB	2,029	6	338
Interaction BC	4,174	18	232
Interaction CA	798	3	266
Residual ABC	4,417	18	245
Total	22,845	55	

It is clear that none of the interactions is significant, so that they can all be lumped together with the residual to give a mean square for error of $11{,}418/45 = 254$, with 45 df. Obviously there is no effect due to differences between the blocks. For the treatments, $F = 1655/254 = 6.52$. Since for $n_1 = 1$ and $n_2 = 45$, the 5% point for F is 4.06 and the 1% point 7.23, there is apparently a significant treatment effect. For exposures, $F = 1590/254 = 6.56$; with $n_1 = 6$ and $n_2 = 45$, the 5% point is 2.31, and the 1% point 3.23, so that the effect of length of exposure must be regarded as highly significant. That is to say, the mere act of burying the seeds in powdered rock, whether radioactive or not, for varying lengths of time apparently affected the length of shoot produced when the seeds were planted out. This is unexpected, as is also the absence of significant interaction between treatment and exposure. One would expect the effect of radiation, if significant at all, to depend on the length of exposure.

It may be noted that, when we have several different estimates of a common variance, the chance that the *largest* ratio will be significant is considerably greater than would be given by the F-test. This test gives the probability that a *random* value of the ratio of two estimates will be exceeded. There is a danger of attributing significance to what, after all, may be just a sampling effect.

9.5 Assumptions Made in Analysis of Variance.
The assumptions underlying the usual techniques of the analysis of variance may be summarized as:

1. Additivity of treatment effects and of environmental effects (such as the variation between blocks).

2. Independence of all the experimental errors.

3. Normality of the distribution of experimental errors.

4. Constancy of the variance of the experimental errors, whatever the magnitude of the treatment or other effects.

It is desirable to know whether the test will be seriously affected when these assumptions do not apply. The assumptions, of course, are not equally serious, but taken together they imply a severe restriction on the type of data to which the techniques of the analysis of variance are strictly relevant. In practice the techniques are applied very widely, so that the conclusions drawn must usually be interpreted with caution.

Non-normality. Attempts to obtain the exact distribution of F, under the null hypothesis, for random samples from a non-normal population have encountered serious mathematical difficulties. E. S. Pearson [2] obtained empirical distributions for samples or 500 of 1000 from six selected non-normal populations, but the samples were not large enough to fix the 5% points, let alone the 1% points, with much accuracy. Nevertheless, from these and some other experiments it appears that the ordinary F-test may be applied without serious error to most types of distributions that are likely to occur. Cochran [1] suggests that a tabular 5% may mean anything between 4 and 7% and a tabular 1% anything between $\frac{1}{2}$ and 2%. As a rule the effect of non-normality is to make results look more significant than they are.

Unless the data are very extensive, it is seldom possible to prove that they are not normal. The standard errors of skewness and kurtosis are so large that only very marked non-normality could be detected in a sample of moderate size. If there is reason to suspect non-normality, from the nature of the data, one may try one of the transformations mentioned in the next section. These, although intended to stabilize the variance, do, as a rule, improve the approximation to normality.

The analysis of variance test has been considered by Pitman,[17] and independently by Welch,[18] from a different standpoint altogether, and in this form the test involves no assumptions about the normality or otherwise of the parent population. Their approach is as follows.

In the simple case of complete randomized blocks, with a blocks and b treatments, the treatments are allocated at random among the b plots in a block. If $x_{ij}(k)$ is the yield of the jth plot in the ith block (the kth treatment being applied to this plot), the null hypothesis is that $x_{ij}(k)$ is independent of k. This means that any one of the treatments would produce the same yield on a particular plot, so that there is no treatment effect. The various yields within each block might, therefore, be rearranged in all the $b!$ possible permutations and all these would on the null hypothesis be equally likely. The whole set of yields actually obtained is regarded as one of the $(b!)^a$ possible and equally likely rearrangements among the experimental plots. This is quite different from the classical point of view, in which the yields in a given block (on the null hypothesis regarding treatments) are considered as random samples from a hypothetical infinite population of yields having a normal distribution.

If we calculate the sums of squares and write

$$S = S_B + S_T + S_E$$

where S is the total SS and S_B, S_T, S_E are the SS due to blocks, treatments, and error respectively, then, on the ordinary theory, the ratio

Sec. 5 Assumptions Made in Analysis of Variance 251

$$W = S_T/(S_T + S_E) = S_T/(S - S_B)$$

has a beta-distribution with parameters $(b-1)/2$, and $(a-1)(b-1)/2$. This is equivalent to saying that $(a-1)W/(1-W)$ has the F-distribution.

From the Pitman and Welch point of view, the observed W is the result of the chance allocation of treatments within a block. In the various permutations that give rise to the different possible values of W the sum of squares *within* blocks remains unchanged. Hence $S_T + S_E$ is constant, so that the distribution of W is that of S_T.

It was shown by Pitman that W has the same expectation a^{-1} as on the ordinary theory, but its variance depends on the different within-block variances. If all these variances are equal (as will be the case when the variates are ranks), the variance of W is $2(a-1)/\{a^3(b-1)\}$. The variance of W on the ordinary theory is $2(a-1)/\{a^3(b-1) + 2a^2\}$, which is not very different if a and b are fairly large. The distribution of W is in fact quite close to a beta-distribution with parameters $p = \frac{1}{2}(b-1) - a^{-1}$, $q = \frac{1}{2}(a-1)(b-1) - (a-1)/a$.

Correlation Between the Errors. Suppose that ϵ_i $(i = 1, 2 \cdots a)$ are the errors of the individual observations on a single treatment, and that these have a common variance σ^2 and a correlation coefficient ρ between each pair. Then Var $(\sum \epsilon_i) = a\sigma^2 + a(a-1)\rho\sigma^2$ (see Problem 20, Chapter IV), so that the true variance of the treatment *mean* will be $\sigma^2[1 + (a-1)\rho]/a$. The estimate of this variance given by the usual method is equal to the sum of squares within the family divided by $a(a-1)$. This sum of squares is $\sum(\epsilon_i - \bar{\epsilon})^2 = \sum \epsilon_i^2 - a\bar{\epsilon}^2$.

Now the expectation of $\sum \epsilon_i^2$ is $a\sigma^2$ and the expectation of $a\bar{\epsilon}^2$ is $E[\sum_i \epsilon_i^2 + \sum_{i \neq j} \epsilon_i \epsilon_j]/a$, so that the expectation of the analysis of variance estimate is $\sigma^2(1-\rho)/a$. This is less than the true value by $\rho\sigma^2$. Hence, if ρ is positive, the treatment mean is less accurate than it is estimated to be. If ρ is negative, it is more accurate. In either case there is a bias in the estimation of the variance. The actual situation is, of course, more complicated than in this simple example, but the general effect of correlation is evident.

Proper randomization will usually remove this difficulty. The plots corresponding to various treatments are laid out in blocks, for example, so that any one treatment is scattered at random over the blocks. Effects due to fertility gradients within the blocks are thus largely eliminated, and the errors may then be treated as though they were independent.

Non-additivity. A reasonable alternative to supposing the effects additive is to take them as multiplicative. For example, in the two-way classification, $x_{jk} = \mu \alpha_j \beta_k (1 + \epsilon_{jk})$. If we suppose that the ϵ_{jk} are all zero, the method of analysis of variance described in § 9.2 will give an *apparent* error variance

$q_3/(a-1)(b-1)$
$$= \mu^2[\sum(\alpha_j\beta_k)^2 - a\bar{\alpha}^2\sum\beta_k^2 - b\bar{\beta}^2\sum\alpha_j^2 + ab\overline{\alpha\beta}^2]/(a-1)(b-1)$$

When the ϵ_{jk} are not zero, the error variance will be increased by an amount due to non-additivity. Unless the error variance is small or the treatment and replication effects are both large this increase will generally be negligible.

If there is reason to suspect non-additivity, it may be well to transform the variables as mentioned in the next section.

Non-uniformity of Variance. The effect of differences between the variances will be to reduce the sensitivity of tests of significance and to increase the uncertainty in the estimation of treatment effects. If a pooled error is used for t-tests between two treatments, the result may be seriously in error.

If all the error variances are known, the observations may be weighted, each being given a weight inversely proportional to its error variance. In practice, the error variances are not known, but it is sometimes possible, when the data are obviously heterogeneous, to separate them into parts for each of which a variance may be estimated.

Another situation arises when the variate x has a distribution (say of the binomial or Poisson type) for which the variance is a function of the expectation. If there are real treatment effects, the variance will clearly not be constant as between treatments. The remedy in such cases is to make a suitable transformation of the variable.

9.6 Transformations to Stabilize Variance.[3] Suppose the original variate x has a distribution for which the expectation is $E(x) = m$ and the variance is Var $(x) = f(m)$, $f(m)$ not being a constant. We wish to find a new variable y, a function of x, for which the variance will be independent (or nearly independent) of m.

Let $y = \phi(x)$. Then for small variations of x around m, we have approximately,[4] by Taylor's Theorem,
$$y = \phi(m) + (x - m)\phi'(m)$$
where ϕ' is the derivative of ϕ. Since $E(x - m) = 0$, it follows that $E(y) = \phi(m)$ and
$$\text{Var }(y) \approx E[(x - m)\phi'(m)]^2$$
$$= [\phi'(m)]^2 \text{ Var }(x)$$
$$= [\phi'(m)]^2 f(m)$$

Hence, if Var $(y) = c^2$, where c is a constant,
$$\phi'(m) \approx c[f(m)]^{-1/2}$$
so that
(9.13) $$\phi(m) \approx c\int [f(m)]^{-1/2} dm$$

If the distribution of x is *binomial*, x being, say, a proportion of successes in a

Sec. 6 Transformations to Stabilize Variance

given number s of trials, $m = \theta$ and $f(m) = \theta(1 - \theta)/s$. Therefore, ignoring the constant,

(9.14) $$\phi(x) = \sin^{-1}(x^{1/2})$$

This is known as the *angular transformation*. A convenient table giving the angles $\phi(x)$ for different values of x (expressed as a percentage) is given by Snedecor.[5] The transformation works quite well except at the extreme values of x. Bartlett has suggested that the ratios $0/s$ and s/s should be counted respectively as $1/4s$ and $(s - 1/4)s$. This transformation improves the approximation to normality, which is very poor for the binomial distribution with moderate values of s and θ near 0 or 1. The approximate variance is $1/(4s)$ if $\phi(x)$ is in radians or $821/s$ if $\phi(x)$ is in degrees.

If the distribution of x is of the *Poisson type* with expectation m, $f(m) = m$, and $\phi(m) = 2c\, m^{1/2}$. Hence the transformation is $\phi(x) = x^{1/2}$. Bartlett has shown that still better results are given by

(9.15) $$\phi(x) = (x + \tfrac{1}{2})^{1/2}$$

where the $\tfrac{1}{2}$ is added as a sort of correction for continuity. This is usually called the *square root transformation*. The variance is fairly constant for $m > 3$, being approximately 0.25.

For many biological populations the standard deviation is approximately proportional to the mean, that is, $f(m) = k^2 m^2$, so that

(9.16) $$\phi(x) = \log x$$

This is the *logarithmic transformation*. It will convert multiplicative effects into additive ones. The empirical transformation

(9.17) $$\phi(x) = \log(1 + x)$$

avoids the difficulty of applying (9.16) when x happens to be zero. The variance is approximately k^2 or $0.189k^2$, according as the logarithms are to base e or to base 10.

The *Fisher transformation* (see § 8.15) may be included here. If $f(m) = k(1 - m^2)^2$, then by (9.13), $\phi(m) = \tfrac{1}{2}\log[(1 + m)/(1 - m)]$. This is the same as (8.70),

$$z' = \tfrac{1}{2}\log\frac{1 + r}{1 - r}$$

as used for transforming sample correlation coefficients. The transformation achieves approximate normality as well as approximate constancy of variance. It is not, of course, needed very often in analysis of variance problems. (See § 9.18.)

Example 4 (Bartlett). Table 24 gives the number of wheat seeds out of 50 which failed to germinate under different treatments, each with 4 replications. Treatments 6 and 7 were actually identical.

TABLE 24

	Treatments						
Replications	1	2	3	4	5	6	7
1	10	11	8	9	7	6	9
2	8	10	3	7	9	3	11
3	5	11	2	8	10	7	11
4	1	6	4	13	7	10	10
Totals	24	38	17	37	33	26	41

The distribution being presumably binomial, but with θ possibly varying from treatment to treatment, the angular transformation is indicated, namely, $y = \sin^{-1}(2x/100)^{1/2}$. The values of y (in degrees) are given in Table 24A.

TABLE 24A

	Treatments						
Replications	1	2	3	4	5	6	7
1	26.6	28.0	23.6	25.1	22.0	20.3	25.1
2	23.6	26.6	14.2	22.0	25.1	14.2	28.0
3	18.4	28.0	11.5	23.6	26.6	22.0	28.0
4	8.1	20.3	16.4	30.7	22.0	26.6	26.6

The analysis of variance in the new variable is

	SS	df	MS
Between treatments	361.5	6	60.25
Within treatments	460.2	21	21.91
Total	821.7	27	

Hence $F = 2.75$. Since with $n_1 = 6$ and $n_2 = 21$, the 5% point is 2.57 and the 1% point is 3.81, the value of F appears barely significant. The estimate of variance 21.9 from the MS within treatments is greater than the value $821/50 = 16.4$ which we should expect if the variability were really binomial.

9.7 Tests of Homogeneity of Variance. If we have sufficient degrees of freedom to estimate the separate variances for different treatments with reasonable accuracy, we can apply certain tests to determine whether the hypothesis of a constant variance from treatment to treatment is acceptable.

Suppose we have b samples, with numbers $N_1, N_2, \cdots N_b$ and squariances $S_1, S_2, \cdots S_b$, each drawn from a normal population with unknown mean and variance. The hypothesis to be tested is that these variances σ_k^2 ($k = 1$,

Sec. 7 Tests of Homogeneity of Variance 255

$2, \cdots b$) are in fact all equal to σ^2. On the null hypothesis the quantities S_k/σ^2 are distributed independently as χ^2 with n_k ($= N_k - 1$) degrees of freedom, and $S/\sigma^2 = \sum S_k/\sigma^2$ is distributed as χ^2 with n ($=\sum n_k$) degrees of freedom. The joint probability density of the S_k is, therefore,

$$(9.18) \qquad P = (2\sigma^2)^{-b} \prod_{k=1}^{b} f_k(S_k/2\sigma^2)$$

where $f_k(x) = x^{\frac{1}{2}n_k - 1} e^{-x}/\Gamma(\frac{1}{2}n_k)$, and the probability density of S is

$$(9.19) \qquad P_0 = (2\sigma^2)^{-1}(S/2\sigma^2)^{(n/2)-1} e^{-S/2\sigma^2}/\Gamma(n/2)$$

In order to test the homogeneity of the variances, we calculate the conditional probability of getting the observed squariances $S_1, S_2, \cdots S_k$, *if the total of these squariances is fixed.* That is, we determine $\Pr\{S_1, \cdots S_b \mid S\}$, which is equal to $\Pr\{S_1, \cdots S_b\}/\Pr\{S\}$ or, apart from differentials, to P/P_0. Now P and P_0 contain σ^2. The ratios S_k/σ^2 and S/σ^2 will be independent of the units in which the variable is measured, but this will not be true of the factor $2\sigma^2$. If, however, we take as our variable $\log S_k$ instead of S_k this difficulty will be removed. If $y_k = \log S_k$, $dy_k = dS_k/S_k$, so that the joint probability density of the y_k is

$$P' = \prod_k f_k'(S_k/2\sigma^2)$$

where $f'_k(x) = x^{n_k/2} e^{-x}/\Gamma(\frac{1}{2}n_k)$, and the probability density of $y = \log S$ is

$$P_0' = (S/2\sigma^2)^{n/2} e^{-S/2\sigma^2}/\Gamma(n/2)$$

Hence the conditional probability density is

$$(9.20) \qquad \frac{P'}{P_0'} = \frac{\Gamma(n/2)}{\prod_k \Gamma(n_k/2)} \cdot \frac{\prod_k \{(S_k/2\sigma^2)^{n_k/2} e^{-S_k/2\sigma^2}\}}{(S/2\sigma^2)^{n/2} e^{-S/2\sigma^2}}$$

The likelihood is the logarithm of this, namely,

$$L = \sum \tfrac{1}{2} n_k \log S_k - \sum S_k/2\sigma^2 - \tfrac{1}{2} n \log S + S/2\sigma^2 + C$$
$$= \sum \tfrac{1}{2} n_k \log S_k - \tfrac{1}{2} n \log S + C$$

since $S = \sum S_k$ and $n = \sum n_k$. The maximum value of L for different possible values of $S_1, S_2, \cdots S_b$, is given by putting $\partial L/\partial S_k = 0$, $k = 1, 2, \cdots b$. That is, $\tfrac{1}{2} n_k/S_k - n/2S = 0$, or $S_k/S = n_k/n$, which is equivalent to $S_k = c n_k$. The maximum value of L is, therefore,

$$L_{\max} = \sum \tfrac{1}{2} n_k \log n_k - \tfrac{1}{2} n \log n + C$$

If we take as our statistic to measure homogeneity of variance

$$(9.21) \qquad \begin{aligned} M &= 2(L_{\max} - L) \\ &= -\sum n_k \log(S_k/n_k) + n \log(S/n) \end{aligned}$$

M will be non-negative and independent of the unknown variance σ^2, and will be a measure of the probability of *not* getting the observed set of squariances $S_1, S_2, \cdots S_b$ for b independent samples from a common population, under the condition of a fixed value for the total $S = \sum S_k$. If M is sufficiently large the null hypothesis of a common σ^2 is rejected. The logarithms are to base e and so are equal to the common logarithms multiplied by 2.303.

It may be noted that S/n is a pooled estimate of the variance σ^2 based on the total variation within samples, while the S_k/n_k are separate estimates of this variance based on the individual samples. If $K = (e^M)^{-1/n}$,

$$K = \{\prod_k (S_k/n_k)^{n_k}\}^{1/n}/(S/n)$$
(9.22)
$$= \{\prod_k (S_k/n_k)^{n_k}\}^{1/n}/\{\sum_k n_k(S_k/n_k)/n\}$$

which is a ratio of the weighted geometric mean of the S_k/n_k to the weighted arithmetic mean, the weights being the degrees of freedom n_k.

It is necessary in order to apply the test to know the distribution of M. It was proved by Bartlett[6] that M is approximately distributed as χ^2 with $b - 1$ df, if the n_k are fairly large. More exactly M/c is so distributed, where c is a correction factor

(9.23) $$c = 1 + \frac{1}{3(b-1)}\left\{\sum\left(\frac{1}{n_k}\right) - \frac{1}{n}\right\}$$

but even with this correction the approximation is not entirely satisfactory when some of the n_k are 3 or less.

Hartley[7] has given a still better approximation, useful even when some of the n_k are down to 1 or 2. Tables based on this approximation have been compiled by Catherine Thompson and M. Merrington.[8] These tables give 5% and 1% points of the distribution of M, for given values of b and c_1, where

(9.24) $$c_1 = \sum(1/n_k) - 1/n$$

Each table gives two entries, denoted by (a) and (b). These correspond to limiting values of a parameter $c_3 = \sum(1/n_k^3) - 1/n^3$. The true 5% (or 1%) point will usually lie near (a), especially when the n_k are nearly equal, but in cases of doubt a separate table is provided to facilitate interpolation.

The criterion L_1 used by Neyman and Pearson[9] was practically the same as K of (9.22), except that the sample numbers N_k were used instead of the degrees of freedom. Tables of L_1, for equal sample sizes, were calculated by P. P. N. Nayer,[10] and are reproduced in various books. These tables may also be used when the N_k vary, by using an average value, provided that none of the N_k is less than 15 or 20.

Example 5. For the data of Example 1, the estimated variances for the different sets of concrete cylinders are given in column 4 of the following table:

Percentage Coal	n_k	S_k	S_k/n_k	$n_k \log_{10}(S_k/n_k)$
0	3	14,250	4,750	11.030
0.05	3	20,019	6,673	11.473
0.1	2	15,817	7,908	7.796
0.5	3	55,425	18,475	12.800
1.0	3	1,150	383	7.750
	14	106,661		50.849

Using Bartlett's test, we have $M = 2.303 \, [14 \log_{10} 106{,}661/14 - 50.849] = 8.056$ and $c = 1 + (\frac{4}{3} + \frac{1}{2} - \frac{1}{14})/12 = 1.147$, so that $M/c = 7.02$. With 4 df this value of χ^2 corresponds to a P of about 0.13, so that the differences of variance, large as they appear at first sight, are not significant in view of the small number of degrees of freedom.

Using Thompson and Merrington's tables, we arrive at the same result. With $c_1 = 1.762$ and $b = 5$, the 5% point for the distribution of M is about 10.7 and the 1% point about 14.9, so that the observed M of 8.06 is not significant.

The degrees of freedom are too few for much reliance to be placed on Nayer's tables of L_1. The value of L_1 is the ratio of the weighted geometric mean of the S_k/N_k to the weighted arithmetic mean, that is, 0.5698. The 5% point and 1% point corresponding to $N = 4$ are 0.491 and 0.370 respectively, again suggesting the non-significance of the observed L_1.

9.8 The Behrens-Fisher Test. The usual t-test for the difference between the means of two random samples assumes that these samples come from populations with a common variance. When the variance is different in the two populations a modification of the test is necessary. Behrens, and later Fisher,[11] suggested a test which depends only on the sample means and variances.

Suppose we have two samples of $N_1 (= n_1 + 1)$ and $N_2 (= n_2 + 1)$ from normal populations with means μ_1, μ_2 and variances σ_1^2, σ_2^2. If $\bar{x}_1$, $\bar{x}_2$, $n_1 s_1^2$, $n_2 s_2^2$ are the sample means and variances, the quantities $t_1 = (\bar{x}_1 - \mu_1)/s_1$ and $t_2 = (\bar{x}_2 - \mu_2)/s_2$ are independently distributed as Student's t, with n_1 and n_2 degrees of freedom respectively.

Let us define a quantity d by

$$\begin{aligned} d &= [\bar{x}_1 - \bar{x}_2 - (\mu_1 - \mu_2)]/(s_1^2 + s_2^2)^{1/2} \\ &= (s_1 t_1 - s_2 t_2)/(s_1^2 + s_2^2)^{1/2} \\ &= t_1 \sin\theta - t_2 \cos\theta \end{aligned}$$

(9.25)

where $\tan\theta = s_1/s_2$. Then d clearly depends only on the difference of the true means and on known quantities. It is independent of the unknown population variances σ_1^2 and σ_2^2.

Now if $f_n(t)$ is the frequency function of the t-distribution with n degrees of freedom, the probability that the two samples will have values of t_1, and t_2, respectively, lying within specified limits, will be

$$\iint f_{n_1}(t_1) f_{n_2}(t_2) \, dt_1 \, dt_2$$

integrated over the appropriate region of the t_1t_2 plane. Let the region be specified by
$$t_1 \sin \theta - t_2 \cos \theta > d_0$$
and let us choose d_0 so that the integral is equal to a fixed quantity $\alpha/2$, say 0.025. Geometrically, this region is the part of the t_1t_2 plane lying below the line L_1, which has the equation

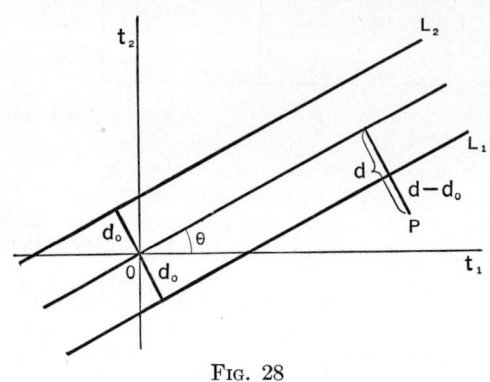

$$t_2 = t_1 \tan \theta - d_0 \sec \theta$$

The quantity d_0 is the perpendicular distance from the origin to L_1 (Figure 28). Because of the symmetry of the distributions of t_1 and t_2, the region corresponding to $d < -d_0$, which is the part of the plane above the line L_2 (parallel to L_1 and equidistant from the origin on the opposite side), will also give an integral equal to $\alpha/2$. The probability, therefore, of the point (t_1, t_2) lying between the lines L_1 and L_2 is $1 - \alpha$, so that

FIG. 28

$$\int_{-\infty}^{\infty} \int_{t_1 \tan \theta - d_0 \sec \theta}^{t_1 \tan \theta + d_0 \sec \theta} f_{n_2}(t_2) f_{n_1}(t_1) \, dt_2 \, dt_1 = 1 - \alpha$$

or, putting $u = t_2 - t_1 \tan \theta$,

(9.26) $$\int_{-\infty}^{\infty} \int_{-d_0 \sec \theta}^{d_0 \sec \theta} f_{n_2}(u + t_1 \tan \theta) \, du \, f_{n_1}(t_1) \, dt_1 = 1 - \alpha$$

From (9.26), for fixed values of θ, n_2 and n_1, we can calculate d_0 corresponding to an assumed value of α. This was done by Sukhatme.[12] The relation $d > d_0$ is equivalent to $\bar{x}_1 - \bar{x}_2 - (\mu_1 - \mu_2) > sd_0$, where $s = (s_1^2 + s_2^2)^{1/2}$, and this may be written $\mu_1 - \mu_2 < \bar{x}_1 - \bar{x}_2 - sd_0$. Similarly the relation $d < -d_0$ is equivalent to $\mu_1 - \mu_2 > \bar{x}_1 - \bar{x}_2 + sd_0$. The region between the lines corresponds, therefore, to

(9.27) $$\bar{x}_1 - \bar{x}_2 - sd_0 \leq \mu_1 - \mu_2 \leq \bar{x}_1 - \bar{x}_2 + sd_0$$

so that we can consider this relation as providing *fiducial limits* for $\mu_1 - \mu_2$ with confidence coefficient $1 - \alpha$. If $\bar{x}_1 - \bar{x}_2 > sd_0$, the probability * that $\mu_1 - \mu_2 < 0$ will be less than $\alpha/2$, and if $\bar{x}_1 - \bar{x}_2 < -sd_0$, the probability that $\mu_1 - \mu_2 > 0$ is less than $\alpha/2$. We may, therefore, regard μ_1 and μ_2 as significantly different at the level α if $|\bar{x}_1 - \bar{x}_2| > sd_0$.

* This is a "fiducial probability" in Fisher's sense, not an *a priori* probability as used in Bayes' Theorem. See the discussions in § 6.3 and in § 12.11.

Sec. 8 The Behrens-Fisher Test

Tables (due to Sukhatme) for the application of this test are given in *Statistical Tables* by Fisher and Yates, Table V 1). These give the 5% and 1% points of d_0 for values of θ at 15° intervals and for n_1 and $n_2 = 6, 8, 12, 24$ and ∞.

Example 6. The mean of 12 observations of a certain quantity is 4.774, with a standard error of 0.0094. The mean of 20 observations by a different method is 4.744, with a standard error of 0.0038. Are these means significantly different?

The F-test for the ratio of the two variances gives

$$F = \frac{12}{20} \frac{(0.0094)^2}{(0.0038)^2} = 3.67$$

The 5% point is 2.34 and the 1% point 3.36 so that the difference of variance is quite definitely significant.

To apply the Behrens-Fisher test, we calculate $\theta = \tan^{-1} 94/38 = 68°$, $n_1 = 11$, $n_2 = 19$, $s = .0101$. The nearest values of n_1 and n_2 in the tables are 8 and 12, 12 and 24 respectively, and for each combination we must interpolate between $\theta = 60°$ and 75°. The values of d_0 for the 5% level and $\theta = 68°$ are

n_2 \ n_1	8	12
12	2.278	2.172
24	2.263	2.156

We now interpolate harmonically* for $n_1 = 11$, giving values

n_2	d_0
12	2.191
24	2.175

A final interpolation for $n_2 = 19$ gives $d_0 = 2.179$, whence $sd_0 = 0.022$. Since $\bar{x}_1 - \bar{x}_2 = 0.030$, the difference is significant at the 5% level. At the 1% level, we find in the same way that $d_0 = 3.034$ and $sd_0 = 0.031$. Hence the observed value of $\bar{x}_1 - \bar{x}_2$ is practically significant at the 1% level.

If we applied the ordinary t-test, disregarding the differences in variance, we should get

$$t = 0.030 \left\{ \frac{32}{12 \times 20} \cdot \frac{132(0.0094)^2 + 380(0.0038)^2}{30} \right\}^{-1/2}$$
$$= 3.44$$

with 30 df. This corresponds to a probability of a little more than 0.001, so that the t-test would here overestimate the significance.

There has been a good deal of discussion over the validity of the Behrens-Fisher test.[13] It is not true that (9.27) will hold in repeated sampling in a proportion $1 - \alpha$ of trials, so that the "fiducial interval" is not strictly a confidence interval. The justification for integrating (9.26) with θ constant is

* Using the reciprocal of n_1 instead of n_1. Thus $2.278 - 0.106(\frac{1}{8} - \frac{1}{11})/(\frac{1}{8} - \frac{1}{12}) = 2.191$.

not obvious, since with *fixed* values of s_1 and s_2, the quantities t_1 and t_2 have a normal distribution and not that of "Student." However, the test seems to be valid on Fisher's theory of fiducial inference which is logically distinct from the Neyman-Pearson theory of confidence intervals, although in many problems the two theories give identical results. (See § 12.11.)

An approximate test for the difference of means of two populations with different variances has been suggested by Cochran and Cox.[14] A weighted mean of critical t values for the two samples, weighted with the respective variances of the means, is calculated and compared with the observed $t = (\bar{x}_1 - \bar{x}_2)(s_1^2 + s_2^2)^{-1/2}$. (Note that s_1 and s_2 are the respective standard errors of $\bar{x}_1$ and $\bar{x}_2$, so that $(s_1^2 + s_2^2)^{1/2}$ is the standard error of $\bar{x}_1 - \bar{x}_2$.)

For the data of Example 6, $t = 0.030/0.0101 = 2.97$. For the first sample, with $n_1 = 11$, the 5% point for t is 2.201, and for the second sample, with $n_2 = 19$, it is 2.093. The weighted $t_{.05}$ is $(2.201 s_1^2 + 2.093 s_2^2)/s^2 = 2.186$. Similarly, the weighted $t_{.01}$ is 3.072. The observed t is, therefore, almost significant at the 1% level, confirming the result of the Behrens-Fisher test.

If the two samples are equal in size, this method reduces to the ordinary t-test for the difference of two means, but with the number of df equal to n instead of $2n$.

9.9 Estimation of Components of Variance. In the usual mathematical model (9.7) underlying the one-way classification, the quantities β_k, characteristic of the kth treatment, are supposed to be fixed parameters which we desire to estimate. However, it is sometimes plausible to consider the β_k as values of a random variable having a normal distribution with mean zero and variance σ_b^2, these values being independent of each other and of the ϵ_{jk}. The latter are supposed independently and normally distributed about zero with variance σ^2.

Now, as we have seen in § 9.3, the β_k, as fixed parameters, can be estimated by $\bar{x}_{.k} - \bar{x}$, and each estimate is independent of the others. In our new model the x_{jk} are normally distributed about μ with variance $\sigma^2 + \sigma_b^2$, but since all the x_{jk} with the same k have a common component β_k they are not independent. In order to express the probability of occurrence of the actual sample it is convenient to make an orthogonal transformation, as in § 4.13, namely:

(9.28)
$$\begin{cases} y_{1k} = (x_{1k} + \cdots + x_{ak})/a^{1/2} = a^{1/2}\bar{x}_{.k} \\ y_{2k} = (x_{1k} - x_{2k})/2^{1/2} \\ y_{3k} = (x_{1k} + x_{2k} - 2x_{3k})/6^{1/2} \\ \cdots \cdots \cdots \cdots \cdots \cdots \cdots \cdots \cdots \cdots \\ y_{ak} = [x_{1k} + \cdots + x_{a-1,k} - (a-1)x_{ak}]/[a(a-1)]^{1/2} \end{cases}$$

Since $x_{1k} - x_{2k} = \epsilon_{1k} - \epsilon_{2k}$, y_{2k} is normally distributed about zero with variance σ^2, and so are $y_{3k}, \cdots y_{ak}$, and these are all independent of each other. Moreover, $a^{-1/2} y_{1k} = \mu + \beta_k + a^{-1} \sum_j \epsilon_{jk}$, and so is normally distributed about

Sec. 9   Estimation of Components of Variance

μ with variance $\sigma_b^2 + a^{-1}\sigma^2$, independently of the other y's. By the properties of the orthogonal transformation, $\sum_j y_{jk}^2 = \sum_j x_{jk}^2$, so that

(9.29) $$\sum_{j=2}^{a} y_{jk}^2 = \sum_j x_{jk}^2 - a^{-1}(\sum_j x_{jk})^2$$

which is the sum of squares within the kth family. The sum of squares within families, q_2, is therefore equal to $\sum_k \sum_{j=2}^{a} y_{jk}^2$, and so is the sum of $b(a-1)$ squares of independent normal variates with mean 0. Hence q_2/σ^2 is distributed as χ^2 with $b(a-1)$ degrees of freedom, and

(9.30) $$E(m_2) = \sigma^2$$

where $m_2 = q_2/[b(a-1)]$ is the mean square within families.

Again, since $y_{1k} = a^{1/2}\bar{x}_{\cdot k}$, and since the sum of squares between families is given by $q_1 = a\sum_k (\bar{x}_{\cdot k} - \bar{x})^2$, it follows that $q_1/(\sigma^2 + a\sigma_b^2)$ is distributed as χ^2 with $b-1$ degrees of freedom. Hence, if $m_1 = q_1/(b-1)$ is the mean square between families,

(9.31) $$E(m_1) = \sigma^2 + a\sigma_b^2$$

so that σ^2 is estimated by m_2 and σ_b^2 by $(m_1 - m_2)/a$.

The simultaneous maximum likelihood estimates of the parameters are not quite the same as these unbiased estimates, as we shall now show.

The probability of the set of independent y's is given by

$$P = (2\pi)^{-ab/2} \sigma^{-b(a-1)} (\sigma^2 + a\sigma_b^2)^{-b/2} e^{-K/2}$$

where

$$K = \frac{1}{\sigma^2} \sum_k \sum_{j=2}^{a} y_{jk}^2 + (\sigma^2 + a\sigma_b^2)^{-1} \sum_k (y_{1k} - a^{1/2}\mu)^2$$

$$= \frac{q_2}{\sigma^2} + a(\sigma^2 + a\sigma_b^2)^{-1} \sum_k (\bar{x}_{\cdot k} - \bar{x} + \bar{x} - \mu)^2$$

$$= \frac{q_2}{\sigma^2} + q_1(\sigma^2 + a\sigma_b^2)^{-1} + ab(\bar{x} - \mu)^2 (\sigma^2 + a\sigma_b^2)^{-1}$$

For convenience let $\theta_1 = \sigma^2$ and $\theta_2 = \sigma^2 + a\sigma_b^2$. Then θ_1, θ_2 and μ may be regarded as the parameters of the distribution. If $L = \log P$, we have

$$2L = C - b(a-1)\log\theta_1 - b\log\theta_2 - K$$
$$= C - b(a-1)\log\theta_1 - b\log\theta_2 - q_2/\theta_1 - q_1/\theta_2 - ab(\bar{x}-\mu)^2/\theta_2$$

Putting $\partial L/\partial \mu$, $\partial L/\partial \theta_1$ and $\partial L/\partial \theta_2 = 0$, we get for the estimated values of μ, θ_1, θ_2 the equations

(9.32)
$$\begin{cases} \bar{x} - \hat{\mu} = 0 \\ -\dfrac{b(a-1)}{\hat{\theta}_1} + \dfrac{q_2}{\hat{\theta}_1^2} = 0 \\ -\dfrac{b}{\hat{\theta}_2} + \dfrac{q_1}{\hat{\theta}_2^2} + \dfrac{ab(\bar{x}-\hat{\mu})^2}{\hat{\theta}_2^2} = 0 \end{cases}$$

Hence

$$\hat{\mu} = \bar{x}, \qquad \hat{\theta}_1 = \frac{q_2}{b(a-1)} = m_2, \qquad \hat{\theta}_2 = \frac{q_1}{b} = \frac{(b-1)m_1}{b}$$

so that the maximum likelihood estimate of $\sigma^2 + a\sigma_b^2$ is biased.

In the *two-way classification,* in which the row, column and interaction effects are all thought of as random variables, normally and independently distributed, the mathematical model for the yield corresponding to the ith row, the jth column and the kth replicate is

$$x_{ijk} = \mu + \alpha_i + \beta_j + \gamma_{ij} + \epsilon_{ijk}$$

where $E(\alpha_i) = E(\beta_j) = E(\gamma_{ij}) = E(\epsilon_{ijk}) = 0$ and the variances of α_i, β_j, γ_{ij} and ϵ_{ijk} are σ_α^2, σ_β^2, σ_γ^2, σ^2 respectively. The variates x_{ijk} are not independent, the covariance of two x's in the same row being, for example, σ_α^2.

If the mean squares for rows, columns, interaction and replicates are denoted by m_1, m_2, m_3, m_4 respectively and if there are a rows, b columns and r replicates, the expectations of these mean squares are given by

$$\begin{aligned}
E(m_1) &= \sigma^2 + r\sigma_\gamma^2 + br\sigma_\alpha^2 \\
E(m_2) &= \sigma^2 + r\sigma_\gamma^2 + ar\sigma_\beta^2 \\
E(m_3) &= \sigma^2 + r\sigma_\gamma^2 \\
E(m_4) &= \sigma^2
\end{aligned}$$

On the null hypothesis that there is no interaction, m_3/m_4 has the F-distribution with $(a-1)(b-1)$ and $ab(r-1)$ df. If this ratio is not significantly different from 1, the squariances and df of interaction and error may be pooled to give a joint mean square with which m_1 and m_2 may be compared. If the interaction is significant, the hypothesis of no row effect is tested by putting $F = m_1/m_3$, with $a-1$ and $(a-1)(b-1)$ df. Similarly, for the column effect, $F = m_2/m_3$ with $b-1$ and $(a-1)(b-1)$ df.

A difficulty arises in extending this method to a *three-way classification,* even when we suppose for simplicity that there is only one member in each sub-class. Suppose that we have a A-classes, b B-classes and c C-classes. If the three main effects, the three interactions and the triple interaction are all thought of as independent random variables with variances σ_α^2, σ_β^2, σ_γ^2, $\sigma_{\alpha\beta}^2$, $\sigma_{\beta\gamma}^2$, $\sigma_{\gamma\alpha}^2$, $\sigma_{\alpha\beta\gamma}^2$ respectively, the expectations of the various mean squares are given by

$$\begin{aligned}
E(m_A) &= bc\sigma_\alpha^2 + b\sigma_{\gamma\alpha}^2 + c\sigma_{\alpha\beta}^2 + \sigma_{\alpha\beta\gamma}^2 \\
E(m_B) &= ca\sigma_\beta^2 + c\sigma_{\alpha\beta}^2 + a\sigma_{\beta\gamma}^2 + \sigma_{\alpha\beta\gamma}^2 \\
E(m_C) &= ab\sigma_\gamma^2 + a\sigma_{\beta\gamma}^2 + b\sigma_{\gamma\alpha}^2 + \sigma_{\alpha\beta\gamma}^2 \\
E(m_{AB}) &= c\sigma_{\alpha\beta}^2 + \sigma_{\alpha\beta\gamma}^2 \\
E(m_{BC}) &= a\sigma_{\beta\gamma}^2 + \sigma_{\alpha\beta\gamma}^2 \\
E(m_{CA}) &= b\sigma_{\gamma\alpha}^2 + \sigma_{\alpha\beta\gamma}^2 \\
E(m_{ABC}) &= \sigma_{\alpha\beta\gamma}^2
\end{aligned}$$

Sec. 10 Limits for the Component of Variance

Since there is no mean square between replicates, the triple interaction gives the only available estimate of error. The significance of the three first-order interactions may be estimated as usual, but it is evident from the above equations that no straightforward F-test will serve to test the significance of the main effects. Each one occurs in combination with *two* interactions.

It is easily verified that

$$E(m_A - m_{AB} - m_{CA} + m_{ABC}) = bc\sigma_\alpha^2$$

so that on the hypothesis that there are no real A-effects, which means that $\sigma_\alpha^2 = 0$,

$$E(m_A + m_{ABC}) = E(m_{AB} + m_{CA})$$

We can therefore make an approximate test of this hypothesis by applying the F-test to the ratio of $m_A + m_{ABC}$ to $m_{AB} + m_{CA}$. The difficulty is to know what degrees of freedom to use. We estimate the df so that the variances of the approximating χ^2 distributions are the same as those of the actual distributions, both for $m_A + m_{ABC}$ and for $m_{AB} + m_{CA}$.

The variance of a χ^2 distribution with n_1 df and expected value μ is $2\mu^2/n_1$. Hence if $m_A + m_{ABC}$ has such a distribution, its variance must be $(2/n_1)[bc\sigma_\alpha^2 + b\sigma_{\gamma\alpha}^2 + c\sigma_{\alpha\beta}^2 + 2\sigma_{\alpha\beta\gamma}^2]^2$. But the variance of m_A is $[2/(a-1)] \times [bc\sigma_\alpha^2 + b\sigma_{\gamma\alpha}^2 + c\sigma_{\alpha\beta}^2 + \sigma_{\alpha\beta\gamma}^2]^2$, since it has a χ^2 distribution with $a - 1$ df. Similarly, the variance of m_{ABC} is $2\sigma_{\alpha\beta\gamma}^4/(a-1)(b-1)(c-1)$. The variance of $m_A + m_{ABC}$ is the sum of the variances of m_A and m_{ABC}, so that on equating the two expressions for this variance we get

$$n_1 = \frac{(bc\sigma_\alpha^2 + b\sigma_{\gamma\alpha}^2 + c\sigma_{\alpha\beta}^2 + 2\sigma_{\alpha\beta\gamma}^2)^2}{(bc\sigma_\alpha^2 + b\sigma_{\gamma\alpha}^2 + c\sigma_{\alpha\beta}^2 + \sigma_{\alpha\beta\gamma}^2)^2/(a-1) + \sigma_{\alpha\beta\gamma}^4/(a-1)(b-1)(c-1)}$$

This is estimated by

$$\frac{(m_A + m_{ABC})^2}{m_A^2/(a-1) + m_{ABC}^2/(a-1)(b-1)(c-1)}$$

In the same way n_2 is estimated by

$$\frac{(m_{AB} + m_{CA})^2}{m_{AB}^2/(a-1)(b-1) + m_{CA}^2/(a-1)(c-1)}$$

The ratio $(m_A + m_{ABC})/(m_{AB} + m_{CA})$ is then approximately distributed as F with n_1 and n_2 df, and serves to determine whether σ_α^2 is significantly different from zero.

The working out of the tests for the other two main effects is left as an exercise.

9.10 Confidence Limits for the Component of Variance Due to Treatment Effects. If we wish to assign confidence limits to σ_b^2 we must know the distribution of the statistic which estimates it. If $v_1 = q_1/(\sigma^2 + a\sigma_b^2)$ and

$v_2 = q_2/\sigma^2$, then v_1 and v_2 are independent χ^2 variables with $b - 1$ and $b(a - 1)$ df respectively. Now

$$\frac{m_1 - m_2}{a} = \frac{\sigma^2 + a\sigma_b^2}{a(b - 1)} v_1 - \frac{\sigma^2}{ab(a - 1)} v_2 = \lambda_1 v_1 - \lambda_2 v_2$$

where λ_1 and λ_2 depend on the parameters σ^2 and σ_b^2. The joint frequency function of v_1 and v_2 is $Cv_1^{\frac{1}{2}n_1-1} v_2^{\frac{1}{2}n_2-1} e^{-\frac{1}{2}(v_1+v_2)}$ where $n_1 = b - 1$, $n_2 = b(a - 1)$. Putting $u = \lambda_1 v_1 - \lambda_2 v_2$, we obtain the joint frequency function of u and v_2,

$$C_1(u + \lambda_2 v_2)^{\frac{1}{2}n_1-1} v_2^{\frac{1}{2}n_2-1} e^{-u/2\lambda_1} e^{-v_2(\lambda_1+\lambda_2)/2\lambda_1}$$

By integrating over the range of v_2, the distribution of u is obtained. Since v_1 goes from 0 to ∞, v_2 goes from $-u/\lambda_2$ to ∞ if u is negative, but from 0 to ∞ if u is positive. The frequency function for u depends, however, on σ^2 as well as on σ_b^2.

A parameter such as σ^2, which appears in a distribution that we want to use to estimate *another* parameter, has been aptly termed by Hotelling a *nuisance parameter*.

The variance of u is given by

$$\text{Var}(u) = \lambda_1^2 \text{Var}(v_1) + \lambda_2^2 \text{Var}(v_2)$$

$$= 2(b - 1)\left[\frac{\sigma^2 + a\sigma_b^2}{a(b - 1)}\right]^2 + 2b(a - 1)\left[\frac{\sigma^2}{ab(a - 1)}\right]^2$$

(9.33)
$$= \frac{2}{a^2}\left[\frac{(\sigma^2 + a\sigma_b^2)^2}{n_1} + \frac{\sigma^4}{n_2}\right]$$

and to a first approximation, for large values of b (say 60 or more) u may be regarded as normally distributed about σ_b^2 with this variance, which is, of course, estimated by $(2/a^2)(m_1^2/n_1 + m_2^2/n_2)$.

From the definition of v_1 and v_2 we can write $\sigma_b^2 = a^{-1}(q_1/v_1 - q_2/v_2)$. On Fisher's theory of fiducial inference, we could regard this relation as giving fiducial limits for σ_b^2, for fixed values of q_1 and q_2. The quantitites v_1 and v_2 are assumed to have the ordinary χ^2 distributions with n_1 and n_2 degrees of freedom, but here, as in the Behrens-Fisher test, we do not have a confidence interval in the ordinary sense.

Another method,[15] also based on Fisher's approach, is to let $F = m_1/m_2$. If F_α and F_α' are the critical points of the ordinary F-distribution for n_1, n_2 and for n_1, ∞ df respectively, we calculate $L = (F - F_\alpha)/(FF_\alpha' - F_\alpha)$. The lower confidence limit for σ_b^2 is then taken as $(m_1 - m_2)L/a$ (zero if $F < F_\alpha$). Similarly we calculate $U = (F - f_\alpha)/(Ff_\alpha' - f_\alpha)$, where $f_\alpha(n_1, n_2)$ is the reciprocal of $F_\alpha(n_2, n_1)$. The upper confidence limit is $(m_1 - m_2)U/a$.

Example 7. In an experiment on counting wireworms in soil (details slightly modified for convenience) there were 25 plots and 6 samples from each. The mean square between plots (m_1) was 72.96 and that within plots (m_2) was 38.44. The degrees of freedom were $n_1 = 24$, $n_2 = 125$.

Sec. 11 Effect of Unequal Numbers in Sub-classes

The hypothesis that the β_k are all zero is rejected at about the 1% level, since $F = 1.90$ and the 1% point is 1.94. On the hypothesis that the β_k are normally distributed, the estimated σ^2 and σ_b^2 are 38.44 and 5.75 respectively. The variance of u is

$$\frac{2}{36}\left\{\frac{(72.96)^2}{24} + \frac{(38.44)^2}{125}\right\} = 12.98$$

so that the normal approximation would give the 90% confidence limits for σ_b^2 as 0 and 11.68.
Fisher's method gives

$$\sigma_b^2 = \frac{24 \times 72.96}{6v_1} - \frac{125 \times 38.44}{6v_2}$$

The 5% upper and lower points for v_1 (with $n_1 = 24$) are 36.415 and 13.848 respectively. The corresponding points for v_2 ($n_2 = 125$) are 151.81 and 99.90 respectively, so that the 90% fiducial limits for σ_b^2 are 2.739 and 13.058.
For the third method we have $F_\alpha = 1.60$, $F_\alpha' = 1.52$, $F = 1.90$, so that $L = 0.233$, and the lower confidence limit is 1.34. Similarly, $f_\alpha = (1.79)^{-1}, f_\alpha' = (1.73)^{-1}$, so that $U = 2.49$ and the upper confidence limit is 14.32. These values are probably the most reliable.

9.11 Effect of Unequal Numbers in the Sub-classes on the Estimation of Treatment Effects.
For the two-way classification of § 9.2, we can readily estimate the class-effects α_j, β_k, provided that all the sub-classes contain the same number of entries.

The joint frequency function for the x_{jk} is

$$(2\pi\sigma^2)^{-ab/2} \exp\left\{-\frac{1}{2\sigma^2}\sum_{jk}(x_{jk} - \alpha_j - \beta_k - \mu)^2\right\}$$

and the maximum likelihood estimates a_j, b_k, m of α_j, β_k, μ are given in the usual way by

(9.34)
$$\begin{cases} \sum_k (x_{jk} - a_j - b_k - m) = 0, & j = 1, 2, \cdots a \\ \sum_j (x_{jk} - a_j - b_k - m) = 0, & k = 1, 2, \cdots b \\ \sum_{jk} (x_{jk} - a_j - b_k - m) = 0 \end{cases}$$

Since $\sum a_j = \sum b_k = 0$, we have, on dividing these equations through by a, b, ab, respectively,

(9.35)
$$\begin{cases} \bar{x}_{j.} - a_j - m = 0 \\ \bar{x}_{.k} - b_k - m = 0 \\ \bar{x} - m = 0 \end{cases}$$

Hence μ is estimated by $\bar{x}$, α_j by $\bar{x}_{j.} - \bar{x}$, and β_k by $\bar{x}_{.k} - \bar{x}$. These estimates are all independent of each other, and the data are said to be *orthogonal*.

Suppose now that in the two-way classification into a A-classes and b B-classes, the number of members in the sub-class $A_j B_k$ is n_{jk} instead of 1 as we assumed before. We can obtain an estimate of σ^2 by pooling the sums of squares within the separate sub-classes. The number of degrees of freedom will be $N - ab$, where $N = \sum n_{jk}$. Let this estimate of variance be denoted by v.

If we ignore the difference between the A and B classifications and regard the data as a one-way classification into ab classes, we can apply (9.7) and obtain as the sum of squares between sub-classes

$$(9.36) \qquad q_1 = \sum_{jk} n_{jk}(\bar{x}_{jk} - \bar{x})^2$$

where $\bar{x}_{jk}$ is the mean of the n_{jk} members of the sub-class $A_j B_k$. Then $q_1/(ab - 1)$ may be compared with v as a test of homogeneity.

Considering the A classification alone, let

$$(9.37) \qquad \bar{x}_{j\cdot} = \frac{1}{b}\sum_k \bar{x}_{jk}$$

Since the variance of $\bar{x}_{jk}$ is σ^2/n_{jk}, we have, on the hypothesis that the α_j are zero,

$$\operatorname{Var}(\bar{x}_{j\cdot}) = \sigma^2 b^{-2} \sum_k (1/n_{jk}) = \sigma^2/N_j$$

where

$$(9.38) \qquad \frac{1}{N_j} = \frac{1}{b^2}\sum_k \left(\frac{1}{n_{jk}}\right)$$

The mean $\bar{x}_{j\cdot}$ has, therefore, the same variance as if it were the mean of N_j quantities with variance σ^2, so that $\bar{x}_{j\cdot}$ has a weight of N_j. If the weighted mean of the a quantities $\bar{x}_{j\cdot}$ is

$$(9.39) \qquad w_a = \sum_j N_j \bar{x}_{j\cdot} / \sum N_j$$

it may be proved that $\sum N_j(\bar{x}_{j\cdot} - w_a)^2$ is distributed as $\chi^2 \sigma^2$ with $a - 1$ df so that an unbiased estimate of σ^2 is given by $Q_1/(a - 1)$, where

$$(9.40) \qquad Q_1 = \sum N_j \bar{x}_{j\cdot}^2 - (\sum_j N_j \bar{x}_{j\cdot})^2 / \sum N_j$$

Since this is independent of v, the A-effects may be tested by the ratio of $Q_1/(a - 1)$ to v.

Similarly for the B-effects, if

$$(9.41) \qquad \frac{1}{M_k} = \frac{1}{a^2}\sum_j \left(\frac{1}{n_{jk}}\right)$$

an unbiased estimate of σ^2 is provided by $Q_2/(b - 1)$, where

$$(9.42) \qquad Q_2 = \sum M_k \bar{x}_{\cdot k}^2 - w_b^2 \sum M_k$$

and

$$(9.43) \qquad w_b = \sum_k M_k \bar{x}_{\cdot k} / \sum M_k$$

The B-effects are tested by the ratio of $Q_2/(b - 1)$ to v.

Sec. 11   Effect of Unequal Numbers in Sub-classes

Let us now consider the question of estimating the parameters μ, α_j, β_k. If x_{jkl} is the lth member of the sub-class A_jB_k, our model is

(9.44) $$x_{jkl} = \mu + \alpha_j + \beta_k + \epsilon_{jkl}$$

when $j = 1, 2 \cdots a$, $k = 1, 2 \cdots b$, $l = 1, 2 \cdots n_{jk}$ and where the ϵ_{jkl} are normally distributed about zero with variance σ^2. The usual procedure for maximum likelihood estimates gives

(9.45) $$\begin{cases} \sum_{kl}(x_{jkl} - a_j - b_k - m) = 0, & j = 1, 2 \cdots a \\ \sum_{jl}(x_{jkl} - a_j - b_k - m) = 0, & k = 1, 2 \cdots b \\ \sum_{jkl}(x_{jkl} - a_j - b_k - m) = 0, & \end{cases}$$

where a_j, b_k, m are estimates of α_j, β_k, μ respectively.

Let us write $N_{j\cdot} = \sum_k n_{jk}$, $N_{\cdot k} = \sum_j n_{jk}$; the equations become

(9.46) $$\begin{cases} \sum_k n_{jk}\bar{x}_{jk} - N_{j\cdot}a_j - \sum_k n_{jk}b_k - N_{j\cdot}m = 0 \\ \sum_j n_{jk}\bar{x}_{jk} - \sum_j n_{jk}a_j - N_{\cdot k}b_k - N_{\cdot k}m = 0 \\ N\bar{x} - \sum_{jk} n_{jk}a_j - \sum_{jk} n_{jk}b_k - Nm = 0 \end{cases}$$

where $\bar{x}$ is the weighted mean of all the $\bar{x}_{jk}$, with weights n_{jk}. If we imagine the a_j and b_k so adjusted that $\sum_{jk} n_{jk}a_j = 0$ and $\sum_{jk} n_{jk}b_k = 0$, which merely means absorbing parts of the constants α_j, β_k into μ, the quantities α_j, β_k, μ are then estimated by a_j, b_k, m as given by the set of $a + b + 1$ equations:

(9.47) $$\begin{cases} N_{j\cdot}a_j + \sum_k n_{jk}b_k = \sum_k n_{jk}\bar{x}_{jk} - N_{j\cdot}\bar{x} \\ \sum_j n_{jk}a_j + N_{\cdot k}b_k = \sum_j n_{jk}\bar{x}_{jk} - N_{\cdot k}\bar{x} \\ m = \bar{x} \\ j = 1, 2 \cdots a, \quad k = 1, 2 \cdots b \end{cases}$$

If all the n_{jk} are equal to 1, these reduce to (9.35), but in the general case the α's and β's cannot be estimated independently. The data are not then orthogonal.

Example 8 [Gowen, quoted by Snedecor in (5).]. The data are mean lengths of life in days for three strains of mice, after inoculation with one of three isolations of typhoid bacillus. In each cell of Table 25 the number in brackets is the number of mice (n_{jk}) in the sub-class.

TABLE 25. SURVIVAL TIME (IN DAYS) FOR MICE INOCULATED WITH TYPHOID BACILLUS

Organism	Strain I	Strain II	Strain III	$\bar{x}_{j\cdot}$	N_j	$N_j\bar{x}_{j\cdot}$
A	4.0000 (34)	4.0323 (31)	3.7576 (33)	3.9300	97.855	384.57
B	6.4545 (66)	6.7821 (78)	4.3097 (113)	5.8488	244.42	1429.56
C	6.6262 (107)	7.8045 (133)	4.1277 (188)	6.1861	405.70	2509.70
$\bar{x}_{\cdot k}$	5.6936	6.2063	4.0650		747.98	4323.83
M_k	166.95	171.11	202.37	540.43		
$M_k\bar{x}_{\cdot k}$	950.55	1061.96	822.63	2835.14		

There are 2 df between strains, 2 between organisms, 8 between sub-classes and 774 between individual mice. The mean square v between individuals (from the original data, not obtainable from Table 25) is 5.015. From (9.36),

$$q_1 = \sum n_{jk}\bar{x}_{jk}^2 - (\sum n_{jk}\bar{x}_{jk})^2/N = 1785.6$$

so that $q_1/(ab - 1) = (1785.6)/8 = 223.2$. The data are obviously not homogeneous.

The computed numbers N_j, M_k are shown in Table 25. From the sums of columns 6 and 7, we get

$$(\sum N_j\bar{x}_{j\cdot})^2/\sum N_j = (4323.83)^2/747.98 = 24{,}994.66$$

Also $\sum N_j\bar{x}_{j\cdot}^2 = 25{,}397.83$, so that $Q_1 = 403.17$. Since $a = 3$, the mean square between organisms is $Q_1/2 = 201.6$, which is highly significant. Similarly,

$$Q_2 = 15{,}346.88 - 14{,}873.37 = 473.51$$

so that $Q_2/2 = 236.8$, which is the mean square between strains and is even more significant.
The analysis of variance is therefore

Variation due to	SS	df	MS
Organisms	403.2	2	201.6
Strains	473.5	2	236.8
Mice	3881.6	774	5.015

The equations for estimating the α_j and β_k are

$$\begin{cases} 98a_1 + 34b_1 + 31b_2 + 33b_3 = 385.00 - 98(5.5556) = -159.45 \\ 257a_2 + 66b_1 + 78b_2 + 113b_3 = 1442.00 - 257(5.5556) = 14.22 \\ 428a_3 + 107b_1 + 133b_2 + 188b_3 = 2523.00 - 428(5.5556) = 145.23 \\ 207b_1 + 34a_1 + 66a_2 + 107a_3 = 1271.00 - 207(5.5556) = 121.00 \\ 242b_2 + 31a_1 + 78a_2 + 133a_3 = 1692.00 - 242(5.5556) = 347.55 \\ 334b_3 + 33a_1 + 113a_2 + 188a_3 = 1387.00 - 334(5.5556) = -468.55 \end{cases}$$

Sec. 12 Interaction with Unequal Sub-class Numbers

We have also
$$\begin{cases} 98a_1 + 257a_2 + 428a_3 = 0 \\ 207b_1 + 242b_2 + 334b_3 = 0 \end{cases}$$

The solution* is

$$a_1 = -1.82356, \quad b_1 = 0.66749$$
$$a_2 = 0.08753, \quad b_2 = 1.44095$$
$$a_3 = 0.36499, \quad b_3 = -1.45773$$

with $m = 5.5556$.

The estimated combined effects, without the error terms, are given by the following table:

Organism	Strain		
	I	II	III
A	4.3995	5.1730	2.2743
B	6.3106	7.0841	4.1854
C	6.5881	7.3615	4.4628

9.12 Interaction with Unequal Sub-class Numbers. In the general case with unequal sub-class numbers, it is not true that we can estimate interaction by subtracting from the total sum of squares the sums due to variation between rows and between columns. Because of the interdependence of the estimates, the "interaction" so calculated is not a valid estimate of σ^2. Thus we **cannot** calculate interaction for Example 8 as follows:

TABLE 26. INCORRECT ANALYSIS OF VARIANCE FOR EXAMPLE 8

Variation	SS	df	MS
Between organisms	403.2 ⎫	2 ⎫	201.6
Between strains	473.5 ⎬ 1785.6	2 ⎬ 8	236.8
"Interaction"	908.9 ⎭	4 ⎭	227.2
Residual	3881.6	774	5.015
Total	5667.2	782	

It is, however, possible to calculate a valid interaction term by deducting from the total sum of squares the amounts due to the fitting of the various constants, namely the α's, β's and μ. On the additive hypothesis, the remainder should be equal to the residual sum of squares. If not, the difference can be attributed to interaction.

By the basic hypotheses of analysis of variance, the sum

$$\sum_{j,k,l}(x_{jkl} - \alpha_j - \beta_k - \mu)^2$$

---

* Found by systematic elimination of the variables. Express a_1, a_2, a_3 in terms of the b's by equations 1, 2, 3, and substitute in equations 4, 5, 6. Eliminate b_1 by equation 8. Solve the resulting pair of equations for b_2 and b_3. For other methods see Chapter X.

is distributed as $\chi^2\sigma^2$ with N degrees of freedom. The difference between an observed x and its estimated value is $x_{jkl} - a_j - b_k - m$. The sum of squares of these discrepancies is

(9.48) $\quad \sum (x_{jkl} - a_j - b_k - m)^2 = \sum_{jkl}(x_{jkl} - \alpha_j - \beta_k - \mu)^2 + \sum_j N_{j.}(a_j - \alpha_j)^2$
$$+ \sum_k N_{.k}(b_k - \beta_k)^2 + N(m - \mu)^2$$

By (9.46), the a_j, b_k and m are linear functions of the x_{jkl}. There are $a + b + 1$ of these quantities, subject to two constraints, namely,

(9.49) $\qquad\qquad \sum_j N_{j.} a_j = 0, \qquad \sum_k N_{.k} b_k = 0$

Hence we can express them in terms of $a + b - 1$ orthogonal normal variates (as in § 4.13), and the sum of squares will be distributed as $\chi^2\sigma^2$ with $a + b - 1$ df. This sum of squares will be equal to the sum of squares for the original variables, namely,

$$\sum_j N_{j.}(a_j - \alpha_j)^2 + \sum_k N_{.k}(b_k - \beta_k)^2 + N(m - \mu)^2$$

Hence, from (9.48) it follows that $\sum_{jkl}(x_{jkl} - a_j - b_k - m)^2$ is independently distributed as $\chi^2\sigma^2$ with $N - a - b + 1$ df.

Now, by writing out the separate terms, we have

$$\sum (x_{jkl} - a_j - b_k - m)^2 = \sum_{jkl} x_{jkl}^2 + \sum_j N_{j.} a_j^2 + \sum_k N_{.k} b_k^2 + Nm^2$$
$$- 2\sum_{jk} a_j n_{jk} \bar{x}_{jk} - 2\sum_{jk} b_k n_{jk} \bar{x}_{jk} - 2mN\bar{x}$$
$$+ 2\sum_{jk} a_j b_k n_{jk} - 2m\sum_{jk} a_j n_{jk} - 2m\sum_{jk} b_k n_{jk}$$
$$= \sum x_{jkl}^2 + \sum_j a_j(N_{j.} a_j + \sum_k n_{jk} b_k - \sum_k n_{jk}\bar{x}_{jk}$$
$$+ N_{j.}\bar{x}) + \sum_k b_k(N_{.k} b_k + \sum_j n_{jk} a_j - \sum_j n_{jk}\bar{x}_{jk}$$
$$+ N_{.k}\bar{x}) + 2Nm(m - \bar{x}) - Nm^2 - \sum_{jk} a_j n_{jk}\bar{x}_{jk}$$
$$- \sum_{jk} b_k n_{jk}\bar{x}_{jk} - \sum_j a_j N_{j.}(\bar{x} + 2m)$$
$$- \sum_k b_k N_{.k}(\bar{x} + 2m)$$

By (9.47), the expressions in parentheses in the second, third and fourth terms on the right-hand side vanish. Also the last two terms vanish by (9.49). We have left

(9.50) $\quad \sum (x_{jkl} - a_j - b_k - m)^2 = \sum x_{jkl}^2 - Nm^2 - \sum_{jk} a_j n_{jk}\bar{x}_{jk} - \sum_{jk} b_k n_{jk}\bar{x}_{jk}$

where the first two terms on the right give the total sum of squares, with $N - 1$ df and the other two terms the reduction due to the fitting of the constants, with $a + b - 2$ df.

We have already seen that the sum of squares due to residuals (v) can be split off from the total, leaving an amount (q_1) with $ab - 1$ df which, on the hypothesis that the α_j, β_k are all zero, is an independent estimate of σ^2. If we subtract from q_1 the sum of squares due to fitting the constants, the remainder with $(a - 1)(b - 1)$ df will also be an independent estimate of σ^2, and may be used to test interaction.

In the foregoing example, $\sum_{jk} a_j n_{jk} \bar{x}_{jk} = 345.0$, $\sum_{jk} b_k n_{jk} \bar{x}_{jk} = 1264.6$, so that the sum of squares due to interaction is $1785.6 - 345.0 - 1264.6 = 176.0$. The correct analysis of variance is therefore as shown in Table 26A.

TABLE 26A. CORRECT ANALYSIS OF VARIANCE FOR EXAMPLE 8

Variation	SS	df	MS
Organisms	403.2	2	201.6
Strains	473.5	2	236.8
Interaction	176.0	4	44.0
Mice	3881.6	774	5.015

There is clearly a definite interaction effect here, although not as great as would have been deduced from Table 26.

The organism effect is tested by the ratio $201.6/44.0$ and not by $201.6/5.015$. The latter would be correct if we intended our inference to apply only to the *same strains of mice* as used in this experiment.

9.13 Proportional Sub-class Numbers. If it happens that the numbers n_{jk}, although unequal, are *proportional* in the different rows (and therefore also in the different columns) the data are still orthogonal. In this case every n_{jk} can be written as the product of l_j and m_k where l_j is a number characteristic of the jth row and m_k is a number characteristic of the kth column. The α_j and β_k can be estimated separately from the means of the A-classes and the B-classes respectively. The sum of squares between A-means can be calculated as in (9.6), and similarly for the sum of squares between B-means. The difference between the sum of squares between classes and the total of these A- and B-sums is attributable to interaction.

9.14 The Missing Plot Technique. It is evident from the analysis in §§ 9.11 and 9.12 that the computations are very much simplified when there is only one individual in each sub-class. If so, however, there is the risk of losing by accident, such as the death of an experimental animal or the ravages of an insect pest on a crop-plant, all the information available about some particular sub-class. If this happens to a *few* sub-classes the situation is not hopeless.

It is possible to form an *estimate* of the missing values and to carry out the analysis with only a minor loss in precision.

On the usual mathematical model, the α_j, β_k and μ are determined so as to minimize the residual sum of squares S_e attributable to error. If some of the x_{jk} are missing, we replace them by estimates X_{jk}, regarded as unknowns, and minimize S_e with respect to these unknowns.

If for convenience we think of a randomized block experiment with a variates or treatments and b blocks, we can denote the treatment totals by $T_j = \sum_k x_{jk}$, the block totals by $B_k = \sum_j x_{jk}$ and the grand total by $G = \sum_{jk} x_{jk}$. The residual sum of squares is then given by

$$(9.51) \qquad S_e = \sum x_{jk}^2 - \frac{1}{a} \sum B_k^2 - \frac{1}{b} \sum T_j^2 + \frac{1}{ab} G^2$$

Assuming that the jkth value is missing, we have, on differentiating with respect to X_{jk} and putting the derivative equal to zero,

$$(9.52) \qquad X_{jk} - B_k/a - T_j/b + G/ab = 0$$

In (9.52) the quantities B_k, T_j, G all include the unknown value X_{jk}. If B_k', T_j', G' represent the totals, *excluding* X_{jk}, we have

$$X_{jk}(1 - 1/a - 1/b + 1/ab) = B_k'/a - T_j'/b + G'/ab$$

or

$$(9.53) \qquad X_{jk} = \frac{bB_k' + aT_j' - G'}{(a-1)(b-1)}$$

If there is only one missing value in the whole table, (9.53) will give the required estimate. If there are two or more, this equation, applied to each value, will give a set of simultaneous equations for the unknowns.

Example 9. Assume that the table represents yields for 5 varieties, each planted in 5 blocks. There are two missing yields, represented by x and y.

Variety	Blocks					Totals
	1	2	3	4	5	
A	9.5	4.0	6.5	4.9	9.3	34.2
B	x	6.2	6.0	7.6	7.6	$27.4 + x$
C	11.8	9.3	15.4	13.2	15.9	65.6
D	6.4	5.4	7.6	8.6	y	$28.0 + y$
E	3.3	5.1	4.6	6.3	6.3	25.6
Totals	$31.0 + x$	30.0	40.1	40.6	$39.1 + y$	$180.8 + x + y$

For the yield x, $B_k' = 31.0$, $T_j' = 27.4$, $G' = 180.8 + y$, and for yield y, $B_k' = 39.1$, $T_j' = 28.0$, $G' = 180.8 + x$. Hence, from (9.53),

Sec. 14 The Missing Plot Technique 273

or
$$x = (165.0 + 137.0 - 180.8 - y)/16$$
$$y = (195.5 + 140.0 - 180.8 - x)/16$$

$$\begin{cases} 16x + y = 121.2 \\ x + 16y = 154.7 \end{cases}$$

whence $x = 7.00$, $y = 9.23$. These are the estimated yields.

The analysis of variance may now be carried out as usual, with the estimated values substituted for x and y, but with 2 df subtracted for both total and error sum of squares. This procedure is not, however, strictly correct. It introduces an upward bias into the mean square between variates which tends to exaggerate the significance of varietal differences. To see this, let us consider the hypothesis that there is no difference between varieties, so that all the β_k are zero. The sum of squares between varieties will then be lumped with the error — the total may be called the *conditional error*. If we minimize the conditional error S_c instead of the residual S_e with respect to the missing values we shall get a different set of values for the unknowns from the set given by (9.53). We have, in fact,

(9.54) $$S_c = \sum x_{jk}^2 - \frac{1}{a} \sum B_k^2$$

and on putting $\partial S_c / \partial X_{jk}' = 0$, we get for the new unknown X_{jk}'

$$X_{jk}' - \frac{B_k}{a} = 0$$

or

$$X_{jk}'\left(1 - \frac{1}{a}\right) = \frac{B_k'}{a}$$

Therefore

(9.55) $$X_{jk}' = B_k'/(a-1) = c_k, \text{ say}$$

The bias in the sum of squares between varieties is due to using (9.53) instead of (9.55) in testing the null hypothesis, although the former should be used to obtain unbiased estimates of the unknowns. The value of S_c using (9.53) is too great by an amount

$$X_{jk}^2 - c_k^2 - \frac{1}{a}(X_{jk} + B_k')^2 + \frac{1}{a}(c_k + B_k')^2 = \frac{a-1}{a}(X_{jk}^2 - c_k^2) - \frac{2B_k'}{a}(X_{jk} - c_k)$$
$$= \frac{a-1}{a}(X_{jk} - c_k)(X_{jk} + c_k - 2c_k)$$
$$\qquad\qquad\qquad\qquad\qquad \text{by (9.55)}$$
$$= \frac{a-1}{a}(X_{jk} - c_k)^2$$

This amount should be subtracted for each missing value from the sum of squares due to varieties in order to correct for bias.

In Example 9, $c_1 = 31.0/4 = 7.75$, $c_5 = 39.1/4 = 9.78$, so that the bias is

$$\tfrac{4}{5}[(7.00 - 7.75)^2 + (9.23 - 9.78)^2] = 0.692$$

The sum of squares between varieties, using the best estimates of x and y, is 186.73 so that the correction here makes very little difference. The analysis of variance is

Variation	SS	df	MS
Blocks	34.40	4	8.60
Varieties	186.04	4	46.51
Residual	39.10	14	2.79
Total	259.54	22	

The 5% point for F with $n_1 = 4$, $n_2 = 14$, is 3.11 and the 1% point is 5.03. There is a barely significant effect between blocks but a highly significant one between varieties.

9.15 Analysis of Covariance. Suppose that in each family or group of a one-way classification we have a number of *pairs* of variates x_{jk}, y_{jk}, and that we are interested in the effect of the classification on the relationship between x and y, as expressed by their covariance. This leads to the *analysis of covariance*.

We may wish to test the hypothesis that the linear regression of y on x is the same for the different families. According to this hypothesis, a linear regression exists in the parent population, expressed by

(9.56) $$\eta - \mu_y = \beta(x - \mu_x)$$

The true regression coefficient β may be estimated by the sample regression as a whole or by the regression of class means or by the various regressions within classes. There is no simple test for the significance of differences or ratios of these observed regressions. We can, however, find estimates of the variance of y after removing the effects of regression, and use these estimates to test for the presence of class effects.

Analogously to (9.4) we have for covariance

(9.57) $$\sum_{jk}(x_{jk} - \bar{x})(y_{jk} - \bar{y}) = \sum_{jk}(x_{jk} - \bar{x}_{.k})(y_{jk} - \bar{y}_{.k})$$
$$+ \sum_{k} n_k(\bar{x}_{.k} - \bar{x})(\bar{y}_{.k} - \bar{y})$$

where n_k is the number of pairs in the kth class.

It is convenient to adopt a notation for the sums of squares and products, due to E. S. Pearson. Let $C_{12k} = \sum_{j}(x_{jk} - \bar{x}_{.k})(y_{jk} - \bar{y}_{.k})$, which is the sum of products in the kth family, and so proportional to the covariance. The

Sec. 15   Analysis of Covariance

corresponding sums of squares for x and y may be denoted by C_{11k} and C_{22k}, and the regression coefficient of y on x by $b_k = C_{12k}/C_{11k}$. A combined regression coefficient within families is given by $b_w = \sum C_{12k}/\sum C_{11k} = C_{12w}/C_{11w}$, say. The sum of products between families is given by $C_{12f} = \sum n_k(\bar{x}_{\cdot k} - \bar{x}) \cdot (\bar{y}_{\cdot k} - \bar{y})$, with corresponding notations for the sums of squares. The regression coefficient between families is $b_f = C_{12f}/C_{11f}$. Finally, the total sum of products is $C_{120} = \sum_{jk}(x_{jk} - \bar{x})(y_{jk} - \bar{y})$, and the corresponding regression coefficient is $b_0 = C_{120}/C_{110}$. With this notation, (9.57) may be written

(9.58) $$C_{120} = C_{12f} + \sum_k C_{12k} = C_{12f} + C_{12w}$$

with similar relations for C_{110} and C_{220}.

We assume that, apart from the effects of regression, y_{jk} is normally distributed, that is,

(9.59) $$y_{jk} = \eta + \epsilon_{jk}$$

where η is given by (9.56) and the ϵ_{jk} are independent normal variates with mean 0 and variance σ^2. As in Chapter VIII, we may calculate the sum of squares of residuals after allowing for regression and hence obtain an estimate of σ^2. For the experiment as a whole, this sum is

(9.60) $$S_0 = \sum_{jk}\{y_{jk} - \bar{y} - b_0(x_{jk} - \bar{x})\}^2 = C_{220} - b_0 C_{120}$$

and $S_0/(N - 2)$ is an unbiased estimate of σ^2. Again, we may calculate the sum of squares of residuals for the family means measured from the regression of the means. This sum is

(9.61) $$S_1 = \sum_k n_k\{\bar{y}_{\cdot k} - \bar{y} - b_f(\bar{x}_{\cdot k} - \bar{x})\}^2 = C_{22f} - b_f C_{12f}$$

and $S_1/(b - 2)$ is another estimate of σ^2. By subtraction, using (9.58), or by direct computation, we can find C_{11w}, C_{22w} and C_{12w}, and hence calculate

(9.62) $$S_2 = C_{22w} - b_w C_{12w}$$

This gives a sum of squares of residuals within families from regression lines with a *common slope* b_w and passing through the respective family means. It is made up of two parts, one (S_3) consisting of the sum of squares of deviations from individual regression within families, and the other (S_4) consisting of the squares of differences between the family regressions and the combined regression. By definition,

(9.63) $$S_3 = \sum_k (C_{22k} - b_k C_{12k}) = C_{22w} - \sum b_k C_{12k}$$

Therefore

$$S_4 = \sum b_k C_{12k} - b_w C_{12w}$$
$$= \sum b_k{}^2 C_{11k} - b_w{}^2 \sum C_{11k}$$
$$= \sum_k (b_k - b_w)^2 C_{11k}$$
(9.64)
$$= \sum_{jk} \{(b_k - b_w)(x_{jk} - \bar{x}_{\cdot k})\}^2$$

The number of degrees of freedom for S_3 is $\sum_k (n_k - 2) = N - 2b$. The number for S_4 is $b - 1$, so that the number for S_2 is $N - b - 1$.

In order to test whether there is any class-effect we may compare the estimate of σ^2 derived from $S_0 - S_3$ (between families) with that derived from S_3 (within families). We put

(9.65) $$F = (S_0 - S_3)(N - 2b)/\{S_3(2b - 2)\}$$

with degrees of freedom $2b - 2$ and $N - 2b$. In doing this we are in effect adjusting for the individual regressions. We may prefer, however, to adjust for the combined regression with coefficient b_w, as this is more accurately determined than the individual values of b_k. If so, we should use S_2 instead of S_3, and test by means of

(9.66) $$F = \frac{(S_0 - S_2)(N - b - 1)}{S_2(b - 1)}$$

with $b - 1$ and $N - b - 1$ df.

The difference in the two methods of adjustment may be more clearly seen in Figure 29. If P is a class mean and M the grand mean, the mean adjusted for individual regression is Q. The adjusted mean $\bar{y}_k$ is given by

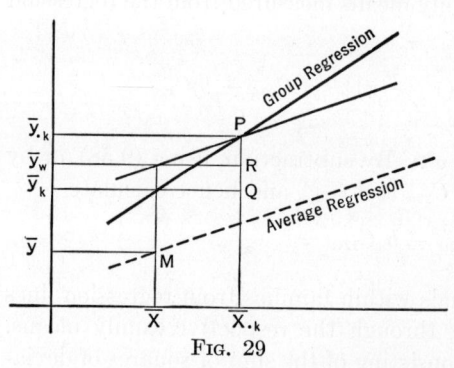

(9.67) $$\bar{y}_k = \bar{y}_{\cdot k} - b_k(\bar{x}_{\cdot k} - \bar{x})$$

If, however, we draw through the class mean a line parallel to the combined regression line (with slope b_w), the adjusted mean is the point R, given by

(9.68) $$\bar{y}_w = \bar{y}_{\cdot k} - b_w(\bar{x}_{\cdot k} - \bar{x})$$

Fig. 29

The significance of differences among the individual regressions may be tested by the ratio

(9.69) $$F = \frac{S_4}{S_3} \frac{N - 2b}{b - 1}$$

with degrees of freedom $b - 1$ and $N - 2b$.

Sec. 15 Analysis of Covariance 277

If this is non-significant, S_3 and S_4 may be pooled as S_2.

Example 10 [Snedecor [5]]. Six groups of rats, 10 to a group, were given different foods and for each rat the food-intake x (in 10-calorie units) and the gain in weight y (in grams) were recorded. The data are given in Table 27.

TABLE 27. FOOD-INTAKE (x) AND GAIN IN WEIGHT (y) FOR 60 RATS

Rat	Group										
	1		2		3		4		5		6	
	x	y	x	y	x	y	x	y	x	y	x	y
1	108	73	99	98	194	94	165	90	124	107	140	49
2	136	102	117	74	198	79	164	76	95	95	177	82
3	138	118	90	56	196	96	161	90	116	97	189	73
4	159	104	141	111	198	98	159	64	112	80	142	86
5	146	81	106	95	210	102	175	86	123	98	216	81
6	141	107	112	88	196	102	135	51	110	74	200	97
7	175	100	110	82	230	108	132	72	137	74	255	106
8	149	87	117	77	222	91	190	90	105	67	173	70
9	174	117	111	86	220	120	145	95	135	89	153	61
10	176	111	122	92	228	105	142	78	126	58	160	82
Total	1502	1000	1125	859	2092	995	1568	792	1183	839	1805	787

In this example each n_k is equal to 10, so that $N = 60$ and $b = 6$.

The sums of squares and products for the separate groups are given in Table 27A.

TABLE 27A. SUMS OF SQUARES, REGRESSION COEFFICIENTS AND ADJUSTED MEANS, FOR DATA OF TABLE 27

k	C_{11k}	C_{22k}	C_{12k}	b_k	S_{3k}	$\bar{y}_{\cdot k}$	$\bar{y}_k$	$\bar{y}_w$
1	4159.6	2062.0	1646.0	0.3957	1410.7	100.0	101.7	101.6
2	1682.5	2030.9	1138.5	0.6767	1260.5	85.9	114.3	100.7
3	1897.6	1072.5	738.0	0.3889	785.5	99.5	78.3	80.2
4	3023.6	1735.6	1184.4	0.3917	1271.6	79.2	78.3	78.4
5	1576.1	2220.9	−58.7	−0.0372	2218.7	83.9	82.5	96.7
6	11630.5	2464.1	3818.5	0.3283	1210.4	78.7	70.2	69.6
Total	23969.9	11586.0	8466.7	(0.3532)	8157.4			

The last three columns give the actual mean gains and the mean gains adjusted for individual regressions and for the combined regression. The last row gives the values of C_{11w}, C_{22w}, C_{12w}, b_w and S_3. By (9.62), $S_2 = 8595.6$, so that $S_4 = 438.2$. From the whole data of Table 27 we find $C_{110} = 91632.6$, $C_{220} = 16198.9$, $C_{120} = 13987.7$, $b_0 = 0.1526$, $S_0 = 14063.7$. From the column totals of Table 27, we get $C_{11f} = 67662.7$, $C_{22f} = 4612.9$, $C_{12f} = 5521.0$, $b_f = 0.0816$, $S_1 = 4162.4$. Note that $C_{110} = C_{11f} + C_{11w}$, with two similar equations, thus checking the arithmetic.

We have, therefore, the following analysis of covariance (Table 27B).

TABLE 27B. ANALYSIS OF COVARIANCE FOR DATA OF TABLE 27

Variation	Residual SS	df	MS
Within groups (S_3)	8157.4	48	169.9
Between regressions (S_4)	438.2	5	87.6
Within groups, from combined regression (S_2)	8595.6	53	162.2
Between groups, from regression of means (S_1)	4162.4	4	1040.6
Difference between b_w and b_f (S_5)	1305.7	1	1305.7
$S_0 - S_2 = S_1 + S_5$	5468.1	5	1093.6
$S_0 - S_3 = S_1 + S_5 + S_4$	5906.3	10	590.6
Total (S_0)	14063.7	58	

The value of F given by (9.65) is 3.48, with 5% and 1% points at 2.03 and 2.71, so that there is clearly a significant difference between the adjusted means $\bar{y}_k$. That is, the different groups of rats show a very significant difference in gain in weight, even when adjusted to a common food-intake. The value of F given by (9.66) is 6.74, with 5% and 1% points at 2.39 and 3.39, so that there is even greater difference between the adjusted means $\bar{y}_w$. From (9.69), F is less than 1, so that there is obviously no significant difference between the regressions. This justifies the procedure of (9.66) in which the regressions are combined.

The regression coefficient for the group means (b_f) is small. The residual mean square for group means (S_1) is highly significant as compared with that for the average regression within groups (S_2), which demonstrates that the group means are very erratic. The quantity S_5 in Table 27B with a single degree of freedom, represents the difference between the regression of group means (b_f) and the average regression within groups (b_w). If S_1 had been non-significant, a significant S_5 would have indicated a different trend for the group means from that for the individuals within a group. Here, of course, the group means show so little trend that this interpretation has no real meaning.

9.16 Experimental Design. It is apparent from the examples in this chapter that the analysis of variance and covariance is a powerful tool for extracting as much information as possible from the results of experiment. It is important, of course, that the experiment should be properly designed in the first place, and a great deal of work has been done in developing efficient experimental designs and procedures. The reader may refer for details to R. A. Fisher's *The Design of Experiments* (5th Edition, 1949) or to Cochran and Cox, *Experimental Designs*, 1950. Some very interesting applications of group theory to problems of design have been made by R. C. Bose, a leading member of the Indian school of statisticians.[20] Here space does not permit of more than a brief reference to some of the commoner designs.

The simplest design is that of *complete randomization*. In a field experiment it would mean that the various replications of a certain variety or treatment are scattered over the whole area [Figure 30(a)]. If there is no particular reason for grouping, this arrangement is satisfactory, as it permits the maximum number of degrees of freedom for error.

If a complete set of treatments are grouped together in a block we have the *randomized block* design, illustrated in Figure 30(b).

Sec. 16   Experimental Design   279

a

C	A	B	D
C	B	A	A
B	A	B	D
D	C	D	C

b

	B	C	A	D
1	B	C	A	D
2	D	A	C	B
3	C	A	D	B
4	C	B	A	D

c

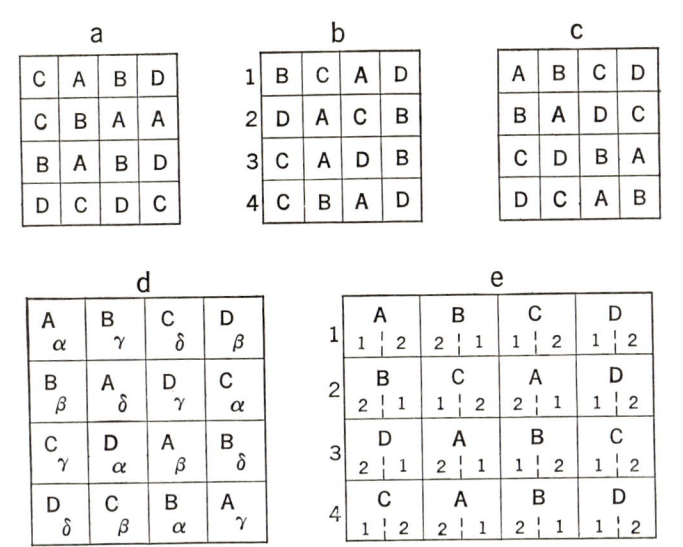

A	B	C	D
B	A	D	C
C	D	B	A
D	C	A	B

d

A α	B γ	C δ	D β
B β	A δ	D γ	C α
C γ	D α	A β	B δ
D δ	C β	B α	A γ

e

	A (1|2)	B (2|1)	C (1|2)	D (1|2)
1	A 1|2	B 2|1	C 1|2	D 1|2
2	B 2|1	C 1|2	A 2|1	D 1|2
3	D 2|1	A 2|1	B 1|2	C 1|2
4	C 1|2	A 2|1	B 2|1	D 1|2

FIG. 30. (a) COMPLETE RANDOMIZATION, (b) RANDOMIZED BLOCKS, (c) LATIN SQUARES, (d) GRAECO-LATIN SQUARES, (e) SPLIT PLOT RANDOMIZED BLOCKS

    This is illustrated in Example 2, at the end of § 9.2, where the blocks consist of types of hog — the animals in one block may be matched in age or weight or may be from the same litter. In a field experiment the blocks may be groups of plots chosen so as to be comparable in respect of soil fertility, etc. If the blocks as a whole are identified with some source of variability, this variability is allowed for and does not affect the experimental error. The experiment is thus more precise than a purely random arrangement.

    The *Latin Square* [Figure 30(c)] is a device for controlling two sources of error at once. In field work the treatments are so allocated among the plots that no treatment occurs more than once in any one row or any one column of the Latin Square. Variability among rows and among columns is removed from the error. This serves to control variability due to gradients of soil fertility in two directions at right angles across the field. In an animal-feeding experiment the treatments might be rations, the rows litters and the columns weights. If, for example, we had four types of ration under investigation, we should use 16 animals, 4 from each of 4 litters, and group them approximately in 4 weight classes so that each class included one animal from each litter. The treatments would then be allocated among the animals according to a Latin Square, and variability between litters and between weights would be removed from error.

    In a Latin Square of a rows and columns, let R_j denote the sum of the jth row, C_k the sum of the kth column, and T_i the sum of the ith treatment, for a variable x $(i, j, k = 1, 2, \cdots a)$. Let G be the grand total. The analysis of variance is

Variability	SS	df	MS
Rows	$S_1 = \sum R_i^2/a - G^2/a^2$	$a - 1$	$S_1/(a-1)$
Columns	$S_2 = \sum C_i^2/a - G^2/a^2$	$a - 1$	$S_2/(a-1)$
Treatments	$S_3 = \sum T_i^2/a - G^2/a^2$	$a - 1$	$S_3/(a-1)$
Error	$S_0 - S_1 - S_2 - S_3$	$(a-1)(a-2)$	$(S_0 - S_1 - S_2 - S_3)/(a-1)(a-2)$
Total	$S_0 = \sum x_{jk}^2 - G^2/a^2$	$a^2 - 1$	

For a large number of treatments it is often difficult to arrange for the right number of rows and columns, and for a small number there are not many degrees of freedom left for error. The Latin Square is ideal for 5 to 8 treatments or varieties.

The number of possible Latin Squares for a given a is very large for the larger values of a, even when restricted to the standard kinds, from which others may be obtained by permutation of rows and columns. A standard square has the letters in their natural order in both the first row and the first column, and $a!\,(a-1)!$ squares may be obtained from it by permutation. There are 4 standard squares for $a = 4$, 56 for $a = 5$ and 9408 for $a = 6$, and the total numbers corresponding are 576, 161280 and 812851200 respectively. Examples of squares up to 12×12 are given in Fisher and Yates' *Statistical Tables*.

If two Latin Squares are superimposed so that each letter of one square occurs once and only once with each letter of the other square (the two squares being then said to be orthogonal), we get a *Graeco-Latin Square*. The arrangement is illustrated in Figure 30(d), where the Greek letters are associated with the Latin ones in the way described. This is a rather specialized and uncommon design, necessitating the picking out of three factors which are real sources of variability. In an animal-feeding experiment the third factor might be the pens. If the pens were lettered, in the example mentioned above, from α to δ and the animals allocated to them according to the Greek letters, the effect of differences among pens would be removed from error. The degrees of freedom for error in an $a \times a$ Graeco-Latin square are $(a^2 - 1) - 4(a - 1) = (a - 1)(a - 3)$, so that the number is rather small unless $a > 4$. No Graeco-Latin square is possible for $a = 6$.

9.17 Split Plots. Confounding. It is often desired to apply the same treatment at different levels. Thus a fertilizer may be applied to experimental plots in several different amounts. A simple example is a *Split Plot* design [Figure 30(e)] in which each plot in a randomized block design is split into two sub-plots for testing some treatment at 2 levels. The allocation of the levels to the sub-plots is random. The purpose of this design is to give maximum accuracy to the comparison of levels.

Sec. 17 Split Plots. Confounding

A good example is given by Goulden.[16] Wheat of two varieties was to be tested for incidence of root-rot. There were 10 different treatments (methods of dusting the seed) and in half the cases the soil was inoculated with a root-rot organism and in the other half not. Two strips of 10 plots each formed a block, one strip being planted with variety A and one with variety B. Each plot was split into two, one half-plot being inoculated and the other half-plot not. There were 4 complete blocks, and hence 160 half-plots altogether. The total number of df was 159, 80 within halves of split plots and 79 between plots. If we ignore for the moment the difference between varieties, there were 8 strips each containing 10 randomized treatments, so that of the 79 df between plots, 7 were between strips, 9 between treatments and 63 belonged to error. But actually, of these 7 df between strips, 1 was between varieties, 3 were between the blocks and 3 belonged to error (the error appropriate to the test of significance between varieties). Also, the 63 df for error contained 9 df attributable to interaction between varieties and treatments, leaving 54 for the error appropriate to a test of significance between treatments.

Finally, of the 80 df within halves of split plots (which naturally contained no direct effects due to blocks, varieties, or treatments), 1 df corresponded to difference between inoculated and uninoculated, 1 to interaction of inoculation with varieties, 9 to interaction with treatments, and 9 to the triple interaction of inoculations with varieties and treatments, leaving 60 for the error appropriate to a test of significance between inoculated and uninoculated soils. Interactions with blocks, and quadruple interactions, have here been included in the error, and the triple interaction might be so included also. The table of degrees of freedom would thus read:

Source of Variation			df	
Between plots	Between blocks	Between strips	3	7 } 79
	Between varieties		1	
	Error (1)		3	
	Between treatments		9	
	Interaction $V \times T$		9	63
	Error (2)		54	
Within halves of split plots	Between I and U		1	80
	Interaction $I \times V$		1	
	Interaction $I \times T$		9	
	Interaction $I \times T \times V$		9	
	Error (3)		60	
Total			159	

In *complete blocks*, as in the examples already given, every treatment is represented, but sometimes this procedure would make the blocks too large for convenience. It is, in many experiments, advisable to use *incomplete blocks*, but this means that it will not be possible to estimate separately all the interactions. Those effects which are not estimable are said to be *confounded*. Thus suppose we wish to test three fertilizers containing nitrogen (N), potassium (K), and phosphorus (P), each at 2 levels (presence and absence). Including the control with no fertilizer, we should have 8 treatments, and with 4 replications this would require 32 plots arranged in 4 blocks. There would be 3 df for main effects, 3 for simple interactions, 1 for a triple interaction, 3 between blocks and 21 for error. The triple interaction $N \times P \times K$ would be the most difficult to interpret and probably the least important, and might well be confounded with block effects. If we choose 8 blocks with 4 plots each, and in 4 of these blocks put the treatments 0, NP, PK, NK, and in the other 4 the treatments N, P, K, NPK, the sum of squares between blocks will include also the triple interaction effect. To see this, let x_{ijk} represent the total yield from all four plots with the ith level of N, the jth level of P and the kth level of K (i, j, k = 0 or 1). The yield from treatment N, for example, is represented by x_{100}. Since the "sum of squares" for two variates is half the square of their difference, the sum of squares between blocks is

$$\tfrac{1}{2} \cdot \tfrac{1}{16} [x_{000} + x_{110} + x_{011} + x_{101} - x_{100} - x_{010} - x_{001} - x_{111}]^2$$

there being 16 plots in each set of 4 like blocks. In a notation similar to that of § 9.4, $\bar{x}_{.jk} = \tfrac{1}{2}(x_{0jk} + x_{1jk})$, etc., and $\bar{x}_{..k} = \tfrac{1}{4}(x_{00k} + x_{01k} + x_{10k} + x_{11k})$, etc. The triple interaction sum of squares is given by

(9.70) $\qquad \tfrac{1}{4}\sum[x_{ijk} - \bar{x}_{.jk} - \bar{x}_{i.k} - \bar{x}_{ij.} + \bar{x}_{i..} + \bar{x}_{.j.} + \bar{x}_{..k} - \bar{x}]^2$

It is easily verified that for every value of i, j, k, the bracket in (9.70) reduces to

$$\pm \tfrac{1}{8} [x_{000} + x_{110} + x_{011} + x_{101} - x_{100} - x_{010} - x_{001} - x_{111}]$$

so that the triple interaction sum of squares is given by exactly the same combination of yields as the sum of squares between blocks. There will now be 3 df for main effects, 7 between blocks, 3 for simple interactions and 18 for error. The advantage of having a greater number of degrees of freedom between blocks is that variation between blocks due to soil heterogeneity is more adequately estimated, the blocks being smaller and more numerous, and this will probably lead to a more accurate estimation of the principal effects than if the design of complete randomized blocks had been chosen.

9.18 Intra-class Correlation. Suppose we have k measurements of a variate x, one on each of k individuals in a family ($k \geq 2$), and we repeat these measurements on N families. The correlation between members of a family is called the *intra-class correlation* and the coefficient is defined by

(9.71) $\qquad r = \dfrac{1}{k(k-1)Ns^2} \sum_{i \neq j} \sum_{\alpha=1}^{N} (x_{i\alpha} - \bar{x})(x_{j\alpha} - \bar{x})$

where $\bar{x}$ is the common mean and s^2 the common variance, calculated from all the kN individuals.

Sec. 18 Intra-class Correlation 283

By definition, the total sum of squares is
$$kNs^2 = \sum_i \sum_\alpha (x_{i\alpha} - \bar{x})^2$$
and the sum of squares between families is
$$k\sum_i (\bar{x}_{\cdot\alpha} - \bar{x})^2 = \frac{1}{k}\sum_\alpha [\sum_i (x_{i\alpha} - \bar{x})]^2$$
$$= \frac{1}{k}\sum_i \sum_\alpha (x_{i\alpha} - \bar{x})^2 + \frac{1}{k}\sum_{i\neq j}\sum_\alpha (x_{i\alpha} - \bar{x})(x_{j\alpha} - \bar{x})$$
$$= Ns^2 + Ns^2(k-1)r$$
$$= Ns^2[(1 + (k-1)r]$$

The intra-class correlation coefficient is therefore never less than $-1/(k-1)$.
The sum of squares within families is given by
$$kNs^2 - Ns^2[1 + (k-1)r] = Ns^2(k-1)(1-r)$$
Fisher[19] has defined a variable z by the relation

(9.72) $$z = \frac{1}{2}\log\frac{1 + (k-1)r}{1-r}$$

which is of the same form as the ordinary Fisher z' of § 8.15 when $k = 2$. This variable z has a distribution which tends to normality for large N, although not as rapidly as when $k = 2$. The variance approximates for large N to $k/[2(k-1)(N-2)]$. If ζ is the population value of z, then for large N
$$E(z) \approx \zeta - \tfrac{1}{2}\log_e [N/(N-1)]$$
so that z may be corrected for bias by adding $\tfrac{1}{2}\log_e [N/(N-1)]$ or approximately $(2N-1)^{-1}$.

In terms of the analysis of variance,
$$z = \tfrac{1}{2}\log(S_B/S_W) + \tfrac{1}{2}\log(k-1)$$
where S_B is the SS between families and S_W the SS within families. Hence $e^{2z} = (k-1)S_B/S_W$.

On the assumption that there is no true correlation between members of a family, so that s^2 is an estimate from kN random observations of a common variance σ^2, the quantity $(k-1)S_B/S_W$ is the ratio of two independent estimates of σ^2. In this case z has the distribution of Fisher's z in § 7.14, or in other words, $[1 + (k-1)r]/(1-r)$ has the Snedecor F-distribution with $N-1$ and $N(k-1)$ df. When the variance between families is significantly greater than that within families, the existence of intra-class correlation is indicated. The test for intra-class correlation may thus be regarded as a test of homogeneity of variance.

Example 11. In Example 1, § 9.1, omitting the fourth column, we have four "families" each consisting of four concrete cylinders. The variable is the breaking strength. The SS between families is 53,830 and the SS within families is 90,844, so that $e^{2z} = (1 + 3r)/(1 - r) = 1.778$, giving $r = 0.163$.

The 5% and 1% points for 3 and 12 df are 3.49 and 5.95, so that there is no reason to doubt the homogeneity of the variance. In other words, the intra-class correlation is not significantly different from zero.

The value of z is 0.288 and the bias correction is $\frac{1}{2}\log_e[N/(N-1)] = 0.144$. The correction is, therefore, very considerable for an N as low as 4, and in this case raises z to 0.432 or F to 2.37. Even this value is non-significant, however.

Problems

1. (*Mills' text, revised.*) Manufacturing industries were classified into those producing perishable, semi-durable, and durable goods. An average of changes occurring between 1929 and 1933 in the selling prices of the products of each of these categories was computed giving the index numbers shown in the $\bar{y}_x$ column of the following table.

Class of industry, x	Number of industries, N_x	Means, $\bar{y}_x$	Computations
Producing perishable goods	34	69.81	$b - 1 = 2, \quad N - b = 82$
Producing semi-durable goods	26	66.41	$q_1 = 2{,}161.8800$
Producing durable goods	25	78.96	$q_2 = 15{,}564.9040$
All industries	85		$Q = 17{,}726.7840$

Compute F and test the null hypothesis that there was no real difference in the price movements of the three different classes of industry for the years 1929–1933.

2. Prove that
$$\sum_{k=1}^{2} N_k(\bar{x}_{.k} - \bar{x})^2 = \frac{N_1 N_2}{N_1 + N_2}(\bar{x}_{.1} - \bar{x}_{.2})^2$$

3. Show that the test for significance between two means is a special case of the test for variation between means of families as given in § 9.1.

Hint. When $b = 2$, q_1 reduces to the expression given in Problem 2. Also q_2 becomes $N_1 s_1^2 + N_2 s_2^2$. Hence
$$F = \frac{q_1}{q_2} \frac{N-b}{b-1}$$
becomes
$$\frac{N_1 N_2}{N_1 + N_2} \frac{N_1 + N_2 - 2}{N_1 s_1^2 + N_2 s_2^2}(\bar{x}_{.1} - \bar{x}_{.2})^2$$
and the square root of this is the t of (7.61).

4. The data represent sugar yield (tons per acre) for 9 varieties of sugar beet, grown each on 5 plots. Assuming that the design consists of 5 blocks each of 9 randomized plots, analyze the variance, and test for a significant difference between varieties.

Block	\multicolumn{9}{c}{Variety}
	A	B	C	D	E	F	G	H	J
1	1.94	1.70	2.23	2.14	1.80	1.82	1.91	1.90	1.98
2	2.08	1.96	2.26	2.08	2.23	2.06	2.06	2.25	2.03
3	1.86	1.83	2.22	2.16	1.67	2.03	2.22	1.92	1.81
4	2.21	1.60	2.08	2.16	2.11	1.96	2.14	1.99	1.77
5	2.03	2.13	2.02	2.17	2.01	2.28	2.28	2.02	1.88

5. A 5 × 5 Latin Square experiment gave the following yields for 5 varieties A to E, planted each in 5 plots in the arrangement indicated.

B	D	E	A	C
5.8	6.4	3.3	9.5	11.8
C	A	B	E	D
9.3	4.0	6.2	5.1	5.4
D	C	A	B	E
7.6	15.4	6.5	6.0	4.6
E	B	C	D	A
6.3	7.6	13.2	8.6	4.9
A	E	D	C	B
9.3	6.3	11.8	15.9	7.6

Construct a table showing sums of squares, degrees of freedom and mean squares, due to rows, columns, varieties and error, and test for significance between varieties.

6. Work out on the lines of § 9.14 the technique of allowing for a single missing plot in a Latin Square design.

Hint. The missing value x occurs in a row sum, a column sum, and a treatment sum. The conditional SS assumes that the treatment effect is zero.

7. Suppose that in the Latin Square experiment of Problem 5, the yield of variety B in row 1 and column 1 had been missing. Estimate this yield. Obtain also the best estimate of the yield of A minus the yield of B, and test whether the difference of these yields is significant.

8. The following data represent yields of millet in 25 plots. Five different spacings of the plants were used, namely 2″, 4″, 6″, 8″ and 10″, and plots with these spacings were arranged in a Latin Square. In the diagram A, B, C, D, E represent the five spacings in order, and the yields are given under the respective letters.

B	E	A	C	D
257	230	279	287	202
D	A	E	B	C
245	283	245	280	260
E	B	C	D	A
182	252	280	246	250
A	C	D	E	B
203	204	227	193	259
C	D	B	A	E
231	271	266	334	338

Test for variations between spacings. Compute the correlation coefficient between mean yield and spacing, and test this coefficient for significance.

9. Treat the data of Problem 8 as a problem in covariance. That is, assume that we have a 2-way classification (rows and columns) with two variables x and y in each cell, x being the spacing and y the yield. Find the mean yields in rows after adjusting for regression on spacing, and test whether there is any significant difference.

10. In a greenhouse experiment on wheat, 4 fertilizer treatments of the soil and 4 chemical treatments of the seed were used (including in each case a control with no treatment). Each combination of treatments was applied to 3 plots, which were placed at random in the available space. The yields are given in the table:

| | Chemical Treatment | | | |
Fertilizer	I	II	III	IV
I	21.4, 21.2, 20.1	20.9, 20.3, 19.8	19.6, 18.8, 16.6	17.6, 16.6, 17.5
II	12.0, 14.2, 12.1	13.6, 13.3, 11.6	13.0, 13.7, 12.0	13.3, 14.0, 13.9
III	13.5, 11.9, 13.4	14.0, 15.6, 13.8	12.7, 12.9, 13.1	12.4, 13.7, 13.0
IV	12.8, 13.8, 13.7	14.1, 13.2, 15.3	14.2, 13.6, 13.3	12.0, 14.6, 14.0

Show that there is a highly significant interaction between chemical treatments and fertilizers.

Hint. The error SS is that within the sub-classes.

11. Suppose that the data represent yields in an experiment with two treatments N and P each at two levels. Only two treatments are applied in each block, as indicated.

Treatment		Blocks					
		Ia	Ib	IIa	IIb	IIIa	IIIb
N_0	P_0	30		30		25	
N_0	P_1	15			10		20
N_1	P_0		30	25			40
N_1	P_1		10		10	15	

Show that there is a *partial confounding*. In the first pair of blocks the N effect is confounded with block difference, in the second pair the P effect is confounded and in the third pair the interaction. Estimate the main effects and the interaction.

Hint. In calculating the sums of squares to estimate any effect, use only the blocks in which that effect is not confounded. Of the total 11 df, 5 are between blocks, 2 for main effects, 1 for interaction, and 3 for error. The SS for the N effect is

$$\tfrac{1}{2} \times \tfrac{1}{4}(65 + 25 - 55 - 30)^2 = 3\tfrac{1}{8}$$

with 1 df, and similarly for P and $N \times P$.

12. The following data (slightly simplified) represent yields in bushels per acre of 4 varieties of flax grown in 3 randomized blocks at 2 distinct locations for 2 years. Carry out a complete analysis of variance, separating the main effects and the interactions beween varieties, blocks, locations and years. Note that since the blocks are numbered arbitrarily there is no connection between, say, block 1 at location G and block 1 at location H. No main effect for blocks is to be expected, and all the interaction terms involving both blocks and varieties may be pooled to give the estimate of error.

YEAR 1948, LOCATION G						YEAR 1949, LOCATION G				
Blocks	Varieties				Blocks	Varieties			
	A	B	C	D		A	B	C	D
1	15	12	18	16	1	14	12	11	8
2	13	16	17	18	2	12	10	12	9
3	17	14	16	20	3	11	13	9	11

Year 1948, Location H				Year 1949, Location H			
Blocks	Varieties				Blocks	Varieties			
	A	B	C	D		A	B	C	D
1	16	14	19	20	1	13	14	13	14
2	15	18	21	24	2	12	11	17	15
3	17	19	23	22	3	15	13	14	17

13. Assume that in the data of Problem 12 the blocks now represent distinct treatments, the same for each year and each location. Carry out the complete analysis of variance, separating out all first order, second order and third order interactions. (The third order interaction mean square is now the only valid estimate of error for testing the other interactions.)

References

For many practical details of application and for the analysis of more complicated experimental designs the student is referred to the following books:

G. W. Snedecor, *Statistical Methods*, 1946.
C. H. Goulden, *Methods of Statistical Analysis*, 1952.
R. A. Fisher, *The Design of Experiments*, 1949 (5th Edition).
W. G. Cochran and G. M. Cox, *Experimental Designs*, 1950.

1. See C. Eisenhart, "The Assumptions Underlying the Analysis of Variance," and W. G. Cochran, "Some Consequences when the Assumptions Are Not Met," both in *Biometrics*, **3**, March 1947.

2. E. S. Pearson, "The Analysis of Variance in Cases of Non-normal Variation," *Biometrika*, **23**, 1931, p. 114.

3. M. S. Bartlett, "The Use of Transformations," *Biometrics*, **3**, 1947, pp. 39–52.

4. A more rigorous mathematical treatment is given by J. H. Curtiss, "Transformations used in the Analysis of Variance," *Ann. Math. Stat.*, **14**, 1943, p. 107.

5. G. W. Snedecor, *Statistical Methods* (4th Edition).

6. M. S. Bartlett, *Proc. Roy. Soc.* **A, 160**, 1937, p. 268.

7. H. O. Hartley, *Biometrika*, **31**, 1940, p. 249.

8. C. M. Thompson and M. Merrington, "Tables for testing the Homogeneity of a Set of Estimated Variances," *Biometrika*, **33**, 1946, p. 296.

9. J. Neyman and E. S. Pearson, "On the Problem of k Samples," *Bull. Acad. Polonaise des Sciences et des Lettres*, **A, 1931**, pp. 460–481.

10. P. P. N. Nayer, "An Investigation into the Application of Neyman and Pearson's L_1 test, with Tables of Percentage Limits," *Statistical Research Memoirs*, Vol. I (1936), p. 38. These tables are reprinted in Croxton and Cowden's *Practical Business Statistics*, p. 519, and in Palmer Johnson's *Statistical Methods in Research* (1949).

11. R. A. Fisher, "The Fiducial Argument in Statistical Inference," *Ann. Eugenics*, **6**, 1935, pp. 391–398.

12. P. V. Sukhatme, "On Fisher and Behrens' test of significance for the difference in means of two normal samples," *Sankhyā*, **4**, 1938, p. 39.

13. See M. G. Kendall, *Advanced Theory of Statistics*, Vol. II, pp. 91–96, and the references there given.

14. See G. W. Snedecor, *Statistical Methods*, 1946, p. 83.

15. This method was worked out by I. J. Bross. The authors are indebted to W. G. Cochran for reference to it.
16. G. H. Goulden, *Methods of Statistical Analysis*, 1939, p. 151.
17. E. J. G. Pitman, "The Analysis of Variance Test," *Biometrika*, **29,** 1937, pp. 322–335.
18. B. L. Welch, "On the z-test in Randomized Blocks and Latin Squares," *Biometrika*, **29,** 1937, pp. 21–52.
19. R. A. Fisher, *Statistical Methods for Research Workers*, 10th Edition, p. 219.
20. R. C. Bose, "On the Construction of Balanced Incomplete Block Designs," *Ann. Eugenics*, London **9,** 1939, pp. 353–399.

CHAPTER X

MATRIX ALGEBRA AND THE METHOD OF LEAST SQUARES[1]

10.1 Introduction. Problems of regression and correlation in several variates require the solution of a set of simultaneous linear equations. The numerical solution of such a set of equations is greatly facilitated by the use of an efficient technique. Moreover, the computation of the standard errors of the variables concerned requires the solution of other related sets of simultaneous equations, or alternatively the calculation of the inverse of a matrix. It is the main purpose of this chapter to give an outline of matrix algebra, as a useful tool in many statistical problems, and of certain computational methods which are convenient in numerical work.

10.2 Normal Equations. Let us suppose that we have a set of N observations on each of $p + 1$ variates, $x_1, x_2, \cdots x_p$ and y ($N > p$), and that we wish to find the "best" linear predicting equation (in the least squares sense),

(10.1) $$Y = b_1 x_1 + b_2 x_2 + \cdots + b_p x_p$$

for obtaining estimates of y to be associated with future values of $x_1, x_2, \cdots x_p$. For example,[2] we may have observations of longitude (x_1), latitude (x_2), altitude (x_3), and rainfall (y) at 57 weather stations, and wish to estimate rainfall at other places. The x_i are the *predictors*, and y is the dependent variable or *predictand*. Equation (10.1) is called a *multiple regression equation*, and the coefficients $b_1, b_2, \cdots b_p$ are the *partial regression coefficients* of y on $x_1, x_2, \cdots x_p$ respectively. They are, of course, estimates of the true regression coefficients $\beta_1, \beta_2, \cdots \beta_p$ and as such are subject to sampling errors.

The whole set of observations may be represented as in Table 28, where $x_{j\alpha}$ is the αth observation on the jth variable ($\alpha = 1, 2, \cdots N, j = 1, 2, \cdots p$).

TABLE 28

x_{11}	x_{12} $\cdots$ $x_{1\alpha}$ $\cdots$ x_{1N}
x_{21}	x_{22} $\cdots$ $x_{2\alpha}$ $\cdots$ x_{2N}
.	. . .
.	. . .
.	. . .
x_{j1}	x_{j2} $\cdots$ $x_{j\alpha}$ $\cdots$ x_{jN}
.	. . .
.	. . .
.	. . .
x_{p1}	x_{p2} $\cdots$ $x_{p\alpha}$ $\cdots$ x_{pN}
y_1	y_2 $\cdots$ y_α $\cdots$ y_N

The true regression equation may be written

(10.2) $$\eta = \sum \beta_j x_j$$

It is assumed that the x_i are either fixed numbers or variates with errors which are negligible in comparison with the error in y. If $\Delta_\alpha = y_\alpha - \eta_\alpha$, the difference between the observed and theoretical values of y for the αth observation, we suppose that the Δ_α are independently distributed about zero with a common variance σ^2, and that the b_i are chosen so as to make the sum of squares of the Δ_α a minimum. We shall use the symbol S to denote summation with respect to α and the symbol $\sum$ to denote summation with respect to j (or other Latin subscript).

Imposing the condition

(10.3) $$S(y_\alpha - \sum \beta_j x_{j\alpha})^2 = \min$$

differentiating (10.3) with respect to $\beta_1, \beta_2, \cdots \beta_p$, and equating the derivatives to zero with $\beta_j = b_j$, we have, as the least squares estimates of the β_j, the values b_j given by

$$S x_{j\alpha}(y_\alpha - \sum b_j x_{j\alpha}) = 0 \quad \text{or}$$

(10.4) $$S \sum_k b_k x_{j\alpha} x_{k\alpha} = S x_{j\alpha} y_\alpha, \quad j = 1, 2, \cdots p$$

This is a system of p equations in the p unknowns $b_1, b_2, \cdots b_p$. Written out in full, they are

(10.5) $$\begin{cases} b_1 S x_{1\alpha}^2 + b_2 S x_{1\alpha} x_{2\alpha} + \cdots + b_p S x_{1\alpha} x_{p\alpha} = S x_{1\alpha} y_\alpha \\ b_1 S x_{2\alpha} x_{1\alpha} + b_2 S x_{2\alpha}^2 + \cdots + b_p S x_{2\alpha} x_{p\alpha} = S x_{2\alpha} y_\alpha \\ \cdots \cdots \cdots \cdots \cdots \cdots \cdots \cdots \cdots \cdots \\ b_1 S x_{p\alpha} x_{1\alpha} + b_2 S x_{p\alpha} x_{2\alpha} + \cdots + b_p S x_{p\alpha}^2 = S x_{p\alpha} y_\alpha \end{cases}$$

The system is called the *normal equations* of the problem. It is clear that the coefficient of b_j in the kth equation is the same as that of b_k in the jth equation. This symmetry in the coefficients is characteristic of normal equations, but any system of p equations in p unknowns may be put into the symmetrical form by a preliminary transformation. (See § 10.11.)

It is of interest to note that the same set of normal equations is obtained by considering the regression problem in different ways. Thus, if we assume normality for the Δ's, the joint probability density is $(\sigma \sqrt{2\pi})^{-N} e^{-S\Delta_\alpha^2/2\sigma^2}$, so that the likelihood function is

(10.6) $$L = C - N \log \sigma - S(\Delta_\alpha^2/2\sigma^2)$$

The condition of maximum likelihood is therefore equivalent to that of minimum $S\Delta_\alpha^2$.

Again, we may consider the b's as linear functions of the observed y's, chosen in such a way as to be unbiased estimates of the β's with minimum variance. (The less the variance the greater the precision of the estimate.)

Sec. 3   **Matrix Algebra**   291

The reason for choosing *linear* functions is that we want the predicting equation to be independent of any change of scale in the y's. If we put $b_j = Sc_{j\alpha}y_\alpha$, and choose the $c_{j\alpha}$ to satisfy the conditions $E(b_j) = \beta_j$, Var (b_j) = min, it may be shown [3] that we arrive at equations (10.5).

10.3 Matrix Algebra. The solution of a system of normal equations like (10.5), and various problems related to this, are conveniently and concisely expressible in matrix notation. In practice some suitable computational technique is required, but the use of matrix algebra facilitates the handling of theoretical problems. We now give a brief account of this algebra.

A system of mn elements arranged in a rectangular array of m rows and n columns is called a matrix of order $m \times n$ or an $m \times n$ *matrix*. When $m = n$, the matrix is said to be *square*. Thus, the set of observations in Table 28 forms a $(p + 1) \times N$ matrix, and the set of coefficients of the b's in (10.5) is a square matrix of order p. A matrix is often denoted by a single letter, as

$$A = \begin{bmatrix} a_{11} & a_{12} & \cdots & a_{1n} \\ a_{21} & a_{22} & \cdots & a_{2n} \\ \cdot & \cdot & & \cdot \\ \cdot & \cdot & & \cdot \\ a_{m1} & a_{m2} & \cdots & a_{mn} \end{bmatrix}$$

To distinguish the matrix from a determinant it is enclosed in square brackets, parentheses, or double vertical lines. We shall adopt the first of these conventions. A convenient short notation is $[a_{jk}]$, $m \times n$.

The elements of a matrix are ordinary numbers, real or complex. In our work they will be real. An ordinary number, as opposed to a matrix, is called a *scalar*. In matrix algebra the whole matrix is regarded as a mathematical entity, subject to algebraic operations which have, of course, to be defined.

A matrix is said to be *null* or *zero* if and only if all of its elements are zero.

Two matrices A and B are said to be *equal* if and only if they have the same number of rows (m) and columns (n) and if $a_{jk} = b_{jk}$ for all j from 1 to m and all k from 1 to n.

Addition. If A and B are both $m \times n$ matrices, the sum $A + B$ is defined as the matrix $C = [c_{jk}]$, $m \times n$, for which $c_{jk} = a_{jk} + b_{jk}$. Matrices which do not have the same number of rows and columns cannot be added, and are said to be not *conformable* for addition.

Multiplication by a Scalar. If c is a scalar (an ordinary number) and $A = [a_{jk}]$, $m \times n$, the product cA is defined as the matrix $P = [p_{jk}]$, $m \times n$, for which $p_{jk} = ca_{jk}$.

Multiplication of Two Matrices. If $A = [a_{ij}]$, $m \times n$, and $B = [b_{jk}]$, $n \times p$, the matrix product AB is defined as the matrix $C = [c_{ik}]$, $m \times p$, for which

(10.7) $$c_{ik} = \sum_j a_{ij} b_{jk}$$

That is, the element in the ith row and kth column of C is found by multiplying together, element by element, the ith row of A and the kth column of B, and adding the products. It is necessary, therefore, that the number of *columns* in A shall be equal to the number of *rows* in B, if A and B are *conformable* for multiplication.

The operation of addition is easily proved to be *commutative* and *associative*. That is, if A, B, and C are conformable for addition, $A + B = B + A$ and $(A + B) + C = A + (B + C)$.

The operation of matrix multiplication is associative but is not, in general, commutative. That is, if A, B, C are conformable for multiplication, $(AB)C = A(BC)$, but AB may not be equal to BA. In fact, if A is of order $m \times n$, B must be of order $n \times m$ for both products to exist. AB is then of order $m \times m$ and BA of order $n \times n$. Even if $m = n$, there is no reason why $\sum_j a_{ij} b_{jk}$ should be equal to $\sum_j b_{ij} a_{jk}$.

Example 1.

$$\begin{bmatrix} 2 & 1 \\ 3 & 4 \end{bmatrix} \cdot \begin{bmatrix} 1 & 6 \\ 2 & -1 \end{bmatrix} = \begin{bmatrix} 4 & 11 \\ 11 & 14 \end{bmatrix}$$

$$\begin{bmatrix} 1 & 6 \\ 2 & -1 \end{bmatrix} \cdot \begin{bmatrix} 2 & 1 \\ 3 & 4 \end{bmatrix} = \begin{bmatrix} 20 & 25 \\ 1 & -2 \end{bmatrix}$$

It is necessary, therefore, to distinguish between "pre-multiplication" and "post-multiplication." The product AB is often referred to as "B multiplied by A on the left" or as "A multiplied by B on the right," and similarly for BA.

The *distributive laws* hold for matrix addition and multiplication, namely, $A(B + C) = AB + AC$ and $(A + B)C = AC + BC$, the matrices, of course, being conformable.

The *product law* does not hold. If AB is a zero matrix (of the appropriate number of rows and columns) it does not follow that either A or B is a zero matrix.

Example 2.

$$\begin{bmatrix} 2 & -1 \\ 10 & -5 \end{bmatrix} \cdot \begin{bmatrix} 1 & 3 \\ 2 & 6 \end{bmatrix} = \begin{bmatrix} 0 & 0 \\ 0 & 0 \end{bmatrix}$$

10.4 Transposition. If the successive columns of matrix A are written as successive rows of a new matrix A', then A' is called the *transpose* of A. The ith column of A' is the ith row of A, and *vice versa*. If A is an $m \times n$ matrix, then A' is an $n \times m$ matrix. For example,

$$A = \begin{bmatrix} 3 & 6 & 2 \\ 2 & 1 & 0 \\ 5 & 9 & 7 \\ 1 & 0 & 6 \end{bmatrix} \qquad A' = \begin{bmatrix} 3 & 2 & 5 & 1 \\ 6 & 1 & 9 & 0 \\ 2 & 0 & 7 & 6 \end{bmatrix}$$

A square matrix is said to be *symmetric* if it is equal to its transpose. That is, $A = [a_{jk}]$, $n \times n$, is symmetric if and only if $a_{jk} = a_{kj}$, for $j, k = 1, 2, \cdots n$.

Sec. 4   **Transposition**

For example, $\begin{bmatrix} -2 & 3 & -4 \\ 3 & 5 & 1 \\ -4 & 1 & 6 \end{bmatrix}$ is symmetric, and so is the matrix of the coefficients of the b's in the normal equations (10.5). In a symmetric matrix, pairs of equal elements are situated symmetrically with respect to its *principal diagonal* (upper left corner to lower right corner).

If $A' = -A$, the matrix is said to be *skew-symmetric*. If so, A must be square and the elements of its principal diagonal must all be zero. For example, $\begin{bmatrix} 0 & 1 & 2 \\ -1 & 0 & 3 \\ -2 & -3 & 0 \end{bmatrix}$ is skew-symmetric.

Theorem 10.1   (*Reversal rule*).

$$(AB)' = B'A'$$

Proof:

If c_{ik}' is the element in the ith row and jth column of $(AB)'$,

$$c_{ik}' = c_{ki} = \sum_j a_{kj} b_{ji}$$

But the element in the ith row and kth row of B' is b_{ji} and the element in the jth row and kth column of A' is a_{kj}. Hence the (i, k)th element of $B'A'$ is

$$\sum_j b_{ji} a_{kj} = c_{ik}'$$

Similarly $(ABC)' = C'B'A'$, etc.

A square matrix in which all the elements except those in the principal diagonal are zero is called a *diagonal matrix*. Diagonal matrices commute with each other, if conformable. Thus,

$$\begin{bmatrix} a_{11} & 0 & 0 \\ 0 & a_{22} & 0 \\ 0 & 0 & a_{33} \end{bmatrix} \cdot \begin{bmatrix} b_{11} & 0 & 0 \\ 0 & b_{22} & 0 \\ 0 & 0 & b_{23} \end{bmatrix} = \begin{bmatrix} a_{11}b_{11} & 0 & 0 \\ 0 & a_{22}b_{22} & 0 \\ 0 & 0 & a_{23}b_{23} \end{bmatrix}$$

$$= \begin{bmatrix} b_{11} & 0 & 0 \\ 0 & b_{22} & 0 \\ 0 & 0 & b_{33} \end{bmatrix} \cdot \begin{bmatrix} a_{11} & 0 & 0 \\ 0 & a_{22} & 0 \\ 0 & 0 & a_{33} \end{bmatrix}$$

A diagonal matrix with all the elements in the principal diagonal equal is called a *scalar matrix*. Multiplication on the left or right by a scalar matrix is equivalent to multiplication by a scalar. Thus

$$\begin{bmatrix} \lambda & 0 & 0 \\ 0 & \lambda & 0 \\ 0 & 0 & \lambda \end{bmatrix} \cdot \begin{bmatrix} a_{11} & a_{12} & a_{13} & a_{14} \\ a_{21} & a_{22} & a_{23} & a_{24} \\ a_{31} & a_{32} & a_{33} & a_{34} \end{bmatrix} = \begin{bmatrix} \lambda a_{11} & \lambda a_{12} & \lambda a_{13} & \lambda a_{14} \\ \lambda a_{21} & \lambda a_{22} & \lambda a_{23} & \lambda a_{24} \\ \lambda a_{31} & \lambda a_{32} & \lambda a_{33} & \lambda a_{34} \end{bmatrix} = \lambda A$$

The Unit Matrix. This is a scalar matrix with $\lambda = 1$. It is denoted by I. For any other matrix A,

(10.8) $$AI = IA = A$$

provided I has the proper number of rows and columns in each case, so as to be conformable. I behaves, therefore, like the number 1 in ordinary multiplication.

10.5 Matrices and Linear Transformations.

The matrix $\begin{bmatrix} y_1 \\ y_2 \\ \cdot \\ \cdot \\ \cdot \\ y_m \end{bmatrix}$, of m rows and one column, is called a *column vector*. Its transpose $[y_1 \; y_2 \cdots y_m]$, of one row and m columns, is called a *row vector*. Let $x = [x_k]$, $n \times 1$, and $y = [y_j]$, $m \times 1$, be column vectors and let $A = [a_{jk}]$, $m \times n$, be a matrix of coefficients. Then the matrix equation

(10.9) $$y = Ax$$

represents the linear transformation

(10.10) $$\begin{cases} y_1 = a_{11}x_1 + a_{12}x_2 + \cdots + a_{1n}x_n \\ y_2 = a_{21}x_1 + a_{22}x_2 + \cdots + a_{2n}x_n \\ \cdots\cdots\cdots\cdots\cdots\cdots\cdots\cdots\cdots \\ y_m = a_{m1}x_1 + a_{m2}x_2 + \cdots + a_{mn}x_n \end{cases}$$

If $A = I$, the transformation reduces to $y_1 = x_1$, $y_2 = x_2$, $\cdots y_n = x_n$, which is the *identical transformation*.

If another linear transformation is made on the y's, say $z_i = \sum_j b_{ij} y_j$, $i = 1, 2, \cdots p$, the relation between the z's and the x's is expressed by $z_i = \sum_j b_{ij} \sum_k a_{jk} x_k = \sum_k (\sum_j b_{ij} a_{jk}) x_k = \sum_k c_{ik} x_k$, where $c_{ik} = \sum_j b_{ij} a_{jk}$. In matrix notation, $z = By = BAx = Cx$, where $C = BA$. The rule of matrix multiplication is, therefore, seen to be quite natural in terms of successive linear transformations.

The *quadratic form* $\sum_{j,k} a_{jk} x_j x_k$ may be written in matrix notation as $x'Ax$, where $x' = [x_1 \; x_2 \cdots x_n]$, $x = \begin{bmatrix} x_1 \\ x_2 \\ \cdot \\ \cdot \\ x_n \end{bmatrix}$ and A is the matrix $[a_{jk}]$, $n \times n$. This is easily verified by carrying out the multiplications according to rule. A is called the matrix of the *quadratic form*. This matrix is symmetric, since $x_j x_k$ is the same as $x_k x_j$.

In the same way the *bilinear form* $\sum_{j=1}^{m} \sum_{k=1}^{n} a_{jk} x_j y_k$ may be written as $x'Ay$, where x and y are column vectors of m and n rows respectively and A is the $m \times n$ matrix of the bilinear form. If, in the bilinear form $x'Ay$, we make

Sec. 6 The Determinant of a Matrix

two linear transformations $x = Hu$ and $y = Kv$, the result is a bilinear form in u and v with matrix $H'AK$. To prove this, we have

$$x'Ay = (u'H')A(Kv)$$
$$= u'(H'AK)v$$

by Theorem 10.1.

If the first p rows of Table 28 are denoted by X and the last row by y', the matrix of coefficients of the b's in (10.5) may be expressed as $A = XX'$. The column vector on the right of (10.5) may be written $g = Xy$, and the whole set of normal equations may, therefore, be concisely represented by

(10.11) $$Ab = g$$

where $b = [b_j]$, $p \times 1$, a column vector.

10.6 The Determinant of a Matrix. If A is a square matrix, of order $n \times n$, the determinant of A, $d(A)$, is a polynomial of the nth degree in the elements of A, denoted by
$$\begin{vmatrix} a_{11} & \cdots & a_{1n} \\ \cdot & & \cdot \\ \cdot & & \cdot \\ \cdot & & \cdot \\ a_{1n} & \cdots & a_{nn} \end{vmatrix}$$
or for short by $|a_{jk}|$.

It is assumed that the reader is familiar with the elementary properties of determinants, as given in most textbooks of college algebra, but we recall a few of these properties for convenience.

The determinant obtained by omitting the jth row and kth column of $d(A)$ is called the *minor of* a_{jk}, and will be denoted by $d(A_{jk})$. The signed minor

$$C_{jk} = (-1)^{j+k} d(A_{jk})$$

is called the *cofactor of* a_{jk}. The formula for the development of $d(A)$ according to the jth row is

(10.12) $$d(A) = \sum_k a_{jk} C_{jk}$$

and similarly for the development according to the kth column,

(10.13) $$d(A) = \sum_j a_{jk} C_{jk}$$

If in these formulas we replace the cofactors of the jth row (or the kth column) by the cofactors of a *different* row or column (what Aitken[4] has called *alien cofactors*) the expression on the right-hand side reduces to zero. That is,

(10.14) $$\sum_k a_{jk} C_{lk} = 0, \quad j \neq l$$

(10.15) $$\sum_j a_{jk} C_{jl} = 0, \quad k \neq l$$

A convenient symbol for expressing such pairs of relations as (10.14) and (10.12) is the *Kronecker delta*, δ_{jk}, defined as equal to 0 when $j \neq k$ and to 1 when $j = k$. The relations

$$\sum_k a_{jk} C_{lk} = \delta_{jl} \, d(A)$$

and

$$\sum_j a_{jk} C_{jl} = \delta_{kl} \, d(A)$$

then express the four equations (10.12) to (10.15).

Even if a matrix is not square, determinants may be constructed from it by crossing out rows and/or columns to leave square arrays. All these are determinants of the matrix. If the matrix is of order $n \times n$, the largest determinant is *the* determinant of the matrix, and is of order n.

The *rank* of a matrix is the order of the determinant (or group of determinants) of highest order that is not equal to zero. A square matrix of order $n \times n$ is called *singular* if its rank is less than n. The determinant of a singular matrix is, of course, equal to zero.

Multiplication of Determinants. If A and B are two square matrices of order $n \times n$, and if $C = AB$, then $d(C) = d(A) \cdot d(B)$. That is, the rule for multiplying together two determinants of the same order is the same as that of multiplying two matrices, except, of course, that a determinant may be transposed without affecting its value and that the order of multiplication is immaterial. Thus,

$$\begin{vmatrix} 3 & 1 \\ 2 & 0 \end{vmatrix} \cdot \begin{vmatrix} 4 & 1 \\ 2 & 5 \end{vmatrix} = \begin{vmatrix} 14 & 8 \\ 8 & 2 \end{vmatrix}$$

which is clearly true, since the determinants have the values -2, 18, and -36 respectively.

The matrices AB and BA are, in general, distinct, but both have the same determinant.

10.7 The Inverse of a Matrix. If a matrix A, $n \times n$, is non-singular, there exists a unique $n \times n$ matrix, denoted by A^{-1}, such that

$$AA^{-1} = I$$

A^{-1} is called the *inverse* or *reciprocal* of A.

The transpose of the matrix of co-factors of the elements of A is called the *adjoint* of A, denoted by adj A. That is,

$$\text{adj } A = [C_{jk}]' = [C_{kj}]$$

Hence $A \cdot \text{adj } A = [\sum_l a_{jl} C_{lk}'] = [\sum_l a_{jl} C_{kl}] = [\delta_{jk} \, d(A)] = d(A)I$, since the element of I in the jth row and kth column is δ_{jk} and $d(A)$ is a scalar. Hence, provided $d(A)$ is not zero,

(10.16) $$A^{-1} = \text{adj } A / d(A)$$

It can be proved in the same way that

$$A^{-1}A = I$$

Sec. 7 The Inverse of a Matrix

We have, therefore, an operation of *matrix division* defined for non-singular square matrices only. As with multiplication, we may pre-divide or post-divide B by A, if B and A are conformable, forming $A^{-1}B$ and BA^{-1}, which are in general different.

Theorem 10.2. *The reversal rule applies to inversion, namely,*

$$(10.17) \qquad (AB)^{-1} = B^{-1}A^{-1}$$

This follows since $(AB)(AB)^{-1} = I = AA^{-1} = ABB^{-1}A^{-1}$.

Theorem 10.3. *The operations of transposition and inversion are commutative, that is,*

$$(10.18) \qquad (A^{-1})' = (A')^{-1}$$

For $A'(A^{-1})' = (A^{-1}A)' = I' = I$, so that $(A^{-1})'$ is the inverse of A'.

The operation of inversion provides a solution in concise symbolic form of a set of simultaneous linear equations, such as the normal equations (10.5), which in matrix notation are written as in (10.11), $Ab = g$.

To solve these equations for the unknown b's, we premultiply by A^{-1}. Then $A^{-1}Ab = A^{-1}g$, or

$$(10.19) \qquad b = A^{-1}g = (\operatorname{adj} A \cdot g)/d(A)$$

The elements of A^{-1} are often written as a^{ik}. Thus, (10.19) is equivalent to

$$(10.20) \qquad b_j = \sum_k a^{ik} g_k = \left(\sum_k C_{kj} g_k\right)/d(A)$$

This is *Cramer's rule*, named after Gabriel Cramer (1704–1752), a Swiss mathematician who first stated it. The numerator of the fraction on the right-hand side of (10.20) is the determinant of the matrix derived from A by replacing the elements of its jth column by $g_1, g_2, \cdots g_p$.

A non-singular matrix A is *orthogonal* if its transpose is equal to its inverse, that is, if

$$AA' = I$$

The matrix $\begin{bmatrix} \cos\theta & -\sin\theta \\ \sin\theta & \cos\theta \end{bmatrix}$ is orthogonal, and is the matrix of the orthogonal transformation

$$x = x'\cos\theta - y'\sin\theta$$
$$y = x'\sin\theta + y'\cos\theta$$

which corresponds geometrically to a rotation of the coordinate axes about the origin through the angle θ.

The general orthogonal transformation of § 4.13 was defined as

$$y_i = \sum_j c_{ij} x_j, \qquad i, j = 1, 2, \cdots n$$

where

$$\sum_k c_{ik} c_{jk} = \delta_{ij} = \sum_k c_{ik} c_{kj}'$$

If C is the matrix of this transformation the orthogonality condition is equivalent to
$$CC' = I$$
so that the matrix of any orthogonal transformation is orthogonal.

10.8 Numerical Solution of Normal Equations. The elegant theoretical solution by means of Cramer's rule is not very useful in practice, particularly for $p > 3$. This is because the computation of determinants of high order by the usual expansion method does not lend itself to compact self-checking numerical schemes. In practice, solutions are usually found by some scheme of systematic elimination of the variables, one by one, a method attributed to Gauss and modified in the direction of greater compactness by Doolittle, Dwyer, and others.[5]

This method transforms the original set of p equations in p unknowns (say $u_1, u_2, \cdots u_p$) to a set of p equations containing, respectively, $p, p-1, \cdots 2, 1$ unknowns. Thus

$$(10.21) \quad \begin{cases} t_{11}u_1 + t_{12}u_2 + \cdots + t_{1,p-1}u_{p-1} + t_{1p}u_p = h_1 \\ \phantom{t_{11}u_1 +\ } t_{22}u_2 + \cdots + t_{2,p-1}u_{p-1} + t_{2p}u_p = h_2 \\ \phantom{t_{11}u_1 + t_{12}u_2 + \cdots +\ } t_{p-1,p-1}u_{p-1} + t_{p-1,p}u_p = h_{p-1} \\ \phantom{t_{11}u_1 + t_{12}u_2 + \cdots + t_{1,p-1}u_{p-1} +\ } t_{pp}u_p = h_p \end{cases}$$

These equations are then easily solved, one by one, beginning with the last and working up. This is known as the "back solution."

The matrix equivalent of (10.21) is

$$(10.22) \quad Tu = h$$

where T is a *triangular matrix*, that is, a square matrix with all elements below (or above) the principal diagonal equal to zero. Written out,

$$T = \begin{bmatrix} t_{11} & t_{12} & \cdots & t_{1,p-1} & t_{1p} \\ 0 & t_{22} & \cdots & t_{2,p-1} & t_{2p} \\ \vdots & & & & \vdots \\ 0 & 0 & \cdots & 0 & t_{pp} \end{bmatrix}$$

The first step in the Gauss solution is, therefore, equivalent to transforming a given square matrix to a triangular matrix.

One method of doing this is known as the *Square Root Method*.[6] If A is a symmetric non-singular matrix, we find a triangular matrix S such that

$$(10.23) \quad S'S = A$$

In a certain sense, S is a "square root" of A. If the matrix equation to be solved is $Au = g$, we have then

$$S'Su = g$$

This is equivalent to the two equations $S'k = g$, $Su = k$, both of which are triangular and, therefore, readily solved.

Sec. 8 Numerical Solution of Normal Equations

Since $S = \begin{bmatrix} s_{11} & s_{12} & \cdots & s_{1p} \\ 0 & s_{22} & \cdots & s_{2p} \\ \vdots & & & \vdots \\ 0 & 0 & \cdots & s_{pp} \end{bmatrix}$, (10.23) is equivalent to

$$\begin{cases} s_{11}^2 = a_{11} \\ s_{11}s_{12} = a_{12} \\ s_{12}^2 + s_{22}^2 = a_{22} \\ \cdots \cdots \cdots \cdots \cdots \cdots \\ s_{1j}^2 + s_{2j}^2 + \cdots + s_{jj}^2 = a_{jj} \\ s_{1j}s_{1k} + s_{2j}s_{2k} + \cdots + s_{jj}s_{jk} = a_{jk} \\ \cdots \cdots \cdots \cdots \cdots \cdots \end{cases}$$

whence we obtain explicit expressions for the elements of S, namely,

(10.24)
$$\begin{cases} s_{11} = (a_{11})^{1/2} \\ s_{12} = a_{12}/s_{11} \\ s_{22} = (a_{22} - s_{12}^2)^{1/2} \\ \cdots \cdots \cdots \cdots \cdots \cdots \\ s_{jj} = (a_{jj} - s_{1j}^2 - s_{2j}^2 - \cdots - s_{j-1,j}^2)^{1/2} \\ s_{jk} = (a_{jk} - s_{1j}s_{1k} - s_{2j}s_{2k} - \cdots - s_{j-1,j}s_{j-1,k})/s_{jj} \\ \cdots \cdots \cdots \cdots \cdots \cdots \end{cases}$$

The next step is to find k from $S'k = g$, or

$$\begin{cases} s_{11}k_1 = g_1 \\ s_{12}k_1 + s_{22}k_2 = g_2 \\ \cdots \cdots \cdots \cdots \cdots \\ s_{1j}k_1 + s_{2j}k_2 + \cdots + s_{jj}k_j = g_j \\ \cdots \cdots \cdots \cdots \cdots \end{cases}$$

whence

(10.25)
$$\begin{cases} k_1 = g_1/s_{11} \\ k_2 = (g_2 - s_{12}k_1)/s_{22} \\ \cdots \cdots \cdots \cdots \cdots \\ k_j = (g_j - s_{1j}k_1 - s_{2j}k_2 - \cdots - s_{j-1,j}k_{j-1})/s_{jj} \\ \cdots \cdots \cdots \cdots \cdots \end{cases}$$

Finally, the u_j are found from $Su = k$, or

$$\begin{cases} s_{11}u_1 + s_{12}u_2 + \cdots + s_{1p}u_p = k_1 \\ s_{22}u_2 + \cdots + s_{2p}u_p = k_2 \\ \cdots \cdots \cdots \cdots \cdots \\ s_{pp}u_p = k_p \end{cases}$$

giving

(10.26)
$$\begin{cases} u_p = k_p/s_{pp} \\ u_{p-1} = (k_{p-1} - s_{p-1,p}u_p)/s_{p-1,p-1} \\ \cdots \cdots \cdots \cdots \cdots \\ u_j = (k_j - s_{j,j+1}u_{j+1} - s_{j,j+2}u_{j+2} - \cdots - s_{jp}u_p)/s_{jj} \\ \cdots \cdots \cdots \cdots \cdots \end{cases}$$

Example 3. Solve the set of equations
$$\begin{bmatrix} 6.86 & 2.56 & 3.39 \\ 2.56 & 8.92 & 1.78 \\ 3.39 & 1.78 & 4.41 \end{bmatrix} \cdot \begin{bmatrix} u_1 \\ u_2 \\ u_3 \end{bmatrix} = \begin{bmatrix} 1.98 \\ 2.93 \\ 1.06 \end{bmatrix}$$

The operations involved in these calculations are well adapted to machine computation. On most types of machine, for example, a quantity like

$$a_{jk} - s_{1j}s_{1k} - s_{2j}s_{2k} - \cdots - s_{j-1,j}s_{j-1,k}$$

may be found in one operation. Square roots may be obtained from Barlow's *Table of Squares, Square Roots, etc.*, or on the machine. The advantages of the method are more evident when the number of unknowns is larger than in this example.

The first step is to calculate the triangular matrix S. Only the result

$$\begin{bmatrix} 2.619 & 0.977 & 1.294 \\ & 2.822 & 0.183 \\ & & 1.644 \end{bmatrix}$$

need actually be set down. The elements are obtained as follows:

$s_{11} = (6.86)^{1/2} = 2.619$
$s_{12} = 2.56/2.619 = 0.977$
$s_{13} = 3.39/2.619 = 1.294$
$s_{22} = [8.92 - (0.977)^2]^{1/2} = 2.822$
$s_{23} = [1.78 - 0.977 \times 1.294]/2.822 = 0.183$
$s_{23} = [4.41 - (1.294)^2 - (0.183)^2]^{1/2} = 1.644$

The k matrix is similarly set down.

$k_1 = 1.98/2.619 = 0.756$
$k_2 = [2.93 - 0.977(0.756)]/2.822 = 0.777$
$k_3 = [1.06 - 1.294(0.756) - 0.183(0.777)]/1.644 = -0.037$

Finally

$u_3 = -0.037/1.644 = -0.023$
$u_2 = [0.777 - 0.183(-0.023)]/2.822 = 0.277$
$u_1 = [0.756 - 0.977(0.277) - 1.294(-0.023)]/2.619 = 0.197$

Hence $u' = [0.197, 0.277, -0.023]$.

Check Sums. It is very desirable in a long computation to have a series of checks as the work proceeds. Such checks are provided by forming a column vector $\bar{g}$ whose elements are the sums of the corresponding rows in A and g. Thus,

(10.27) $$\bar{g}_j = a_{j1} + a_{j2} + \cdots + a_{jp} + g_j$$

The second and third steps of the computation are repeated with $\bar{g}$ instead of g, giving new vectors $\bar{k}$ and $\bar{u}$. Apart from errors due to the rounding off of decimals, which should not affect more than the last one or two places unless p is large, we should find

(10.28) $$\bar{k}_j = s_{jj} + s_{j,j+1} + \cdots + s_{jp} + k_j$$

and

(10.29) $$\bar{u}_j = u_j + 1$$

Sec. 9   Calculation of the Inverse of a Matrix   301

A convenient tabular form for the square root method, including the checks, is set out in Table 29. The first row of S is calculated, followed by k_1 and $\bar{k}_1$. This gives the first check. Each row of S, in turn, has its own check. In calculating the elements of u, u_p is first obtained and then $\bar{u}_p$, followed by u_{p-1} and $\bar{u}_{p-1}$, and so on, until the check of $\bar{u}_1$ with $u_1 + 1$. As a final check, the values $u_1, u_2, \cdots u_p$ should be substituted in the normal equations.

TABLE 29

				g	$\bar{g}$
A	6.86	2.56 8.92	3.39 1.78 4.41	1.98 2.93 1.06	14.79 16.19 10.64
S	2.619	0.977 2.822	1.294 0.183 1.644	k 0.756 0.777 −0.037	$\bar{k}$ 5.647 3.782 1.606
u'	0.197	0.277	−0.023		
$\bar{u}'$	1.197	1.277	0.977		

Note that, in writing out the symmetrical matrix A, it is unnecessary to include the elements below the principal diagonal. These must be included, however, in summing to form the column vector $\bar{g}$. We can do this, in effect, by summing down the column to each diagonal element and then across. The omitted elements in S are all zeros.

Observe also that the checks all hold except for an occasional single unit in the third decimal place.

In a long calculation it is advisable to retain two or three more significant figures than are desired at the end. Figures can always be dropped, but they cannot be replaced later in the calculation. This applies particularly in Analysis of Variance problems, where the subtraction of two nearly equal numbers may mean the loss of several significant figures in one step.

10.9 Calculation of the Inverse of a Matrix. As we shall see later, some of the elements of the matrix A^{-1} in (10.19) are required for testing the significance of the partial regression coefficients b_j. The inverse matrix is used also in dropping a variable from the regression equation if it does not seem to be contributing much information.

When the inverse matrix is required, a good method of solving the normal equation $Au = g$ is to invert A and calculate $u = A^{-1}g$ by matrix multiplication. When only a few elements of A^{-1} are wanted, however, it may be a waste of time to invert the whole matrix.

Since $AA^{-1} = I$, the kth column of A^{-1} is the solution U_k of the matrix equation $AU_k = G_k$, where G_k is a column matrix of zeros, except that the element in the kth row is 1. Thus,

$$U_1 = \begin{bmatrix} a^{11} \\ a^{21} \\ \cdot \\ \cdot \\ a^{p1} \end{bmatrix} \text{ is given by solving the equation } AU_1 = \begin{bmatrix} 1 \\ 0 \\ \cdot \\ \cdot \\ 0 \end{bmatrix}$$

There are p separate sets of equations to solve, but they all have a common coefficient matrix A, so that a compact solution is possible. The method here suggested (there are many others) consists of three steps:

1. Finding the square root triangular matrix S, as described above.
2. Inverting S (which is much easier than inverting A).
3. Calculating $A^{-1} = (S'S)^{-1} = S^{-1}(S^{-1})'$, by Theorem 10.3.

If s^{jk} is the typical element of S^{-1}, it is easy to see from the rules of matrix multiplication as applied to $S^{-1}S = I$, that all the $s^{jk} = 0$ when $j > k$. Hence S^{-1} is also a triangular matrix. Moreover, the diagonal elements $s^{ii} = 1/s_{ii}$, and when $j < k$,

(10.30) $\qquad s^{jk} = (-s^{j,k-1}s_{k-1,k} - s^{j,k-2}s_{k-2,k} - \cdots - s^{jj}s_{jk})/s_{kk}$

Thus,

$$\begin{cases} s^{11} = 1/s_{11} \\ s^{21} = 0 \\ s^{12} = -s^{11}s_{12}/s_{22} \\ s^{22} = 1/s_{22} \\ \qquad \text{etc.} \end{cases}$$

The simplest way to perform this inversion is probably to write S^{-1} in its transposed form, and to remember that the jth *column* of $(S^{-1})'$ multiplied by the kth column of S is equal to δ_{jk}. Thus, to invert the matrix S of Example 3, we should have

$$(S^{-1})' = \begin{bmatrix} s^{11} & 0 & 0 \\ s^{12} & s^{22} & 0 \\ s^{13} & s^{23} & s^{33} \end{bmatrix}$$

where the elements are given by

$\qquad s^{11} = 1/2.619 = 0.382$
$\qquad s^{22} = 1/2.822 = 0.354$
$\qquad s^{12} = [0 - 0.977(0.382)]/2.822 = -0.132$
$\qquad s^{33} = 1/1.644 = 0.608$
$\qquad s^{23} = [0 - 0.183(0.354)]/1.644 = -0.039$
$\qquad s^{13} = [0 - 1.294(0.382) - 0.183(-0.132)]/1.644 = -0.286$

These results are entered as obtained in the appropriate places in $(S^{-1})'$, giving

Sec. 9 Calculation of the Inverse of a Matrix 303

$$(S^{-1})' = \begin{bmatrix} 0.382 & 0 & 0 \\ -0.132 & 0.354 & 0 \\ -0.286 & -0.039 & 0.608 \end{bmatrix}$$

Finally, the j, kth element of A^{-1}, a^{jk}, is found by multiplying together the jth and kth columns of $(S^{-1})'$. Thus,

$$a^{11} = (0.382)^2 + (-0.132)^2 + (-0.286)^2 = 0.245$$
$$a^{12} = -0.132 \times 0.354 + 0.286 \times 0.039 = -0.036$$
$$\text{etc.}$$

The final result is

$$A^{-1} = \begin{bmatrix} 0.245 & -0.036 & -0.174 \\ -0.036 & 0.127 & -0.024 \\ -0.174 & -0.024 & 0.370 \end{bmatrix}$$

The solution of the equations of Example 3 may now be obtained from equation (10.19), $u = A^{-1}g$, where $g = \begin{bmatrix} 1.98 \\ 2.93 \\ 1.06 \end{bmatrix}$.

The result is $u = \begin{bmatrix} 0.195 \\ 0.275 \\ -0.023 \end{bmatrix}$, which agrees with the solution found before except for errors of rounding-off.

Check Sums. The method of checking the computation, step by step, as described in § 10.8 may be used in calculating A^{-1}. The check for the first step consists in forming a column vector a whose elements are the sums of the corresponding rows in A,

(10.31) $$a_j = \sum_k a_{jk}, \qquad j = 1, 2, \cdots p$$

The equation $s'S = a'$ is solved for s' along with $S'S = A$ (this involves only one extra column) and the check is provided by

$$s_j = \sum_k s_{jk}, \qquad j = 1, 2, \cdots p$$

except for rounding-off errors. The explicit formula for s_j is

(10.32) $$s_j = (a_j - s_{1j}s_1 - s_{2j}s_2 - \cdots - s_{j-1,j}s_{j-1})/s_{jj}$$

The check for the second step (inversion of S) consists in forming a row vector i', whose elements are all unity, and computing the row vector t' for which $t'S = i'$, so that

(10.33) $$t_j = (1 - s_{1j}t_1 - s_{2j}t_2 - \cdots - s_{j-1,j}t_{j-1})/s_{jj}$$

The check is

$$t_k = \sum_j s^{jk}, \qquad k = 1, 2, \cdots p$$

If the transposed matrix $(S^{-1})'$ is computed instead of S^{-1} (as suggested above) it is convenient to compute the column vector t instead of t'. The checks are then on the rows of $(S^{-1})'$.

Finally, the third step, $A^{-1} = S^{-1}(S^{-1})'$, may be checked by computing $b' = t'(S^{-1})'$. The checks are provided by

$$b_j = \sum_k a^{jk}, \qquad j = 1, 2, \cdots p$$

A compact tabular form for carrying out the whole inversion process, with checks, is indicated in Table 30.

TABLE 30. INVERSION OF SYMMETRIC MATRIX

b_1	$\begin{pmatrix} a_{11} \\ a^{11} \end{pmatrix}$	a_{12}	$\cdots \; a_{1p}$	a_1
b_2	a^{21}	$\begin{pmatrix} a_{22} \\ a^{22} \end{pmatrix}$	$\cdots \; a_{2p}$	a_2
		$\cdots \cdots \cdots$		
b_p	a^{p1}	a^{p2}	$\cdots \begin{pmatrix} a_{pp} \\ a^{pp} \end{pmatrix}$	a_p
t_1	$\begin{pmatrix} s_{11} \\ s^{11} \end{pmatrix}$	s_{12}	$\cdots \; s_{1p}$	s_1
t_2	s^{12}	$\begin{pmatrix} s_{22} \\ s^{22} \end{pmatrix}$	$\cdots \; s_{2p}$	s_2
		$\cdots \cdots \cdots$		
t_p	s^{1p}	s^{2p}	$\cdots \begin{pmatrix} s_{pp} \\ s^{pp} \end{pmatrix}$	s_p

The matrices A and A^{-1} are superimposed, but because of the symmetry of both matrices, only the diagonal spaces in the table have two entries. The omitted entries must of course be included in forming the check sums. In the same way S and $(S^{-1})'$ are superimposed, but here the omitted entries are all zeros.

The complete set of calculations required to invert the matrix of Example 3 is given in Table 31, following the arrangement of Table 30.

The sums of rows check with the s, t, and b columns within one unit in the last decimal place. The last figure of the sum is placed in parentheses after the figure it is supposed to check.

10.10 Moving Decimal Points in Matrix Elements. If the elements of a coefficient matrix vary in size by several orders, as may happen in multiple regression when the independent variables are measured in widely differing units, the computations become difficult to handle. It is desirable to have the elements of the principal diagonal, in particular, between the limits of 0.1 and

Sec. 10 Moving Decimal Points in Matrix Elements

TABLE 31

0.036(5)	$\begin{pmatrix} 6.86 \\ 0.245 \end{pmatrix}$	2.56	3.39	12.81
0.068(7)	−0.036	$\begin{pmatrix} 8.92 \\ 0.127 \end{pmatrix}$	1.78	13.26
0.172(2)	−0.174	−.024	$\begin{pmatrix} 4.41 \\ 0.370 \end{pmatrix}$	9.58
0.382(2)	$\begin{pmatrix} 2.619 \\ 0.382 \end{pmatrix}$	0.977	1.294	4.891(0)
0.222(2)	−0.132	$\begin{pmatrix} 2.822 \\ 0.354 \end{pmatrix}$	0.183	3.005(5)
0.283(3)	−0.286	−0.039	$\begin{pmatrix} 1.644 \\ 0.608 \end{pmatrix}$	1.643(4)

10. This is achieved by choosing (by inspection) a diagonal matrix D whose non-zero elements are suitable powers of 10, and transforming A to B ($= DAD$). The column vector g is transformed to $h = Dg\lambda$ where λ is a suitable scalar power of 10 chosen so that the elements of h are of about the same order as those of B. The equation $Bv = h$ is then solved and the solution of the original equation $Au = g$ is given by

(10.34) $$u = Dv\lambda^{-1}$$

The inverse of A is obtained from that of B by

(10.35) $$A^{-1} = DB^{-1}D$$

The proof is as follows:

$$v = B^{-1}h = (DAD)^{-1}h$$
$$= D^{-1}A^{-1}D^{-1}Dg\lambda$$
$$= D^{-1}A^{-1}g\lambda$$
$$= D^{-1}u\lambda$$

whence

$$u = Dv\lambda^{-1}$$

The proof that $A^{-1} = DB^{-1}D$ is readily extracted from the above proof.

Example 4. Given the set of normal equations

$$\begin{bmatrix} 68{,}634 & 25.61 & 338.8 \\ 25.61 & 0.0892 & 0.178 \\ 338.8 & 0.178 & 4.41 \end{bmatrix} \cdot \begin{bmatrix} x_1 \\ x_2 \\ x_3 \end{bmatrix} = \begin{bmatrix} 19.8 \\ 0.0293 \\ 0.106 \end{bmatrix}$$

we may take

$$D = \begin{bmatrix} 0.01 & 0 & 0 \\ 0 & 10 & 0 \\ 0 & 0 & 1 \end{bmatrix}$$

Then

$$B = \begin{bmatrix} 6.86 & 2.56 & 3.39 \\ 2.56 & 8.92 & 1.78 \\ 3.39 & 1.78 & 4.41 \end{bmatrix}$$

all numbers being rounded off to three significant figures. We obtain

$$Dg = \begin{bmatrix} 0.198 \\ 0.293 \\ 0.106 \end{bmatrix}$$

so that a suitable value of λ is 10, giving

$$h = \begin{bmatrix} 1.98 \\ 2.93 \\ 1.06 \end{bmatrix}$$

The solution of the transformed equations (carried out in Example 3) is

$$v' = [0.197, 0.277, -0.023]$$

Then

$$u = \begin{bmatrix} 0.01 & 0 & 0 \\ 0 & 10 & 0 \\ 0 & 0 & 1 \end{bmatrix} \cdot \begin{bmatrix} 0.197 \\ 0.277 \\ -0.023 \end{bmatrix} \cdot 10^{-1}$$

so that

$$u' = [0.000197, 0.277, -0.0023]$$

An alternative method of solution (which is really equivalent to the Gaussian elimination method and which avoids the necessity of extracting square roots) is to find a triangular matrix T, with diagonal elements equal to unity, and a diagonal matrix D, such that $T'DT = A$. If the matrix equation to be solved is $Au = g$, we have $T'DTu = g$, which is equivalent to the three equations

$$T'l = g, \quad Dk = l, \quad Tu = k$$

each of which is triangular (or diagonal) in form.

If the matrices T and D are of the forms

$$T = \begin{bmatrix} 1 & t_{12} & \cdots & t_{1p} \\ 0 & 1 & \cdots & t_{2p} \\ \cdot & \cdot & \cdot & \cdot \\ 0 & 0 & \cdots & 1 \end{bmatrix}$$

$$D = \begin{bmatrix} d_1 & 0 & \cdots & 0 \\ 0 & d_2 & \cdots & 0 \\ \cdot & \cdot & \cdot & \cdot \\ 0 & 0 & \cdots & d_p \end{bmatrix}$$

the equation $T'DT = A$ is equivalent to the set of relations

$$d_1 = a_{11}$$
$$t_{12}d_1 = a_{12}$$
$$t_{13}d_1 = a_{13}$$
$$\cdots\cdots\cdots$$
$$t_{12}^2 d_1 + d_2 = a_{22}$$
$$t_{12}t_{13}d_1 + t_{23}d_2 \quad a_{23}$$
$$t_{13}^2 d_1 + t_{23}^2 d_2 + d_3 = a_{33}$$
$$\cdots\cdots\cdots\cdots\cdots$$

The total number of equations, $\frac{1}{2}p(p+1)$, is just sufficient to determine the $\frac{1}{2}p(p-1)$ values of t_{ij} and the p values of d_i.

Sec. 11 Non-symmetric Matrix Equations

The inverse of the matrix A is then given by
$$A^{-1} = T^{-1}D^{-1}(T^{-1})'$$
where T and D, being triangular and diagonal respectively, are readily inverted.

10.11 Non-symmetric Matrix Equations. If M is a square non-symmetric matrix, and $Mu = n$, we may use a preliminary transformation given by Aitken[7] to bring the equation to the symmetric form. This consists in multiplying through on the left by M'. If $M'M = A$ and $M'n = g$, the result is the equation $Au = g$, in which A is now symmetric. Since $A^{-1} = (M'M)^{-1} = M^{-1}(M')^{-1}$, the inverse of M is given by

(10.36) $$M^{-1} = A^{-1}M$$

Two additional steps of matrix multiplication are therefore required for the process of inversion. However, in most practical cases, the matrices that we need to invert are symmetric to start with, although non-symmetric matrices do arise in correlation theory.

Another method of dealing with a non-symmetric matrix is to orthogonalize the rows. That is, given the square non-symmetric matrix M we find a new matrix N of which the first row is the same as that of M, the second row is a linear combination of the first and second rows of M orthogonal to the first row, and so on. If the elements of N are denoted by n_{ij}, we have, therefore,

$$n_{11}n_{21} + n_{12}n_{22} + \cdots + n_{1p}n_{2p} = 0$$

or, in general,

$$n_{i1}n_{j1} + n_{i2}n_{j2} + \cdots + n_{ip}n_{jp} = 0, \quad i \neq j$$

It is then readily seen that $NN' = D$, where D is a diagonal matrix. The transformation of M to N is equivalent to multiplying M by a triangular matrix T of which the diagonal elements are all equal to unity. Thus $TM = N$, where

$$T = \begin{bmatrix} 1 & 0 & 0 & \cdots \\ t_{21} & 1 & 0 & \cdots \\ t_{31} & t_{32} & 1 & \cdots \\ \cdots & \cdots & \cdots & \cdots \end{bmatrix}$$

is equivalent to the set of relations

$$m_{11} = n_{11}, \quad m_{12} = n_{12}, \cdots$$
$$t_{21}m_{11} + m_{21} = n_{21}, \quad t_{21}m_{12} + m_{22} = n_{22}, \cdots$$

If, then, we have the equation to solve

$$Mu = n$$

we can write $TM(TM)' = D$, and $(TM)'v = u$ so that
$$Dv = TMu = Tn$$
$$v = D^{-1}Tn$$

and
$$u = (TM)'D^{-1}Tn$$
$$= M'T'D^{-1}Tn$$

10.12 Improvement of an Approximation to the Inverse Matrix. It has been pointed out by Hotelling [8] that, owing to the rapid accumulation of rounding-off errors in a long calculation, the solution of a set of p equations in p unknowns with coefficients of the order of unity may possibly be in error by as much as 4^{p-1} times the maximum error in the coefficients themselves. The situation is similar in the process of inverting the matrix of coefficients. It is obvious, then, that if p is at all large the number of significant figures in the final result will be seriously cut down. An iteration method of improving a fairly crude approximation is desirable.

Let us denote A^{-1} by C, and let C_0 be an approximation to C. Then a better approximation is

(10.37) $$C_1 = C_0(2I - AC_0)$$

and this approximation may be improved step by step, by calculating at each step

(10.38) $$C_{m+1} = C_m(2I - AC_m), \quad m = 0, 1, 2, \cdots$$

One or two steps will usually be sufficient in practice.

If $D_0 = I - AC_0$, D_0 will be a matrix whose elements are all small, assuming that C_0 is a reasonably good approximation to A^{-1}. The size of a matrix is estimated by its *norm*, which is the positive square root of the sum of squares of its elements. We now prove that

(10.39) $$C_m = A^{-1}[I - (D_0)^{2^m}]$$

This is clearly true for $m = 0$. If it is true for m, it is true for $m + 1$, since then
$$C_{m+1} = C_m(2I - AC_m)$$
$$= A^{-1}[I - (D_0)^{2^m}][I + (D_0)^{2^m}]$$
$$= A^{-1}[I - (D_0)^{2^{m+1}}]$$

It is, therefore, true for $m = 0, 1, 2, \cdots$. Hence

(10.40) $$C - C_m = A^{-1}(D_0)^{2^m}$$
$$= C_0(I - D_0)^{-1}(D_0)^{2^m}$$

It may be proved from this that if the norm of D_0, $N(D_0)$, is equal to $k < 1$,

(10.41) $$N(C - C_m) \leq N(C_0)(k)^{2^m}(1 - k)^{-1}$$

and so tends to zero as m increases.

Example 5. Let
$$A = \begin{bmatrix} 1.0 & 0.4 & 0.5 & 0.6 \\ & 1.0 & 0.3 & 0.4 \\ & & 1.0 & 0.2 \\ & & & 1.0 \end{bmatrix}$$

Sec. 13   Variance and Covariance   309

Suppose that a first approximation to the inverse of this is

$$C_0 = \begin{bmatrix} 2.1 & -0.2 & -0.8 & -1.0 \\ & 1.3 & -0.2 & -0.4 \\ & & 1.4 & 0.3 \\ & & & 1.7 \end{bmatrix}$$

Then

$$D_0 = I - AC_0 = \begin{bmatrix} -0.02 & 0.02 & 0 & 0.01 \\ 0 & 0 & -0.02 & 0.03 \\ 0.01 & -0.01 & 0 & -0.02 \\ -0.02 & 0.04 & -0.02 & 0 \end{bmatrix}$$

so that

$$N(D_0) = 0.072$$

The second approximation is

$$C_1 = \begin{bmatrix} 2.1 & -0.2 & -0.8 & -1.0 \\ & 1.3 & -0.2 & -0.4 \\ & & 1.4 & 0.3 \\ & & & 1.7 \end{bmatrix} \cdot \begin{bmatrix} 0.98 & .02 & 0 & 0.01 \\ 0 & 1 & -0.02 & 0.03 \\ .01 & -0.01 & 1 & -0.02 \\ -0.02 & 0.04 & -0.02 & 1 \end{bmatrix}$$

$$= \begin{bmatrix} 2.070 & -0.190 & -0.776 & -1.011 \\ & 1.282 & -0.218 & -0.355 \\ & & 1.398 & 0.274 \\ & & & 1.692 \end{bmatrix}$$

which is not in error by more than two units in the third decimal place. One more step gives the result correct within two or three units in the sixth decimal place.

For further discussion of error control see references 8 and 9.

10.13 Variance and Covariance of the Regression Coefficients in Linear Regression. If we suppose that the y_α of § 10.2 are all independent and are distributed about their respective true values η_α with a common variance σ^2, we can prove that

(10.42) $$E(b_j) = \beta_j$$

and

(10.43) $$\text{Cov}(b_j, b_k) = \sigma^2 a^{jk}$$

We have, by definition, $g_j = Sx_{j\alpha}y_\alpha$ and, by the solution of the normal equations, $b_j = \sum_k a^{jk} g_k$. Therefore

$$E(b_j) = \sum_k a^{jk} Sx_{k\alpha} \eta_\alpha$$
$$= \sum_k a^{jk} Sx_{k\alpha} \sum_l \beta_l x_{l\alpha}$$
$$= \sum_l \beta_l \sum_k a^{jk} a_{kl}$$
$$= \sum_l \beta_l \delta_{jl} = \beta_j$$

Also, by hypothesis,

(10.44) $$\text{Cov}(y_\alpha, y_\beta) = \sigma^2 \delta_{\alpha\beta}$$

so that
$$\operatorname{Cov}(g_j, g_k) = \underset{\alpha\beta}{SS} x_{j\alpha} x_{k\beta} \operatorname{Cov}(y_\alpha, y_\beta)$$
$$= \sigma^2 \underset{\alpha\beta}{SS} \delta_{\alpha\beta} x_{j\alpha} x_{k\beta}$$
$$= \sigma^2 S x_{j\alpha} x_{k\alpha} = \sigma^2 a_{jk}$$

Accordingly
$$\operatorname{Cov}(b_j, b_k) = \sum_l \sum_m a^{jl} a^{km} \operatorname{Cov}(g_l, g_m)$$
$$\sigma^2 \sum_l \sum_m a^{jl} a^{km} a_{lm}$$
$$= \sigma^2 \sum_l a^{jl} \delta_{kl} = \sigma^2 a^{jk}$$

That is, the matrix A^{-1}, multiplied by σ^2, is the *covariance matrix* of the coefficients $b_1, b_2, \cdots b_p$. The elements of the principal diagonal give the *variance* of the respective coefficients. Equation (10.43) is one of the statistician's main reasons for needing to invert A.

The variance of a linear function of the b's may be found from (10.43). In particular, if $Y = \sum b_j x_j$ is a *predicted value* of y based on a new set of values $x_1, x_2, \cdots x_p$ of the independent variates,
$$\operatorname{Var}(Y) = \sum_{j,k} x_j x_k \operatorname{Cov}(b_j, b_k)$$
$$= \sigma^2 \sum_{j,k} a^{jk} x_j x_k$$

This is the variance arising out of the *uncertainty in the coefficients* b_j. To get the variance of the *observed* y which would correspond to the observed $x_1, \cdots x_p$, we must add σ^2, so that

(10.45)
$$\sigma_y^2 = \sigma^2 [1 + \sum_{j,k} a^{jk} x_j x_k]$$

This indicates one of the dangers of extrapolation, since σ_y^2 may become very large for values of $x_1, \cdots x_p$ far outside the range of the original observations.

10.14 Residuals. The difference between the observed and estimated values of the independent variable y, corresponding to a given set of observations of the x's, is called the *residual*,

(10.46)
$$v_\alpha = y_\alpha - Y_\alpha$$

It is not the same as the *error* Δ_α, which is defined by
$$\Delta_\alpha = y_\alpha - \eta_\alpha$$

If v is the column vector with elements $v_1, v_2, \cdots v_N$, and X is the matrix $[x_{j\alpha}]$, $p \times N$, then
$$Xv = X(y - Y) = g - XX'b = g - Ab$$
since $g = Xy$ and $Y = X'b$. But the normal equations give $Ab = g$, so that

Sec. 15 Distribution of Sum of Squares of Residuals

(10.47) $$Xv = 0$$

The residuals are, therefore, said to be *orthogonal* to each of the predictors.

In the ordinary notation, (10.47) is written

(10.48) $$Sx_{j\alpha}v_\alpha = 0, \qquad j = 1, 2, \cdots p$$

If, for example, $x_{1\alpha} = 1$, for all α, which means that there is a constant term in the regression equation, (10.48) becomes for $j = 1$

(10.49) $$Sv_\alpha = 0$$

This provides a useful check on the residuals.

In matrix notation, Sv_α^2 may be written as $v'v$, which is a scalar, and we therefore have

$$\begin{aligned} Sv_\alpha^2 &= (y' - Y')v \\ &= y'v - Y'v \\ &= y'v \end{aligned}$$

since

$$Y'v = b'Xv = 0, \text{ by (10.47)}$$

Hence

$$\begin{aligned} v'v &= y'(y - Y) \\ &= y'(y - X'b) \\ &= y'y - g'b \end{aligned}$$

which in scalar notation becomes

(10.50) $$Sv_\alpha^2 = Sy_\alpha^2 - \sum b_j g_j$$

This is usually a convenient way to compute the sum of squares of residuals, provided enough figures are retained in the b_j. There is a danger that in the subtraction almost all the significant figures will be lost. It is worth while actually to compute the separate residuals, in any event, in order to make sure that they do not show any systematic tendencies.

10.15 Distribution of Sum of Squares of Residuals. We now prove that

(10.51) $$E(Sv_\alpha^2) = (N - p)\sigma^2$$

so that an unbiased estimate of σ^2 is provided by

(10.52) $$s^2 = Sv_\alpha^2/(N - p)$$

This is not the same as the maximum likelihood estimate, which has N instead of $N - p$, and is found by maximizing L simultaneously with respect to σ^2, $\beta_1, \cdots \beta_p$, assuming that the Δ_α are independently and normally distributed about zero with common variance σ^2. The proof of (10.51) does not require the assumption of normality.

$$\begin{aligned} E(y_\alpha^2) &= E(\eta_\alpha + \Delta_\alpha)^2 = \eta_\alpha^2 + \sigma^2 \\ &= \sum_{j,k} \beta_j \beta_k x_{j\alpha} x_{k\alpha} + \sigma^2 \end{aligned}$$

so that
$$E(Sy_\alpha^2) = N\sigma^2 + \sum_{j,k}\beta_j\beta_k a_{jk}$$
Also
$$\sum b_j g_j = \sum_{j,k} a_{jk} b_j b_k$$
so that
$$E(\sum b_j g_j) = \sum_{j,k} a_{jk} E(b_j b_k)$$
$$= \sum_{j,k} a_{jk}(\beta_j\beta_k + \sigma^2 a^{jk}), \text{ by } (10.43)$$

Since $\sum_{j,k} a_{jk} a^{jk} = \sum_j \delta_{jj} = p$, we have on substituting in (10.50),
$$E(Sv_\alpha^2) = (N-p)\sigma^2$$

The estimate in (10.52) is usually preferred to the maximum likelihood estimate, not only because it is unbiased, but chiefly because its distribution on the assumption of normality is the same as that of the sample variance, discussed in Chapter VII, with $n = N - p$ degrees of freedom. That is, $(N-p)s^2/\sigma^2$ has the χ^2 distribution with $N - p$ degrees of freedom. Moreover, with the same assumption, the distribution of s^2 is quite independent of that of the b's (which are normal variates), so that we can use Student's t-distribution to fix confidence limits for the β's.

We first prove that Cov $(v_\alpha, b_j) = 0$ for all α and all j. Since
$$v_\alpha = y_\alpha - Y_\alpha$$
$$= \Delta_\alpha + \eta_\alpha - \sum b_j x_{j\alpha}$$
(10.53)
$$= \Delta_\alpha - \sum(b_j - \beta_j)x_{j\alpha}$$

and since $E(b_j - \beta_j) = 0$, we have

(10.54)
$$E(v_\alpha) = 0$$

Also

(10.55) $\quad \text{Cov } (v_\alpha, b_j) = E\{v_\alpha(b_j - \beta_j)\}$
$$= E\{\Delta_\alpha(b_j - \beta_j)\} - E\{\sum_k (b_j - \beta_j)(b_k - \beta_k)x_{k\alpha}\}$$

Now
$$E\{\Delta_\alpha(b_j - \beta_j)\} = E(\Delta_\alpha b_j)$$
$$= E(\Delta_\alpha \sum_k a^{jk} g_k)$$
$$= E\{\Delta_\alpha \sum_k a^{jk} Sx_{k\beta}(\eta_\beta + \Delta_\beta)\}$$
$$= \sum_k a^{jk} Sx_{k\beta} E(\Delta_\alpha \Delta_\beta)$$
$$= \sum a^{jk} x_{k\alpha} \sigma^2$$

by (10.44). Also
$$E\{(b_j - \beta_j)(b_k - \beta_k)\} = \text{Cov } (b_j, b_k) = a^{jk}\sigma^2$$

Sec. 15 Distribution of Sum of Squares of Residuals 313

Substituting these results in (10.55), we obtain
(10.56) $$\text{Cov }(v_\alpha, b_j) = 0$$

This, of course, proves only that the residuals and the regression coefficients are *uncorrelated*, not that they are independent. But if the Δ_α have a multivariate normal distribution, so have the y_α, which differ from the Δ_α only by constants. The g_j are linear functions of the y_α, the b_j are linear functions of the g_j, and the Y_α are linear functions of the b_j. Hence the v_α and the b_j are expressible as linear functions of the Δ_α, and so they too have a joint multivariate normal distribution. The absence of correlation for this distribution implies that the joint frequency function can be split up into a factor depending only on the b's and a factor depending only on the v's. In other words the b's and the v's are independent.

From (10.53) and (10.48)
$$\begin{aligned} Sv_\alpha^2 &= S\Delta_\alpha^2 - \sum_{j,k}(b_j - \beta_j)(b_k - \beta_k)Sx_{j\alpha}x_{k\alpha} \\ &= S\Delta_\alpha^2 - \sum_{j,k}(b_j - \beta_j)(b_k - \beta_k)a_{jk} \\ &= S\Delta_\alpha^2 - \sum_{j,k} a_{jk}u_j u_k \end{aligned}$$

where $u_j = b_j - \beta_j$. Let us now make a linear transformation of the variables u to new variables w, chosen so that the quadratic form $\sum a_{jk}u_j u_k$ reduces to a sum of squares. That is, if

(10.57) $$w_k = \sum_l \lambda_{kl} u_l$$

then
(10.58) $$Sv_\alpha^2 = S\Delta_\alpha^2 - \sum w_k^2$$

Since Cov $(u_j, u_k) = \sigma^2 a^{jk}$, we have
(10.59) $$\text{Var }(w_k) = \sum_l \sum_m \lambda_{kl}\lambda_{km}\sigma^2 a^{lm}$$

Now if we actually carry out the transformation (10.57), the first step is to put
$$w_1 = \sum a_{1j}u_j / (a_{11})^{1/2}$$
for then
$$\begin{aligned} w_1^2 &= (a_{11})^{-1}\sum a_{1j}a_{1k}u_j u_k \\ &= (a_{11})^{-1}[a_{11}^2 u_1^2 + 2a_{11}\sum_{j=2}^p a_{1j}u_1 u_j + \sum_{j,k=2}^p a_{1j}a_{1k}u_j u_k] \end{aligned}$$

Hence
$$\sum_{j,k=1}^p a_{jk}u_j u_k = w_1^2 + \sum_{j,k=2}^p b_{jk}u_j u_k$$

where $b_{jk} = (a_{11}a_{jk} - a_{1j}a_{1k})/a_{11}$. In exactly the same way
$$\sum_{j,k=2}^p b_{jk}u_j u_k = w_2^2 + \sum_{j,k=3}^p c_{jk}u_j u_k$$

where $w_2 = \sum b_{2j}u_j/(b_{22})^{1/2}$, and so on. Hence, in (10.57),
$$\lambda_{1l} = a_{1l}/(a_{11})^{1/2}$$
$$\lambda_{2l} = b_{2l}/(b_{22})^{1/2}, \text{ etc.}$$
where $b_{22} = \dfrac{1}{a_{11}} \begin{vmatrix} a_{11} & a_{12} \\ a_{21} & a_{22} \end{vmatrix}$, etc.

If D_r is the determinant of the first r rows and columns of A, so that
$$D_1 = a_{11}$$
$$D_2 = \begin{vmatrix} a_{11} & a_{12} \\ a_{21} & a_{22} \end{vmatrix}, \text{ etc.}$$

we have $b_{22} = D_2/D_1$, $c_{33} = D_3/D_2$, etc. From (10.59),
$$\begin{aligned}
\operatorname{Var}(w_1) &= \sum_{l,m} a_{1l}a_{1m}\sigma^2 a^{lm}/a_{11} \\
&= \sum_l \delta_{1l}a_{1l}\sigma^2/a_{11} \\
&= \sigma^2 \\
\operatorname{Var}(w_2) &= \sigma^2 \sum_{l,m} b_{2l}b_{2m} a^{lm}/b_{22} \\
&= \frac{\sigma^2}{D_1 D_2} \sum_{l,m} a^{lm}(a_{11}a_{2l} - a_{12}a_{1l})(a_{11}a_{2m} - a_{12}a_{1m}) \\
&= \frac{\sigma^2}{D_1 D_2} \sum_{l,m} a^{lm}(a_{11}^2 a_{2l}a_{2m} - a_{11}a_{12}a_{2l}a_{1m} - a_{11}a_{12}a_{1l}a_{2m} + a_{12}^2 a_{1l}a_{1m}) \\
&= \frac{\sigma^2}{D_1 D_2}(a_{11}^2 a_{22} - a_{11}a_{12}^2 - a_{11}a_{12}^2 + a_{12}^2 a_{11}) \\
&= \sigma^2(a_{11}a_{22} - a_{12}^2)/D_2 = \sigma^2
\end{aligned}$$

In the same way, each of the new variables may be shown to have the same variance σ^2.

Also, being linear functions of the b's, they are independent of the v's. We have, therefore,
$$S(v_\alpha^2/\sigma^2) = S(\Delta_\alpha^2/\sigma^2) - \sum w_k^2/\sigma^2$$
where the terms on the right are the sums of squares of N and of p independent normal standard variates respectively, and are therefore distributed as χ^2, with N and p df. It follows that $S(v_\alpha^2/\sigma^2)$ is distributed as χ^2 with $N - p$ df.

10.16 Confidence Limits for the True Regression Coefficients. Since b_j is normally distributed about β_j with variance $\sigma^2 a^{jj}$, and since s^2 is an unbiased estimate of σ^2 with a χ^2 distribution, independent of the b_j, it follows that

(10.60) $$t = (b_j - \beta_j)/s(a^{jj})^{1/2}$$

has Student's t-distribution with $N - p$ df. If, therefore, t_α is the value of t corresponding to the confidence coefficient $1 - \alpha$, the confidence limits for β_j are given by

Sec. 17   Omission of Variates in Multiple Regression   315

(10.61) $$b_j - s(a^{jj})^{1/2}t_\alpha < \beta_j < b_j + s(a^{jj})^{1/2}t_\alpha$$

If b_1 and b_2 are two of the regression coefficients, the variance of the difference is given by

(10.62) $$\text{Var}(b_1 - b_2) = \text{Var}(b_1) + \text{Var}(b_2) - 2\,\text{Cov}(b_1, b_2)$$
$$= \sigma^2(a^{11} + a^{22} - 2a^{12})$$

Hence on the null hypothesis that $\beta_1 = \beta_2$ the quantity

(10.63) $$t = \frac{b_1 - b_2}{s(a^{11} + a^{22} - 2a^{12})^{1/2}}$$

has the Student distribution with $N - p$ df, and so may be used to test whether the two coefficients differ significantly.

Sometimes the same set of predictors may be used for different sets of y's. An example is given in Fisher's *Statistical Methods for Research Workers* (10th Edition, p. 136), where the yields of grain from two adjacent plots of land, differently treated with fertilizers, are compared over a period of thirty years. If the yields are estimated by $Y = a + bx$ and $Y' = a' + b'x$, where x represents time, the question is whether $b - b'$ is significantly different from zero. Owing to the strong correlation between Y and Y' we do not compute the values of b and b' separately. Instead we take $Y'' = Y - Y' = a'' + b''x$, and test the significance of b'' from this third regression equation.

If it is necessary in a multiple regression problem to calculate two equations, for different sets of y's, a good procedure would be to calculate A^{-1} and then use the relations

$$b_j = \sum_k a^{jk} g_k, \qquad \bar{b}_j = \sum_k a^{jk} \bar{g}_k$$

where g_k and $\bar{g}_k$ correspond to the two sets y and $\bar{y}$ respectively.

10.17 Omission of Variates in Multiple Regression. Suppose that we have found the regression of y on the variables $x_1, x_2, \cdots x_p$ and that we would like to drop x_1, since it does not seem to contribute significantly to the regression. That is, we know the b_j as given by the normal equations

$$\sum_{j=1}^{p} b_j a_{jk} = g_k, \qquad k = 1, 2, \cdots p$$

and require the b_j' given by

$$\sum_{j=2}^{p} b_j' a_{jk} = g_k, \qquad k = 2, 3, \cdots p$$

If we let $\delta b_j = b_j - b_j'$, we have on subtraction

(10.64) $$b_1 a_{1k} + \sum_{2}^{p} \delta b_j a_{jk} = 0, \qquad k = 2, 3, \cdots p$$

But if a_{jk} is the typical element of A^{-1}, we know that

(10.65) $$\sum_{j=1}^{p} a^{1j} a^{jk} = 0, \qquad k = 2, 3 \cdots p$$

Hence the coefficients of $a_{1k}, a_{2k}, \cdots a_{pk}$ in (10.64) are proportional to those in (10.65), so that
$$b_1/a^{11} = \delta b_j/a^{1j}$$
or

(10.66) $$\delta b_j = a^{1j} b_1/a^{11}$$

Hence, to drop the variable x_1, we reduce each b_j by $a^{1j}b_1/a^{11}$. If the matrix A has been inverted these corrections are easily obtained.

The variance of the new coefficients b_j' is given by

(10.67) $$\begin{aligned}\text{Var}(b_j') &= \text{Var}(b_j - a^{1j}b_1/a^{11}) \\ &= \text{Var}(b_j) + (a^{1j}/a^{11})^2 \text{Var}(b_1) - 2(a^{1j}/a^{11}) \text{Cov}(b_1, b_j) \\ &= \sigma^2[a^{jj} - (a^{1j})^2/a^{11}]\end{aligned}$$

In general the jkth element of the new inverted matrix is
$$(a')^{jk} = a^{jk} - a^{1j}a^{1k}/a^{11}$$

10.18 Solution of a Set of Linear Equations with More Equations than Unknowns.

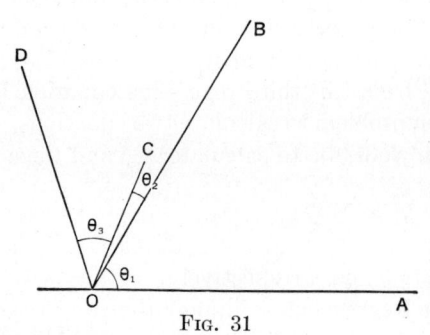

One of the oldest applications of least squares methods is to problems of surveying, where various check measurements are made and the results adjusted by calculation. Thus, if O, A, B, C, D (Figure 31) represent survey stations, and the angles $\theta_1, \theta_2, \theta_3$ between OA, OB, OC and OD are required, the surveyor at O can take six different angular measurements, as shown in Table 32.

Fig. 31

Table 32

Observation	Stations	Measured Angle	Adjusted Angle (seconds)
1	A, B	62°59'40.3''	40.35
2	A, C	64°11'35.0''	34.40
3	A, D	100°20'29.1''	29.65
4	B, C	1°11'54.0''	54.05
5	B, D	37°20'49.3''	49.30
6	C, D	36° 8'55.8''	55.25

Let the corrections to be added to these measured angles be denoted by $\Delta_1, \Delta_2 \cdots \Delta_6$. Then, if the measured angles are $\alpha_1, \alpha_2, \cdots \alpha_6$, we have a set of *observation equations*:

Sec. 18 Solution of a Set of Linear Equations

(10.68)
$$\begin{cases} \theta_1 = \alpha_1 + \Delta_1 \\ \theta_1 + \theta_2 = \alpha_2 + \Delta_2 \\ \theta_1 + \theta_2 + \theta_3 = \alpha_3 + \Delta_3 \\ \theta_2 = \alpha_4 + \Delta_4 \\ \theta_2 + \theta_3 = \alpha_5 + \Delta_5 \\ \theta_3 = \alpha_6 + \Delta_6 \end{cases}$$

It is obvious by examining the data for consistency that the errors are only a few tenths of a second in magnitude. If we write

$$\theta_1 = 62°59'40'' + x$$
$$\theta_2 = 1°11'54'' + y$$
$$\theta_3 = 36° \ 8'55'' + z$$

the equations for x, y and z (measured in tenths of seconds) will be

(10.69)
$$\begin{cases} x = 3 + \Delta_1 \\ x + y = 10 + \Delta_2 \\ x + y + z = 1 + \Delta_3 \\ y = 0 + \Delta_4 \\ y + z = 3 + \Delta_5 \\ z = 8 + \Delta_6 \end{cases}$$

The general pattern of such a set of equations is, therefore,

(10.70) $$\sum_{j=1}^{n} c_{j\alpha} x_j = k_\alpha + \Delta_\alpha, \qquad \alpha = 1, 2 \cdots m$$

where we have m equations in n unknowns ($m > n$), and where the $c_{j\alpha}$ and the k_α are known constants. The x_j are adjusted so as to make $S\Delta_\alpha{}^2$ a minimum.

Writing $S\Delta_\alpha{}^2 = S(\sum c_{j\alpha} x_j - k_\alpha)^2$, differentiating with respect to x_j, and equating the derivatives to zero, we get for the *estimated* x_j

$$Sc_{j\alpha}(\sum c_{j\alpha} x_j - k_\alpha) = 0, \qquad j = 1, 2 \cdots n$$

Writing $a_{jk} = Sc_{j\alpha} c_{k\alpha}$, $g_j = Sc_{j\alpha} k_\alpha$, we arrive at the *normal equations:*

(10.71) $$\sum_k a_{jk} x_k = g_j, \qquad j = 1, 2 \cdots n$$

If $A = [a_{jk}]$, $n \times n$, $x = [x_j]$, $n \times 1$, and $g = [g_j]$, $n \times 1$, these may be written as a matrix equation $Ax = g$, with the solution $x = A^{-1}g$. Moreover, if the Δ_α have a common variance σ^2 and are independent, $A^{-1}\sigma^2$ is the variance-covariance matrix of the x_j, so that, for example, the standard error of x_j is $\hat{\sigma}(a^{jj})^{1/2}$. As before, $\hat{\sigma}$ is estimated from the residuals by the equation

(10.72) $$\hat{\sigma}^2 = Sv_\alpha{}^2/(m - n)$$

where

(10.73) $$v_\alpha = k_\alpha - \sum c_{j\alpha} x_j$$

Also

(10.74) $$Sc_{k\alpha}v_\alpha = g_k - \sum_j a_{jk}x_j = 0$$

by (10.71), and so

$$Sv_\alpha^2 = Sv_\alpha(k_\alpha - \sum c_{j\alpha}x_j)$$
$$= Sv_\alpha k_\alpha, \text{ by (10.74)}$$
(10.75) $$= Sk_\alpha^2 - \sum g_j x_j$$

In the above example the $c_{j\alpha}$ are all either 1 or 0. The normal equations are

$$3x + 2y + z = 14$$
$$2x + 4y + 2z = 14$$
$$x + 2y + 3z = 12$$

which have the solution $x = 3.5$, $y = 0.5$, $z = 2.5$.

The residuals are -0.5, 6.0, -5.5, -0.5, 0, and 5.5, so that $Sv_\alpha^2 = 97.0$. As a check, $Sk_\alpha^2 = 183$ and $\sum g_j x_j = 14 \times 3.5 - 14 \times 0.5 - 12 \times 2.5 = 86$. Hence our estimate of σ^2 is $97/3 = 32.3$. The diagonal elements of A^{-1} are 0.5, 0.5 and 0.5, so that the standard errors of x, y and z are each $[(32.3)/2]^{1/2} = 4.0$ (in tenths of a second of arc). The best values for θ_1, θ_2, θ_3 are, therefore, $62°59'40.35'' \pm 0.40''$, $1°11'54.05'' \pm 0.40''$, $36°8'55.25'' \pm 0.40''$.

10.19 Weighted Observations. An observer will sometimes allot different weights to different observations, the weight being an estimate of the precision of measurement. Thus, if a particular measurement is the mean of four readings of equal accuracy, the variance of the mean would be one quarter that of a single reading, and the mean might therefore be given a weight of 4 as compared with a weight of 1 for a single reading. The precision is here regarded as inversely proportional to the variance.

If the observations k_α in (10.70) have weights w_α, we may regard each equation as equivalent to w_α identical equations. Alternatively, we may multiply each of the observation equations by the square root of the weight and treat the new coefficients just as we did the old ones. The normal equations remain unchanged, but now

$$a_{jk} = Sw_\alpha c_{j\alpha} c_{k\alpha}$$
$$g_j = Sw_\alpha c_{j\alpha} k_\alpha$$

The residuals now satisfy the relations

$$Sw_\alpha c_{k\alpha} v_\alpha = 0$$
$$Sw_\alpha v_\alpha^2 = Sw_\alpha k_\alpha^2 - \sum g_j x_j$$

The estimate of σ^2 is $mS(w_\alpha v_\alpha^2)/[(m - n)Sw_\alpha]$, which reduces to the value in (10.72) when all the w_α are equal.

10.20 Condition Equations or Equations of Constraint. In the solution of a set of observation equations there may be one or more exact equations which must be satisfied by the adjusted values. Thus, if the four angles of a quadri-

Sec. 20 Equations of Constraint 319

lateral are measured, it is known that the true values must add up to exactly 360°. If the measured angles are $\alpha_1, \alpha_2, \alpha_3, \alpha_4$, with weights w_1, w_2, w_3, w_4, the corrections $x_1, \cdots x_4$, to be added, are given by the observation equations $x_1 = 0, x_2 = 0, x_3 = 0, x_4 = 0$, with the *condition equation*

$$x_1 + x_2 + x_3 + x_4 = 360° - (\alpha_1 + \alpha_2 + \alpha_3 + \alpha_4) = e, \text{ say}.$$

The condition equation is used to eliminate one of the variables, say x_4, and we then have $x_1 = 0, x_2 = 0, x_3 = 0, x_1 + x_2 + x_3 = e$, with weights w_1, w_2, w_3, w_4, respectively. The normal equations are

(10.76)
$$\begin{cases} (w_4 + w_1)x_1 + w_4 x_2 + w_4 x_3 = w_4 e \\ w_4 x_1 + (w_4 + w_2)x_2 + w_4 x_3 = w_4 e \\ w_4 x_1 + w_4 x_2 + (w_4 + w_3)x_3 = w_4 e \end{cases}$$

whence $x_i = (e/w_i)/\sum(1/w_i)$, $i = 1, 2, 3$, the sum being over all values of i from 1 to 4. Then x_4 is given by the equation of condition as $(e/w_4)/\sum(1/w_i)$. The standard errors of x_1, x_2, x_3 are found by the usual rule. That of x_4 is obvious from symmetry, but may be found by repeating the calculation with one of the other variables eliminated instead of x_4.

In the general case, if we require to minimize $Sw_\alpha(\sum_j c_{j\alpha} x_j - k_\alpha)^2$, subject to the q linear constraints ($q < m$) expressed by

(10.77)
$$\sum_j b_{ij} x_j = m_i, \quad i = 1, 2 \cdots q$$

the procedure is to use Lagrange multipliers[10] $\lambda_1, \lambda_2 \cdots \lambda_q$, and minimize (without constraints) the quantity

$$\tfrac{1}{2} S w_\alpha (\sum c_{j\alpha} x_j - k_\alpha)^2 + \sum_i \lambda_i \sum_j b_{ij} x_j$$

The ½ is introduced simply as a matter of convenience, to avoid the occurrence of a factor 2 in the normal equations. We thus obtain the equations

(10.78)
$$\sum_k a_{jk} x_k + \sum_i \lambda_i b_{ij} = g_j, \quad j = 1, 2 \cdots n$$

where

$$a_{jk} = S w_\alpha c_{j\alpha} c_{k\alpha}, \quad g_j = S w_\alpha c_{j\alpha} k_\alpha$$

Equations (10.77) and (10.78) together give $n + q$ equations for the $n + q$ unknowns x_k and λ_i. The matrix of coefficients is

$$A = \begin{bmatrix} a_{11} & \cdots & a_{1n} & b_{11} & \cdots & b_{q1} \\ \vdots & & \vdots & \vdots & & \vdots \\ a_{n1} & \cdots & a_{nn} & b_{1n} & \cdots & b_{qn} \\ b_{11} & \cdots & b_{1n} & 0 & \cdots & 0 \\ \vdots & & \vdots & \vdots & & \vdots \\ b_{q1} & \cdots & b_{qn} & 0 & \cdots & 0 \end{bmatrix}$$

In the example of the quadrilateral given above, the set of equations will be

(10.79)
$$\begin{cases} w_1 x_1 + \lambda = 0 \\ w_2 x_2 + \lambda = 0 \\ w_3 x_3 + \lambda = 0 \\ w_4 x_4 + \lambda = 0 \\ x_1 + x_2 + x_3 + x_4 = e \end{cases}$$

The solution is as given above, with $\lambda = - e/\sum(1/w_i)$, and the standard errors are easily found from the matrix of coefficients, which has five rows and columns.

Problems

1. Prove that the derivative of $d(A)$ with respect to an element a_{jk} is the co-factor of a_{jk}.

2. If the elements of the determinant $\begin{vmatrix} \alpha & \beta \\ \gamma & \delta \end{vmatrix}$ are differentiable functions of x, prove that the derivative of the determinant with respect to x is equal to

$$\begin{vmatrix} \alpha' & \beta \\ \gamma' & \delta \end{vmatrix} + \begin{vmatrix} \alpha & \beta' \\ \gamma & \delta' \end{vmatrix}$$

where $\alpha' = d\alpha/dx$, etc. Generalize this result for the n-rowed determinant $|a_{jk}|$.

3. Prove that the determinant of a skew-symmetric matrix of odd order is equal to zero.

4. Verify by computation that the matrix C of the linear orthogonal transformation (4.82) satisfies the equation $CC' = I$.

5. Compute AB and BA, if

$$A = \begin{bmatrix} 2 & 3 & 0 & 0 \\ 5 & 2 & 0 & 0 \\ 0 & 0 & 4 & 0 \\ 0 & 0 & 0 & 2 \end{bmatrix}, \quad B = \begin{bmatrix} 1 & 0 & 0 & 0 \\ 0 & 1 & 0 & 0 \\ 1 & 2 & 1 & 0 \\ 3 & 4 & 0 & 1 \end{bmatrix}$$

6. Calculate the inverse of the matrix

$$A = \begin{bmatrix} 1 & 2 & -2 \\ -1 & 3 & 0 \\ 0 & -2 & 1 \end{bmatrix}$$

Check your answer by computing AA^{-1}.

7. Solve the normal equations [5]

$$\begin{bmatrix} 1.000 & 0.313 & 0.280 \\ 0.313 & 1.000 & 0.652 \\ 0.280 & 0.652 & 1.000 \end{bmatrix} \cdot \begin{bmatrix} u_1 \\ u_2 \\ u_3 \end{bmatrix} = \begin{bmatrix} 0.495 \\ 0.650 \\ 0.803 \end{bmatrix}$$

Ans. $u' = [0.271, 0.158, 0.625]$.

8. Compute the inverse matrix of coefficients and solve the system. (This problem and the answers are due to D. B. De Lury.)

$$575.88 u_1 + 227.28 u_2 + 429.26 u_3 = 1600$$
$$227.28 u_1 + 781.10 u_2 + 1683.56 u_3 = 19100$$
$$429.24 u_1 + 1683.56 u_2 + 10962.36 u_3 = 2400$$

Ans.
$$A^{-1} = \begin{bmatrix} 19.6370 & -6.0638 & 0.1624 \\ -6.0644 & 21.0097 & -2.9892 \\ 0.1624 & -2.9891 & 1.3649 \end{bmatrix} \times 10^{-4}$$
$$u' = [-8.4020, 38.4408, -5.3557]$$

Problems

9. The quantities a, b, c, d are to be determined from the following measurements, all of equal weight: $a - b = 1168$, $a - c = 1877$, $b - c = 712$, $c - d = 669$, $b - d = 1377$, $a - d = 2547$, $d = 165$. Find by the method of least squares the best values for a, b, c, d and their standard errors.

10. The means of three sets of measurements, one on each of the angles of a plane triangle, are respectively $45°13'5'' \pm 5.3''$, $39°17'10'' \pm 8.4''$, $95°29'32'' \pm 11.6''$. Find the best values to assume for these angles. The stated errors may be taken as standard errors, and the means are to be weighted inversely as the variances.

11. Solve the following set of normal equations by the square root method:

$$\begin{aligned} 84x + 18y - 50z - 12u + 17v &= -693.7 \\ 18x + 85y - 45z + 3u - 15v &= -812.7 \\ -50x - 45y + 84z + 43u - 26v &= 2376.0 \\ -12x + 3y + 43z + 44u - 16v &= 2050.4 \\ 17x - 15y - 26z - 16u + 129v &= 1307.8 \end{aligned}$$

Hint: Divide the coefficients on the left by 10 and the numbers on the right by 1000. Multiply the answers obtained by 100.

Ans. $x = 12.761$, $y = 9.735$, $z = 36.438$, $u = 20.907$, $v = 19.525$.

12. The accompanying table gives the results of measurements at various dates on the velocity of light in vacuum, together with an estimate by R. T. Birge[11] of the probable error. The velocities are the excess in kilometers per second over 299,000 km/sec.

Date	Velocity	Probable Error
1874	990	200
1879	910	50
1882	860	30
1882	853	60
1902	901	84
1906	784	10
1923	782	30
1926	798	15
1928	786	10
1932	774	4
1936	771	10
1937	771	10
1940	776	6

Find the weighted average and its probable error (the probable error is assumed to be 0.6745 times the standard error).

Ans. $299,777.8 \pm 2.6$ km/sec.

13. The four angles of a plane quadrilateral are measured as

$$\begin{aligned} A &= 101°13'22'', \text{ weight } 3 \\ B &= 93°49'17'', \text{ weight } 2 \\ C &= 87° 5'39'', \text{ weight } 2 \\ D &= 77°52'40'', \text{ weight } 1 \end{aligned}$$

Adjust these results, and find the standard errors of the adjusted values.

Ans. The seconds of arc are $A = 14'' \pm 14''$, $B = 5'' \pm 17''$, $C = 27'' \pm 17''$, $D = 15'' \pm 20''$.

14. In a plane quadrilateral $ABCD$ the following angles were measured. All the measurements may be assumed of equal weight. Adjust these observations.

$$\begin{aligned}
CAB &= 64°\ 8'34'', & DAC &= 41°\ 58'47'' \\
ABC &= 66°34'\ 9'', & ACD &= 53°\ 53'50'' \\
BCA &= 49°17'23'', & DAB &= 106°\ 7'30'' \\
CDA &= 84°\ 7'18'', & BCD &= 103°\ 11'\ 3''
\end{aligned}$$

Hint: Denote the true values of the first six angles by $\theta_1, \theta_2 \cdots \theta_6$. These are subject to two independent condition equations. Use the second of arc as a unit.

15. Solve the equations (10.76) and compute the standard errors of x_1, x_2, x_3, x_4. Also obtain the same results by solving the system (10.79).

Ans. The standard error of x_1 is equal to

$$\frac{(w_2 w_3 + w_2 w_4 + w_3 w_4)^{1/2} \sigma}{(w_1 w_2 w_3 + w_1 w_2 w_4 + w_1 w_3 w_4 + w_2 w_3 w_4)^{1/2}}$$

and the others are symmetrical expressions.

References

1. Some of the material in this chapter is adapted from a monograph *On the Solution of Normal Equations and Related Topics*, by D. B. Duncan and J. F. Kenney (Edwards Bros , 1946).

2. R. A. Fisher, *Statistical Methods for Research Workers*, 4th Edition, p. 160.

3. Harold Hotelling, "Problems of Prediction," *Amer. Jour. Sociology*, **48**, 1942, pp. 61–76.

4. A. C. Aitken, *Determinants and Matrices* (Oliver & Boyd), 3rd Edition, 1944.

5. See P. S. Dwyer, "The Solution of Simultaneous Equations," *Psychometrika*, **6**, 1941, pp. 101–129.

6. P. S. Dwyer, "The Square Root Method and Its Use in Correlation and Regression," *J. Amer. Stat. Ass.*, **40**, 1945, pp. 493–503. This method was previously published by Banachiewicz (*Astronomical Journal*, **50**, 1942, pp. 38–41, and earlier in Poland) and it was also described by Choleski.

A brief discussion of various numerical methods for solving systems of linear equations, including the square root method, has been given by A. S. Householder (*Amer. Math. Monthly*, **57**, 1950, pp. 453–459).

7. A. C. Aitken, "Studies in Practical Mathematics. The Evaluation, with Applications, of a Certain Triple Product Matrix," *Proc. Roy. Soc. Edin.*, **57**, 1937, pp. 172–181.

8. Harold Hotelling, "Some New Methods in Matrix Calculation," *Ann. Math. Stat.*, **14**, 1943, pp. 1–34. See also a letter by Hotelling in the same volume, p. 440.

A very full discussion of the sources of errors in computation with high order matrices is contained in a paper "Numerical Inverting of Matrices of High Order" by J. von Neumann and H. H. Goldstine, *Bull. Amer. Math. Soc.*, **53**, 1947, pp. 1021–1099.

9. F. E. Satterthwaite, "Error Control in Matrix Calculation," *Ann. Math. Stat.*, **15**, 1944, pp. 373–387.

10. See, for example, I. S. and E. S. Sokolnikoff, *Higher Mathematics for Engineers and Physicists*, 1941, pp. 163–167, or L. Page, *Introduction to Theoretical Physics*, 1935, p. 311.

11. R. T. Birge, *Reports on the Progress of Physics*, 1941.

CHAPTER XI

CURVILINEAR REGRESSION; MULTIPLE AND PARTIAL CORRELATION

11.1 The Correlation Ratio. In Part I of this work * the calculation and use of the correlation ratio are described. We recall that the correlation ratio is a measure of relationship appropriate to a bivariate distribution *grouped in arrays*. For convenience we consider x-arrays (columns in the usual table), but with minor changes in notation the results apply equally well to y-arrays (rows).

Let N_i be the number of observations in the ith array ($i = 1, 2 \cdots p$), and let $N = \sum N_i$. Let $\bar{y}_i$ be the mean of observations in the ith array and $\bar{y}$ the general mean. Then the sample correlation ratio E_{yx} is defined by

(11.1) $$E_{yx}^2 = \sum N_i(\bar{y}_i - \bar{y})^2 / S(y - \bar{y})^2$$

the denominator being summed over all the N observations in the sample. A similar expression holds for E_{xy}, which in general has a different value from E_{yx}.

It may be noted that if a straight line is fitted by least squares to the means of arrays so that the weighted sum of squares of residuals is a minimum (the weights being equal to the array frequencies) this line is the ordinary regression line of y on x

(11.2) $$Y - \bar{y} = b(x - \bar{x})$$

where $b = rs_y/s_x$. Also

(11.3) $$S(y - \bar{y})^2 = S(y - \bar{y}_i + \bar{y}_i - \bar{y})^2 = S(y - \bar{y}_i)^2 + \sum N_i(\bar{y}_i - \bar{y})^2$$

since the N_i observations in one column have a common value of $\bar{y}_i - \bar{y}$. Hence from (11.1)

$$Ns_y^2 = S(y - \bar{y}_i)^2 + Ns_y^2 E_{yx}^2$$

or

(11.4) $$E_{yx}^2 = 1 - \frac{S(y - \bar{y}_i)^2}{Ns_y^2}$$

This may be compared with the formula

(11.5) $$r^2 = 1 - \frac{S(y - Y)^2}{Ns_y^2}$$

and shows that $1 - E_{yx}^2$ is the proportion of the total sum of squares due to

* Kenney, J. F. and Keeping, E. S., *Mathematics of Statistics*, Part One, D. Van Nostrand Co., Inc., 1954.

fluctuation about the line of column means, just as $1 - r^2$ is the proportion due to fluctuation about the straight regression line.

The usual notation for the correlation ratio η_{yx} is here reserved for the *population value*. If η and E are taken to refer to either pair η_{yx} and E_{yx} or η_{xy} and E_{xy}, the distribution of E^2 when $\eta = 0$ has been worked out by Hotelling.[1]

If the various y-arrays (or x-arrays as the case may be) are normally distributed with a common variance, then E^2 is a $\beta(\frac{1}{2}n_1, \frac{1}{2}n_2)$ variate, where $n_1 = p - 1$ and $n_2 = N - p$. It follows readily that $n_2 E^2/n_1(1 - E^2)$ has the F-distribution with n_1 and n_2 degrees of freedom.

The significance of an observed E^2 may, therefore, be tested by means of the table of F, or K. Pearson's *Tables of the Incomplete Beta Function*. A special table which may be used when N is large (as it usually is for a sample for which we would calculate E^2) was prepared by Woo.[2]

If η is not zero, but the number of observations in each array is the same for all samples, the frequency function for E^2 is

$$(11.6) \qquad f(E^2) = e^{-\lambda}(E^2)^{a-1}(1 - E^2)^{b-1} H(\lambda E^2)/B(a, b)$$

where

$$(11.7) \qquad \lambda = N\eta^2/2(1 - \eta^2), \qquad a = n_1/2, \qquad b = n_2/2$$

and

$$(11.8) \qquad H(x) = 1 + \frac{a+b}{1!\,a} x + \frac{(a+b)(a+b+1)}{2!\,a(a+1)} x^2 + \cdots$$

which is the *confluent hypergeometric function*.

The function given by (11.6) obviously reduces to the frequency function for a $\beta(a, b)$ variate when $\lambda = 0$. It is, when λ is not zero, an example of a *non-central distribution*. Since this distribution is of some importance and arises in other problems (see § 12.18), the function has been tabulated by Tang.[21] The tables give the values of $\int_0^{E_\alpha^2} f(E^2)\, dE^2$, where E_α^2 is determined by

$$\int_{E_\alpha^2}^{1} f(E^2 \mid \lambda = 0)\, dE^2 = \alpha$$

α being chosen as either 0.01 or 0.05.

11.2 A Test for Linearity of Regression. The weighted sum of squares between column means which occurs in (11.1) can be split up into a part depending on linear regression and a part depending on the deviation from linear regression.

Since $\bar{y}_i - \bar{y} = \bar{y}_i - Y_i + Y_i - \bar{y}$, we have

$$(11.9) \qquad \sum N_i(\bar{y}_i - \bar{y})^2 = \sum N_i(\bar{y}_i - Y_i)^2 + \sum N_i(Y_i - \bar{y})^2$$

(It is easily proved that the cross-product term vanishes by putting $Y_i = a + bx_i$ and using the normal equations for a and b which are obtained

Sec. 2   A Test for Linearity of Regression   325

in fitting this line to the column means by least squares.) Equation (11.9) can be written

(11.10) $$B = B_1 + B_2$$

where by (11.1) $B = Ns_y^2 E_{yx}^2$. Also as in Chapter VIII, $B_2 = Ns_y^2 r^2$, so that

(11.11) $$B_1 = Ns_y^2(E_{yx}^2 - r^2)$$

This expression represents the part of the sum of squares between column means which cannot be accounted for by linear regression. If this part is excessive, compared with the random sampling fluctuations that might be expected under the null hypothesis that the true regression is linear, we reject the null hypothesis. The basis for comparison is the variation within arrays, $W = S(y - \bar{y}_i)^2$, which by (11.4) is equal to $Ns_y^2(1 - E_{yx}^2)$. Since for each array the sum of squares of $y - \bar{y}_i$ is distributed as $\chi^2 \sigma^2$ with $N_i - 1$ df, W itself is distributed as $\chi^2 \sigma^2$ with $N - p$ df.

Again, since the variance of $\bar{y}_i$ is σ^2/N_i, $\sum N_i(\bar{y}_i - \bar{y})^2$ is distributed as $\chi^2 \sigma^2$ with $p - 1$ df. Also $B_2 = \sum N_i b^2(x_i - \bar{x})^2$, and so is independent of regression except for b^2. Since, as shown in § 8.7, b is a normal variate with variance

$$\sigma^2(1 - \rho^2)/Ns_x^2 = \sigma^2(1 - \rho^2)/\sum N_i(x_i - \bar{x})^2$$

it follows that on the assumption of an uncorrelated parent distribution, B_2 is the square of a normal variate with variance σ^2 and therefore is distributed as $\chi^2 \sigma^2$ with 1 df. Hence B_1 is distributed as $\chi^2 \sigma^2$ with $p - 2$ df, independently of W, so that

(11.12) $$\frac{B_1}{W}\frac{N - p}{p - 2} = \frac{E_{yx}^2 - r^2}{1 - E_{yx}^2}\frac{N - p}{p - 2}$$

has the F-distribution with $p - 2$ and $N - p$ df. A significant value of F indicates a significant departure from linearity. A similar test is, of course, available for E_{xy}.

The situation may be clarified by an Analysis of Variance Table. Thus

Variation	SS	df	MS
About regression line (B_1)	$Ns_y^2(E_{yx}^2 - r^2)$	$p - 2$	$Ns_y^2(E_{yx}^2 - r^2)/(p - 2)$
Due to regression (B_2)	$Ns_y^2 r^2$	$N - p$	$Ns_y^2 r^2/(N - p)$
Total (B)	$Ns_y^2 E_{yx}^2$	$N - 2$	

Example 1. In an investigation of the relationship between percentage illiteracy (y) and percentage Negro population (x) for 82 counties in the State of Mississippi (1920), it was found that the regression line of y on x was $y = 0.299x + 2.02$, but the line of column means appeared appreciably curved. The values of x were grouped in ten classes, "under 10," "10 and under 20," etc. Calculation gave $r^2 = 0.7134$, $E_{yx}^2 = 0.7803$, with $p = 10$, $N = 82$. Hence $F = 2.74$. The 5% and 1% points for $n_1 = 8$ and $n_2 = 72$ are about 2.07 and 2.76 respectively so that the true trend is rather definitely curved.

11.3 Fitting a Polynomial of Second or Higher Degree. The least squares method of § 10.2 for obtaining a linear predicting equation $Y = \sum b_i x_i$ makes no assumption as to the independence of the x_i. We can, therefore, take $x_1 = 1$, $x_2 = x$, $x_3 = x^2$, $\cdots x_p = x^{p-1}$, and use this method for fitting a polynomial of degree $p - 1$ to a set of observations of pairs of values x_α, y_α, the assumption being that the x_α are either fixed values or variates with a negligible error compared with that of y. It is often possible to choose the x_α so that they are equally spaced on the x-axis and thus simplify the computations.

The a_{jk} of (10.20) are now given by $Sx_{j\alpha}x_{k\alpha} = Sx_\alpha{}^{j+k}$, so that the matrix A is

$$\begin{bmatrix} N & Sx & Sx^2 & \cdots & Sx^{p-1} \\ Sx & & & & \\ \vdots & & & & \vdots \\ Sx^{p-1} & \cdots & \cdots & \cdots & Sx^{2p-2} \end{bmatrix}$$

and g_j is $Sx_\alpha{}^j y_\alpha$.

Then $b_j = \sum_k a^{jk} g_k$, and the variance of b_j is $a^{jj}\sigma^2$.

For example, to fit the quadratic

$$Y = b_1 + b_2 x + b_3 x^2$$

we have the equations

(11.13) $$\begin{bmatrix} N & Sx & Sx^2 \\ Sx & Sx^2 & Sx^3 \\ Sx^2 & Sx^3 & Sx^4 \end{bmatrix} \cdot \begin{bmatrix} b_1 \\ b_2 \\ b_3 \end{bmatrix} = \begin{bmatrix} Sy \\ Sxy \\ Sx^2 y \end{bmatrix}$$

to be solved for b_1, b_2, b_3.

If we choose the unit of x, so that the values (supposed equally spaced) change by 1 from one observation to the next, and if we choose the origin of x midway in the range (at the middle value if N is even and half way between the two middle values if N is odd), then in the simplest case of one observation of y at each value of x, we have

$$Sx = Sx^3 = 0$$
$$Sx^2 = N(N^2 - 1)/12$$
$$Sx^4 = N(N^2 - 1)(3N^2 - 7)/240$$

The equations (11.13) then reduce to

(11.14) $$\begin{cases} Nb_1 + \{N(N^2-1)/12\}b_3 = Sy \\ N(N^2-1)b_2/12 = Sxy \\ N(N^2-1)b_1/12 + N(N^2-1)(3N^2-7)b_3/240 = Sx^2 y \end{cases}$$

Example 2. Given the following values of x and y,

x	5	15	25	35	45	55	65	75	85	95
y	10.0	8.1	9.3	12.1	13.6	17.5	20.0	24.0	30.0	42.5
u	−4.5	−3.5	−2.5	−1.5	−0.5	0.5	1.5	2.5	3.5	4.5

calculate (a) a straight and (b) a parabolic trend line, and find the effect of each on the sum of squares of y.

In terms of a new variable $u = (x - 50)/10$ the equations for the straight trend line are

$$\begin{cases} Nb_1 = Sy = 187.1 \\ N(N^2 - 1)b_2/12 = Suy = 273.45 \end{cases}$$

giving $b_1 = 18.71$, $b_2 = 3.3145$. Hence $Y = 18.71 + 0.33145(x - 50) = 0.3314x + 2.138$.

The equations for a parabolic trend line are

$$\begin{cases} 10b_1' + 82.5b_3' = 187.1 \\ 82.5b_2' = 273.45 \\ 82.5b_1' + 1208.6b_3' = 1817.98 (=Su^2y) \end{cases}$$

These give $b_2' = 3.3145$, $b_1' = 14.422$, $b_3' = 0.5197$, so that $Y' = 14.4225 + 0.33145(x - 50) + 0.005197(x - 50)^2 = 10.842 - 0.1882x + 0.005197x^2$.

The calculated values of Y and Y' are as shown:

y	10.0	8.1	9.3	12.1	13.6	17.5	20.0	24.0	30.0	42.5
Y	3.794	7.109	10.423	13.738	17.053	20.367	23.682	26.996	30.311	33.626
Y'	10.030	9.188	9.384	10.620	12.895	16.210	20.564	25.957	32.390	39.862

The analysis of variance table is given in the next section (omitting the part dealing with cubic regression). Since the mean square for parabolic regression is 45 times the mean square for deviations from parabolic regression, the parabolic term is highly significant.

11.4 Orthogonal Polynomials. The procedure of § 11.3 has the disadvantage that if it is required to introduce an additional term into the regression equation all the coefficients have to be calculated afresh. A method suggested by R. A. Fisher involves the fitting of a series of *orthogonal polynomials*, each term being independent of all the others. This means that each regression coefficient can be calculated independently, and the tests of significance are facilitated.

Two polynomials $P_1(x)$ and $P_2(x)$ are orthogonal if $S(P_1P_2) = 0$ where S is the sum over a specified set of values of x. If x were a continuous variable in the range from a to b, the condition of orthogonality would be $\int_a^b P_1P_2 \, dx = 0$.

It is easily verified, as in the following table, that the polynomials $P_0 = 1$, $P_1 = x - 4$, $P_2 = x^2 - 8x + 12$, $P_3 = x^3 - 12x^2 + 41x - 36$ are all orthogonal for the set of integral values of x from 1 to 7.

x	P_0P_1	P_0P_2	P_0P_3	P_1P_2	P_1P_3	P_2P_3
1	−3	5	−6	−15	18	−30
2	−2	0	6	0	−12	0
3	−1	−3	6	3	−6	−18
4	0	−4	0	0	0	0
5	1	−3	−6	−3	−6	18
6	2	0	−6	0	−12	0
7	3	5	6	15	18	30
	0	0	0	0	0	0

It can be proved [3] that any polynomial in x of degree k, for a specified set of values of x, can be expressed as a linear function of $k + 1$ orthogonal polynomials, say

(11.15) $$Y = A_0\xi_0 + A_1\xi_1 + A_2\xi_2 + \cdots + A_k\xi_k$$

where $\xi_0 = 1$, and ξ_i is a polynomial of degree i ($i = 1, 2, \cdots k$). If x takes the values $1, 2, 3 \cdots N$, the first four of these polynomials are

$$\xi_1 = \lambda_1(x - \bar{x})$$
$$\xi_2 = \lambda_2[(x - \bar{x})^2 - (N^2 - 1)/12]$$
$$\xi_3 = \lambda_3[(x - \bar{x})^3 - (x - \bar{x})(3N^2 - 7)/20]$$
$$\xi_4 = \lambda_4[(x - \bar{x})^4 - (x - \bar{x})^2(3N^2 - 13)/14 + 3(N^2 - 1)(N^2 - 9)/560]$$

where $\bar{x}$ is the mean value of x and the λ's are usually and conveniently chosen so as to make the values of these polynomials integers (as small as possible) for all values of x from 1 to N. Thus if $N = 7$, we have $\bar{x} = 4$, $\lambda_1 = 1$, $\lambda_2 = 1$, $\lambda_3 = 1/6$, $\lambda_4 = 7/12$.

The sets of values of these polynomials are

x	ξ_1	ξ_2	ξ_3	ξ_4
1	−3	5	−1	3
2	−2	0	1	−7
3	−1	−3	1	1
4	0	−4	0	6
5	1	−3	−1	1
6	2	0	−1	−7
7	3	5	1	3

All the polynomials with even subscripts have a set of values symmetric about the middle. All those with odd subscripts are skew-symmetric (the signs changing but not the magnitudes). Hence only one half the table, together with the middle line if any, need be given. In the tables the *lower* halves only are printed.

The regression coefficients $A_0, A_1, \cdots A_k$ are calculated by least squares so as to make $S(y - Y)^2$ a minimum. The normal equations are

$$\begin{cases} A_0 S(\xi_0\xi_0) + A_1 S(\xi_0\xi_1) + \cdots + A_k S(\xi_0\xi_k) = S(y\xi_0) \\ A_0 S(\xi_0\xi_1) + A_1 S(\xi_1\xi_1) + \cdots + A_k S(\xi_1\xi_k) = S(y\xi_1) \\ \text{etc.} \end{cases}$$

but because of the orthogonal property of these polynomials, and because $\xi_0 = 1$, these equations reduce to

(11.16) $$\begin{cases} A_0 N = S(y) \\ A_1 S(\xi_1)^2 = S(y\xi_1) \\ \cdots \cdots \cdots \\ A_k S(\xi_k)^2 = S(y\xi_k) \end{cases}$$

Sec. 4   Orthogonal Polynomials

It is evident, therefore, that each regression coefficient can be calculated independently of all the others.

The sum of squares of deviations from regression is given by

(11.17) $\quad\quad S(y^2) - A_0 S(y) - A_1 S(y\xi_1) - \cdots - A_k S(y\xi_k)$

The first two terms give the total sum of squares about the mean, since $A_0 = \bar{y}$. The 3rd term gives the reduction due to linear regression, the 4th term the additional reduction due to parabolic regression, and so on.

The actual fitting of the polynomials is greatly facilitated by tables giving the values assumed by ξ_1 to ξ_5 for all necessary x. For values of N up to 75 these tables are given in Fisher and Yates' *Statistical Tables* (3rd Edition). They have been extended to $N = 104$ by Anderson and Houseman.[4] New tables by DeLury [22] give the polynomials up to ξ_{N-1} for $N \leq 26$, and also the integrals of these polynomials, $I_r = \int_0^{N-1} \xi_r(x)\,dx$ and $J_r = \int_{-1/2}^{N-1/2} \xi_r(x)\,dx$ for $r \leq 14$, $N \leq 26$. These integrals are useful in estimating the total amount of some variable X from a systematic sample, such as is often obtained in forestry, ore-drilling, etc., when samples are selected at regularly spaced points, along a preassigned straight line or series of such lines.

The use of orthogonal polynomials may be illustrated by fitting a cubic to the data of Example 2, in which $N = 10$. The last three columns are read from the tables, and $u = (x + 5)/10$.

x	u	y	ξ_1	ξ_2	ξ_3
5	1	10.0	-9	$+6$	-42
15	2	8.1	-7	$+2$	$+14$
25	3	9.3	-5	-1	$+35$
35	4	12.1	-3	-3	$+31$
45	5	13.6	-1	-4	$+12$
55	6	17.5	$+1$	-4	-12
65	7	20.0	$+3$	-3	-31
75	8	24.0	$+5$	-1	-35
85	9	30.0	$+7$	$+2$	-14
95	10	42.5	$+9$	$+6$	$+42$

We calculate $S(y) = 187.1$, $S(y\xi_1) = 546.9$, $S(y\xi_2) = 137.2$, $S(y\xi_3) = 252.2$. The values of $S(\xi_1)^2 = 330$, $S(\xi_2)^2 = 132$ and $S(\xi_3)^2 = 8580$ are read from the tables. Then $A_0 = 187.1/10 = 18.71$, $A_1 = 546.9/330 = 1.6573$, $A_2 = 137.2/132 = 1.0394$, $A_3 = 252.2/8580 = 0.029394$.

The total sum of squares is 1071.33. The reduction due to linear regression is $A_1 S(y\xi_1) = 906.38$, the additional reduction due to parabolic regression is $A_2 S(y\xi_2) = 142.61$, and the further reduction due to cubic regression is $A_3 S(y\xi_3) = 7.41$. The analysis of variance table is, therefore,

Variation	SS	df	MS
Total	1071.33	9	
Linear regression	906.38	1	908.38
Deviations	164.95	8	20.62
Parabolic regression	142.61	1	142.61
Deviations	22.34	7	3.19
Cubic regression	7.41	1	7.41
Deviations	14.93	6	2.49

The cubic regression term is not significant, so that a parabolic trend line would probably be quite satisfactory. The parabolic regression term is highly significant, indicating a well-marked deviation from linearity. There is, of course, no guarantee that because one term is non-significant all higher terms are also non-significant, but one can often form an opinion from the relation of the plotted curve to the scatter diagram of the original data.

In this particular example the addition of a fourth degree term reduces the SS for deviations to 1.39 and the mean square to 0.28, while a fifth degree term reduces the SS to 1.16 and raises the mean square to 0.29. The mean squares for quartic and quintic regression are 13.54 and 0.23 respectively, so that, based on the deviations from quintic regression, the third and fourth degree terms, but not the fifth degree term, appear highly significant.

If the second and fourth degree curves are plotted on a graph showing the original data, the parabola clearly gives a good general description of the course of the data, but the fit of the quartic is much closer. With a ninth degree curve we could fit the observed data *exactly*, but such a complicated curve is obviously not desirable. One must compromise between the desire for simplicity and the desire to get a good fit, and the parabola would appear in this example to give a satisfactory compromise.

The equation of the parabola is

$$Y = A_0 + A_1\xi_1 + A_2\xi_2$$
$$= A_0 + A_1\lambda_1(u - \bar{u}) + A_2\lambda_2[(u - \bar{u})^2 - (N^2 - 1)/12]$$

The values of λ_1 and λ_2, from the tables, are 2 and $\frac{1}{2}$ respectively, and $(N^2 - 1)/12 = 33/4$, so that

$$Y = 18.71 + 3.3146(u - 5.5) + 0.5197(u - 5.5)^2 - 8.25$$
$$= 11.913 - 2.4021u + 0.5197u^2$$
$$= 11.913 - 0.2402(x + 5) + 0.005197(x + 5)^2$$
$$= 10.842 - 0.1882x + 0.005197x^2$$

which agrees with the equation previously obtained. In calculating values of Y for plotting a curve, it is simpler to work with the values of the ξ's rather than x.

11.5 Seidel's Method of Successive Approximations. Sometimes approximate values of the constants in a regression curve may be obtained from a graph. These values can then be improved by least squares.

Sec. 5   Seidel's Method of Successive Approximations   331

Let the true curve be $Y = f(x, \alpha, \beta)$ where for convenience we suppose only two parameters, and let a and b be approximate values of α and β respectively. Then, if $\delta a = \alpha - a$, $\delta b = \beta - b$, both δa and δb may be presumed small, and, to a first approximation, squares, products, and higher powers can be neglected. Hence

(11.18) $$Y = f(x, a + \delta a, b + \delta b)$$
$$= f(x, a, b) + \delta a f_a + \delta b f_b$$

approximately, where f_a and f_b are the partial derivatives of f with respect to a and b. Replacing Y by the observed y, we have a set of observation equations for the unknowns δa and δb. By forming the normal equations and solving them, δa and δb are obtained, and these values, added to a and b, give improved values of the parameters. The process can then be repeated as often as necessary. It usually converges quite rapidly, and two or three stages will generally give a satisfactory result.

Example 3. The following data were obtained in a physical experiment. (E represents the energy radiated from a carbon filament lamp per cm² per sec and T the absolute temperature of the filament in thousands of degrees C.)

T	1.309	1.471	1.490	1.565	1.611	1.680
E	2.138	3.421	3.597	4.340	4.882	5.660

By plotting on logarithmic graph paper it is seen that the data follow a law of the type

$$E = aT^b$$

with $a = 0.725$, and $b = 3.96$ approximately. Here $\partial E/\partial a = T^b$, $\partial E/\partial b = aT^b \log T$, so that $E - aT^b = T^b \delta a + aT^b \log T \, \delta b$. Using the approximate values of a and b, we obtain a set of six equations for δa and δb. On forming the normal equations and solving them, we get $\delta a = 0.0434$, $\delta b = -0.102$, so that the new values are $a = 0.7684$, $b = 3.858$.

If we repeat the process with these new values, we get $\delta a = 0.0004$, $\delta b = 0.0024$, so that $a = 0.7688$, $b = 3.8604$. From the sum of squares of residuals, the standard errors of a and b are 0.009 and 0.033 respectively, so that it is quite sufficiently accurate to take $a = 0.769$, $b = 3.86$.

If $f(x, a, b)$ is a *linear* function of a and b, the Seidel method is exact, since the second and higher derivatives of f all vanish. The method may thus be used in fitting straight lines or polynomial curves, and has the advantage that it is not necessary to carry many decimals.

In the example of § 11.4, suppose that the approximate parabola is

$$Y = 12 - 2.5u + 0.5u^2$$

Putting $\alpha = 12 + \delta a$, $\beta = -2.5 + \delta b$, $\gamma = 0.5 + \delta c$, and forming the normal equations, we obtain

$$10 \, \delta a + 55 \, \delta b + 385 \, \delta c = 12.1$$
$$55 \, \delta a + 385 \, \delta b + 3025 \, \delta c = 92.5$$
$$385 \, \delta a + 3025 \, \delta b + 25333 \, \delta c = 761.7$$

The solution is $\delta c = 0.020$, $\delta b = 0.098$, $\delta a = -0.086$, so that the corrected parabola is
$$Y = 11.914 - 2.402u + 0.520u^2$$

11.6 Exponential and Modified Exponential Regression. The exponential curve

(11.19) $$Y = be^{px}$$

is of fairly frequent occurrence, implying that the observed variable y increases or decreases at an approximately uniform *percentage* rate as x increases. The curve

(11.20) $$Y = a + be^{px}$$

has been termed a *modified exponential* curve, and arises also in a number of problems.

The customary procedure in fitting (11.19) is to write it in the form

(11.21) $$\log Y = \log b + px$$

and fit a straight line to the observed values of $\log y$ as plotted against x. This means that the sum of squares of deviations for $\log y$ is minimized, instead of the corresponding quantity for y. Since $d(\log y) = dy/y$, the procedure is strictly correct in those problems in which the standard deviation of y increases in direct proportion to y. For problems in which the variance of y is independent of y, the effect of the customary procedure is to give undue weight to the smaller values of y. For many data in the field of economics the assumption of a standard deviation proportional to y seems reasonable, but there are problems in other fields where an exponential trend accompanied by a constant standard deviation may fairly be assumed.[23]

The exact least squares solution is laborious. It requires us to calculate b and p from the equations

(11.22) $$\begin{cases} S(y_\alpha e^{px_\alpha}) = bSe^{2px_\alpha} \\ S(x_\alpha y_\alpha e^{px_\alpha}) = bS(x_\alpha e^{2px_\alpha}) \end{cases}$$

or, for the modified equation (11.20), a, b and p from

(11.23) $$\begin{cases} Sy_\alpha = Na + bSe^{px_\alpha} \\ S(y_\alpha e^{px_\alpha}) = aSe^{px_\alpha} + bSe^{2px_\alpha} \\ S(x_\alpha y_\alpha e^{px_\alpha}) = aS(x_\alpha e^{px_\alpha}) + bS(x_\alpha e^{2px_\alpha}) \end{cases}$$

Rough approximations to b and p may be found for (11.19) by fitting a straight line graphically to the values of $\log y$ plotted against x; these approximations may be improved by Seidel's method.

Tables for use in fitting exponential curves may be found in Glover's *Tables*,[5] but these cover a very limited range of values of p (from 0 to 0.0953, e^p between 1.0 and 1.1). Cowden[6] has given a method of finding approximate values of a, b, and $q(=e^p)$. This consists in plotting the data, drawing a

Sec. 6   Exponential and Modified Regression

tentative trend line, selecting three equidistant ordinates, and calculating a from the formula

(11.24) $$a = \frac{Y_0 Y_2 - Y_1^2}{Y_0 + Y_2 - 2Y_1}$$

(This formula is readily proved by putting $x - h$, x and $x + h$ for x in the right-hand side of (11.20) and equating the results to Y_0, Y_1, Y_2 respectively.) Values of $Y - a$ are now plotted on semi-logarithmic paper, and a is further adjusted if necessary so that a straight line fits the points reasonably well. Then b is the ordinate of this straight line at $x = 0$ and $q^{x_N - x_1}$ is the ratio of the ordinates at x_N and x_1. These values of a, b, and q may be improved by Seidel's process.

A method of fitting the exponential curve (11.19), which in practice gives satisfactory results, is to calculate the straight line regression of $\log y$ on x with the observations *weighted* in proportion to y. This procedure approximately counteracts the automatic weighting (nearly proportional to $1/y$) which results from using $\log y$ instead of y. If the fitted curve has the equation

(11.25) $$\log Y = c + px, \qquad c = \log b$$

the weighted least squares condition is

(11.26) $$\sum y (\log y - c - px)^2 = \min$$

This gives rise to the normal equations

$$c \sum y + p \sum xy = \sum y \log y$$
$$c \sum xy + p \sum x^2 y = \sum xy \log y$$

whence p and b ($= e^c$) are determined.

The following example is given by Snedecor,[7] x being the age in days of chick embryos, and y the dry weight in grams.

x	y	$\log_{10} y$
6	0.029	−1.538
7	0.052	−1.284
8	0.079	−1.102
9	0.125	−0.903
10	0.181	−0.742
11	0.261	−0.583
12	0.425	−0.372
13	0.738	−0.132
14	1.130	0.053
15	1.882	0.275
16	2.812	0.449

(Common logarithms have been used, so that the calculated c and p must be multiplied by 2.303. Alternatively, the equation may be written in the form $Y = b10^{px}$, with $c = \log_{10} b$.)

The normal equations have the solution (after multiplication) $p = 0.4581$, $c = -6.2794$, so that the exponential equation is

$$Y = 0.001875 \exp(.4581x)$$

The equation obtained without weighting is

$$Y = 0.002046 \exp(.4511x)$$

while the exact least squares solution is

$$Y = 0.001895 \exp(.4573x)$$

It is clear that the weighted regression of $\log y$ on x gives in this example a good approximation.

The method of weighting could be applied also to the *modified exponential* equation, the weighting being now proportional to $y - a$. Preliminary values of a, b, and q having been obtained by Cowden's method, these values could be improved by a *weighted* Seidel process.[8] The least squares condition for the weighted process is

$$\sum (y-a)\{\log(y-a) - \delta a/(y-a) - xp - x\,\delta p - \log b - \delta b/b\}^2 = \min$$

11.7 Fitting a Simple Harmonic Curve to a Series of Observations. Many phenomena appear to be more or less cyclical, and in such cases it may seem reasonable to fit a simple harmonic curve to a series of observations. Let the curve be

(11.27) $$Y = A \cos \omega x + B \sin \omega x + C$$

where the period is $2\pi/\omega$, and the series extends over an integral number of periods. The normal equations are

(11.28) $$\begin{cases} AS(\cos^2 \omega x) + BS(\cos \omega x \sin \omega x) + CS(\cos \omega x) = S(y \cos \omega x) \\ AS(\cos \omega x \sin \omega x) + BS(\sin^2 \omega x) + CS(\sin \omega x) = S(y \sin \omega x) \\ AS(\cos \omega x) + BS(\sin \omega x) + CN = S(y) \end{cases}$$

On the assumption of an integral number of complete periods, $S(\cos \omega x) = S(\sin \omega x) = 0$. Also $S(\cos^2 \omega x) = S(\sin^2 \omega x) = N/2$, since $S(1 - 2\sin^2 \omega x) = S(2\cos^2 \omega x - 1) = S(\cos 2\omega x) = 0$, and $S(\sin \omega x \cos \omega x) = \frac{1}{2}S(\sin 2\omega x) = 0$. Equations (11.28), therefore, reduce to

(11.29) $$\begin{cases} A = \dfrac{2}{N} S(y \cos \omega x) \\ B = \dfrac{2}{N} S(y \sin \omega x) \\ C = \bar{y} \end{cases}$$

The coefficient matrix of (11.28) is

$$\begin{bmatrix} N/2 & 0 & 0 \\ 0 & N/2 & 0 \\ 0 & 0 & N \end{bmatrix}$$

Sec. 7 Fitting a Simple Harmonic Curve

so that the variance-covariance matrix, which is the inverse of this, is

$$\begin{bmatrix} 2/N & 0 & 0 \\ 0 & 2/N & 0 \\ 0 & 0 & 1/N \end{bmatrix}$$

The sum of squares of residuals is

(11.30) $\quad S(v^2) = S(y^2) - \sum b_i g_i$

$= S(y^2) - \dfrac{N}{2} A^2 - \dfrac{N}{2} B^2 - N\bar{y}^2$

$= S(y^2) - \dfrac{2}{N}[S(y \cos \omega x)]^2 - \dfrac{2}{N}[S(y \sin \omega x)]^2 - N\bar{y}^2$

The number of degrees of freedom is $N - 3$. Since (11.27) corresponds to a wave of amplitude $(A^2 + B^2)^{1/2}$, or intensity $A^2 + B^2$, the test for reality of the wave or harmonic is a test of whether $A^2 + B^2$ is significantly different from zero. Since on the usual assumptions for regression A and B are normally distributed, it follows from the variance-covariance matrix that they are independent and have a common variance $2\sigma^2/N$. Hence $(A^2 + B^2)N/2\sigma^2$ has the χ^2 distribution with 2 degrees of freedom. This provides a test for the significance of the observed $A^2 + B^2$, provided that σ^2 can be estimated with considerable accuracy, say from a long series of observations. If only a comparatively short series is available we may estimate σ^2 by $S(v_\alpha^2)/(N-3)$, where v_α is a residual, and use the fact that $N \dfrac{A^2 + B^2}{2} \bigg/ \dfrac{S(v^2)}{N-3}$ has the F-distribution with 2 and $N - 3$ degrees of freedom.

If we calculate the value of $x = A^2 + B^2$ for a number of different periods p, and draw a graph of x against p, the result is called a *periodogram*. If the periodogram has well-marked peaks at certain points, which cannot reasonably be attributed to sampling fluctuations, these values of p may be regarded as the periods of genuine harmonic terms.

If P is the probability of getting a periodic component of intensity at least equal to x,

(11.31) $\quad P = 1 - \displaystyle\int_0^{Nx/4\sigma^2} e^{-\frac{1}{2}\chi^2} d(\tfrac{1}{2}\chi^2)$

$= e^{-Nx/4\sigma^2}$

since $Nx/2\sigma^2$ has the χ^2 distribution with 2 df. If x is calculated for n selected periods, and $\hat{x}$ is the maximum value of x, then the probability $\hat{P}$ that *at least one* intensity will exceed $\hat{x}$ by pure chance is given by

(11.32) $\quad 1 - \hat{P} = (1 - e^{-N\hat{x}/4\sigma^2})^n$

assuming that the selected periods are all independent. This formula was given by Walker.[9] Since we do, in fact, pick out the largest intensities for examination, Walker's formula should be used rather than (11.31) for judging significance. The test requires a knowledge of σ^2, but Fisher[10] has given a method which avoids the necessity of knowing σ^2. If the number of observations $N = 2n + 1$, and if $x_1, x_2, \cdots x_n$ are the intensities corresponding to trial periods of N, $N/2$, $N/3$, $\cdots N/n$, Fisher has obtained the distribution of $g = \hat{x}/2v$, where $\hat{x}$ is the maximum value of x_1 to x_n and $v = S(Y - \bar{y})^2 = (x_1 + x_2 + \cdots + x_n)/2$. He finds that the probability of a value of g at least as great as a given value is

$$(11.33) \quad P = n(1-g)^{n-1} - n\frac{(n-1)}{2}(1-2g)^{n-1} + \cdots$$
$$+ (-1)^{m-1}\binom{n}{m}(1-mg)^{n-1}$$

the series stopping as soon as $1 - mg$ ceases to be positive.

H. T. Davis[11] has calculated tables of P and also of $\hat{P}$ in (11.32) useful in the analysis of economic time series. A general discussion of the problem and of the difficulties of assessing the reality of apparent cyclical or oscillatory movements may be found in Kendall's *Advanced Theory of Statistics*, Vol. II, Chapter 30.

11.8 Estimation of x for a Given y in Curvilinear Regression. Suppose our estimated regression equation is $Y = b_0 + b_1 x + b_2 x^2$. Our estimate of x for $y = y_0$ will be a real root of $y_0 = b_0 + b_1 x + b_2 x^2$, lying within the range of x for which the regression is presumed to hold. There may, of course, be no such root or there may be two roots. If a real root exists, we should like to have confidence limits for it.

Let us replace x by a parameter λ, and let $T = b_0 + b_1 \lambda + b_2 \lambda^2$. Then the expectation of T is given by

$$(11.34) \qquad E(T) = \beta_0 + \beta_1 \lambda + \beta_2 \lambda^2$$

and the variance by

$$(11.35) \quad \text{Var}(T) = E[T - \beta_0 - \beta_1 \lambda - \beta_2 \lambda^2]^2$$
$$= E[(b_0 - \beta_0) + (b_1 - \beta_1)\lambda + (b_2 - \beta_2)\lambda^2]^2$$
$$= \sigma^2(a^{00} + a^{11}\lambda^2 + a^{22}\lambda^4 + 2a^{01}\lambda + 2a^{02}\lambda^2 + 2a^{12}\lambda^3)$$

by (10.43). Hence $\{T - E(T)\}/\{\text{Var}(T)\}^{1/2}$ is normally distributed about 0 with variance 1. If $V'(T)$ is equal to Var (T) with σ^2 replaced by its estimate $s^2 = S(y - Y)^2/(N - 3)$, then

$$\{T - E(T)\}/\{V'(T)\}^{1/2}$$

has Student's t-distribution with $N - 3$ df. If t_α is the value of t such that $100(1 - \alpha)\%$ of the distribution lies between $\pm t_\alpha$, the $100(1 - \alpha)\%$ confidence limits are given by

$$(11.36) \quad [(b_0 - \beta_0) + (b_1 - \beta_1)\lambda + (b_2 - \beta_2)\lambda^2]^2$$
$$= \frac{t_\alpha^2 S(y - Y)^2}{N - 3}(a^{00} + a^{11}\lambda^2 + a^{22}\lambda^4 + 2a^{01}\lambda + 2a^{02}\lambda^2 + 2a^{12}\lambda^3)$$

Sec. 9   Maximum or Minimum in Regression   337

If when $y = y_0$ the true value of x is λ,
$$y_0 = \beta_0 + \beta_1\lambda + \beta_2\lambda^2$$
so that on substituting in (11.36) we have

(11.37) $(N - 3)(b_0 + b_1\lambda + b_2\lambda^2 - y_0)^2$
$$= t_\alpha^2 S(y - Y)^2(a^{00} + a^{11}\lambda^2 + a^{22}\lambda^4 + 2a^{01}\lambda + 2a^{02}\lambda^2 + 2a^{12}\lambda^3)$$

This is a quartic in λ. One root goes with the upper confidence limit and one with the lower. There are two extraneous roots.

11.9 Estimation of Maximum or Minimum in Curvilinear Regression.[12]
If the true regression is given by
$$\eta = \beta_0 + \beta_1 x + \beta_2 x^2$$
$d\eta/dx = 0$ when $\beta_1 + 2\beta_2 x = 0$, so that the true maximum (or minimum) is given by
$$\xi = -\beta_1/2\beta_2$$

The maximum likelihood estimate of ξ is $\hat{x} = -b_1/2b_2$. If we let $T = b_1 + 2b_2\lambda$, then $E(T) = \beta_1 + 2\beta_2\lambda = 0$ when $\lambda = \xi$. Also
$$\text{Var}(T) = E[b_1 - \beta_1 + 2(b_2 - \beta_2)\lambda]^2$$
$$= \sigma^2(a^{11} + 4a^{22}\lambda^2 + 4a^{12}\lambda)$$
so that

(11.38) $$t = \frac{(b_1 + 2b_2\lambda)}{s(a^{11} + 4a^{22}\lambda^2 + 4a^{12}\lambda)^{1/2}}$$

has Student's t-distribution with $N - 3$ df. Hence confidence limits for x can be established.

The same procedure can be used to find the *point of inflection* of a cubic curve. If the true regression equation is
$$\eta = \beta_0 + \beta_1 x + \beta_2 x^2 + \beta_3 x^3$$
$$\frac{d^2\eta}{dx^2} = 2\beta_2 + 6\beta_3 x$$
and this is equal to 0 when $x = \xi$ if
$$\xi = -\beta_2/3\beta_3$$
The estimate is $\hat{x} = -b_2/3b_3$, and the confidence limits are obtained as before.

Again, suppose Y is a *quadratic function of two variables* u and v, so that

(11.39) $$Y = b_1 + b_2 u + b_3 v + b_4 u^2 + b_5 uv + b_6 v^2$$

This is another special case (see § 11.3) of the general multivariate regression of Chapter X. Here $x_1 = 1$, $x_2 = u$, $x_3 = v$, $x_4 = u^2$, $x_5 = uv$, $x_6 = v^2$.

The point at which Y is a maximum or minimum is given by $\partial Y/\partial u = 0$, $\partial Y/\partial v = 0$, and is estimated from the equations

(11.40) $$\begin{cases} b_2 + 2b_4 u + b_5 v = 0 \\ b_3 + b_5 u + 2b_6 v = 0 \end{cases}$$

If λ and μ are two parameters, and if

(11.41)
$$\begin{cases} T_1 = b_2 + 2b_4\lambda + b_5\mu \\ T_2 = b_3 + b_5\lambda + 2b_6\mu \end{cases}$$

then T_1 and T_2 have a joint bivariate normal distribution with a known variance-covariance matrix $A_{ij}\sigma^2$ (i, $j = 1, 2$). We have

$$E(T_1) = \beta_2 + 2\beta_4\lambda + \beta_5\mu = 0$$

and
$$\text{Var}(T_1) = \sigma^2(a^{22} + 4a^{44}\lambda^2 + a^{55}\mu^2 + 4a^{24}\lambda + 4a^{45}\lambda\mu + 2a^{25}\mu)$$
$$= \sigma^2 A_{11}$$

Similarly, $E(T_2) = 0$
$$\text{Var}(T_2) = \sigma^2(a^{33} + a^{55}\lambda^2 + 4a^{66}\mu^2 + 2a^{35}\lambda + 4a^{56}\lambda\mu + 4a^{36}\mu)$$
$$= \sigma^2 A_{22}$$

and
$$\text{Cov}(T_1 T_2) = \sigma^2[a^{23} + 2a^{45}\lambda^2 + 2a^{56}\mu^2 + (a^{25} + 2a^{34})\lambda$$
$$+ (a^{35} + 2a^{26})\mu + (a^{55} + 4a^{46})\lambda\mu]$$
$$= \sigma^2 A_{12}$$

If $S_T = \sum_{i,j} A^{ij} T_i T_j$, S_T/σ^2 can be written as a sum of squares of two independent normal standard variates ξ_1 and ξ_2. For if

$$\xi_1 = (A^{11})^{1/2}(T_1 + A^{12} T_2/A^{11})$$
$$\xi_2 = [A^{22} - (A^{12})^2/A^{11}]^{1/2} T_2$$

then
$$\xi_1^2 + \xi_2^2 = A^{11} T_1^2 + A^{22} T_2^2 + 2A^{12} T_1 T_2 = S_T$$

Also $E(\xi_1) = E(\xi_2) = 0$, and

$$\text{Var}(\xi_1) = A^{11}[\text{Var}(T_1) + (A^{12}/A^{11})^2 \text{Var}(T_2) + 2(A^{12}/A^{11}) \text{Cov}(T_1 T_2)]$$
$$= \sigma^2 A^{11}[A_{11} + (A^{12}/A^{11})^2 A_{22} + 2(A^{12} A_{12})/A^{11}]$$
$$= \sigma^2(A^{11} A_{11} + A^{12} A_{12}) + \sigma^2(A^{12}/A^{11})(A^{12} A_{22} + A^{11} A_{12})$$
$$= \sigma^2$$

Similarly $\text{Var}(\xi_2) = \sigma^2$ and $\text{Cov}(\xi_1 \xi_2) = 0$. Hence S_T/σ^2 has the χ^2 distribution with 2 df. If $S_m = S(y - Y)^2$, then, as we have proved in Chapter X, S_m/σ^2 has the χ^2 distribution with $N - 6$ df (there being 6 variables x_0 to x_5 in the regression). Consequently

$$F = \frac{S_T}{S_m} \frac{N - 6}{2}$$

has the F-distribution with 2 and $N - 6$ df. For a fixed value of F, this provides a relation between λ and μ, the two-dimensional analogue of a confidence limit. The values of λ and μ given by (11.41), with $T_1 = T_2 = 0$, are the estimated values of u and v corresponding to the maximum or minimum of Y.

Sec. 10 Geometrical Picture of Multiple Regression

11.10 The Geometrical Picture of Multiple Regression and Correlation.
The term *multiple correlation* refers to a theory of correlation involving three or more variables. For ease in exposition we shall restrict the derivation of formulas to the three-variable case although the method is perfectly general. When the three-variable case is understood the formulas can be generalized for k variables.

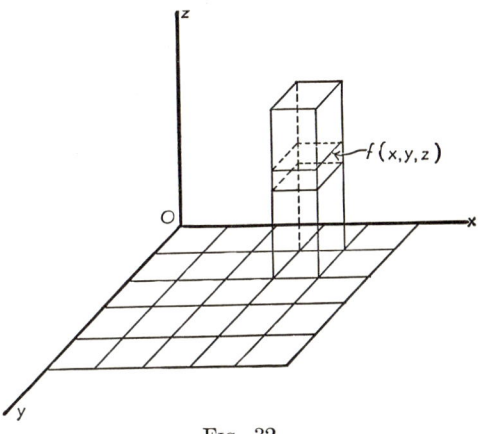

The framework of a two-way table was a rectangle in the xy-plane which was divided into cells by lines parallel to the axes. The analogue in the case of three variables, which we shall denote by x, y, and z, is a rectangular parallelepiped divided into cells by slicing planes parallel to the axes.

Fig. 32

We shall denote the frequency in the cell whose mid-point has the coordinates (x, y, z) by $f(x, y, z)$. A pair of (x, y) values fixes a z column (Figure 32), and the sum of the frequencies in such a column is the "column total":

$$(11.42) \qquad \sum_z f(x, y, z) = f(x, y)$$

where here and subsequently the symbol $\sum$ together with the variable underneath denotes a summation in the direction of that variable. Now consider all those columns which have the same y. Their total frequency, denoted by

$$(11.43) \qquad \sum_x f(x, y) = f(y)$$

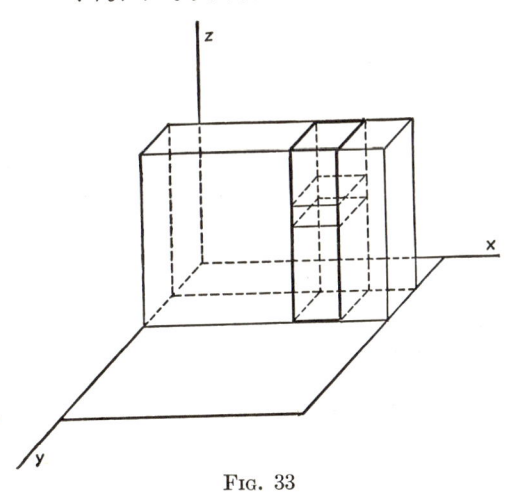

Fig. 33

may appropriately be called a "slab total" (Figure 33). Finally, if we add all the slab totals we get the total frequency N. Thus

$$(11.44) \qquad \sum_y f(y) = N$$

By making use of (11.42) we may, if we wish, express (11.43) as the double sum

Multiple and Partial Correlation

(11.45) $$\sum_x \sum_z f(x, y, z) = f(y)$$

and hence express (11.44) as the triple sum

(11.46) $$\sum_x \sum_y \sum_z f(x, y, z) = N$$

(a) The aggregate of the column totals $f(x, y)$ forms a two-way frequency table. If we imagine the numerical values of these frequencies written in the cells of the xy-plane it is easy to see that they constitute a correlation table (Figure 34). For this table, the simple correlation coefficient r_{xy} is called the

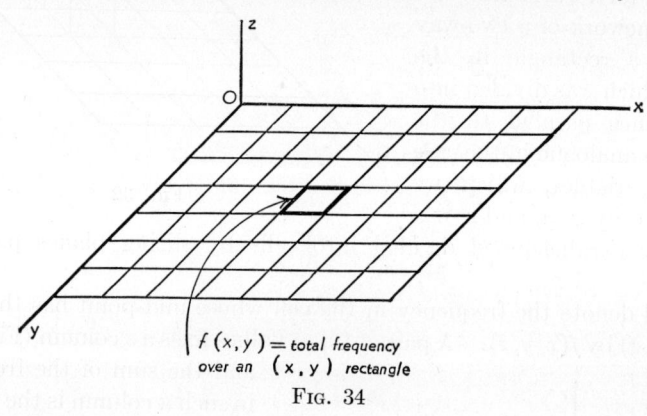

$f(x, y) =$ total frequency over an (x, y) rectangle

FIG. 34

total correlation (in contradistinction to a partial correlation coefficient to be defined later) and the regression curves are called the total regressions of y on x and x on y. Discussions analogous to (a) may be given for horizontal columns parallel (b) to Ox and (c) to Oy.

The mean of a column at (x, y) is defined by

(11.47) $$\bar{z}(x, y) = \frac{1}{f(x, y)} \sum_z z f(x, y, z)$$

Similarly, the mean of an x column at (y, z) is

(11.48) $$\bar{x}(y, z) = \frac{1}{f(y, z)} \sum_x x f(x, y, z)$$

and the mean of a y column at (x, z) is

(11.49) $$\bar{y}(x, z) = \frac{1}{f(x, z)} \sum_y y f(x, y, z)$$

The *regression plane* of z on xy is that plane which fits the means of the z columns best in a weighted least-squares sense. This should not be confused with the true regression surface, z on xy, which is defined as the locus of the mean points of the z columns. More accurately, it is the locus of these points

Sec. 10 Geometrical Picture of Multiple Regression

as the dimensions of the cells approach zero and as $N \to \infty$. The regression plane, z on xy, is that plane which fits best the true regression surface, z on xy. Corresponding statements hold for the regression planes of y on xz and of x on yz.

So far, it was convenient to designate our variables by the conventional letters used in representing three-dimensional space. We are now about to obtain the equations of the regression planes and in order to extend our results to k variables it will be desirable to change to a new set of symbols which will lend themselves more readily to generalization. The switch will cause no difficulty. We shall now use x_1 in place of x, x_2 in place of y, and x_3 in place of z. The relations between the r's in the old notation and the new are $r_{xy} = r_{12}$, $r_{yz} = r_{23}$, $r_{xz} = r_{13}$.

We shall now derive the equation of the regression plane of x_1 on x_2 and x_3. In determining, under a least-squares criterion, the parameters in its equation it will simplify the exposition if we assume that the variables are measured from their respective means as origin. This may be assumed without loss of generality. Let the desired equation be of the form

(11.50) $$x_1 = Ax_2 + Bx_3 + C$$

Then we may determine the parameters in (11.50) so that the sum of the squares of the residuals

(11.51) $$U = \sum_{2,3}(x_1 - Ax_2 - Bx_3 - C)^2 f$$

is a minimum, f being short for $f(x_1, x_2, x_3)$, and $\sum_{2,3}$ for $\sum_{x_2}\sum_{x_3}$. Equating to zero the first partial derivatives of U with respect to A, B, and C, we obtain the equations

$$\sum x_2(x_1 - Ax_2 - Bx_3 - C)f = 0$$
$$\sum x_3(x_1 - Ax_2 - Bx_3 - C)f = 0$$
$$C = 0$$

The simplification of the last equation is a consequence of our choice of origin since $\sum x_1 f = \sum x_2 f = \sum x_3 f = 0$ when the origin of x_i is at the mean of its N values. The first two equations may be written in the form

(11.52) $$\begin{cases} A\sum x_2^2 f + B\sum x_2 x_3 f = \sum x_1 x_2 f \\ A\sum x_2 x_3 f + B\sum x_3^2 f = \sum x_1 x_3 f \end{cases}$$

Let s_i^2 be the variance of x_i and let r_{ij} be the correlation coefficient between x_i and x_j. Then by definition,

$$\sum x_i^2 f(x_1, x_2, x_3) = N s_i^2$$
$$\sum x_i x_j f(x_1, x_2, x_3) = N s_i s_j r_{ij}$$

So (11.52) becomes

(11.53) $$\begin{cases} NAs_2^2 + NBs_2s_3r_{23} = Ns_1s_2r_{12} \\ NAs_2s_3r_{23} + NBs_3^2 = Ns_1s_3r_{13} \end{cases}$$

Solving for A and B we have

$$A = \frac{s_1}{s_2} \frac{\begin{vmatrix} r_{12} & r_{23} \\ r_{13} & 1 \end{vmatrix}}{\begin{vmatrix} 1 & r_{23} \\ r_{23} & 1 \end{vmatrix}}$$

$$B = \frac{s_1}{s_3} \frac{\begin{vmatrix} 1 & r_{12} \\ r_{23} & r_{13} \end{vmatrix}}{\begin{vmatrix} 1 & r_{23} \\ r_{23} & 1 \end{vmatrix}}$$

It is convenient both for simplicity and for the purpose of generalizing to k variables to define the determinant R by

$$R = \begin{vmatrix} r_{11} & r_{12} & r_{13} \\ r_{21} & r_{22} & r_{23} \\ r_{31} & r_{32} & r_{33} \end{vmatrix}$$

and to let R_{ij} be the cofactor of r_{ij}. Thus,

$$R_{12} = -\begin{vmatrix} r_{21} & r_{23} \\ r_{31} & r_{33} \end{vmatrix}$$

$$R_{13} = \begin{vmatrix} r_{21} & r_{22} \\ r_{31} & r_{32} \end{vmatrix}$$

Clearly, $r_{11} = r_{22} = r_{33} = 1$, and $r_{12} = r_{21}$, etc., so the expressions for A and B may be written

$$A = -\frac{s_1 R_{12}}{s_2 R_{11}}$$

$$B = -\frac{s_1 R_{13}}{s_3 R_{11}}$$

Hence (11.50) becomes

(11.54) $$\frac{x_1}{s_1} R_{11} + \frac{x_2}{s_2} R_{12} + \frac{x_3}{s_3} R_{13} = 0$$

This equation gives the estimate of x_1 for assigned values of x_2 and x_3, provided that the true regression is not far from being linear. It is an important equation because it shows how, on the average, changes in x_2 and x_3 affect x_1. The student will observe that the R's involve only simple correlation coefficients and that all the necessary computations for the terms in (11.54) were explained in Part I.

There are two analogous equations for the regression planes of x_2 on x_1 and x_3, and x_3 on x_1 and x_2, which can be obtained readily from (11.54) by a cyclical permutation of the subscripts on x and R. They are

Sec. 10 Geometrical Picture of Multiple Regression

(11.55) $$\frac{x_2}{s_2} R_{22} + \frac{x_3}{s_3} R_{23} + \frac{x_1}{s_1} R_{21} = 0$$

when x_2 is the dependent variable, and

(11.56) $$\frac{x_3}{s_3} R_{33} + \frac{x_1}{s_1} R_{31} + \frac{x_2}{s_2} R_{32} = 0$$

when x_3 is the dependent variable. Referred to an arbitrary origin (11.54) would have been

(11.57) $$\frac{X_1 - \bar{X}_1}{s_1} R_{11} + \frac{X_2 - \bar{X}_2}{s_2} R_{12} + \frac{X_3 - \bar{X}_3}{s_3} R_{13} = 0$$

where $X_i - \bar{X}_i = x_i$. Analogous adjustments of (11.55) and (11.56) are obvious when the variables are referred to an arbitrary origin.

The three-dimensional case can now be generalized. By methods similar to those employed above we can derive the linear regression equation for k variables. Thus we have the hyperplane x_1 on $x_2, x_3, \cdots, x_k$,

(11.58) $$\frac{x_1}{s_1} R_{11} + \frac{x_2}{s_2} R_{12} + \cdots + \frac{x_k}{s_k} R_{1k} = 0$$

where R_{ij} is the cofactor of r_{ij} in

(11.59) $$R = \begin{vmatrix} r_{11} & \cdots & r_{1k} \\ & r_{22} & \\ \cdots & \cdots & \cdots \\ r_{k1} & \cdots & r_{kk} \end{vmatrix}$$

When expressed in standard units, (11.58) becomes

(11.60) $$t_1 = -\frac{1}{R_{11}} \sum_{i=2}^{k} R_{1i} t_i$$

where $t_i = x_i/s_i$. Then t_1 may be regarded as a weighted mean of the contributions of the other variables. The factor R_{1i} represents the force or weight of t_i when all these variables are given an opportunity to predict the value of t_1.

It may be noted that (11.58) is simply a rewriting in different notation of the regression equation (10.1), in which the b_j are given by (10.20). For if the x's are all measured from their means and if y is written as x_1, we have

$$a_{ij} = r_{ij} s_i s_j, \qquad g_j = r_{1j} s_1 s_j, \qquad (i, j = 2, 3, \cdots k)$$

Then in the equation

(11.61) $$x_1 = b_2 x_2 + b_3 x_3 + \cdots + b_k x_k$$

the b_i are given by $b_i = \sum_j a^{ij} g_j$. By writing out the matrix $A = [a_{ij}]$, it is easily seen that its determinant is equal to $s_2^2 s_3^2 \cdots s_k^2 R_{11}$, so that $a_{ij} = R_{11 \cdot ij}/s_i s_j R_{11}$, where $R_{11 \cdot ij}$ is the cofactor of r_{ij} in R_{11}. Also by the rule for expanding determinants $\sum_{j=2}^{k} r_{1j}R_{11 \cdot ij}$ is equal to $-R_{i1}$, and hence $b_i = -s_1 R_{i1}/(s_i R_{11})$. Equation (11.61) can, therefore, be written

$$\frac{R_{11}x_1}{s_1} + \frac{R_{21}x_2}{s_2} + \cdots + \frac{R_{k1}x_k}{s_k} = 0$$

which, because of the symmetry of the correlation matrix, is equivalent to (11.58).

11.11 Variance about the Regression Plane. Let v be the distance, measured parallel to the x_1-axis, between the regression plane and the point (x_1, x_2, x_3). That is, $v = $ observed $x_1 - $ estimated x_1, where the estimated x_1 is given by (11.54). Let

(11.62) $$s_{1.23}^2 = \frac{1}{N} \sum v^2 f(x_1, x_2, x_3)$$

where $\sum$ denotes summation over all the points (x_1, x_2, x_3). Then

$$Ns_{1.23}^2 = \sum f \left\{ x_1 + \frac{s_1}{R_{11}} \left(\frac{R_{12}}{s_2} x_2 + \frac{R_{13}}{s_3} x_3 \right) \right\}^2$$
$$= \left(\frac{s_1}{R_{11}} \right)^2 \sum f \left(\frac{R_{11}x_1}{s_1} + \frac{R_{12}x_2}{s_2} + \frac{R_{13}x_3}{s_3} \right)^2$$

Since $\sum f x_1^2 = N s_1^2$, $\sum f x_1 x_2 = N r_{12} s_1 s_2$, etc., we have

$$s_{1.23}^2 = \left(\frac{s_1}{R_{11}} \right)^2 (R_{11}^2 + R_{12}^2 + R_{13}^2 + 2R_{11}R_{12}r_{12} + 2R_{11}R_{13}r_{13} + 2R_{12}R_{13}r_{23})$$
$$= \left(\frac{s_1}{R_{11}} \right)^2 [R_{11}(R_{11} + r_{12}R_{12} + r_{13}R_{13}) + R_{12}(R_{12} + r_{12}R_{11} + r_{23}R_{13})$$
$$\quad + R_{13}(R_{13} + r_{13}R_{11} + r_{23}R_{12})]$$
$$= \left(\frac{s_1}{R_{11}} \right)^2 R_{11} R$$

by the familiar rules for determinants. Hence we have

(11.63) $$s_{1.23}^2 = s_1^2 \frac{R}{R_{11}}$$

The square root of this is usually called the *standard error of estimate* of x_1 for assigned values of x_2 and x_3. As in the corresponding case of two variables (see §§ 8.6 and 8.7), $s_{1.23}^2 \frac{N}{N-3}$ is an unbiased estimate of the corresponding population parameter $\sigma_1^2 P/P_{11}$, where P is the determinant $|\rho_{ij}|$, $i, j = 1, 2, 3$, and P_{11} is the cofactor of ρ_{11} in P. Moreover, as in § 8.9, the sampling error of the coefficients in the regression equation introduces additional terms into the standard error of estimate of x_1, so that the s.e. of an observed x_1 is actually given by the square root of

$$\frac{N}{N-3} s_{1.23}^2 \left[1 + \frac{1}{N} + \frac{x_2^2}{Ns_2^2} + \frac{x_3^2}{Ns_3^2} \right]$$

Sec. 13   The Multiple Correlation Coefficient   345

11.12 Variance Due to Regression. The variance of x_1 due to the regression (11.54) is given by

$$s_{123}^2 = \frac{1}{N}\sum fx_1^2$$

where x_1 is the estimated value from (11.54). Hence, as in § 11.11,

$$s_{123}^2 = \left(\frac{s_1}{R_{11}}\right)^2 (R_{12}^2 + R_{13}^2 + 2R_{12}R_{13}r_{23})$$

$$= \left(\frac{s_1}{R_{11}}\right)^2 [R_{12}(R_{12} + r_{23}R_{13}) + R_{13}(R_{13} + r_{23}R_{12})]$$

$$= \left(\frac{s_1}{R_{11}}\right)^2 [-R_{12}r_{12}R_{11} - R_{13}r_{13}R_{11}]$$

$$= \left(\frac{s_1}{R_{11}}\right)^2 R_{11}(R_{11} - R)$$

Consequently

(11.64) $$s_{123}^2 = s_1^2(1 - R/R_{11})$$

It follows from (11.63) and (11.64) that

(11.65) $$s_1^2 = s_{1.23}^2 + s_{123}^2$$

11.13 The Multiple Correlation Coefficient. With two variables the proportion of the total variance explained by regression is equal to r^2, where r is the ordinary coefficient of correlation. So here, the quantity

(11.66) $$r_{1.23}^2 = \frac{s_{123}^2}{s_1^2} = 1 - \frac{R}{R_{11}}$$

is the square of the *multiple correlation coefficient* of x_1 on x_2 and x_3. This coefficient may be regarded also as the ordinary correlation coefficient between the *observed* x_1 and the *estimated* x_1. If we denoted the estimated x_1 by x_{123}, we have for this correlation

$$r_{1.23} = \frac{\sum x_1 x_{123}}{N s_1 s_{123}} = \frac{1}{N R_{11} s_{123}} \sum x_1 \left(-\frac{R_{12}x_2}{s_2} - \frac{R_{13}x_3}{s_2}\right)$$

$$= -\frac{1}{R_{11}s_{123}}[R_{12}r_{12}s_1 + R_{13}r_{13}s_1]$$

$$= \frac{s_1}{s_{123}}\left(1 - \frac{R}{R_{11}}\right)$$

(11.67) $$= \left(1 - \frac{R}{R_{11}}\right)^{1/2}$$

which agrees with (11.66). By a cyclical permutation of the subscripts we can write at once the formulas for the multiple correlation coefficients of x_2 on x_1 and x_3, and of x_3 on x_1 and x_2. They are

(11.68) $$r_{2.31} = \left(1 - \frac{R}{R_{22}}\right)^{1/2}$$

(11.69) $$r_{3.12} = \left(1 - \frac{R}{R_{33}}\right)^{1/2}$$

By writing (11.63) in the form
$$s_{1.23}^2 = s_1^2\left\{1 - \left(1 - \frac{R}{R_{11}}\right)\right\}$$
we obtain the formula

(11.70) $$s_{1.23}^2 = s_1^2(1 - r_{1.23}^2)$$

which is quite analogous to the expression for $\sigma_{\cdot y}^2$ in simple correlation. It is clear from (11.70) that

(11.71) $$-1 \leq r_{1.23} \leq 1$$

Each of the formulas (11.67) to (11.69) may be generalized for k variables. Thus the multiple correlation coefficient of order $k - 1$ of x_1 with the other $k - 1$ variables is

(11.72) $$r_{1.23\cdots k} = \left(1 - \frac{R}{R_{11}}\right)^{1/2}$$

where now R_{ij} is the cofactor of r_{ij} in R as defined in (11.59).

Example 4. Three variables have in pairs simple correlation coefficients given by
$$r_{12} = 0.8 \qquad r_{13} = -0.7 \qquad r_{23} = -0.9$$
Find the multiple correlation coefficient $r_{1.23}$ of x_1 on x_2 and x_3.
Solution.
$$R = \begin{vmatrix} 1 & .8 & -.7 \\ .8 & 1 & -.9 \\ -.7 & -.9 & 1 \end{vmatrix} = 0.068$$
$$R_{11} = 0.19 \qquad r_{1.23} = 0.80$$

Example 5. Suppose it is found that $r_{12} = 0.6$, $r_{13} = -0.4$, $r_{23} = 0.7$. Comment on these results.

Solution. $R = -.346$, $R_{11} = .51$, $r_{1.23} = 1.29$. This is an impossible value of $r_{1.23}$. It is clear from equations (11.67) to (11.69) that R_{11}, R_{22}, and R_{33} must all have the same sign as R if the multiple correlation coefficients are to be numerically less than 1. In this example suspicion might be aroused by noting that while r_{12} and r_{23} are both fairly large and positive, r_{13} is fairly large and negative, contrary to what one would expect.

11.14 Some Limiting Cases of Multiple Correlation.

Theorem 11.1. *The necessary and sufficient condition for coincidence of the three regression planes* (11.54), (11.55), *and* (11.56) *is*

(11.73) $$r_{12}^2 + r_{13}^2 + r_{23}^2 - 2r_{12}r_{13}r_{23} = 1$$

For these planes are coincident if and only if the coefficients are proportional. This will be so if $R_{11}/R_{21} = R_{12}/R_{22} = R_{13}/R_{23}$ and $R_{21}/R_{31} = R_{22}/R_{32} = R_{23}/R_{33}$.

On writing out the cofactors in terms of r_{ij} it will be found that these relations are equivalent to (11.73).

Theorem 11.2. *If $r_{1.23} = \pm 1$, then* (11.73) *is satisfied and the regression is linear.*

Sec. 14 Some Limiting Cases of Multiple Correlation

For by (11.66) the condition for perfect multiple correlation is $R = 0$, and this is equivalent to (11.73).

Example 6. Given the following data, $r_{12} = 0.6$, $r_{13} = 0.4$. Find the value of r_{23} in order that $r_{1 \cdot 23} = 1$.

Solution. Substituting the given values in (11.73) we have

$$r^2 - 0.48r - 0.48 = 0,$$

where the subscripts are dropped for the moment. Solving, we find $r = 0.24 \pm 0.73$. So $r_{23} = 0.97$.

The example shows that even though r_{12} and r_{13} are individually small, it does not follow that there cannot be high correlation between x_1, x_2, and x_3. Indeed two variables which individually with a third variable have correlations which are apparently worthless for predicting purposes may be very valuable when the three variables are taken together and multiple regression employed. On the other hand, it may be possible to get as good a prediction from r_{12} or r_{13} using simple regression as from multiple regression. This situation will be clarified by the following theorems.

Theorem 11.3. *If $r_{23} = 1$, then $r_{1 \cdot 23}{}^2 = r_{12}{}^2 = r_{13}{}^2$, and $s_{1 \cdot 23}{}^2 = s_1{}^2(1 - r_{12}{}^2)$.*

Proof: When $r_{23} = 1$, $R = 2r_{12}r_{13} - r_{12}{}^2 - r_{13}{}^2 = -(r_{12} - r_{13})^2$. But also in this case $R_{11} = 0$, so that $R = 0$ from (11.67). Hence $r_{12} = r_{13}$. Now when $r_{12} = r_{13}$ the general expression for $1 - \dfrac{R}{R_{11}}$ reduces to $\dfrac{2r_{12}{}^2}{1 + r_{23}}$ so that if we now put $r_{23} = 1$, (11.66) gives $r_{1 \cdot 23}{}^2 = r_{12}{}^2 = r_{13}{}^2$, and (11.63) gives $s_{1 \cdot 23}{}^2 = s_1{}^2(1 - r_{12}{}^2)$.

In this case, then, multiple regression has no advantage over the simple regression x_1 on x_2 or x_1 on x_3, because the standard error is exactly what it would be if the third variable were not added. Since $r_{23} = 1$, there is perfect linear dependence between x_2 and x_3. Geometrically, all the data lie in the regression plane.

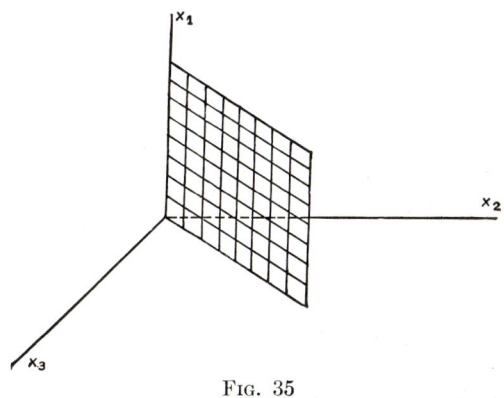

FIG. 35

Theorem 11.4. *If $r_{23} = 0$, then $r_{1.23}^2 = r_{12}^2 + r_{13}^2$.*

For $R_{11} = 1$, and $R = 1 - r_{12}^2 - r_{13}^2$, so that $1 - \dfrac{R}{R_{11}} = r_{12}^2 + r_{13}^2$.
Therefore

(11.74) $$s_{1.23}^2 = s_1^2(1 - r_{12}^2 - r_{13}^2)$$

Hence, when x_2 and x_3 are completely independent, multiple regression gives a better prediction than would be given by either of the simple regressions x_1 on x_2 or x_1 on x_3; very much better if also r_{12} and r_{13} are nearly equal. If they are exactly equal their maximum value is $(\tfrac{1}{2})^{1/2} = 0.707$. This theorem shows that one has a good regression equation for predicting when each of two variables is highly correlated with the third variable but not with the other.

11.15 The Distribution of the Multiple Correlation Coefficient for Samples from an Uncorrelated Parent Population. In the notation of Chapter X, the regression of y on the variables $x_1, x_2, \cdots x_p$ is given by

$$Y = \sum_i b_i x_i$$

and the multiple correlation coefficient of y with $x_1, x_2, \cdots x_p$ is

(11.75) $$r_{yY} = S(yY)/\{S(y^2)S(Y^2)\}^{1/2}$$

This is the ordinary correlation coefficient of the observed y values with the estimated Y values, measured from their means.

The normal equations for the regression coefficients b_i are

$$\sum_j a_{ij} b_j = g_i, \quad i = 1, 2 \cdots p$$

where

$$a_{ij} = Sx_{i\alpha}x_{j\alpha}, \quad g_i = Sx_{i\alpha}y_\alpha$$

For convenience we may suppose the variables standardized, so that the means are all 0 and the variances 1. If x_0 is written for y, we then have

$$a_{ij} = r_{ij}, \quad g_i = r_{i0}$$

and the normal equations become

(11.76) $$\sum_j r_{ij} b_j = r_{i0}$$

If the residuals v are given by $v = y - Y$,

$$\begin{aligned} S(vx_i) &= S(y - Y)x_i = S(x_0 - \sum b_j x_j)x_i \\ &= r_{0i} - \sum b_j r_{ij} \\ &= 0, \text{ by (11.76)} \end{aligned}$$

Hence $S(vY) = \sum_i b_i S(vx_i) = 0$, and therefore, since $S(vY) = S(yY) - S(Y^2)$,

(11.77) $$S(yY) = S(Y^2)$$

Sec. 16   Coefficient for a Correlated Parent Population   349

Now
$$S(v^2) = S(y^2 - 2yY + Y^2)$$
$$= S(y^2) - 2S(yY) + S(Y^2)$$
$$= S(y^2) - S(Y^2)$$

by (11.77), so that from (11.75) we have

(11.78) $$r_{yY}^2 = \frac{S(Y^2)}{S(v^2) + S(Y^2)}$$

This may be written

(11.79) $$r_{yY}^2 / (1 - r_{yY}^2) = S(Y^2)/S(v^2)$$

If the $x_1, x_2, \cdots x_p$ all have a fixed set of values and if y is a random normal variate independent of $x_1 \cdots x_p$ (that is, the multiple correlation coefficient in the parent population is zero) then $S(Y^2)$ and $S(v^2)$ are independently distributed as χ^2 with p and $N - p - 1$ degrees of freedom. Hence the quantity

(11.80) $$F = \frac{S(Y^2)}{S(v^2)} \frac{N - p - 1}{p}$$

is distributed as Snedecor's F with p and $N - p - 1$ df. This means that r_{yY}^2 is a Beta-variate with parameters $\frac{1}{2}(N - p - 1)$ and $\frac{1}{2}p$. The distribution of r_{yY}^2 is, therefore, identical with that of the square of the correlation ratio, E^2 (see § 11.1), with $p + 1$ instead of p. We are now dealing with $p + 1$ variables, y and $x_1, x_2, \cdots x_p$ and so have p degrees of freedom for the regression of y on the x's.

11.16 The Distribution of the Multiple Correlation Coefficient for a Correlated Parent Population. A geometrical picture of multiple correlation may be helpful to some readers. For the jth variate x_j we have N observations such as $x_{j\alpha}$ ($\alpha = 1, 2, \cdots N$). In a flat (Euclidean) space of N dimensions the whole set of observations may be represented by a single point, of coordinates $x_{j\alpha}$, or by a single vector joining this point to the origin.

If the $x_{j\alpha}$ are measured from their mean the square of the length of this vector is equal to Ns_j^2, where s_j is the standard deviation of x_j. Also if Ox_i and Ox_j are the vectors corresponding to the variates x_i and x_j, the cosine of the angle between them is equal to $S(x_{i\alpha}x_{j\alpha})/[S(x_{i\alpha}^2)S(x_{j\alpha}^2)]^{\frac{1}{2}} = r_{ij}$, the correlation coefficient for x_i and x_j.

If we consider the case of $p = 2$, the two vectors Ox_1 and Ox_2 will determine a plane (Fig. 36) and the vector OY, where $Y = b_1 x_1 + b_2 x_2$, will lie in this plane.

The vector Oy will in general lie outside the plane, but since OY is determined so as to make $S(y - Y)^2$ a minimum, Y is the foot of the perpendicular from y on to this plane. If θ is the angle between Oy and OY,

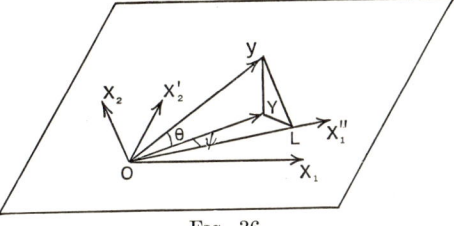

Fig. 36

$$\cos \theta = S(yY)/\{S(y^2) \cdot S(Y^2)\}^{1/2}$$

and so is equal to the multiple correlation coefficient of y with x_1 and x_2. If the number of predictors (p) is greater than 2, the same general picture holds, but there is no unique perpendicular to the space determined by $x_1, x_2, \cdots x_p$. There is instead a $(p-1)$-dimensional sub-space, but we will not pursue this matter further.

It was proved by Fisher [13] that the distribution of r_{yY} for a given sample size and for a given number of predictors is a function of the multiple correlation coefficient ρ in the parent population, and of this alone. To show this, we first apply to the x_j a non-singular linear transformation so as to get new variables x_j' which are *uncorrelated*. We may, for example, let $x_1' = x_1$, $x_2' = x_{2.1}$ (the deviations of x_2 from the regression of x_2 on x_1), $x_3' = x_{3.21}$ (the deviations from the regression of x_3 on x_2 and x_1), and so on. This transformation will leave Y and therefore r_{yY} invariant. Geometrically it consists in choosing new vectors Ox_j' which are mutually perpendicular, but the angle θ of Figure 36 is unchanged.

We can now apply an orthogonal transformation so that the correlation between y and one of the new variables x_1'' is a maximum *in the parent population*. Then y is uncorrelated with all the other new variables and the multiple correlation coefficient becomes the ordinary correlation coefficient ρ between y and x_1''. Since all the other correlations in the parent population are now zero, and since these transformations leave r_{yY} invariant, the frequency function of r_{yY} must be a function of ρ.

The function is a complicated one, namely,

$$(11.81) \quad f(r^2) = (1-\rho^2)^{\frac{N-1}{2}} (1-r^2)^{\frac{N-p-3}{2}} (r^2)^{\frac{p-2}{2}}$$
$$\times F\left(\frac{N-1}{2}, \frac{N-1}{2}, \frac{p}{2}; \rho^2 r^2\right) \, \mathrm{B}\left(\frac{p}{2}, \frac{N-p-1}{2}\right)$$

where r is written for r_{yY}, F is the hypergeometric function and B is the Beta function. For $\rho = 0$, r^2 is a Beta-variate.

It may be proved that the expected value of r_{yY}^2 is given by

$$(11.82) \quad E(r_{yY}^2) = 1 - \frac{N-p-1}{N-1}(1-\rho^2) F\left(1, 1, \frac{N+1}{2}; \rho^2\right)$$
$$= 1 - \frac{N-p-1}{N-1}(1-\rho^2)\left(1 + \frac{2\rho^2}{N+1} + \frac{8\rho^4}{(N+1)(N+3)} + \cdots\right)$$

which, when $\rho = 0$, reduces to

$$(11.83) \quad E(r_{yY}^2) = \frac{p}{N-1}$$

11.17 Partial Correlation. Assume, as before, that the variables x_1, x_2, x_3 are referred to their own means as origin. Suppose that we wish to know what the correlation between x_1 and x_2 would be if the influence of x_3 were eliminated.

Sec. 17   Partial Correlation

Let us subtract from the x_1 of each point that part of x_1 which is due to the influence of x_3, as indicated by the regression of x_1 on x_3, and denote the residual by $x_{1.3}$. Thus we have

(11.84)
$$\begin{cases} x_{1.3} = x_1 - r_{13}\dfrac{s_1}{s_3}x_3 \\ x_{2.3} = x_2 - r_{23}\dfrac{s_2}{s_3}x_3 \end{cases}$$

We now define the *partial correlation coefficient* ($r_{12.3}$) of x_1 and x_2 in the trivariate distribution of x_1, x_2 and x_3 as the ordinary correlation coefficient of $x_{1.3}$ and $x_{2.3}$. By definition,

(11.85)
$$r_{12.3} = \frac{\sum x_{1.3}x_{2.3}f(x_1, x_2, x_3)}{N s_{1.3} s_{2.3}}$$

The numerator may be written, using (11.84), as

$$\sum x_1 x_2 f - r_{13}\frac{s_1}{s_3}\sum x_2 x_3 f - r_{23}\frac{s_2}{s_3}\sum x_1 x_3 f + r_{13}r_{23}\frac{s_1 s_2}{s_3^2}\sum x_3^2 f$$
$$= N s_1 s_2 (r_{12} - r_{13}r_{23} - r_{23}r_{13} + r_{13}r_{23})$$
$$= N s_1 s_2 (r_{12} - r_{13}r_{23})$$

In the denominator of (11.85), $s_{1.3}^2$ is the residual variance of x_1 after eliminating the regression on x_3, and hence

(11.86) $$s_{1.3}^2 = s_1^2(1 - r_{13}^2)$$

Similarly

(11.87) $$s_{2.3}^2 = s_2^2(1 - r_{23}^2)$$

Substituting in (11.85) we obtain the result

(11.88) $$r_{12.3} = \frac{r_{12} - r_{13}r_{23}}{[(1 - r_{13}^2)(1 - r_{23}^2)]^{1/2}} = -\frac{R_{12}}{[R_{11}R_{22}]^{1/2}}$$

If $b_{12.3}$ and $b_{21.3}$ are the *partial regression coefficients* of $x_{1.3}$ on $x_{2.3}$ and of $x_{2.3}$ on $x_{1.3}$ respectively,

(11.89)
$$\begin{cases} b_{12.3} = \dfrac{\sum x_{1.3}x_{2.3}f}{\sum x_{2.3}^2 f} = r_{12.3}\dfrac{s_{1.3}}{s_{2.3}} \\ b_{21.3} = \dfrac{\sum x_{1.3}x_{2.3}f}{\sum x_{1.3}^2 f} = r_{12.3}\dfrac{s_{2.3}}{s_{1.3}} \end{cases}$$

so that

(11.90) $$r_{12.3}^2 = b_{12.3}b_{21.3}$$

From equations (11.86) to (11.89) we readily obtain

$$b_{12.3} = -\frac{s_1}{s_2}\frac{R_{12}}{R_{11}}$$

and hence $b_{12.3}$ is identical with the b_2 of equation (11.61). In the same way, $b_{13.2} = b_3$, so that in the present notation the regression plane of x_1 on x_2 and x_3 may be written

$$x_1 = b_{12.3}x_2 + b_{13.2}x_3$$

The partial correlation coefficient may also be regarded as the correlation between x_1 and x_2 *when x_3 is held constant*. That is, we limit attention to a sub-set of the whole set of observations, a slab parallel to the x_1x_2 plane, and calculate the ordinary correlation coefficient for this sub-set. A classical example is the correlation between statures of fathers and sons, when the stature of the mother has a particular value, say 62 inches.

The partial correlation coefficient defined in this way depends in general, however, on the value of x_3 selected. Necessary and sufficient conditions that this coefficient is independent of x_3, and is equal to $r_{12.3}$ as defined by (11.85), are that:

(a) The bivariate regression of x_1 on x_3 (ignoring x_2) is linear, and the standard deviations of all the x_1 arrays (x_3 constant) are equal.

(b) The trivariate regression of x_1 on x_2 and x_3 is linear and the standard deviation of all the x_1 arrays (x_2 and x_3 constant) are equal.

If these conditions are satisfied, and if $r_{12.3}$ is the correlation coefficient for x_1 and x_2 with x_3 constant,

$$s_{1.23}^2 = s_{1.3}^2(1 - r_{12.3}^2)$$

and

$$s_{1.3}^2 = s_1^2(1 - r_{13}^2) = s_1^2 R_{22}$$

By (11.66) and (11.70), $s_{1.23}^2 = s_1^2 R/R_{11}$, so that $1 - r_{12.3}^2 = R/R_{11}R_{22}$, whence $r_{12.3}^2 = R_{12}^2/R_{11}R_{22}$, in agreement with (11.88).

Tables of $(1 - r^2)^{1/2}$ and of $1 - r^2$ have been prepared by J. R. Miner [14] to facilitate the computation of $r_{12.3}$. By letting $\sin \theta = r$, $\cos \theta = (1 - r^2)^{1/2}$, one can use ordinary trigonometric tables for the same purpose.

The conditions (a) and (b) given above are not likely to be satisfied very accurately in practical applications. The calculated value of $r_{12.3}$ will be a sort of average value of the correlations which could be obtained for all assignments of x_3.

Example 7. In a study of the factors which influence "academic success," May [15] obtained the following results (among others) based on the records of 450 students at Syracuse University.

X_1 = honor points X_2 = general intelligence X_3 = hours of study
$\bar{X}_1 = 18.5$ $\bar{X}_2 = 100.6$ $\bar{X}_3 = 24$
$s_1 = 11.2$ $s_2 = 15.8$ $s_3 = 6$
$r_{12} = 0.60$ $r_{13} = 0.32$ $r_{23} = -0.35$

One purpose of the study was to find to what extent honor points were related to general intelligence, when hours of study (per week) are held constant. Using (11.88) it is found that $r_{12.3} = 0.80$.

Sec. 19   Distribution of Partial Correlation Coefficient   353

The other partial correlations are $r_{13.2} = 0.71$, $r_{23.1} = -0.72$, so that for all three pairs of variates the correlations are stronger when the effect of the third variable is eliminated.

11.18 Partial Correlations with k Variables. The formulas of § 11.17 may be extended to more than three variates. If there are k variates altogether, the partial correlation coefficient of x_1 and x_2, with all the rest eliminated, is denoted by $r_{12.34\ldots k}$ and defined as the ordinary correlation coefficient between the residuals v_1 and v_2 for the multiple regressions of x_1 and x_2 on the other variates. This definition gives

$$(11.91) \qquad r_{12.34\ldots k} = - R_{12}/(R_{11}R_{22})^{1/2}$$

where R_{ij} is the cofactor of r_{ij} in the k-rowed determinant (11.59).

Partial correlations may be defined of all orders from 1 to $k - 2$. Thus when $k = 4$, there will be two first-order partial correlations of x_1 and x_2, namely, $r_{12.3}$ and $r_{12.4}$, and a second-order partial correlation $r_{12.34}$. A partial correlation of any order may be expressed in terms of partial correlations of order one lower, by a relation similar to (11.88). For example,

$$(11.92) \qquad r_{12.34} = \frac{r_{12.4} - r_{13.4}r_{23.4}}{[(1 - r_{13.4}^2)(1 - r_{23.4}^2)]^{1/2}}$$

11.19 The Distribution of the Partial Correlation Coefficient. As already described, the set of values $x_{1\alpha}$ ($\alpha = 1, 2, \cdots N$) may be regarded as fixing a point X_1 or a vector OX_1 in N-dimensional space. If these values are all measured from their mean, $Sx_{1\alpha} = 0$, so that one degree of freedom is lost, and the point X_1 is in a space of $N - 1$ dimensions. (X_1 is the projection of the original X_1 on the hyperplane $Sx_{1\alpha} = 0$.)

Let OX_1, OX_2, OX_3 (Figure 37) represent the sets of values of x_1, x_2, x_3 in this $(N - 1)$-dimensional space. If X_1A and X_2B are drawn perpendicular to OX_3, X_1A and X_2B represent the vectors $X_{1.3}$ and $X_{2.3}$ respectively, which are such that $Sx_{1.3}^2$ and $Sx_{2.3}^2$ are minimized. If then θ is the dihedral angle between the planes X_1OX_3 and X_2OX_3, $\cos \theta$ is the coefficient of partial correlation between x_1 and x_2, with x_3 eliminated. From the diagram we see that θ is the angle between the projections of OX_1 and OX_2 on the $(N - 2)$-dimensional space perpendicular to OX_3. It follows that the sampling distribution of $r_{12.3}$ is the same as that of r_{12} (see (8.68)), but with $N - 2$ instead of $N - 1$ and with $\rho_{12.3}$ instead of ρ. With k variables altogether the distribution of $r_{12.3\ldots k}$ has $N - k + 1$ instead of $N - 1$.

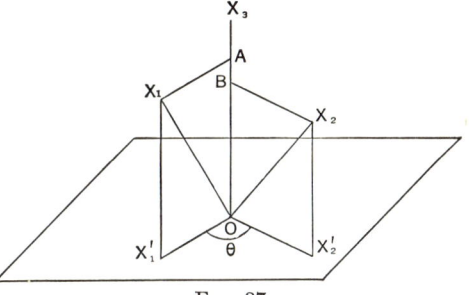

Fig. 37

Further discussion of the trigonometrical aspects of correlation will be found in a paper by Dunham Jackson.[16]

11.20 Correlograms. In a time series where a variable x is measured as a function of the time t, it will often happen that the observations are correlated. The graph of $r_{x_1 x_2}$ as a function of the time $(t_2 - t_1)$ between x_1 and x_2 is called a *correlogram*. A theoretical correlogram is shown in Figure 38. This model arises if we suppose that only *consecutive* observations really influence each other. That is, the partial correlation between x_1 and x_3, eliminating the influence of x_2, is zero.

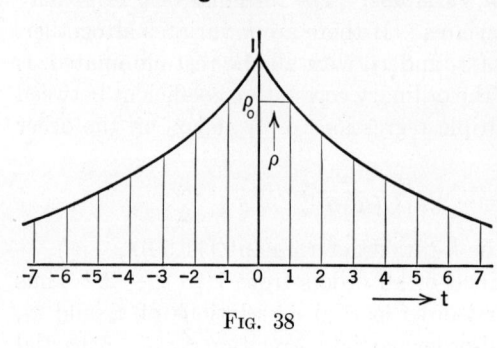

FIG. 38

Since
$$\rho_{13.2} = \frac{\rho_{13} - \rho_{12}\rho_{23}}{[(1 - \rho_{12}^2)(1 - \rho_{23}^2)]^{1/2}} = 0$$

this implies that $\rho_{13} = \rho_{12}\rho_{23}$. If the correlation is constant between successive consecutive pairs of members of the time series, $\rho_{23} = \rho_{12}$, so that $\rho_{13} = \rho_{12}^2$. In the same way, $\rho_{14.23} = 0$, implying $\rho_{14.3} = \rho_{12.3}\rho_{24.3}$, whence we readily obtain $\rho_{14} = \rho_{12}^3$. In general $\rho_{\alpha\beta} = \rho_{12}^{|\alpha-\beta|}$. If the observation x_α corresponds to $t = \alpha$, and if $\rho_{12} = \rho_0$, the correlation between two observations separated by time t is given by
$$\rho = \rho_0^{|t|}$$

This is the curve shown in Figure 38.

Given a set of values such as the x_α, correlated in this way, we can form a new set of uncorrelated quantities by means of a linear transformation. Thus, if all the x_α have the same variance σ^2 and if x_α and x_β have covariance $\sigma^2 \rho^{|\alpha-\beta|}$ let us put
$$y_1 = x_1(1 - \rho^2)^{1/2}$$
$$y_2 = x_2 - \rho x_1$$
$$\cdots\cdots\cdots\cdots$$
$$y_N = x_N - \rho x_{N-1}$$

Then
$$\text{Var}(y_1) = \sigma^2(1 - \rho^2)$$
$$\text{Var}(y_2) = \sigma^2(1 - 2\rho^2 + \rho^2) = \sigma^2(1 - \rho^2)$$
$$\cdots\cdots\cdots\cdots\cdots\cdots\cdots\cdots$$
$$\text{Var}(y_N) = \sigma^2(1 - \rho^2)$$

Also
$$\text{Cov}(y_1, y_j) = (1 - \rho^2)^{1/2}\sigma^2(\rho^{j-1} - \rho \cdot \rho^{j-2}) = 0$$

and
$$\text{Cov}(y_i, y_j) = \sigma^2[\rho^{j-i} - \rho \cdot \rho^{j-i-1} - \rho \cdot \rho^{j-i+1} + \rho^2 \cdot \rho^{j-i}]$$
$$= 0, \; 2 \leq i < j \leq N$$

Sec. 21   Discriminant Functions   355

Hence the quantities $y_1, y_2, \cdots y_N$ are uncorrelated and have a common variance $\sigma^2(1 - \rho^2)$. The ordinary least squares theory can be applied to these new variables. Thus if we wish to construct a regression equation for a variable x_0 in terms of $x_1, x_3, \cdots x_p$, and if successive observations on all these variables are correlated in the manner described above, the regression equation will be of the form

$$Y_\alpha = \sum_j b_j y_{j\alpha} = \sum_j b_j(x_{j\alpha} - \rho x_{j,\alpha-1})$$

and will be used to predict values of $x_{0\alpha} - \rho x_{0,\alpha-1}$, instead of $x_{0\alpha}$.

11.21 Discriminant Functions. Suppose we have several criteria $x_1, x_2, \cdots x_p$, each of which may be used to distinguish between two populations, I and II. Thus for x_1 the two population distributions may be somewhat as shown in Figure 39. It is obvious that, since these overlap, we shall sometimes make a mistake in allotting an individual to one of the two populations on the basis of the x_1 value alone. The problem arises, therefore, of finding what function of $x_1, x_2, \cdots x_p$ will give the smallest probability of error in assigning individuals to one or the other of these two populations. An example is the use of aptitude tests, intelligence tests, and the like, to make an appraisal of a student's chance of success in, say, a university engineering course. On the basis of these tests a student may be classified as I (likely to make a success of engineering) or II (unlikely to do so). The vocational adviser wishes to know what function of the test-scores available will serve to discriminate most accurately between these two classes.

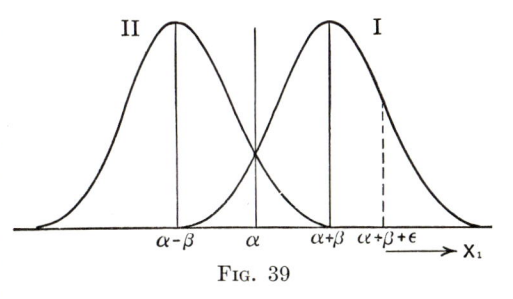

Fig. 39

If the two distributions in Figure 39 are adjusted in scale so that the area of each is unity, we should naturally take α as the dividing point for classification. An individual with an x_1 greater than α would be put in population I. The probability of mis-classifying a II as a I would be $1 - \Phi(\beta)$, where

$$\Phi(\beta) = (2\pi)^{-1/2} \int_{-\infty}^\beta e^{-t^2/2}\, dt,$$

the distributions being assumed normal. The probability of mis-classifying a I as a II is identical. If $\beta = 0$, this probability is $\frac{1}{2}$, and therefore there is no effective discrimination.

If we imagine a hypothetical perfect discriminant y which can take only two values -1 and $+1$, -1 for all individuals in II and $+1$ for all individuals in I, and if

$$x_1 = \alpha + \beta y + \epsilon$$

where ϵ is normally distributed about zero, we have the situation depicted in Figure 39. It is necessary that the β of this regression equation shall be significantly greater than zero, if x_1 is to serve as a useful discriminant.

In the more general case, suppose that there are N_1 and N_2 individuals in the populations I and II respectively, and that there are p variates $x_1, x_2, \cdots x_p$ which may serve as criteria for discrimination. The hypothetical perfect discriminant y may be supposed to take the value $\dfrac{N_2}{N_1 + N_2}$ for all individuals in I and $-\dfrac{N_1}{N_1 + N_2}$ for all in II. This ensures that $\bar{y} = 0$ for the combined populations. If now we calculate the regression equation of y on $x_1, x_2, \cdots x_p$, say $Y = \sum_{i=1}^{p} b_i x_i$, then Y will be the best possible linear combination of the x_i for discriminating between I and II. It will give the best estimate of the perfect discriminant y. It is called the *discriminant function*.

Let $x_{ir\alpha}$ be the αth value of x_i for the rth population, so that r is either 1 or 2, and $\alpha = 1, 2, \cdots N_r$. Let $\bar{x}_{i1}$ be the mean of x_i for population I and $\bar{x}_{i2}$ the mean for population II. It is supposed as usual that the mean of x_i for the *combined* population is zero. Then the least squares criterion for the choice of the b_i is that

$$\sum_r S_\alpha (y_{r\alpha} - \sum_i b_i x_{ir\alpha})^2 = \min$$

Differentiating with respect to b_i and putting the derivatives equal to zero, we obtain the normal equations

$$\sum_r S_\alpha x_{ir\alpha}(y_{r\alpha} - \sum_j b_j x_{jr\alpha}) = 0, \quad i = 1, 2, \cdots p$$

or

(11.93) $$\sum_j a_{ij} b_j = g_i, \quad i = 1, 2, \cdots p$$

where

(11.94) $$a_{ij} = \sum_r S_\alpha x_{ir\alpha} x_{jr\alpha}$$

and

(11.95) $$g_i = \sum_r S_\alpha x_{ir\alpha} y_{r\alpha}$$

Since when $r = 1$, $y_{r\alpha} = N_2/(N_1 + N_2)$ and when $r = 2$, $y_{r\alpha} = -N_1/(N_1 + N_2)$ for all α, we have from (11.95)

$$g_i = \frac{N_2}{N_1 + N_2} S x_{i1\alpha} - \frac{N_1}{N_1 + N_2} S x_{i2\alpha}$$

$$= \frac{N_1 N_2}{N_1 + N_2} (\bar{x}_{i1} - \bar{x}_{i2})$$

(11.96) $$= \lambda^2 d_i$$

where $\lambda^2 = N_1 N_2/(N_1 + N_2)$ and $d_i = \bar{x}_{i1} - \bar{x}_{i2}$, the distance between the means of the two populations for the variate x_i. Again, from (11.94),

Sec. 21 Discriminant Functions 357

$$a_{ij} = \underset{\alpha}{S} x_{i1\alpha} x_{j1\alpha} + \underset{\alpha}{S} x_{i2\alpha} x_{j2\alpha}$$
$$= \underset{\alpha}{S}\{(x_{i1\alpha} - \bar{x}_{i1})(x_{j1\alpha} - \bar{x}_{j1}) + (x_{i2\alpha} - \bar{x}_{i2})(x_{j2\alpha} - \bar{x}_{j2})\}$$
$$+ N_1 \bar{x}_{i1} \bar{x}_{j1} + N_2 \bar{x}_{i2} \bar{x}_{j2}$$

Let us denote the combined sum of products for the variables x_i and x_j for the two populations taken separately by S_{ij}. Then

(11.97) $$a_{ij} = S_{ij} + N_1 \bar{x}_{i1} \bar{x}_{j1} + N_2 \bar{x}_{i2} \bar{x}_{j2}$$

Now since the mean of x_i for the whole population is zero,

$$N_1 \bar{x}_{i1} + N_2 \bar{x}_{i2} = 0$$

that is,

$$N_1 \bar{x}_{i1} + N_2 (\bar{x}_{i1} - d_i) = 0$$

or

(11.98) $$\bar{x}_{i1} = \frac{N_2 d_i}{N_1 + N_2} = \lambda^2 \frac{d_i}{N_1}$$

Similarly $\bar{x}_{i2} = \lambda^2 d_i / N_2$. Hence from (11.97)

$$a_{ij} = S_{ij} + \lambda^4 d_i d_j \left(\frac{1}{N_1} + \frac{1}{N_2} \right)$$
(11.99) $$= S_{ij} + \lambda^2 d_i d_j$$

The normal equations (11.93), therefore, become, on substituting from (11.96) and (11.99),

$$\sum_j b_i (S_{ij} + \lambda^2 d_i d_j) = \lambda^2 d_i$$

or

(11.100) $$\sum_j b_j S_{ij} = \lambda^2 d_i (1 - \sum b_j d_j)$$

If the matrix $[S^{ij}]$ is the inverse of the matrix $[S_{ij}]$, it follows that the b_j are proportional to $\sum_k d_k S^{jk}$. If α^2 is the constant of proportionality, we have from (11.100) that

$$\alpha^2 \sum_{j,k} d_k S_{ij} S^{jk} = \lambda^2 d_i (1 - \alpha^2 \sum_{j,k} d_j d_k S^{jk})$$

and since $\sum_j S_{ij} S^{jk} = \delta_i{}^k$, this becomes

$$\alpha^2 d_i = \lambda^2 d_i (1 - \alpha^2 D^2)$$

where

(11.101) $$D^2 = \sum_{j,k} d_j d_k S^{jk}$$

so that

(11.102) $$\alpha^2 = \lambda^2 / (1 + \lambda^2 D^2)$$

The significance of the regression may be tested by the usual methods. The total sum of squares for y is

(11.103) $$S(y^2) = N_1\left(\frac{N_2}{N_1+N_2}\right)^2 + N_2\left(\frac{N_1}{N_1+N_2}\right)^2$$
$$= \lambda^2$$

The sum of squares due to regression is

(11.104) $$S(Y^2) = \sum_r S \sum_\alpha \sum_{i,j} b_i b_j x_{ir\alpha} x_{jr\alpha}$$
$$= \sum_{i,j} a_{ij} b_i b_j$$
$$= \sum_i b_i g_i$$
$$= \lambda^2 \sum b_i d_i, \quad \text{by (11.96)}$$
$$= \alpha^2 \lambda^2 D^2, \quad \text{by (11.101)}$$
$$= \lambda^2 - \alpha^2$$

Hence the residual sum of squares is
$$\lambda^2(1 - \alpha^2 D^2) = \alpha^2$$
and the analysis of variance is

	SS	df	MS
Regression	$\lambda^2 \sum b_i d_i$	p	$\lambda^2 \sum b_i d_i / p$
Residual	$\lambda^2(1 - \sum b_i d_i)$	$N_1 + N_2 - p - 1$	$\lambda^2(1 - \sum b_i d_i)/(N_1 + N_2 - p - 1)$
Total	λ^2	$N_1 + N_2 - 1$	

By the property of the multiple correlation coefficient given in (11.78) it is evident that the quantity $\sum b_i d_i$, which is the ratio of the sum of squares due to regression to the total sum of squares, is simply the square of the *multiple correlation coefficient* of y with $x_1, x_2, \cdots x_p$. That is,

$$r_{yY}^2 = \sum b_i d_i = \alpha^2 \sum d_i d_j S^{ij} = \alpha^2 D^2$$

so that the quantity D of (11.101) is proportional to the multiple correlation coefficient.

Although y is not a random variable while the x's are random variables (an inversion of the usual state of affairs), the F-test remains valid for the non-vanishing of the b_i.

Also, if s^2 is the residual mean square and if S^{ii} is the ith diagonal term in the matrix $[S^{ij}]$, then $b_i/s(S^{ii})^{1/2}$ is distributed as Student's t, with N_1+N_2-p-1 degrees of freedom, on the hypothesis that β_i (the true value of b_i) is zero.

We may also test a *theoretical discriminant function* with coefficients proposed arbitrarily. If Y_0 represents such a function, the regression on Y_0 will have only one degree of freedom, and the difference of the sum of squares for regression on Y and on Y_0 will have $p - 1$ degrees of freedom. The significance of

Sec. 21   Discriminant Functions

this difference may be estimated by the F-test, by comparison of the mean square for the difference of regressions and the residual mean square after allowing for regression on Y.

Example 8 (D. M. Seath). The amount of Dutch clover in a forage stand was estimated by a mechanical counter (x_1) and by eye (x_2). The two treatments to be discriminated were randomized in 15 blocks of two plots each, so that 14 df could be taken out for block differences, giving an analysis of variance:

	df	SS(x_1)	SS(x_2)	SP($x_1 x_2$)
Between populations	1	13.47	8.43	10.65
Between blocks	14	93.11	54.69	60.95
Within populations	14	20.44	6.41	4.89
Total	29	127.02	69.53	76.49

The SS and SP (sum of products) between populations are the quantities symbolized as $\lambda^2 d_i d_j (i, j = 1, 2)$, where $\lambda^2 = 15/2$. The quantities d_i were 1.34 and 1.06 respectively. The S_{ij} are now the sums of squares and products within populations, so that the a_{ij} of the normal equations are the sums of the items in the first and third rows of the above table. The normal equations are, therefore,

$$33.91 b_1 + 15.54 b_2 = 10.05$$
$$15.54 b_1 + 14.84 b_2 = 7.95$$

the solution of which is

$$b_1 = 0.0976, \quad b_2 = 0.4336$$

so that the best discriminant function is

$$Y = 0.09762 x_1 + 0.4336 x_2$$

The inverse matrix a^{ij} is

$$\begin{bmatrix} 0.0568 & -0.0595 \\ -0.0595 & 0.1297 \end{bmatrix}$$

The analysis of variance for the *perfect discriminant* is

	SS	df	MS
Regression	4.428	2	2.214
Residual	3.072	13	0.236
Total	7.5	15	

Note that in the above example

$$\sum b_i d_i = 0.0976(1.34) + 0.4335(1.06) = 0.590$$

so that $\lambda^2 \sum b_i d_i = 4.428$. From the residual mean square 0.236 and the inverse matrix a^{ij}, we obtain the standard errors of b_1 and b_2. These are respectively $(0.0568 \times 0.236)^{1/2} = 0.1158$ and $(0.1297 \times 0.236)^{1/2} = 0.1751$.

It is, therefore, clear that b_1 does not differ significantly from zero. The matrix S_{ij} is

$$\begin{bmatrix} 20.44 & 4.89 \\ 4.89 & 6.41 \end{bmatrix}$$

so that

$$S^{ij} = \begin{bmatrix} 0.0598 & -0.04565 \\ -0.04565 & 0.1908 \end{bmatrix}$$

Hence $D^2 = \sum d_i d_j S^{ij} = 0.1928$. The coefficient of correlation between y and Y is given by $r_{yY}^2 = 4.428/7.5 = 0.5904 = 3.072 D^2$.

Suppose we now ask whether the best discriminant is significantly better than a proposed discriminant, say $z = x_1 + x_2$. The SS for z is equal to $33.91 + 14.84 + 2 \times 15.54 = 79.83$. The SP for y and z is

$$S y x_1 + S y x_2 = \lambda^2 (d_1 + d_2) = 18.00$$

The coefficient of correlation between y and z is given by

$$r_{yz}^2 = \frac{(18.0)^2}{\frac{15}{2} \times 79.83} = 0.5411$$

so that the SS due to regression on z is $\lambda^2 \times 0.5411 = 4.058$.

We have then the following table:

	SS	df	MS
Regression on z	4.058	1	
Additional for regression on Y	0.370	1	0.370
Residual	0.072	13	0.236
Total	7.5	15	

The additional sum of squares for regression on Y over and above that on z is not significant. Hence $z = x_1 + x_2$ would be as good a discriminant as the one calculated, as far as the available data go.

Finally we may consider the analysis of variance for the *observed discriminant* Y. The total SS $= S(Y^2) = \lambda^2 \sum b_i d_i = 4.428$, and that between populations is $N_1 \overline{Y}_1^2 + N_2 \overline{Y}_2^2 = \lambda^2 (\sum b_i d_i)^2 = 2.614$, with 2 df since here $p = 2$. The analysis of variance is

	SS	df	MS
Between populations	2.614	2	1.307
Within populations	1.814	13	0.139
Total	4.428	15	

The standard error of the observed difference $\bar{Y}_1 - \bar{Y}_2$ is $(0.139)^{1/2} = 0.373$. Since the actual difference is $\sum b_i d_i = 0.590$, the significance of this difference can be estimated.

11.22 An Alternative Approach to Discriminant Functions. We may ask what linear function of the x_i, say

(11.105) $$L = \sum l_i x_i, \qquad i = 1, 2, \cdots p$$

will give the greatest possible value for the ratio of the sum of squares *between* populations to the sum of squares and products *within* populations. The sum of squares between populations for the variable x_i is

$$N_1 \bar{x}_{i1}^2 + N_2 \bar{x}_{i2}^2 = \lambda^4 d_i^2 \left(\frac{1}{N_1} + \frac{1}{N_2} \right) = \lambda^2 d_i^2$$

by (11.98). Hence the sum of squares between populations for L is

(11.106) $$B = \lambda^2 (\sum l_i d_i)^2 = \lambda^2 \sum_{i,j} l_i l_j d_i d_j$$

The SS for x_i and the SP for x_i, x_j, within the populations, are the quantities denoted above by S_{ii} and S_{ij}. Hence the total sum of squares and products within populations for L is

(11.107) $$W = \sum_{i,j} S_{ij} l_i l_j, \qquad (i, j = 1, 2, \cdots p)$$

We require to choose the l_i so as to make the ratio B/W a maximum. Since $\frac{\partial B}{\partial l_i} = 2\lambda^2 d_i \sum l_j d_j = 2\lambda B^{1/2} d_i$ and $\frac{\partial W}{\partial l_i} = 2 \sum_j S_{ij} l_j$, the condition $\frac{\partial}{\partial l_i} \left(\frac{B}{W} \right) = 0$ gives

$$\frac{\lambda B^{1/2}}{W} d_i - \frac{B}{W^2} \sum_j S_{ij} l_j = 0$$

or

(11.108) $$\sum_j S_{ij} l_j = \gamma d_i, \qquad i = 1, 2, \cdots p$$

where $\gamma = \lambda W B^{-1/2}$. Therefore

(11.109) $$l_j = \gamma \sum_i d_i S^{ij}$$

so that apart from a constant of proportionality, l_j is equal to b_j as given by the regression approach described in the previous section. The L of (11.105) is, therefore, in effect the same discriminant function as Y, since, of course, it is only the *ratio* of the coefficients that really matters in choosing a discriminant function.

Since from (11.107), (11.108), and (11.109)

$$W = \gamma \sum l_i d_i = \gamma^2 \sum d_i d_j S^{ij} = \frac{\lambda^2 W^2}{B} \sum d_i d_j S^{ij}$$

we have

$$\frac{B}{W} = \lambda^2 \sum d_i d_j S^{ij}$$

It was shown by Hotelling [18] that $\frac{B}{W} \frac{N_1 + N_2 - p - 1}{p}$ is distributed as Snedecor's F with p and $N_1 + N_2 - p - 1$ degrees of freedom, on the assumption that the populations are actually identical.

The discriminant function is closely related to a measure of *generalized distance* between two populations, proposed by Mahalanobis,[17] and also to a *generalized T-test*, suggested by Hotelling [18], for distinguishing between the means of different multivariate normal populations.

Given two samples of sizes N_1 and N_2, with p variates measured for each sample, any one observation on the ith variate for the rth sample will be assumed to be given by

(11.110) $$x_{ir\alpha} = \mu_{ir} + \epsilon_{ir\alpha}$$

where $i = 1, 2, \cdots p$, $r = 1, 2$, $\alpha = 1, 2, \cdots N_r$, and where the $\epsilon_{ir\alpha}$ have a multivariate normal distribution with mean 0 and covariance matrix $[\sigma_{ij}]$. The difference of the means for the two *populations* for the variate x_i is

$$\delta_i = \mu_{i1} - \mu_{i2}$$

and the generalized distance is given by

(11.111) $$\Delta^2 = \frac{1}{p} \sum_{i,j} \sigma^{ij} \delta_i \delta_j$$

where $[\sigma^{ij}]$ is the inverse of $[\sigma_{ij}]$.

Bose and Roy [19] have studied the sampling distribution of the studentized statistic

(11.112) $$pD^2 = \sum s^{ij} d_i d_j$$

where s_{ij} is an estimate of σ_{ij} from the pooled sum of squares within samples. In the notation of § 11.21, $s_{ij} = S_{ij}/(N_1 + N_2 - 2)$.

There is a bias in this value of D^2 since $E(D^2) = \Delta^2 + \lambda^2$, but this is small if N_1 and N_2 are large. However, if we define D_0^2 as $D^2 - \lambda^2$, we have

(11.113) $$E(D_0^2) = \Delta^2$$
$$\text{Var}(D_0^2) = \frac{2\lambda^4}{p}\left(1 + \frac{2\Delta^2}{\lambda^2}\right)$$

The distribution of D_0^2 is complicated. It is in effect what is known as *non-central* χ^2. If $x = p\, D\Delta/\lambda^2$, and $t = \lambda^2/p\Delta^2$, so that $xt = D/\Delta$,

(11.114) $$f(x) = (xt)^{\frac{p}{2}} e^{-\left(\frac{tx^2}{2} + \frac{1}{2t}\right)} I_{\frac{p-2}{2}}(x)$$

where $I_n(x)$ is a Bessel function of imaginary argument, the properties of which may be studied in Whittaker and Watson's *Modern Analysis* or in Watson's *Treatise on Bessel Functions*.

The function D (or D_0) has been used in anthropology for classifying and distinguishing between certain human populations, on the basis of a considerable number of measurable traits.

Example 9. In a certain experiment (actual details somewhat simplified), each of a number of rabbits received both a high dose and a low dose of insulin (in random order) and the bloodsugar was measured at 1, 2, and 3 hours after each dose. Denoting these measured values by x_1, x_2, and x_3, the SS and SP are given by the following table:

	df	SS x_1^2	SS x_2^2	SS x_3^2	SP $x_1 x_2$	SP $x_1 x_3$	SP $x_2 x_3$
Between populations ($\lambda^2 d_i d_j$)	1	519	3503	5645	1349	1712	4447
Within populations (S_{ij})	34	2677	2358	3223	1278	1814	1966

The inverted matrix S^{ij} is proportional to

$$\begin{bmatrix} 3.735 & -0.553 & -1.765 \\ -0.553 & 5.337 & -2.947 \\ -1.765 & -2.945 & 4.679 \end{bmatrix}$$

If d_i is the mean low-insulin value minus the mean high-insulin value for x_i, the data give values of d_1, d_2, d_3 proportional to 353, 917, 1164. Hence, from (11.109), the values of l_1, l_2, l_3 are proportional to -1.243, 1.272, 2.123 respectively. (Constant multipliers are disregarded throughout all these calculations.) A close approximation to the best discriminant would, therefore, be

$$L = -3x_1 + 3x_2 + 5x_3$$

On evaluating B and W for this discriminant, by (11.106) and (11.107), we obtain $B = 235{,}091$, $W = 107{,}446$. Since $p = 3$ and $N_1 + N_2 = 36$, the value of F is 23.3, with df 3 and 32.

If, instead, we try as a discriminant the mean of the three observations x_1, x_2, and x_3, or equivalently

$$L = x_1 + x_2 + x_3$$

we find

$$B = 24{,}683, \quad W = 18{,}374, \quad F = 14.3$$

It appears that the first discriminant function is distinctly better than the second. By the regression method of the previous section it may be shown that the difference is significant at the 5% level.

Problems

1. Prove the statement in § 11.1 that if a straight line $Y = a + bx$ is fitted to the array means in such a way that $S = \sum N_i(\bar{y}_i - Y_i)^2$ is a minimum, then this line is the ordinary regression line of y on x.

2. Prove that if E^2 has the distribution given by (11.6) with $\lambda = 0$ then $n_2 E^2 / \{n_1(1 - E^2)\}$ has the F-distribution with n_1 and n_2 df, where $n_1 = p - 1$, $n_2 = N - p$.

3. Prove that the sum of the squares of N numbers differing by 1 and centered at 0 is $N(N^2 - 1)/12$, whether N is odd or even.

For N odd, the numbers are $\cdots -3, -2, -1, 0, 1, 2, 3, \cdots$, for N even they are $\cdots -2\tfrac{1}{2}, -1\tfrac{1}{2}, -\tfrac{1}{2}, \tfrac{1}{2}, 1\tfrac{1}{2}, 2\tfrac{1}{2} \cdots$.

Prove also that the sum of the fourth powers is $N(N^2 - 1)(3N^2 - 7)/240$. (See § 11.3.)

Hint. See (1.28) and (1.30). These results may be proved by induction.

4. Prove that the variance of the jth coefficient A_j in the expression of Y as a sum of $k + 1$ orthogonal polynomials is $\sigma^2/S(\xi_j)^2$, and that the covariance of any two A_i, A_j, $(i \neq j)$ is zero. Show that the estimate of σ^2 is

$$\{S(y^2) - A_0 S(y) - \cdots - A_k S(y\xi_k)\}/(N - k - 1)$$

5. Verify the computations of Example 3, § 11.5, by writing out the observation equations and the normal equations and solving the latter.

6. Prove that the exact least squares solution of the problem of fitting $Y = a + be^{px}$ is given by equations (11.23).

7. Write out the full discussions analogous to (a) of § 11.10 for columns parallel to Ox and to Oy.

8. Show that the Gompertz curve $Y = cB^{q^x}$ and the logistic curve $Y = A/(1 + ce^{qx})$ are similar in form to the modified exponential curve if for the Gompertz log Y is expressed as a function of x and for the logistic $1/Y$ is so expressed. Hence Cowden's method of fitting may be applied to these curves by plotting log Y (or $1/Y$) against x (see Reference 6).

The Gompertz curve has been used in actuarial work, and the logistic in population studies. Both are curves with horizontal asymptotes.

9. Find the multiple correlation coefficients and the regression equations for the data in Example 7, §11.17.

10. (*Garrett*) The r for intelligence and school achievement in a group of children 8 to 14 years old is 0.80. The r for intelligence and age in the same group is 0.70. The r for school achievement and age is 0.60. What will be the correlation between intelligence and school achievement in children of the same age?

11. (*Yule* and *Kendall*) The following means, standard deviations, and correlations are found for

X_1 = seed-hay crops in cwts. per acre
X_2 = spring rainfall in inches
X_3 = accumulated temperature above 42° F. in spring

in a certain district in England during 20 years.

$\bar{X}_1 = 28.02 \quad s_1 = 4.42 \quad r_{12} = 0.80$
$\bar{X}_2 = 4.91 \quad s_2 = 1.10 \quad r_{13} = -0.40$
$\bar{X}_3 = 594 \quad s_3 = 85 \quad r_{23} = -0.56$

Find the partial correlations and the regression equation for hay crop on spring rainfall and accumulated temperature.

12. The following data relate to land values and crops in twenty-five Iowa counties.

X_1 = average value per acre of farm land on January 1, 1920
X_2 = average yield of corn per acre in bushels 1910–1919
X_3 = per cent of farm land in small grain
X_4 = per cent of farm land in corn

County No.	X_1	X_2	X_3	X_4
1	$ 87	40	11	14
2	133	36	13	30
3	174	34	19	30
4	385	41	33	39
5	363	39	25	33
6	274	42	23	34
7	235	40	22	37
8	104	31	9	20
9	141	36	13	27
10	208	34	17	40
11	115	30	18	19
12	271	40	23	31
13	163	37	14	25
14	193	41	13	28
15	203	38	24	31
16	279	38	31	35
17	179	24	16	26
18	244	45	19	34
19	165	34	20	30
20	257	40	30	38
21	252	41	22	35
22	280	42	21	41
23	167	35	16	23
24	168	33	18	24
25	115	36	18	21

(a) Find the linear regression equation of X_1 on $X_2 X_3 X_4$.
(b) Estimate the first five values of X_1, using the equation obtained in (a).
(c) Calculate $s_{1.234}$ and $r_{1.234}$.

13. (*Pearl and Surface*)[20]. In a biometrical study of egg production in the domestic fowl, measurements of length, breadth and weight were made on 453 eggs. From all these, the value of $r_{12.3}$ was -0.8955. If the 42 eggs weighing from 53 to 53.9 gm are considered alone, the ordinary correlation coefficient r_{12} between length and breadth is -0.9117. Similarly the 46 eggs between 56 and 56.9 gm give $r_{12} = -0.8911$ and the 13 eggs between 62 and 62.9 gm give $r_{12} = -0.8739$.

Show that the weighted mean of these values of r_{12} is very close to $r_{12.3}$, thus verifying for this example the interpretation of $r_{12.3}$ given at the end of § 11.17.

References

1. Harold Hotelling, *Proc. Nat. Acad. Sci.*, **11**, 1925, pp. 657–662.
2. T. L. Woo, *Biometrika*, **21**, 1929, pp. 1–66, reprinted in Pearson's *Tables for Statisticians and Biometricians*, Part II, pp. 16–72.
3. F. E. Allan, "The General Form of the Orthogonal Polynomials for Simple Series with Proofs of their Simple Properties," *Proc. Roy. Soc. Edin.*, **50**, 1935, pp. 310–320.
4. R. L. Anderson and E. E. Houseman, "Tables of Orthogonal Polynomial Values Extended to N = 104," Research Bulletin No. 297, 1942, Iowa State College, Ames, Iowa.
5. J. W. Glover, *Tables of Applied Mathematics*, 1923, pp. 468–481.
6. D. J. Cowden, "Simplified Methods of Fitting Certain Types of Growth Curves," *Jour. Amer. Stat. Ass.*, **42**, 1947, pp. 585–590.
7. G. W. Snedecor, *Statistical Methods*, 4th Edition, p. 375.

8. For the theory of the Seidel process, see Whittaker and Robinson, *The Calculus of Observations*, pp. 255–257.

9. Sir Gilbert Walker, "On the Criterion for the Reality of Relationships or Periodicities," *Calcutta Ind. Met. Memoirs*, **21**, 1914, Part 9.

10. R. A. Fisher, "Tests of Significance in Harmonic Analysis," *Proc. Roy. Soc.*, A, **125**, 1929, p. 54.

11. H. T. Davis, *The Analysis of Economic Time Series* (1941).

12. The method used in this section is due to Prof. B. A. Griffith (unpublished), based on a result of E. C. Fieller, *Quart. J. Pharm. Pharmacol.*, **17**, 1945, pp. 117–123.

13. R. A. Fisher, "The General Sampling Distribution of the Multiple Correlation Coefficient," *Proc. Roy. Soc.*, A, **121**, 1928, p. 654.

14. J. R. Miner, *Tables of $\sqrt{1-r^2}$ and $1-r^2$ for Use in Partial Correlation and in Trigonometry* (Johns Hopkins Press, 1922).

15. M. A. May, "Predicting Academic Success," *Jour. Ed. Psych.*, **14**, 1923, pp. 429–440.

16. Dunham Jackson, "The Trigonometry of Correlation," *Amer. Math. Monthly*, **31**, 1924, pp. 275–280.

17. P. C. Mahalonobis, "On the Generalized Distance in Statistics," *Proc. National Inst. for Science and Industry*, **12**, 1936, pp. 49–55.

18. Harold Hotelling, "The Generalization of Student's Ratio," *Ann. Math. Stat.*, **2**, 1931, pp. 360–378.

19. R. C. Bose and S. N. Roy, "The Exact Distribution of the Studentized D^2-Statistic," *Sankhyā*, **4**, 1938, pp. 19–31.

20. Quoted in Pearl's *Medical Biometry and Statistics*, 2nd Edition, p. 397.

21. P. C. Tang, "The Power Function of the Analysis of Variance Tests, with Tables and Illustrations of Their Use," *Stat. Res. Mem.*, **2**, 1938, pp. 126–157.

22. D. B. DeLury, "Values and Integrals of the Orthogonal Polynomials Up to $n = 26$" (Univ. of Toronto Press, 1950).

23. E. S. Keeping, "A Significance Test for Exponential Regression," *Ann. Math. Stat.*, **22**, 1951, pp. 180–198.

CHAPTER XII

FURTHER CONSIDERATIONS ON STATISTICAL INFERENCE

12.1 Introduction. The importance of inference in statistical theory and practice has been repeatedly emphasized in previous chapters. Apart from the purely descriptive side of statistics, in which the characteristics of a given finite population are represented graphically or summarized by a few measures such as the mean and standard deviation, almost all interesting statistical problems are concerned with estimation. Usually we have to estimate the parameters of a parent population from a sample, the form of the distribution being known or assumed, and to assign confidence limits for these estimates, but there are also problems of *non-parametric inference*, when we wish to infer, for instance, something about the form of a distribution and are not concerned with the numerical value of the parameters.

In this chapter we give a sketch of certain methods of estimation and in particular of Fisher's method of maximum likelihood and the Neyman-Pearson theory of statistical inference, both of which have been referred to occasionally in previous chapters. Closely connected with this theory are the sampling practices which have been developed in industry in recent years and which go under the general name of *quality control*.

12.2 The Best Unbiased Estimate of a Parameter. Fisher's Inequality.
Let us suppose that we wish to estimate a single parameter θ of a parent population, by means of a statistic T which is calculated from a sample of N independent observations $x_1, x_2, \cdots x_N$ of a variate x. The statistic T is an *unbiased* estimate of θ if

$$(12.1) \qquad E(T) \equiv \theta$$

whatever the values of any other parameters, $\theta', \theta'' \cdots$ which may occur in the frequency function for the variate x.

It is the *best unbiased estimate* if its variance is at least as small as that of any other unbiased estimate of θ. That is,

$$(12.2) \qquad E[(T - \theta)^2] = \min$$

Fisher's inequality states that

$$(12.3) \qquad \text{Var}(T) \geq \frac{1}{NE\left[\left(\frac{\partial \log f}{\partial \theta}\right)^2\right]} = \frac{1}{N \int_{-\infty}^{\infty} \left(\frac{\partial \log f}{\partial \theta}\right)^2 f \, dx}$$

where f stands for $f(x, \theta, \theta' \cdots)$, the frequency function for x. We now give a proof of this statement.

Since the observations are independent, the probability density of the observed sample is

$$P = f(x_1, \theta, \theta' \cdots) f(x_2, \theta, \theta' \cdots) \cdots f(x_N, \theta, \theta' \cdots)$$

Let us make a change of variables from $x_1, x_2 \cdots x_N$ to $\xi_1, \xi_2 \cdots \xi_{N-1}, T$, where the ξ's, like T, are suitable functions of the x's, not depending on θ. Let the frequency function for T be $g(T, \theta, \theta' \cdots)$ and let the conditional joint frequency function for the ξ's, given T, be $h(\xi_1, \xi_2 \cdots \xi_{N-1} \mid T, \theta, \theta' \cdots)$. Then by the ordinary formula for change of variable,

(12.4) $\quad P \, dx_1 \, dx_2 \cdots dx_N = gh \, dT \, d\xi_1 \cdots d\xi_{N-1} = gh \mid J \mid dx_1 \cdots dx_N$

where J is the Jacobian of the ξ's and T with respect to the x's and is independent of θ. The functions f, g, h all depend on θ, and it is assumed that these functions, as well as Tg, satisfy the conditions given in § 3.1 for differentiating with respect to θ under the sign of integration. If so, T is said to be a *regular* estimate of θ.

Since f, g, h are frequency functions,

$$\int f \, dx = 1, \qquad \int g \, dT = 1, \qquad \int \cdots \int h \, d\xi_1 \cdots d\xi_{N-1} = 1$$

Differentiating these equations with respect to θ, we obtain

$$\int \frac{\partial f}{\partial \theta} \, dx = \int \frac{\partial g}{\partial \theta} \, dT = \int \cdots \int \frac{\partial h}{\partial \theta} \, d\xi_1 \cdots d\xi_{N-1} = 0$$

These may be written

(12.5) $\quad \int \frac{\partial}{\partial \theta}(\log f) f \, dx = 0, \qquad \int \frac{\partial}{\partial \theta}(\log g) g \, dT = 0$

$$\int \cdots \int \frac{\partial}{\partial \theta}(\log h) h \, d\xi_1 \cdots d\xi_{N-1} = 0$$

Also, from (12.4), $\log P = \log g + \log h + \log \mid J \mid$, whence on differentiating,

(12.6) $\quad \dfrac{\partial \log P}{\partial \theta} = \dfrac{\partial \log g}{\partial \theta} + \dfrac{\partial \log h}{\partial \theta}$

$\mid J \mid$ being independent of θ. Squaring both sides of (12.6), multiplying each side by the corresponding side of (12.4) and integrating, we have

(12.7) $\quad \displaystyle\int \cdots \int \left(\frac{\partial \log P}{\partial \theta}\right)^2 P \, dx_1 \cdots dx_N$

$$= \int \cdots \int \left(\frac{\partial \log g}{\partial \theta} + \frac{\partial \log h}{\partial \theta}\right)^2 gh \, dT \, d\xi_1 \cdots d\xi_{N-1}$$

Since $\log P = \sum_i \log f(x_i, \theta)$, the left-hand side of (12.7) may be written

Sec. 2　Best Unbiased Estimate of a Parameter

$$\int \cdots \int \left[\sum_i \left(\frac{\partial \log f_i}{\partial \theta}\right)^2 + \sum_{i \neq j} \frac{\partial \log f_i}{\partial \theta} \frac{\partial \log f_j}{\partial \theta} \right] f_1 f_2 \cdots f_N \, dx_1 \cdots dx_N$$

where f_i stands for $f(x_i, \theta, \theta' \cdots)$. The second sum vanishes on integration by virtue of the first equation of (12.5). The first sum has N terms all identical after integration, and may be written

$$N \int \left(\frac{\partial \log f}{\partial \theta}\right)^2 f \, dx$$

The right-hand side of (12.7), with the second equation of (12.5), gives

$$\int \left(\frac{\partial \log g}{\partial \theta}\right)^2 g \, dT + \int \left(\frac{\partial \log h}{\partial \theta}\right)^2 gh \, dT \, d\xi_1 \cdots d\xi_{N-1}$$

The second term in this expression is essentially non-negative, so that we have

(12.8) $$N \int \left(\frac{\partial \log f}{\partial \theta}\right)^2 f \, dx \geq \int \left(\frac{\partial \log g}{\partial \theta}\right)^2 g \, dT$$

the sign of equality occurring only when h is independent of θ, so that $(\partial \log h)/\partial \theta = 0$. Equation (12.1) is equivalent to

$$\int T g(T, \theta, \theta' \cdots) \, dT = \theta$$

and on differentiating with respect to θ, we obtain

$$\int T \frac{\partial g}{\partial \theta} \, dT = 1$$

Since

$$\int \frac{\partial g}{\partial \theta} \, dT = 0$$

it follows that

$$\int (T - \theta) \frac{\partial g}{\partial \theta} \, dT = 1$$

or

(12.9) $$\int (T - \theta) g^{1/2} (g^{1/2} \, \partial \log g/\partial \theta) \, dT = 1$$

Now, there is a useful lemma, known as *Schwarz's inequality*, which states that if ϕ and ψ are real functions of x with integrable squares over a given range,

(12.10) $$\left(\int \phi \psi \, dx\right)^2 \leq \int \phi^2 \, dx \int \psi^2 \, dx$$

This is readily proved by noting that the quadratic form in u and v,

$$\int (u\phi + v\psi)^2 \, dx = u^2 \int \phi^2 \, dx + 2uv \int \phi\psi \, dx + v^2 \int \psi^2 \, dx$$

is non-negative for all real values of u and v. But the condition that $Au^2 + 2Buv + Cv^2$ is non-negative is that $B^2 \leq AC$, and this condition immediately gives the Schwarz inequality. Applying this to the two functions in (12.9), we have

(12.11) $$1 \leq \int (T - \theta)^2 g \, dT \int g(\partial \log g/\partial \theta)^2 \, dT$$

The first factor on the right-hand side is Var (T), and hence, by (12.8)

$$\text{Var }(T) \geq \frac{1}{N \int (\partial \log f/\partial \theta)^2 f \, dx}$$

which is *Fisher's inequality*.[17]

The sign of equality in (12.10) can occur only if $u\phi + v\psi = 0$, which means that ψ is proportional to ϕ. In this case it means that

(12.12) $$\partial \log g/\partial \theta = k(T - \theta)$$

where k is independent of θ.

Example 1. If T is a statistic used to estimate the mean of a normal distribution, for which
$$f = (2\pi\sigma^2)^{-1/2} \exp\{-(x - \mu)^2/2\sigma^2\}$$
we have
$$\frac{\partial \log f}{\partial \mu} = \frac{x - \mu}{\sigma^2}$$
so that
$$N \int \left(\frac{\partial \log f}{\partial \mu}\right)^2 f \, dx = \frac{N}{\sigma^4} \int_{-\infty}^{\infty} (x - \mu)^2 f \, dx$$
$$= N/\sigma^2$$

Hence the variance of $T \geq \sigma^2/N$. Since σ^2/N is actually the variance of the sample mean $\bar{x}$, $\bar{x}$ is the best possible unbiased estimate of μ.

In this example
$$g(\bar{x}) = (N/2\pi)^{1/2}\sigma^{-1} \exp\{-N(\bar{x} - \mu)^2/2\sigma^2\}$$
so that $\partial \log g/\partial \mu = N(\bar{x} - \mu)/\sigma^2$. This is of the form (12.12) with $k = N/\sigma^2$.

12.3 Consistent and Efficient Statistics. A statistic T is said to be *consistent*, as an estimate of a parameter θ, if when the size of the sample N is increased indefinitely T tends in the stochastic sense to the value θ. That is, for any given $\epsilon > 0$.

$$\Pr\{|T - \theta| > \epsilon\} \to 0 \quad \text{as } N \to \infty$$

The arithmetic mean $\bar{x}$ of a sample from a normal parent population with parameters μ and σ is, as we have seen in Chapter VI, normally distributed about μ with variance σ^2/N. Hence

$$\Pr\{|\bar{x} - \mu| > \epsilon\} = \Pr\left\{\frac{|\bar{x} - \mu|N^{1/2}}{\sigma} > \frac{\epsilon N^{1/2}}{\sigma}\right\}$$
$$= 2\{1 - \Phi(\epsilon N^{1/2}/\sigma)\}$$

where $\Phi(x)$ is the distribution function of the normal law. For fixed ϵ and σ, N can be taken so large that $\Phi(\epsilon N^{1/2}/\sigma)$ is arbitrarily near to 1. This proves the consistency of $\bar{x}$.

If T is such that (1) $E(T) \to \theta$, (2) Var $(T) \to 0$ as $N \to \infty$, then it follows from the Bienaymé-Tchebycheff inequality (§ 4.14) that T is a consistent statistic for the estimation of θ. This is a useful rule for determining consistency.

The less the sampling variance of a statistic the more reliable the statistic will be as an estimate of a parameter θ. It is, therefore, natural to take the efficiency of a statistic as inversely proportional to its variance. The expression on the right-hand side of (12.3) is the minimum value $V_{\min}$ of the variance of any unbiased statistic used to estimate θ. The ratio of this minimum value to the actual variance of T is called the *efficiency* of T. A statistic with an efficiency of 100% is called a *most-efficient* statistic. When a most-efficient statistic exists it can be found by the method of maximum likelihood (§ 12.4).

Example 2. The mean and the median of a sample of N from a normal population with parameters μ and σ are both consistent statistics for estimating μ. Their variances are σ^2/N (for any N) and $\pi\sigma^2/2N$ (for large N). Hence, at least for large N, the median is less efficient than the mean; its efficiency is approximately $2/\pi$ or 63.7%. This means that an estimate of μ from a sample of 64 observations, using the mean, is just about as reliable as an estimate from a sample of 100, using the median.

Example 3. Suppose that σ^2 is the parameter to be estimated in a normal parent population, μ being known.

$$\frac{\partial \log f}{\partial \sigma^2} = -\frac{1}{2\sigma^2} + \frac{(x-\mu)^2}{2\sigma^4}$$

so that

$$\int_{-\infty}^{\infty} \left(\frac{\partial \log f}{\partial \sigma^2}\right)^2 f\, dx = \frac{1}{4\sigma^4} - \frac{\sigma^2}{2\sigma^6} + \frac{3\sigma^4}{4\sigma^8}$$

$$= \frac{1}{2\sigma^4}$$

The variance of a most-efficient estimate of σ^2 is, therefore, $2\sigma^4/N$. Now the sample variance, multiplied by $N/(N-1)$, is an unbiased estimate of σ^2, and its variance is $2\sigma^4/(N-1)$. Its efficiency is, therefore, $(N-1)/N$ and it is only asymptotically most-efficient. However, the estimate $S(x_\alpha - \mu)^2/N$ has a smaller variance but is biased.

12.4 Sufficient Statistics. The Method of Maximum Likelihood.

In the proof of Fisher's inequality, we saw that the sign of equality in (12.3) can occur only when *two* conditions are satisfied:

(a) h is independent of θ,
(b) $\partial \log g/\partial \theta = k(T - \theta)$.

If condition (a) is satisfied, T is called a *sufficient* statistic, whether or not (b) is satisfied also. The probability density P is then, from (12.4), expressible in the form

$$P = gh\,|J|$$

where g is a function of T and θ, and $h\,|J|$ is independent of θ.

If we let $L = \log P$, and call L the *likelihood*,

(12.13) $$L = L_1(T, \theta) + L_2$$

where L_2 is independent of θ. Knowledge of L_2 does not contribute anything, therefore, to the estimation of θ, and it is for this reason that T is called sufficient. In other words, T gives all the information that the sample can supply about the parameter θ.

The condition of sufficiency does not determine T uniquely, since any function of T will satisfy the condition (12.13) equally well. We naturally choose a function which will give a consistent estimate of θ, and if possible one that is unbiased.

A way of obtaining estimates, known as the *method of maximum likelihood*, is due to R. A. Fisher and has already been used several times in earlier chapters. It is the most important general method of estimation known, at least theoretically. In practice, the equations to which it leads are often intractable, but it is usually possible in such cases to improve the estimate given by a less efficient statistic by means of an iterative process, one or at most two repetitions of which will give a result practically as good as the maximum likelihood estimate (see § 12.7).

The method of maximum likelihood consists in taking as an estimate of θ that value for which P is a maximum. Since L is a monotone increasing function of P, L is also a maximum for the same value of θ, and it is generally more convenient to work with L. Hence if the equations

(12.14) $$\frac{\partial L}{\partial \theta} = 0, \qquad \frac{\partial^2 L}{\partial \theta^2} < 0$$

are satisfied for $\theta = T$, then T is a maximum likelihood estimate of θ. A solution which is a mere constant is disregarded.

If there are two or more parameters, say $\theta, \theta' \cdots$, it may happen that T can be found to maximize L whatever the values of the other parameters may be. In that case there is a unique maximum likelihood estimate of θ. Even if there is no unique estimate, it is often possible to estimate two or more parameters simultaneously.

Example 4. For the normal distribution of Example 3,
$$P = (2\pi\sigma^2)^{-N/2} \exp\{-S(x_\alpha - \mu)^2/2\sigma^2\}$$
where the sum is from 1 to N for α. Hence
$$L = C - \tfrac{1}{2}N \log \sigma^2 - S(x_\alpha - \mu)^2/2\sigma^2$$
$$\frac{\partial L}{\partial \sigma^2} = -N/2\sigma^2 + S(x_\alpha - \mu)^2/2\sigma^4 = 0$$
$$\frac{\partial^2 L}{\partial(\sigma^2)^2} = N/2\sigma^4 - S(x_\alpha - \mu)^2/\sigma^6 = -N/2\sigma^4$$

The maximum likelihood estimate of σ^2 is $T = (1/N)S(x_\alpha - \mu)^2$, which depends on μ. If, however, we maximize L simultaneously for σ^2 and μ by solving together the equations

Sec. 4   Sufficient Statistics   373

we obtain
$$\frac{\partial L}{\partial \mu} = 0, \quad \frac{\partial L}{\partial \sigma^2} = 0$$

$$\mu = S x_\alpha / N = \bar{x} \quad \text{and} \quad \sigma^2 = S(x_\alpha - \bar{x})^2 / N = s^2$$

so that the sample mean and sample variance are simultaneous maximum likelihood estimates of μ and σ^2 respectively.

The importance of the maximum likelihood method depends on the following properties. *If a most-efficient statistic exists, the method will give it. If a sufficient estimate T_0 exists, any solution of (12.14) will be a function of T_0.* For a sufficient statistic, h is independent of θ, so that from (12.6)

$$\frac{\partial L}{\partial \theta} = \frac{\partial \log g(T_0, \theta)}{\partial \theta}$$

If this is zero, g is a function of T_0 but not of θ. If the statistic is also most-efficient,

$$\partial (\log g)/\partial \theta = k(T_0 - \theta)$$

so that the equation $\partial L/\partial \theta = 0$ has the unique solution $T = T_0$.

Another important property of maximum likelihood statistics is that, under certain conditions, they tend to normality for large N and have in the limit minimum variance. In other words they are *asymptotically normal* and *asymptotically most-efficient*.[1]

Conditions strong enough to ensure the approach to normality are: (1) if f is the frequency function $f(x, \theta)$, then the first three derivatives of f with respect to θ exist, for all θ in some interval containing the true value θ_0; (2) these derivatives are integrable over all x; and (3)

$$\int_{-\infty}^{\infty} \left(\frac{\partial \log f}{\partial \theta} \right)^2 f \, dx$$

is finite and positive for all θ in this interval.

For any θ in this interval, we have by Taylor's theorem

$$\frac{\partial \log f}{\partial \theta} = \left(\frac{\partial \log f}{\partial \theta} \right)_0 + (\theta - \theta_0) \left(\frac{\partial^2 \log f}{\partial \theta^2} \right)_0 + \tfrac{1}{2}(\theta - \theta_0)^2 R(x)$$

where we assume that $|R(x)|$ has an upper bound independent of θ, and where the subscript 0 means that θ is to be put equal to θ_0.

Since $L = S \log f(x_\alpha, \theta)$, we therefore obtain

(12.15) $$\frac{1}{N} \frac{\partial L}{\partial \theta} = B_0 + B_1(\theta - \theta_0) + \tfrac{1}{2} B_2 (\theta - \theta_0)^2 = 0$$

where

$$B_0 = \frac{1}{N} S \left(\frac{\partial \log f}{\partial \theta} \right)_0$$

$$B_1 = \frac{1}{N} S \left(\frac{\partial^2 \log f}{\partial \theta^2} \right)_0$$

and
$$B_2 = \frac{1}{N} S R(x_\alpha)$$

Now since $\int_{-\infty}^{\infty} f \, dx = 1$, f being a frequency function, it follows that

(12.16) $$\int_{-\infty}^{\infty} \frac{\partial f}{\partial \theta} \, dx = \int_{-\infty}^{\infty} \frac{\partial^2 f}{\partial \theta^2} \, dx = 0$$

for every θ in the interval. Consequently

(12.17) $$E\left(\frac{\partial \log f}{\partial \theta}\right)_0 = \int \left(\frac{1}{f} \frac{\partial f}{\partial \theta}\right)_0 f(x, \theta_0) \, dx$$
$$= \int \left(\frac{\partial f}{\partial \theta}\right)_0 dx = 0$$

and

(12.18) $$E\left(\frac{\partial^2 \log f}{\partial \theta^2}\right)_0 = \int \left[\frac{1}{f}\frac{\partial^2 f}{\partial \theta^2} - \left(\frac{1}{f}\frac{\partial f}{\partial \theta}\right)^2\right]_0 f(x, \theta_0) \, dx$$
$$= \int \left(\frac{\partial^2 f}{\partial \theta^2}\right)_0 dx - E\left[\left(\frac{\partial \log f}{\partial \theta}\right)_0\right]^2$$
$$= -E\left[\left(\frac{\partial \log f}{\partial \theta}\right)_0\right]^2$$
$$= -k^2$$

by the condition (3) mentioned above.

Hence B_0 is the arithmetic mean of N independent random variables with the same distribution and with expectation zero and variance k^2. By the central limit theorem it follows that B_0 converges in probability to zero and that NB_0 is asymptotically normal with variance Nk^2. In the same way, B_1 converges to $-k^2$. It may further be proved that for sufficiently large N the equation (12.15) has, with probability arbitrarily near to 1, a root arbitrarily near to θ_0.

Moreover, if T is this root, we can write equation (12.15) as

(12.19) $$T - \theta_0 = \frac{B_0}{-B_1 - \frac{1}{2}B_2(T - \theta_0)}$$

Since B_2 remains finite as N increases, the denominator in (12.19) tends to k^2 as N increases. Writing (12.19) in the equivalent form

$$k\sqrt{N}(T - \theta_0) = \frac{\frac{1}{k\sqrt{N}}(NB_0)}{-\frac{1}{k^2}[B_1 + \frac{1}{2}B_2(T - \theta_0)]}$$

we see that the denominator tends to 1 and that the numerator is asymptotically normal with mean 0 and variance 1.

Sec. 4 Sufficient Statistics 375

Hence the maximum likelihood estimate T is, in the limit for large N, normally distributed about the true value θ_0 with variance given by

(12.20) $$\frac{1}{\sigma_T^2} = Nk^2 = - NE\left(\frac{\partial^2 \log f}{\partial \theta^2}\right)_0$$
$$= - E\left(\frac{\partial^2 L}{\partial \theta^2}\right)_0$$

This is a very useful way of finding the standard error of a maximum likelihood estimate. The quantity $1/\sigma_T^2$ is regarded by Fisher as a measure of the *information* relevant to θ provided by the sample.

If T_1 and T_2 are simultaneous maximum likelihood estimates of two parameters, θ_1 and θ_2, and if these estimates have a bivariate normal distribution with variances σ_1^2 and σ_2^2 and covariance $\rho\sigma_1\sigma_2$, then it may be shown that σ_1^2 and σ_2^2 are the cofactors of the terms in the principal diagonal of the determinant

(12.21) $$D = \begin{vmatrix} -E\left(\dfrac{\partial^2 L}{\partial \theta_1^2}\right) & -E\left(\dfrac{\partial^2 L}{\partial \theta_1\, \partial \theta_2}\right) \\ -E\left(\dfrac{\partial^2 L}{\partial \theta_1\, \partial \theta_2}\right) & -E\left(\dfrac{\partial^2 L}{\partial \theta_2^2}\right) \end{vmatrix}$$

divided by the determinant D itself. The derivatives are evaluated at the true values θ_1^0 and θ_2^0. This theorem may be extended to more than two parameters.

Example 5. For a parent population with a probability θ of "success" in a single trial, the probability of r successes in N trials is $\binom{N}{r}\theta^r(1-\theta)^{N-r}$. The likelihood function is, therefore,

(12.22) $$L = \log\binom{N}{r} + r \log \theta + (N - r) \log (1 - \theta)$$

The maximum likelihood estimate of the parameter θ is given by

$$\frac{\partial L}{\partial \theta} = \frac{r}{\theta} - \frac{N - r}{1 - \theta} = 0$$

whence the estimate is found to be

$$\hat{\theta} = r/N$$

Also,

$$\frac{\partial^2 L}{\partial \theta^2} = -\frac{r}{\theta^2} - \frac{N - r}{(1 - \theta)^2}$$

Now the expected value of r is $N\theta$, so that

$$E\left(\frac{\partial^2 L}{\partial \theta^2}\right) = -\frac{N}{\theta} - \frac{N}{1 - \theta}$$
$$= -\frac{N}{\theta(1 - \theta)}$$

The variance of $\hat{\theta}$ is therefore $\theta(1 - \theta)/N$, which is the well-known formula. The standard error is given by substituting for θ its estimate r/N. Each trial contributes an amount of information measured by $[\theta(1 - \theta)]^{-1}$.

12.5 Curve-fitting by the Method of Maximum Likelihood. It was pointed out in Chapter V that the method of moments, as frequently used for curve-fitting, is not the most efficient method possible, except in certain special cases. R. A. Fisher [2] has shown that the maximum likelihood estimates of the parameters in various Pearson types of distribution curves have variances which are generally less, and often much less, than those of the estimates furnished by the method of moments. Thus, if we know that the frequency curve is that of a Gamma variate (Type III) with a single parameter $\lambda > 0$ to be estimated, we have

$$f(x) = \frac{1}{\Gamma(\lambda)} x^{\lambda-1} e^{-x}, \quad x \geq 0$$

and

$$L = -N \log \Gamma(\lambda) + (\lambda - 1) S \log x_\alpha - S x_\alpha$$

Then

(12.23) $$\frac{\partial L}{\partial \lambda} = -N \frac{d}{d\lambda} \log \Gamma(\lambda) + S \log x_\alpha = 0$$

and the estimate of λ is the unique positive root $\hat{\lambda}$ of (12.23). This root may be found from a table of the Digamma function.[3] The variance is found from

(12.24) $$\frac{\partial^2 L}{\partial \lambda^2} = -N \frac{d^2}{d\lambda^2} \log \Gamma(\lambda) = -\frac{1}{\sigma_{\hat{\lambda}}^2}$$

by the help of tables of the Trigamma function.[3]

By the method of moments, we estimate λ from the mean $\bar{x}$ of the distribution. Since $E(x) = \lambda$ and $\text{Var}(x) = \lambda$, this estimate is $\bar{x}$ itself, with variance λ/N. The efficiency of the moment estimate is, therefore,

$$\left[\lambda \frac{d^2}{d\lambda^2} \log \Gamma(\lambda) \right]^{-1}$$

and this is always less than 1, tending to zero as $\lambda \to 0$. Since the skewness is $2\lambda^{-1/2}$, the more skew the curve the less the accuracy of estimation of λ by the method of moments. For a skewness of 1, the efficiency is about 88%.

In practice, however, we usually require to determine *three* parameters of a Type III curve in order to fit an empirical distribution such as that of Example 3 in § 5.14. If the equation of the curve is

(12.25) $$f = K(t + \lambda^{1/2})^{\lambda-1} e^{-\lambda^{1/2} t}, \quad \lambda > 2$$

where $t = (x - \mu)/\sigma$, $\lambda = 4/\gamma_1^2$, $K = \lambda^{\lambda/2} e^{-\lambda}/[\sigma \Gamma(\lambda)]$, the parameters μ, σ^2, and γ_1 are, by the method of moments, estimated by the statistics k_1, k_2, and g_1 respectively. The variance of k_1 is σ^2/N, and that of k_2 is

$$\frac{\kappa_4}{N} + \frac{2\kappa_2^2}{N-1} = 2\sigma^4 \left(\frac{1}{N-1} + \frac{3}{N\lambda} \right)$$

Sec. 6 The Chi-square Test of Goodness of Fit 377

The variance of g_1 is difficult to evaluate exactly but for large N it approximates to $\frac{6}{N}\left(1 + \frac{6}{\lambda} + \frac{5}{\lambda^2}\right)$.

The likelihood function is

$$(12.26) \quad L = N\left(\frac{\lambda}{2}\log \lambda - \lambda - \log \Gamma(\lambda) - \log \sigma\right) \\ + (\lambda - 1)S \log\left(\frac{x - \mu}{\sigma} + \lambda^{1/2}\right) - \lambda^{1/2} S\left(\frac{x - \mu}{\sigma}\right)$$

and the estimation of μ, σ, and λ would require the simultaneous solution of the equations $\partial L/\partial \mu = 0$, $\partial L/\partial \sigma = 0$, $\partial L/\partial \lambda = 0$. This is clearly a formidable task. We can, however, estimate these parameters one at a time, assuming the others fixed. Thus for the estimation of μ we have

$$S\left[\frac{x - \mu}{\sigma} + \lambda^{1/2}\right]^{-1} = \frac{N\lambda^{1/2}}{\lambda - 1}$$

and

$$\frac{\partial^2 L}{\partial \mu^2} = -\frac{\lambda - 1}{\sigma^2} S\left[\frac{x - \mu}{\sigma} + \lambda^{1/2}\right]^{-2}$$

The expectation of $-\frac{\partial^2 L}{\partial \mu^2}$ is $\frac{\lambda}{\lambda - 2}\frac{N}{\sigma^2}$, so that the variance of the estimate of μ is $\frac{\lambda - 2}{\lambda}\frac{\sigma^2}{N}$. The efficiency of the moment estimate is, therefore, $(\lambda - 2)/\lambda = 1 - \frac{1}{2}\gamma_1^2$. This is practically equal to 1 for very small skewness but for $\gamma_1 = 1$ is only 50%.

12.6 The Chi-square Test of Goodness of Fit. If Np_i is the expected number of observations in the ith class, and if f_i is the observed frequency in that class, we have seen in § 5.12 that the quantity

$$(12.27) \quad \chi_s^2 = \sum_{i=1}^{k}(f_i - Np_i)^2/Np_i$$

is in the limit as $N \to \infty$ distributed as χ^2 with $k - 1$ degrees of freedom.

If the quantities p_i depend upon some parameter θ, θ may be estimated by maximizing the likelihood. By equation (5.75) the probability of the observed sample is

$$(12.28) \quad \frac{N!}{f_1! f_2! \cdots f_k!} p_1^{f_1} p_2^{f_2} \cdots p_k^{f_k}$$

so that

$$(12.29) \quad L = C + \sum f_i \log p_i$$

The equation for estimating θ is, therefore,

$$(12.30) \quad \frac{\partial L}{\partial \theta} = \sum \frac{f_i}{p_i}\frac{\partial p_i}{\partial \theta} = 0$$

and the variance in random samples of this estimate of θ is given by

$$\frac{1}{\sigma^2} = - E\left(\frac{\partial^2 L}{\partial \theta^2}\right)$$

$$= - E\sum\left\{\frac{f_i}{p_i}\frac{\partial^2 p_i}{\partial \theta^2} - \frac{f_i}{p_i^2}\left(\frac{\partial p_i}{\partial \theta}\right)^2\right\}$$

(12.31)
$$= - N\sum\frac{\partial^2 p_i}{\partial \theta^2} + N\sum\frac{1}{p_i}\left(\frac{\partial p_i}{\partial \theta}\right)^2$$

since $E(f_i) = Np_i$.

Remembering that $\sum p_i = 1$, we see that the first term in (12.31) vanishes, so that

(12.32)
$$\frac{1}{\sigma^2} = N\sum\frac{1}{p_i}\left(\frac{\partial p_i}{\partial \theta}\right)^2$$

Now from (12.27)

$$\chi_s^2 = \sum\frac{f_i^2}{Np_i} - N$$

so that if θ is estimated by making χ_s^2 a minimum, the condition is

(12.33)
$$\sum\frac{f_i^2}{Np_i^2}\frac{\partial p_i}{\partial \theta} = 0$$

which is not quite the same as (12.30) since f_i in general differs from Np_i. However, as $N \to \infty$, the ratio $f_i/Np_i \to 1$, for every value of i, so that in large samples the method of maximum likelihood is practically equivalent to minimizing χ_s^2. It should be remembered that it is only for very large samples that χ_s^2 has exactly the χ^2 distribution.

Now, in curve fitting, the true values of p_i have usually to be estimated from the sample. If the method of estimation is most-efficient, the value of χ_s^2 will be a minimum or very near it, but if the p_i are estimated by an inefficient method the calculated χ_s^2 will be too large, depending not only on the deviations of the observations from hypothesis but also on the errors of estimation of the parameters.[4]

Let $m_i = Np_i$, the true expected frequency in the ith class, and m_i' the frequency calculated from a most-efficient estimate T of a parameter of which the true value is θ. Writing $\delta T = \theta - T$, we have

$$\frac{1}{m_i} = \frac{1}{m_i'} + \delta T\frac{\partial}{\partial T}\left(\frac{1}{m_i'}\right) + \frac{1}{2}(\delta T)^2\frac{\partial^2}{\partial T^2}\left(\frac{1}{m_i'}\right) + \cdots$$

If $\chi_s'^2$ is the calculated value of χ_s^2,

$$\chi_s^2 - \chi_s'^2 = \sum f_i^2\left(\frac{1}{m_i} - \frac{1}{m_i'}\right)$$

$$= - \delta T\sum\frac{f_i^2}{m_i'^2}\frac{\partial m_i'}{\partial T}$$

$$+ \frac{1}{2}(\delta T)^2\sum\frac{f_i^2}{m_i'^3}\left\{2\left(\frac{\partial m_i'}{\partial T}\right)^2 - \frac{\partial^2 m_i'}{\partial T^2}m_i'\right\} + \cdots$$

Sec. 6   The Chi-square Test of Goodness of Fit

Since $\chi_s'^2$ is a minimum, $\sum \dfrac{f_i^2}{m_i'^2} \dfrac{\partial m_i'}{\partial T} = 0$, so that

$$\chi_s^2 - \chi_s'^2 = \frac{1}{2}(\delta T)^2 \sum \frac{f_i^2}{m_i'^3}\left\{2\left(\frac{\partial m_i'}{\partial T}\right)^2 - m_i'\frac{\partial^2 m_i}{\partial T^2}\right\} + \cdots$$

As the size of the sample increases, T approaches θ, so that $\delta T \to 0$, and also $f_i/m_i' \to 1$. For large N, therefore, we have approximately

(12.34)
$$\chi_s^2 - \chi_s'^2 = (\delta T)^2 \sum \left\{\frac{1}{m_i'}\left(\frac{\partial m_i'}{\partial T}\right)^2 - \frac{1}{2}\frac{\partial^2 m_i'}{\partial T^2}\right\}$$
$$= (\delta T)^2 \sum \frac{1}{m_i'}\left(\frac{\partial m_i'}{\partial T}\right)^2$$

since $\sum m_i' = N$, which is independent of T.

Now since m_i' is calculated from a most-efficient statistic T, the variance of this statistic is given by

$$\frac{1}{\sigma^2} = \sum \frac{1}{m_i'}\left(\frac{\partial m_i'}{\partial T}\right)^2$$

whence

(12.35) $$\chi_s^2 - \chi_s'^2 = (\delta T/\sigma)^2$$

Since $E(T - \theta) = 0$ and $\text{Var}(T - \theta) = \sigma^2$, $\delta T/\sigma$ is a standard normal variate. It is, moreover, independent of $\chi_s'^2$, which is a minimum value for variations in T. It was shown in § 5.12 that χ_s^2 is distributed as a sum of squares of $k - 1$ independent standard normal variates. Hence we see from (12.35) that $\chi_s'^2$ is distributed as a sum of squares of $k - 2$ independent standard normal variates. That is, $\chi_s'^2$ has the χ^2 distribution with $k - 2$ degrees of freedom.

This, however, is true only when we use a most-efficient statistic. If $\chi_s''^2$ is the value calculated by using a statistic T' of efficiency e and therefore of variance σ^2/e, we have, by the same argument as above,

(12.36) $$\chi_s''^2 - \chi_s'^2 = \left(\frac{\delta T'}{\sigma}\right)^2$$

where $\delta T' = T' - T$. The variance of $\delta T'$ is given by

$$\text{Var}(\delta T') = \text{Var}(T') + \text{Var}(T) - 2\,\text{Cov}(T, T')$$
$$= \sigma^2(1/e + 1) - 2\sigma^2 \rho_{T, T'}/e^{1/2}$$

Now the coefficient of correlation [5] between a statistic of efficiency e and a most-efficient statistic for estimating the same parameter is $e^{1/2}$, so that

(12.37) $$\text{Var}(\delta T') = \sigma^2(1/e - 1)$$

The mean value of $\chi_s''^2 - \chi_s'^2$ is, therefore, $1/e - 1$, and since the mean value of $\chi_s'^2$ is $k - 2$, that of $\chi_s''^2$ is $k - 3 + 1/e$. The distribution, however, is not that of χ^2, so that, when e is low, the mean value of the usual chi-square is altered and the tables of goodness of fit no longer apply.

12.7 The Correction of an Inefficient Estimate.

Since inefficient estimates are often much more easily obtained than efficient ones (for example, by the method of moments) and since, if the distribution is not very far from normal, the loss of efficiency may not be serious, it is sometimes worth while to apply a small correction to an inefficient estimate rather than go through the labor of finding the most efficient one.

If T is a most-efficient estimate and T' an estimate of efficiency e, then, as we have seen in (12.37), the variance of $T' - T$ is $\sigma^2(1/e - 1)$. If L is the likelihood, $\left(\frac{\partial L}{\partial \theta}\right)_T = 0$, and also, for large N, $-\frac{1}{\sigma_T^2} = \left(\frac{\partial^2 L}{\partial \theta^2}\right)_T$, approximately. Now, by Taylor's theorem,

$$\left(\frac{\partial L}{\partial \theta}\right)_{T'} = \left(\frac{\partial L}{\partial \theta}\right)_T + (T' - T)\left(\frac{\partial^2 L}{\partial \theta^2}\right)_T + \cdots$$
$$= -(T' - T)/\sigma_T^2$$

if squares and higher powers of $T' - T$ may be neglected. Since for values of e near 1 the variance of $T' - T$ is a small fraction of σ^2, this approximation is justified if the efficiency of T' is fairly high. We have, therefore, as an approximation

(12.38) $$T = T' + \sigma_T^2 \left(\frac{\partial L}{\partial \theta}\right)_{T'}$$

which enables us to correct T' to bring it nearer to T.

Example 6. In § 12.5 we saw that the moment estimate of the parameter μ of a Type III distribution with given σ^2 and λ is $T' = \bar{x}$, while the maximum likelihood estimate T is given by solving the equation

$$S\left[\frac{x-T}{\sigma} + \lambda^{1/2}\right]^{-1} = N\lambda^{1/2}(\lambda - 1)^{-1}$$

which is of degree N. The variance of T is $\frac{\lambda - 2}{\lambda} \frac{\sigma^2}{N}$. Hence, from (12.26) and (12.38) we have approximately

(12.39) $$\begin{aligned}T &= \bar{x} - \frac{\lambda - 2}{\lambda}\frac{\sigma^2}{N}\left[\frac{\lambda - 1}{\sigma}S\left(\frac{x - \bar{x}}{\sigma} + \lambda^{1/2}\right)^{-1} - \frac{N\lambda^{1/2}}{\sigma}\right] \\ &= \bar{x} - \frac{\sigma(\lambda - 2)}{\lambda}\left[(\lambda - 1)\frac{1}{N}S\left(\frac{x - \bar{x}}{\sigma} + \lambda^{1/2}\right)^{-1} - \lambda^{1/2}\right]\end{aligned}$$

From the data of Example 3 in § 5.14, assuming that the parent population is of Type III with $\sigma = 138$ milliseconds and $\gamma_1 = 0.4$ ($\lambda = 25$), we have $T' = 204$ milliseconds. The value of $\frac{1}{N}S\left(\frac{x - \bar{x}}{\sigma} + \lambda^{1/2}\right)^{-1}$ for the grouped distribution turns out to be 0.2085, whence $T = 203.5$ milliseconds. The correction in this case is quite small.

Example 7. Ability to taste phenyl-thio-carbamide is known to be inherited as a Mendelian dominant character. If p is the probability of possessing the gene T and q that of possessing t, the only non-tasters are those with two t genes, while individuals with TT or Tt are tasters. In a random collection, therefore, the probability that any given individual is a non-taster is q^2.

The value of q was estimated for chimpanzees from a collection of 28 animals. Of these, 23 were unrelated and included 5 non-tasters. The probability of this sample is $C(q^2)^5(1 - q^2)^{18}$.

Sec. 8   The Neyman-Pearson Theory   381

A group of 3 animals (2 parents and a child) were all non-tasters. Since if both parents possess tt genes the child is necessarily a non-taster, the probability of this group is q^4. Another group of 2 (mother and child) were both tasters. It can be shown by working out the various possible cases that the probability of this combination is $(1 - q)(1 + q - q^2)$.

For the whole sample the proportion of non-tasters was 2/7, which gives as a rough estimate of q the value $(2/7)^{1/2} = 0.5345$.

The probability of the combined sample is $P = Cq^{10}(1 - q^2)^{18}q^4(1 - q)(1 + q - q^2)$, so that $L = C_1 + 10 \log q + 18 \log (1 - q^2) + 4 \log q + \log (1 - q) + \log (1 + q - q^2)$. Hence

$$\frac{\partial L}{\partial q} = \frac{14}{q} - \frac{36q}{1 - q^2} - \frac{1}{1 - q} - \frac{2q - 1}{1 + q - q^2}$$

The maximum likelihood equation for q is thus a fourth degree algebraic equation,

$$14 + 14q - 68q^2 - 51q^3 + 53q^4 = 0$$

This can be solved by systematic trial and error (bracketing) and gives the estimate $\hat{q} = 0.5141$.

In order to use the approximation (12.38) we need to evaluate $\partial L/\partial q$ for $q = 0.5345$ (which gives -2.95) and to estimate $\sigma_{\hat{q}}^2$. The latter can be found from $\partial^2 L/\partial q^2$ and is 0.00685. The corrected rough estimate of q is, therefore, $0.5345 - .00685 \times 2.95 = 0.5143$, extremely close to the true maximum likelihood value.

12.8 The Neyman-Pearson Theory of Confidence Intervals.[6]   Several examples of estimation by confidence intervals have been given in earlier chapters. In general terms the problem is to find two functions of the sample S, say $\underline{\theta}(S)$ and $\bar{\theta}(S)$, such that

(12.40) $\Pr \{\underline{\theta}(S) \leq \theta_0 \leq \bar{\theta}(S) \mid \theta_0\} = 1 - \alpha$

where α is a fixed number between 0 and 1, say 0.05. That is, the probability that the interval between $\underline{\theta}(S)$ and $\bar{\theta}(S)$ includes, or covers, the true value θ_0 is to be 0.95, whatever this true value may be.

Let T be a statistic used to estimate θ, and let $g(T, \theta)$ be the frequency function of T. For any value of θ we can find two quantities γ_1 and γ_2 (depending on θ and α) such that

$$\Pr \{\gamma_1 < T < \gamma_2 \mid \theta\} = \int_{\gamma_1}^{\gamma_2} g(T, \theta) \, dT = 1 - \alpha$$

This can be done in infinitely many ways, since all that is necessary is that the sum of the areas of the two tails, one from $-\infty$ to γ_1 and the other from γ_2 to ∞ shall be equal to α. As θ varies, the points (γ_1, θ) and (γ_2, θ) describe curves C_1 and C_2 in the plane of T and θ, and in most cases each of these curves will be cut by a straight line parallel to the axis of θ in one point only. (See Figure 16, Chapter VI.) If the ordinates of the points on C_1 and C_2 where the curves are cut by a vertical line $T = $ constant are $\bar{\theta}(T)$ and $\underline{\theta}(T)$, where these functions depend, of course, on α, then the region between the curves C_1 and C_2 is characterized equally well by $\gamma_1 < T < \gamma_2$ for all θ, or by $C_2 < \theta < C_1$ for all T. Hence it follows that

$$\Pr \{\underline{\theta} < \theta < \bar{\theta} \mid \theta\} = 1 - \alpha$$

where $\underline{\theta}$ and $\bar{\theta}$ are functions of T and therefore of the sample S, since T is a statistic calculated from S. The probability is interpreted in the sense explained in § 6.4.

The quantities $\underline{\theta}(T)$ and $\bar{\theta}(T)$ are lower and upper *confidence limits* respectively, corresponding to the *confidence coefficient* $1 - \alpha$, or, to phrase it differently, at the level α. The risk of accepting the hypothesis that the confidence interval includes the true value when in fact it does not do so is α.

There are several arbitrary elements about this procedure:

1. The *choice of the statistic T*. The same parameter may be estimated by more than one statistic. The population mean, for example, may be estimated by the sample mean or the sample median.

2. The *choice of the confidence coefficient*. This depends on the risk of error one is prepared to take, and will vary according to the seriousness of the consequences that may follow from making an error of this kind.

3. The *division of the risk* between the upper and lower tails of the distribution. The risk that θ is below $\underline{\theta}(S)$ need not be equal (although it often is so) to the risk that θ is above $\bar{\theta}(S)$. In some cases we may be particularly desirous not to *underestimate* θ, and in other cases not to *overestimate* it.

4. *The sample size*. The larger the sample the more accurately θ can be estimated from it, and hence the narrower the confidence interval for a given confidence coefficient.

It is clearly desirable, as a general rule, to have a confidence interval as short as possible. The confidence interval δ from $\underline{\theta}$ to $\bar{\theta}$ is said to be a *shortest confidence interval*, corresponding to the coefficient α, if the condition (12.40) is satisfied and if, δ' being any other confidence interval from $\underline{\theta}'$ to $\bar{\theta}'$ also satisfying (12.40), δ is less likely than δ' to cover a *false* value θ_1 when the true value is θ_0. Symbolically,

$$(12.41) \qquad \Pr\{\underline{\theta} \leq \theta_1 \leq \bar{\theta} \mid \theta_0\} \leq \Pr\{\underline{\theta}' \leq \theta_1 \leq \bar{\theta}' \mid \theta_0\}$$

for all values of θ_1 and whatever the true value θ_0 may be. Unfortunately it is quite exceptional to be able to find such a shortest confidence interval. It may be remarked that the word "shortest" as used here does not necessarily mean shortest in the sense of having minimum length, and Kendall has proposed to use instead the term "most selective."

A confidence interval is *unbiased* if the probability that it covers θ_0 when the true value is θ_0 is $1 - \alpha$ but the probability that it covers θ_1 when the true value is θ_0 is always equal to or less than $1 - \alpha$, whatever the values of θ_1 and θ_0. The probability of covering a false value θ_1 is, therefore, never greater than the probability of covering the true value, no matter on which side of the true value θ_1 may lie. This is the sense in which the interval is "unbiased." If condition (12.41) is satisfied when both the confidence intervals mentioned are unbiased, then δ is a *shortest unbiased confidence interval*. Sometimes we can find *shortest one-sided confidence intervals*, for which $\Pr\{\delta \text{ covers } \theta_1 \mid \theta_0\} \leq$

Sec. 9 Geometrical Illustration of Confidence Intervals 383

Pr $\{\delta' \text{ covers } \theta_1 \mid \theta_0\}$ for all θ_1 on one side only of θ_0, that is, for which $\theta_1 - \theta_0$ is always positive or always negative.

12.9 A Geometrical Illustration of Confidence Intervals. It is often convenient to think of a set of sample values $x_1, x_2, \cdots x_N$ as determining a point E in an N-dimensional Euclidean space, the sample space W. The frequency function of x determines a density associated with each point.

We suppose that the frequency function depends on several parameters $\theta, \theta', \theta'' \cdots$, of which we desire to estimate θ. We add a new dimension to the sample space, providing an axis of θ, as shown in Figure 40 for the case $N = 2$. For each point E the quantities $\underline{\theta}(E)$ and $\bar{\theta}(E)$ determine points U and L on a line through E parallel to the axis of θ.

For any given value of θ, say θ_1, the space W in the diagram is plane. Let E be the point corresponding to a particular set of sample values, and let the line through E parallel to the axis of θ cut the space W in E_1. Then all the points E_1 which are such that the points L and U lie on opposite sides of E_1 constitute the region of acceptance A, and the interval from L to U covers or includes E_1. If, on the other hand, E_1 is outside the region of acceptance, say at E_1', the points L and U lie on the *same* side of E_1, and the interval does not include θ_1. Hence, for any fixed θ_1,

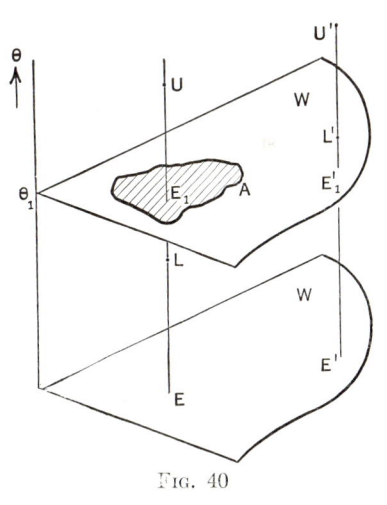

$$\Pr\{\underline{\theta} \leq \theta_1 \leq \bar{\theta}\} = \Pr\{E \epsilon A(\theta_1) \mid \theta, \theta' \cdots\}$$

where the notation $E \epsilon A(\theta_1)$ means that E is an element of the region of acceptance corresponding to the value θ_1 of the parameter θ. (The points E and E_1 are the same, as far as the sample space is concerned.) It follows that, if the confidence limits are determined so that $\Pr\{\underline{\theta} \leq \theta \leq \bar{\theta} \mid \theta, \theta', \cdots\} = 1 - \alpha$, then for all θ,

(12.42) $$\Pr\{E \epsilon A(\theta) \mid \theta, \theta' \cdots\} = 1 - \alpha$$

Fig. 40

The region $A(\theta)$ cannot, therefore, be empty for any permissible value of θ.

If the functions $\underline{\theta}$ and $\bar{\theta}$ are single-valued and determined for all points E, there must be at least one region of acceptance for every E. Moreover, if a sample point falls in the regions $A(\theta_1)$ and $A(\theta_2)$ corresponding to two values θ_1 and θ_2 of θ, it will fall in the region $A(\theta_3)$ corresponding to any θ_3 between θ_1 and θ_2, and vice versa. These conditions are sufficient, as well as necessary, so that in order to find the confidence limits for any given sample we can take the upper and lower bounds of the interval of θ for which E lies within the region of acceptance $A(\theta)$.

12.10 The Determination of Confidence Intervals. If we have a *sufficient* statistic T for estimating θ, the likelihood function is

$$L = L_1(T, \theta) + L_2(x_1, x_2 \cdots x_N, \theta', \theta'' \cdots)$$

The equation $T = $ constant determines a set of surfaces in W, and the condition $T \leq k$ determines a region K. The probability that E falls in K depends only on T and θ, and by appropriately choosing k we can make this probability equal to $1 - \alpha$. Confidence intervals can then be set up as in § 12.9.

Example 8. For a normal population with mean μ and variance σ^2, the sample mean $\bar{x}$ is a sufficient statistic for estimating μ. The likelihood function can be written

$$L = C - N \log \sigma - \frac{N}{2\sigma^2}(\bar{x} - \mu)^2 - \frac{1}{2\sigma^2} S(x_\alpha - \bar{x})^2$$

which shows the sufficiency. It is known that $\bar{x}$ is normally distributed with mean μ and variance σ^2/N, so that if the region K is determined by $|\bar{x} - \mu| \leq \tau_\alpha \sigma/\sqrt{N}$, where τ_α is that value of a standard normal variate for which $2\int_{\tau_\alpha}^{\infty} \phi(t) \, dt = \alpha$, then $\Pr\{E \epsilon K\} = 1 - \alpha$.

The confidence limits are given by

$$\bar{x} - \tau_\alpha \sigma N^{-1/2} \leq \mu \leq \bar{x} + \tau_\alpha \sigma N^{-1/2}$$

We are here supposing that σ is known, even though μ is unknown.

If the standard deviation or other scale parameter is unknown, we can sometimes use the method of "studentization." Suppose that in Example 8 above, both μ and σ are unknown. Since $\bar{x}$ is normally distributed, and since the sample variance s^2 is distributed as $\sigma^2 \chi^2/N$ independently of $\bar{x}$, the quantity $t = \dfrac{\bar{x} - \mu}{s/n^{1/2}}$, where $n = N - 1$, has the Student t-distribution, given by

$$f(t) = k\left(1 + \frac{t^2}{n}\right)^{-\frac{n+1}{2}}$$

If we now choose t_α so that $\int_{-\infty}^{-t_\alpha} f(t) \, dt = \int_{t_\alpha}^{\infty} f(t) \, dt = \alpha/2$, we have

$$\Pr\{-t_\alpha \leq t \leq t_\alpha\} = 1 - \alpha$$

which is equivalent to

$$\Pr\{\bar{x} - n^{-1/2} s t_\alpha \leq \mu \leq \bar{x} + n^{-1/2} s t_\alpha\} = 1 - \alpha$$

The confidence interval is now a function of the sample values only, once α is given.

This method depends upon the possibility of finding a function of the parameter to be estimated whose distribution is independent of any unknown parameters. Such a fortunate state of affairs does not occur very frequently.

Sec. 11 Confidence Intervals and Fiducial Inference

Example 9 (Neyman [7]). Suppose the variables x_1 and x_2 are independently and rectangularly distributed on the range from 0 to θ. It is required to determine a confidence interval for θ from a single sample of the two variables, with confidence coefficient 3/4.

The joint frequency function is

$$f(x_1, x_2) = \frac{1}{\theta^2}, \quad 0 < x_1 < \theta, \quad 0 < x_2 < \theta$$

and zero elsewhere.

If in Figure 41 (a), we regard the shaded region as a region of acceptance corresponding to the value θ, and consider the set of all such regions for all values of θ (lying in parallel planes

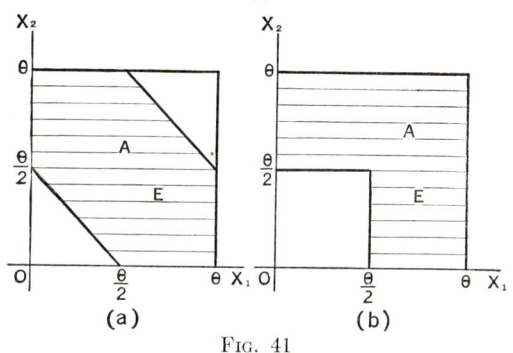

Fig. 41

as in Figure 40), then it is easy to verify that the conditions governing regions of acceptance given at the end of § 12.9 are fulfilled. The point $E(x_1, x_2)$ lies in the region $A(\theta)$ if $\theta/2 \leq x_1 + x_2 \leq 3\theta/2$, and this condition may be expressed as $\frac{2}{3}(x_1 + x_2) \leq \theta \leq 2(x_1 + x_2)$. Hence the confidence limits are $\frac{2}{3}(x_1 + x_2)$ and $2(x_1 + x_2)$.

Various other confidence limits corresponding to the same confidence coefficient may be assigned. Thus the shaded region in Figure 41(b) is also a region of acceptance, which may be characterized by $\theta/2 \leq L \leq \theta$, where L is the larger of the two values x_1 and x_2. Expressing this condition as $L \leq \theta \leq 2L$, we see that the confidence limits are L and $2L$. Since L is certainly less than $\frac{4}{3}(x_1 + x_2)$, the confidence interval in case (b) is shorter than that in case (a). It may be shown that case (b) actually gives a shortest interval in Neyman's sense.

12.11 Confidence Intervals and Fiducial Inference. R. A. Fisher has developed in a series of papers [8] a theory of fiducial inference which is distinct in principle from the Neyman-Pearson theory, although in most practical problems the two theories give identical results. One problem in which they differ has been discussed in § 9.8, namely, the Behrens-Fisher problem.

In the theory of fiducial inference we imagine a hypothetical distribution of conceivable values of the parameter θ to be estimated. It is not, of course, necessary to assume some actual *a priori* distribution of θ, for then we should be doing what Bayes did (§ 1.10). If T is a statistic used to estimate θ, and if it is a *sufficient* statistic, the fiducial distribution of θ, which is derived from that of T, is unique. No problem of selecting the "best" or "shortest" interval arises if sufficient statistics alone are used.

If $F(T, \theta)$ is the distribution function for T, the frequency function is given by

(12.43) $$dF = \frac{\partial F(T, \theta)}{\partial T} dT$$

Now $F(T_1, \theta)$ is the probability that for a fixed value of θ a random value of T *will not* exceed T_1, and this is taken as the fiducial probability that for a fixed value of T_1 a random value of θ *will* exceed T_1. Note that in Figure 16 of § 6.4, the locus of the lower bound of t as θ varies is also the locus of the upper bound of θ as t varies. The fiducial distribution of θ is therefore given by

(12.44) $$dF = -\frac{\partial F(T, \theta)}{\partial \theta} d\theta = f(\theta) d\theta$$

It is assumed that the variate x is continuously distributed. The fiducial distribution of θ is not an *a priori* probability and is not to be interpreted in a frequency sense. The idea is (the word "fiducia" means trust) that $\int_{\theta_1}^{\theta_2} f(\theta) d\theta$ is a measure of our belief that θ lies between θ_1 and θ_2.

Example 10. For a normal population with mean μ and variance σ^2, where σ^2 is known and μ is to be estimated, the distribution of the sample mean $\bar{x}$ is given by

$$dF = \frac{N^{1/2}}{(2\pi)^{1/2}\sigma} \exp\{-N(\bar{x} - \mu)^2/2\sigma^2\} d\bar{x}$$

since $\bar{x}$ is normally distributed about μ with variance σ^2/N. Hence

$$F(\bar{x}, \mu) = \int_{-\infty}^{\bar{x}} (N/2\pi)^{1/2}\sigma^{-1} \exp\{-N(u - \mu)^2/2\sigma^2\} du$$

and

$$-\frac{\partial F(\bar{x}, \mu)}{\partial \mu} = (N/2\pi)^{1/2}\sigma^{-1} \int_{-\infty}^{\bar{x}} \frac{2N}{2\sigma^2}(u - \mu)e^{-N(u-\mu)^2/2\sigma^2} du$$
$$= (N/2\pi)^{1/2}\sigma^{-1}e^{-N(\bar{x}-\mu)^2/2\sigma^2}$$

The fiducial distribution of μ is, therefore, a normal distribution with mean $\bar{x}$ and variance σ^2/N. Consequently the fiducial limits are precisely the same as the confidence limits of Example 8, with known σ.

The Behrens-Fisher problem is concerned with the difference of the means of two independent normal populations with possibly different variances. If $x_{11}, x_{12}, \cdots x_{1N}$ is a random sample of N observations from the first population, in the order in which they are observed, and if $x_{21}, x_{22}, \cdots x_{2N'}$ is a random sample of N' observations from the second population ($N' > N$), also in the order of occurrence, then by sacrificing some of the observations from the second sample, we can form confidence limits for the difference δ of the two means.

If $u_i = x_{1i} - x_{2i}$, $i = 1, 2, \cdots N$, we have

(12.45) $$\begin{cases} E(u_i) = \delta \\ \text{Var}(u_i) = \sigma_1^2 + \sigma_2^2 \end{cases}$$

where σ_1^2 and σ_2^2 are the two variances. The consecutive u_i are normal and independent and we shall have the confidence interval

(12.46) $$\bar{u} - t_\alpha S \leq \delta \leq \bar{u} + t_\alpha S$$

where $\bar{u}$ is the mean of the u_i, $S^2 = \sum(u_i - \bar{u})^2/N(N-1)$ which is an unbiased estimate of $(\sigma_1^2 + \sigma_2^2)/N$, and t_α is the value of Student's t (with $N-1$ degrees of freedom) corresponding to the confidence coefficient $1 - \alpha$.

In an experiment consisting of repeated sampling from a pair of normal populations, the relative frequency of cases in which the statement (12.46) would be true, whatever the values of the respective means and variances, would be approximately $1 - \alpha$.

Fisher's solution of the problem has been given in § 9.8, leading to fiducial limits expressed by (9.27) and calculated with the help of Sukhatme's tables. However, as pointed out in that section, these fiducial limits are not confidence limits.

12.12 Tests of Hypotheses. In many practical problems samples are examined in order to test some hypothesis about the parent population, for example, that the mean is not greater than some specified value, or that the proportion of individuals with some definite characteristic lies within assigned limits.

Two kinds of errors may be made regarding this hypothesis: (1) The hypothesis may be rejected when it is really true (this is called an *error of the first kind*); (2) the hypothesis may *not* be rejected when it is really false (this is called an *error of the second kind*). The usual testing procedure is designed so as to limit the risk of errors of the first kind to a specified value (such as 0.05) and at the same time to reduce as far as possible the risk of errors of the second kind.

As a simple example, consider the estimation of the mean of a normal population from samples of a fixed size. If the true mean is, say, 100 and if the standard error of a sample mean is 1, then, for a confidence coefficient of 0.95, the region of acceptance of the hypothesis that the true mean is 100 can be chosen in many ways, including the three indicated in Figure 42. The intervals (a) 98.35 to ∞ and (b) 98 to 102 and (c) − ∞ to 101.65 are each such that if a sample mean falls *outside* this interval, which will happen with a

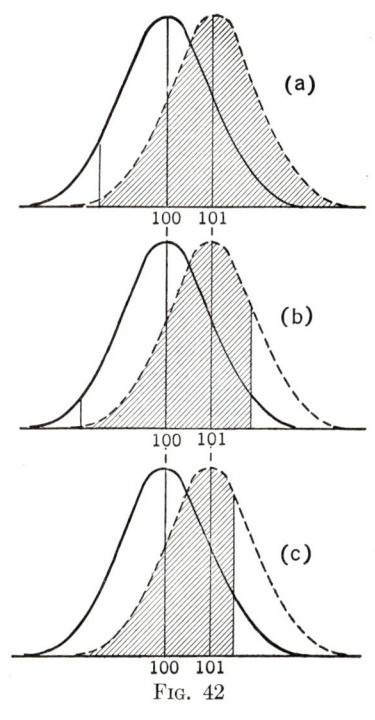

FIG. 42

probability of 0.05, the hypothesis that the true mean is 100 will be rejected even though in fact this hypothesis is true. The risk of an error of the first kind is, therefore, in each case 0.05. If, however, the true mean is 100, the probability of accepting a value different from 100, say 101, is greater in (a) than in (b) and greater in (b) than in (c), the probabilities being indicated by the shaded areas under the dotted curves with mean 101. The probability of committing an error of the second kind is, therefore, least with the interval (c) and greatest with (a), and this will be true whenever the false mean is greater than the true mean. For a false mean less than the true mean, say 99, the conditions are reversed and the probability of an error of the second kind is least with the interval (a) and greatest with (c).

In the general problem of testing a hypothesis we have a set of random variables $X_1, X_2 \cdots X_N$, with a joint probability distribution $F(x_1, x_2 \cdots x_N)$. The statistical hypothesis H_ω is that $F(x_1, \cdots x_N)$ belongs to a certain subclass ω of distribution functions out of the whole class Ω of possible distribution functions. If the class ω consists of a single element, the hypothesis is said to be *simple*. Otherwise, it is called *composite*. The hypothesis that the variables are normally and independently distributed with mean 0 and variance 1 would be a simple hypothesis, because this specification determines F uniquely.

The set of observations $X_1, X_2 \cdots X_N$ determines, as noted previously, a point E in the sample space W. In order to test the hypothesis H_ω we have to choose a certain region A in W such that, whenever E falls outside A, H_ω is to be rejected, and whenever E falls within A, H_ω may be accepted. The region A is called the *region of acceptance*. Commonly we have, or assume, a certain amount of information about the function $F(x_1, \cdots x_N)$, as for instance that the variables are independently and normally distributed with the same distribution. In this case

$$dF = \prod_i \phi(x_i)dx_i, \text{ where } \phi(x_i) = \frac{1}{\sqrt{2\pi}} e^{-(x_i-\mu)^2/2\sigma^2}$$

and the hypothesis can refer only to the magnitudes of μ or σ or both.

Problems of testing hypotheses and problems of estimation are both parts of statistical inference, although they do not cover the whole field. The following problem, for instance, which arises in the quality control of manufactured products, is not precisely in either of the above classes. Assuming that in respect of some measurable quality the product should lie between certain specified limits, we have to decide on the basis of a sample whether a given batch of material should be classified as (a) between these limits, (b) above the upper limit, or (c) below the lower limit.

12.13 The Power of a Test. The size of the region of acceptance A is measured by the probability that the sample point E falls within A, calculated on the assumption that the hypothesis H_ω is true. In other words, the size

Sec. 13   The Power of a Test

of this region is $1 - \alpha$ if the probability of committing an error of the first kind is α. Thus if the distribution function $F(x_1, x_2 \cdots x_N)$ depends on a certain unknown parameter θ, and if the hypothesis H_0 is that $\theta = \theta_0$,

(12.47)
$$\Pr \{E \epsilon A \mid \theta_0\} = \int_{(A)} dF(x_1, x_2 \cdots x_N, \theta_0)$$
$$= 1 - \alpha$$

If the alternative hypothesis H_1 is that $\theta = \theta_1$, the probability of committing an error of the second kind, that is, of accepting H_0 when H_1 is true, is

$$\Pr \{E \epsilon A \mid \theta_1\} = \beta$$

The quantity $1 - \beta$ is called the *power* of the region A with respect to the alternative hypothesis $\theta = \theta_1$.

If the power is plotted for different values of θ_1 we get the *power curve* of the region A.

Example 11. If $x_1, x_2 \cdots x_N$ is a sample of N independent observations from a normal population with variance 1 and unknown mean μ,

(12.48) $dF(x_1, x_2 \cdots x_N, \mu) = (2\pi)^{-N/2} \exp[-\tfrac{1}{2} \sum (x_i - \mu)^2] \, dx_1 \cdots dx_N$

Let the hypothesis H_0 be that $\mu = 0$. The region of acceptance for a confidence coefficient of 0.95 may be selected as that region A for which $|\bar{x}| \leq 1.96 N^{-1/2}$, since

$$\Pr \{E \epsilon A \mid \mu = 0\} = (2\pi)^{-N/2} \int_{(A)} \cdots \int e^{-\tfrac{1}{2}\Sigma x_i^2} \, dx_1 \cdots dx_N$$

and if we make an orthogonal transformation to new variables $y_1, \cdots y_N$, of which $y_1 = \bar{x} N^{1/2}$, we obtain

(12.49)
$$\Pr \{E \epsilon A \mid \mu = 0\} = (2\pi)^{-\tfrac{1}{2}} \int_{-1.96}^{1.96} e^{-\tfrac{1}{2} y_1^2} \, dy_1$$
$$= 0.95$$

If the alternative hypothesis H_1 is that $\mu = \mu_1$, the probability of accepting H_0 when H_1 is true is

$$\Pr \{E \epsilon A \mid \mu = \mu_1\} = (2\pi)^{-N/2} \int_{(A)} \cdots \int \exp[-\tfrac{1}{2} \sum (x_i - \mu_1)^2] \, dx_1 \cdots dx_N$$

By a similar transformation to that used in (12.49) we can show that

(12.50)
$$\Pr \{E \epsilon A \mid \mu = \mu_1\} = (2\pi)^{-\tfrac{1}{2}} \int_{\delta_1}^{\delta_2} e^{-\tfrac{1}{2} y_1^2} \, dy_1$$
$$= \Phi(\delta_2) - \Phi(\delta_1)$$

where $\delta_1 = -1.96 - \mu_1 N^{1/2}$ and $\delta_2 = 1.96 - \mu_1 N^{1/2}$.

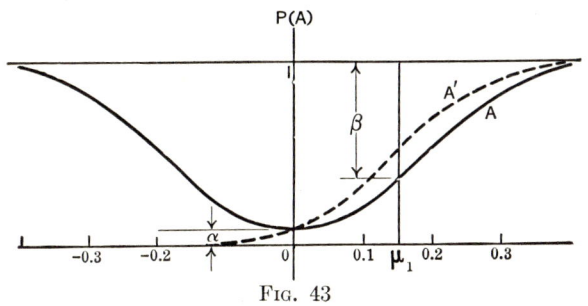

FIG. 43

Hence the power of the region with respect to the hypothesis H_1 is $1 + \Phi(\delta_1) - \Phi(\delta_2)$. This is plotted for different values of μ_1 (and for $N = 100$) in Figure 43.

12.14 Uniformly Most Powerful Tests. The region of acceptance corresponding to a given value of α can, in general, be chosen in many ways. If A and A' are two regions of the same size, and if the power curve of A' is below that of A for all values of θ_1, then A' is not as good as A for testing the hypothesis $\theta = \theta_1$. For it is clear that since A and A' are of the same size, the probability (α) of an error of the first kind is the same for both, but the probability (β) of an error of the second kind is less for A than it is for A'. That is, in the long run we shall more frequently go wrong if we use the region A' to distinguish between the hypotheses H_0 and H_1 than if we use the region A, no matter what the true value of θ may be. We then say that the test using A is *uniformly more powerful* than the test using A'. If this is so for all possible alternative regions A' of the same size as A, the test using A is a *uniformly most powerful* test. If such a test can be found we shall naturally be quite satisfied with it, as no better one could be devised for distinguishing between H_0 and H_1 at the specified level α. This situation, however, rarely arises. Usually the power curve for another region A' will be above that for A in some parts of the range of θ and below it in other parts.

Thus, in Example 11 above, we can choose as A' the region for which $\bar{x} \leq 1.65 N^{-1/2}$, which also has a size 0.95. The power of A' with respect to H_1 is $1 - \Phi(1.65 - \mu_1 N^{1/2})$. The curve is plotted in Figure 43, and is above that for A when $\mu_1 > 0$ and below that for A when $\mu_1 < 0$. Hence if we have reason to believe that the unknown μ is positive, we shall prefer a test using A' to a test using A, but if we have no reason to expect positive values rather than negative values we shall probably prefer the test using A, which is more symmetrical.

The test using A, in fact, satisfies another criterion introduced by Neyman and Pearson, namely, that of being *unbiased*. A test is unbiased if its power curve for testing the hypothesis that $\theta = \theta_0$ has a minimum at the value θ_0. If so, the probability of rejecting the hypothesis is smaller if θ is really θ_0 than if θ is really some neighboring value θ_1, and this is naturally desirable. Since it is usually impossible to find a uniformly most powerful unbiased test (one which is *uniformly* more powerful than any other unbiased test), Neyman and Pearson have suggested using an unbiased test which is *most powerful in the neighborhood* of θ_0. That is, if $P(A \mid \theta)$ is the power of the region A with respect to the hypothesis that the unknown parameter is equal to θ, then we should choose A so that

(12.51) $\quad$ (a) $\left[\dfrac{\partial P(A \mid \theta)}{\partial \theta}\right]_{\theta=\theta_0} = 0$

$\qquad\qquad$ (b) $\left[\dfrac{\partial^2 P(A \mid \theta)}{\partial \theta^2}\right]_{\theta=\theta_0} \geq \left[\dfrac{\partial^2 P(A' \mid \theta)}{\partial \theta^2}\right]_{\theta=\theta_0}$

Sec. 15   Regions with More than One Parameter

for all A' satisfying (a) and of the same size as A. The second condition requires the curvature of the power curve at the minimum to be greater for A than for any unbiased alternative A'.

It may be proved that these two conditions can be satisfied in many practical cases. In Example 11 above, the region A satisfies the more stringent conditions of being a uniformly most powerful unbiased test.

The chief objection to the criterion (12.51) is that in practice we are more interested in distinguishing between widely separated values θ_0 and θ_1 than between values which are close together. For very large samples, however, the difficulties of finding uniformly most powerful tests are greatly lessened, and *asymptotically most powerful* [9] tests may be shown to exist in most cases of practical interest. A similar situation exists with regard to confidence intervals. It is frequently possible to obtain *asymptotically shortest unbiased confidence intervals*, even in cases where shortest unbiased confidence intervals in the sense defined in § 12.8 do not exist.

12.15 Confidence Regions with More than One Parameter. Let us suppose that the distribution function of the population depends on a set of parameters $\theta_1, \theta_2 \cdots \theta_h$, of which we desire to estimate a sub-set, $\theta_1 \cdots \theta_m (m < h)$. The remaining parameters are nuisance parameters. Any one particular set of values of $\theta_1, \theta_2 \cdots \theta_m$ determines a point P in an m-dimensional parameter space. If we can find a region A_θ of this space, determined entirely by the sample, such that $\Pr\{P \epsilon A_\theta\} = 1 - \alpha$, whatever the true values of any of the parameters $\theta_1, \theta_2 \cdots \theta_h$, then A_θ is a confidence region for P with confidence coefficient $1 - \alpha$.

It will be seen that the estimation of a single parameter is a special case of this, where the region A_θ reduces to a line interval, bounded by $\underline{\theta}$ and $\bar{\theta}$.

Example 12. Suppose we have two independent samples of sizes N_1 and N_2 from normal populations with different means μ_1 and μ_2 and a common variance σ^2. It is required to find a confidence region for the two means.

The quantities $S_1/\sigma^2, S_2/\sigma^2, N_1 d_1^2/\sigma^2$ and $N_2 d_2^2/\sigma^2$, where S_1 and S_2 are the sums of squares for the two samples, $d_1 = \bar{X}_1 - \mu_1$, and $d_2 = \bar{X}_2 - \mu_2$, are independently distributed as χ^2 with $N_1 - 1, N_2 - 1, 1$ and 1 degrees of freedom respectively. Hence $(S_1 + S_2)/\sigma^2$ and $(N_1 d_1^2 + N_2 d_2^2)/\sigma^2$ are distributed as χ^2 with $N_1 + N_2 - 2$ and 2 degrees of freedom, so that

$$F = \frac{N_1 + N_2 - 2}{2} \cdot \frac{N_1 d_1^2 + N_2 d_2^2}{S_1 + S_2}$$

has the Snedecor F distribution with 2 and $N_1 + N_2 - 2$ degrees of freedom. If F_α is determined by $\int_0^{F_\alpha} f(F)\, dF = 1 - \alpha$, $f(F)$ being the frequency function for F, the probability that $F \leq F_\alpha$ is $1 - \alpha$.

This is the probability that

$$N_1(\bar{X}_1 - \mu_1)^2 + N_2(\bar{X}_2 - \mu_2)^2 \leq 2F_\alpha(S_1 + S_2)/(N_1 + N_2 - 2)$$

that is, the probability that the point (μ_1, μ_2) in the $\mu_1 \mu_2$ plane lies inside the ellipse with equation

$$(12.52) \quad N_1(\bar{X}_1 - \mu_1)^2 + N_2(\bar{X}_2 - \mu_2)^2 = 2F_\alpha(S_1 + S_2)/(N_1 + N_2 - 2)$$

The ellipse is the confidence region A in the two-dimensional parameter space of μ_1 and μ_2. In this example the nuisance parameter σ^2 disappears.

12.16 Composite Hypotheses.

If the distribution under test depends on $r + s$ parameters $\theta_1 \cdots \theta_r, \theta_{r+1} \cdots \theta_{r+s}$, a null hypothesis H_0 which specifies the form of the distribution and the s parameters $\theta_{r+1} \cdots \theta_{r+s}$, while leaving the others unspecified, is a *composite hypothesis* of r degrees of freedom. Additional specification of the parameters $\theta_1 \cdots \theta_r$ will give a simple hypothesis, H_1, and the problem is to find a region of acceptance of a fixed size, whatever the values of $\theta_1 \cdots \theta_r$, such that errors of the second kind are minimized for all admissible simple alternatives H_1.

Example 13. A sample of size N is taken from a normal population of mean μ and variance σ^2. If σ is unspecified, the hypothesis H_0 (that $\mu = \mu_0$) has 1 degree of freedom.

We wish to find a critical region A such that $\int_{(A)} p_0 \, dx_1 \cdots dx_N = 1 - \alpha$, whatever the value of σ, p_0 being the probability of the sample calculated on the hypothesis H_0. Among the admissible regions we then have to find the best (that is, the one which minimizes error of the second kind) for the alternative simple hypothesis H_1 (that $\mu = \mu_1$ and $\sigma = \sigma_1$).

Now the likelihood L is given by

$$(12.53) \quad L = \log p_0 = -\frac{N}{2} \log(2\pi\sigma^2) - \frac{1}{2\sigma^2} \sum (x_i - \mu_0)^2$$
$$= C - N \log \sigma - \frac{N}{2\sigma^2}[(\bar{x} - \mu_0)^2 + s^2]$$

where $\bar{x}$ and s^2 are the sample mean and variance respectively. Hence p_0 is constant over the surface of the hypersphere

$$\sum_i (x_i - \mu_0)^2 = \text{constant}$$

and A may be chosen by taking on each hypersphere an area which is a fraction $1 - \alpha$ of its total area and combining these fractions. This area is clearly independent of σ.

Our problem is now to minimize $\int_{(A)} p_1 \, dx_1 \cdots dx_N$, where p_1 is the probability of the sample calculated on hypothesis H_1, subject to the condition $\int_{(A)} p_0 \, dx_1 \cdots dx_N = 1 - \alpha$. If we can do this we reduce the chance of error of the second kind to a minimum while retaining the chance of error of the first kind at the fixed value α.

The problem is equivalent to that of minimizing (without restriction) the integral $\int_{(A)} (p_1 - \lambda p_0) \, dx_1 \cdots dx_N$, where λ is a Lagrange undetermined multiplier. If we choose for the region A all points for which $p_1 - \lambda p_0 \leq 0$ and exclude all points for which $p_1 - \lambda p_0 > 0$ we shall obviously make this integral as small as possible. The boundary of the region A is, therefore, given by

$$p_1 = \lambda p_0$$

or

$$\log p_1 - \log p_0 = \lambda_1$$

If

$$(12.54) \quad L_1 = \log p_1$$
$$= C - N \log \sigma_1 - \frac{N}{2\sigma_1^2}[(\bar{x} - \mu_1)^2 + s^2]$$

and if in (12.53) we put $\sigma = \sigma_1$ (since the choice of A is independent of the value of σ), we obtain

$$\lambda_1 = \frac{N}{2\sigma_1^2}[(\bar{x}-\mu_0)^2 - (\bar{x}-\mu_1)^2]$$

or

$$\bar{x}(\mu_1 - \mu_0) = \sigma_1^2 \lambda_1/N + \tfrac{1}{2}(\mu_1^2 - \mu_0^2) = c_1(\mu_1 - \mu_0), \text{ say.}$$

The region A on a given hypersphere should therefore be taken as the whole surface outside the "cap" cut off by the hyperplane $\bar{x} = c_1$, c_1 being chosen so that the area of this cap is a fraction α of the area of the hypersphere. The boundaries of these caps all lie on a hyper-circular cone with vertex at the point $(\mu_0, \mu_0 \cdots \mu_0)$ and axis equally inclined to all the coördinate axes.

If $\mu_1 > \mu_0$ the region corresponds to $\bar{x} \leq c_1$, and if $\mu_1 < \mu_0$ it corresponds to $\bar{x} \geq c_1$, and these regions are independent of μ_1. Hence either for $\mu_1 > \mu_0$ or for $\mu_1 < \mu_0$ (but not for both) the test using this region of acceptance A is a uniformly most powerful test.

From the geometry of the hypersphere it follows that the fractional area of the "cap," which is equal to α, is given by

(12.55) $$\alpha = \frac{1}{n^{1/2} B\left(\frac{n}{2}, \frac{1}{2}\right)} \int_{t_\alpha}^{\infty} \left(1 + \frac{t^2}{n}\right)^{-\frac{1}{2}(n+1)} dt$$

where $t = n^{1/2}(\bar{x} - \mu_0)/s$ and $n = N - 1$. But this means that t_α is the value of Student's t as given by the Fisher tables corresponding to $P = 2\alpha$. The one-tailed t-test, according to which the hypothesis H_0 is rejected when $t > t_\alpha$, is, therefore, a uniformly most powerful test for the class of admissible alternative hypotheses H_1 ($\mu = \mu_1 > \mu_0$), whatever σ and σ_1 may be. A similar statement holds when $\mu_1 < \mu_0$, the hypothesis being rejected when $-t > t_\alpha$. If μ_1 may be either greater or less than μ_0 no uniformly most powerful test exists, but the common procedure of the *two-tailed t-test*, that is, rejecting H_0 when $|t| > t_\alpha$, t_α being now the value of t corresponding to $P = \alpha$, provides a *uniformly most powerful unbiased test*.

12.17 The Power of the *t*-Test. If we can calculate the power function of the t-test for some value μ_1 different from μ_0, we can determine the probability $(1 - \beta)$ of rejecting the hypothesis H_0 if the alternative hypothesis H_1 is true. We naturally want this probability to be reasonably large. Unfortunately the power function is not independent of σ, and indeed Dantzig [10] has shown that no test of the composite hypothesis H_0 ($\mu = \mu_0$, whatever the value of σ), can have a power function independent of σ. In many practical cases we have little or no prior knowledge of σ, but if we can estimate it roughly we can use tables of the power function to assist in laying out an experiment designed to detect a difference between μ_0 and μ_1 of a given order of magnitude.

Neyman and Tokarska [11] have tabulated the power function for Student's t-test (one-tailed), and more recently Lehmer [12] has given inverse tables of probabilities of errors of the second kind. Johnson and Welch [16] have provided fairly extensive tables of the *non-central t-distribution*, the probability integral of which gives the power of the t-test. In Neyman and Tokarska's tables the argument is $\rho = N^{1/2} \Delta/\sigma$, where $\Delta = \mu_1 - \mu_0$. The alternative hypothesis is that $\mu = \mu_1$, where $\mu_1 > \mu_0$. This type of hypothesis is suggested when, for example, a new treatment is under investigation for increasing some desirable property of a crop, such as the sugar yield of beet. If the mean yield μ_1 under the new treatment is definitely superior to that under the old, μ_0, it may be worth while to change over to the new treatment, but we shall not be interested in changing if $\mu_1 < \mu_0$.

The probability of accepting the hypothesis that $\mu = \mu_0$, when in fact $\mu = \mu_1$, is equal to the probability that t in (12.55) is less than t_α, calculated on the assumption that $\mu = \mu_1$. This is the probability that $n^{1/2}(\bar{x} - \mu_0) < t_\alpha s$ when the joint probability density for $\bar{x}$ and s is given by (see eq. (7.33))

$$(12.56) \quad f(\bar{x}, s) = \left(\frac{n+1}{2\pi}\right)^{1/2} \frac{1}{\sigma} e^{-\frac{n+1}{2\sigma^2}(\bar{x}-\mu_1)^2} \frac{2}{\Gamma(n/2)} \left(\frac{n+1}{2\sigma^2}\right)^{n/2} s^{n-1} e^{-\frac{(n+1)}{2\sigma^2}s^2}$$

This expression can be written down at once by remembering that for a normal parent population $\bar{x}$ is normally distributed about μ_1 with variance σ^2/N, and Ns^2/σ^2 is independently distributed as χ^2 with $N - 1$ $(=n)$ degrees of freedom.

The probability of error of the second kind is, therefore, given by integrating $f(\bar{x}, s)$ for $\bar{x}$ from $-\infty$ to $\mu_0 + t_\alpha s n^{-1/2}$ and for s from 0 to ∞. Hence

(12.57)
$$\beta = \left(\frac{n+1}{2}\right)^{\frac{n+1}{2}} \frac{2^{3/2}}{\Gamma(n/2)\sigma^{n+1}} \int_0^\infty s^{n-1} e^{-\frac{(n+1)s^2}{2\sigma^2}} \int_{-\infty}^{\mu_0 + t_\alpha s n^{-\frac{1}{2}}} (2\pi)^{-1/2} e^{-\frac{(n+1)(\bar{x}-\mu_1)^2}{2\sigma^2}} d\bar{x}\, ds$$

On putting $z = \frac{(n+1)^{1/2}(\bar{x} - \mu_1)}{\sigma}$, $v = \left(\frac{n+1}{n}\right)^{1/2} \frac{t_\alpha s}{\sigma}$, equation (12.57) reduces to

$$(12.58) \quad \beta = \frac{2}{\Gamma(n/2)} \left(\frac{n}{2t_\alpha^2}\right)^{n/2} \int_0^\infty v^{n-1} e^{-nv^2/2t_\alpha^2} \int_{-\infty}^{v-\rho} (2\pi)^{-1/2} e^{-z^2/2} dz\, dv$$

$$= \frac{2}{\Gamma(n/2)} \left(\frac{n}{2t_\alpha^2}\right)^{n/2} \int_0^\infty v^{n-1} e^{-nv^2/2t_\alpha^2} \Phi(v - \rho)\, dv$$

where $\rho = (n + 1)^{1/2} \Delta/\sigma$. For a given α, (12.58) expresses β as a function of n and ρ. The integral can be evaluated numerically for given n and ρ, and we then have the power of the t-test for a given value of Δ.

The tables can be used to determine the value of μ_1 necessary to reduce the risk of errors of the second kind to a specified value. Suppose, for example, that $\mu_0 = 100$ and $\sigma = 10$, with $N = 16$, and that we wish to determine μ_1 so that the risk is equal to the same value 0.05 for each kind of error. With $\alpha = \beta = 0.05$, we find from the table that when $n = 15$, $\rho = 3.45$. Since $\rho = 4\Delta/\sigma$, this gives $\Delta = 8.62$. If, therefore, μ_1 is at least as great as 108.6, there is at least a 95% chance of detecting the difference between μ_1 and μ_0 in a sample of 16, at the 0.05 level of significance. This level indicates that the probability of rejecting the hypothesis that $\mu = \mu_0$, when in fact it is so, is 0.05. If the hypothesis is that $\mu \leq \mu_0$, the probability of unjustly rejecting it is not greater than 0.05.

Again, suppose that two samples of 8 give means of $\bar{x}_1$ and $\bar{x}_2$. If the true population means are μ_1 and μ_2, and if the hypothesis H_0 is that $\mu_2 - \mu_1 \leq 0$, then to establish the alternative hypothesis H_1 that $\mu_2 > \mu_1$ it will be necessary to reject H_0. If we want the risk of error in so doing to be not greater than 0.01, we must take $\alpha = 0.01$. The difference $\Delta = \mu_2 - \mu_1$ will be estimated by the difference of the means $\bar{x}_2 - \bar{x}_1$, with a standard error of $\sigma(2/8)^{1/2} = \sigma/2$, σ being the standard deviation of the populations concerned (assumed the same for both). The number of degrees of freedom for the estimation of σ is 14, and this is the number that must be used for n in entering the table. For $n = 14$, $\alpha = 0.01$ and $\beta = 0.2$, we find that $\rho = 3.51$. Now ρ is the ratio of Δ to its standard error and so is here to be taken as $2\Delta/\sigma$. Hence $\Delta/\sigma = 1.75$. That is, a difference in yields amounting to 1.75 times the standard deviation has a reasonable chance (0.8) of being detected at the 0.01 level of significance (when the probability of unjustly rejecting H_0 is not greater than 0.01).

12.18 The Power Function of Analysis of Variance Tests. Suppose that k "treatments" are to be compared, each being replicated N times, and that it is desired to test whether any significant difference exists between these treatments, as expressed in the value of some variate X which will be called the "yield."

The usual procedure is to compute Snedecor's F and to reject the null hypothesis if the observed F is greater than the tabulated F_α corresponding to an assigned level of significance α. In tabulating the power function of this test, P. C. Tang [13] found it convenient to use $E^2 = f_1 F/(f_2 + f_1 F)$, where
f_1 = number of degrees of freedom for treatment mean square $= k - 1$, and
f_2 = number of degrees of freedom for error mean square $= k(N - 1)$.

If q_1 and q_2 are the treatment sum of squares and the error sum of squares respectively, it is easily seen from the definition of F that

(12.59) $$E^2 = q_1(q_1 + q_2)^{-1}$$

It may be noted that the squared correlation ratio given in (11.1) is a special case, the treatment means being replaced by means of arrays.

If the true effect of the ith treatment is α_i and if the origin is so chosen that $\sum \alpha_i = 0$, the standard deviation of the treatment effects is

$$\sigma_T = \left(\frac{1}{k}\sum_{i=1}^{k}\alpha_i^2\right)^{1/2}$$

If σ is an estimate of the standard deviation of individual yields the standard error of a treatment mean is $(\sigma^2/N)^{1/2} = \sigma_M$. The ratio

(12.60) $$\phi = \sigma_T/\sigma_M$$

is used in both Tang's and Lehmer's tables as an argument. Tang has shown that when ϕ is not zero the frequency function for q_1/σ^2 (denoted by χ'^2) is

(12.61) $$f(\chi'^2) = \tfrac{1}{2}e^{-\lambda}(\chi'^2/2)^{\frac{1}{2}k-1}e^{-\frac{1}{2}\chi'^2}\sum_{m=0}^{\infty}\left\{\frac{(\frac{1}{2}\lambda\chi'^2)^m}{m!\,\Gamma(m+k/2)}\right\}$$

where $\lambda = k\phi^2/2$.

This is known as the *non-central* χ^2 *distribution*. When $\phi = 0$, it reduces to the ordinary χ^2 distribution with k degrees of freedom. The quantity q_1/q_2 is the ratio of a non-central χ^2 variate to an ordinary χ^2 variate, and from its distribution that of E^2 is obtained. The result is

(12.62) $\quad f(E^2 \mid \lambda) = e^{-\lambda}(E^2)^{\frac{1}{2}f_1 - 1}(1 - E^2)^{\frac{1}{2}f_2 - 1} H(\lambda E^2)[B(\tfrac{1}{2}f_1, \tfrac{1}{2}f_2)]^{-1}$

where $H(\lambda E^2)$ is the confluent hypergeometric series defined in (11.8). For $\lambda = 0$, E^2 is a Beta-variate. The null hypothesis H_0 is that $\phi = 0$, that is, $\lambda = 0$. The alternative hypothesis H_1 is that λ is not 0. For a given significance level α (the probability of error of the first kind), the critical value E_α^2 is given by

(12.63) $$\alpha = \int_{E_\alpha^2}^{1} f(E^2 \mid \lambda = 0)\, dE^2$$

The probability of error of the second kind is then

(12.64) $$\beta = \int_{0}^{E_\alpha^2} f(E^2 \mid \lambda)\, dE^2$$

and can be calculated numerically for a given E_α^2.

The special case when $k = 2$ was considered in the previous section. Then $\alpha_1 = \tfrac{1}{2}(\mu_0 - \mu_1)$ and $\alpha_2 = \tfrac{1}{2}(\mu_1 - \mu_0)$, so that $\sigma_T = \Delta/2$. Hence $\phi = N^{1/2}\Delta/2\sigma = \rho/\sqrt{2}$, where ρ is the argument used by Neyman and Tokarska. However, Tang's tables are for the symmetric two-tailed test, whereas Neyman's are for the asymmetric one-tailed test, so that Tang's level $\alpha = 0.01$ (with $f_1 = 1$) corresponds to Neyman's level $\alpha = 0.005$.

Example 14. If the estimated value of σ is 10, and if the true effects for 4 treatments, in 5 replications each, are $-5, -4, 3, 6$, we have

$$\sigma_T = \left(\frac{86}{4}\right)^{1/2} = 4.64$$
$$\sigma_M = 10/5^{1/2} = 4.47$$
$$\phi = 1.04, f_1 = 3, f_2 = 16$$

Taking $\alpha = 0.05$, we find from the tables that β is about 0.7. That is, in about 3 experiments in 10 we should find the suggested combination of treatments significant at the 5% level. Except for $k = 2$, there are, of course, infinitely many sets of α's which would give the same value of ϕ. The tables do, however, permit one to estimate what order of magnitude of treatment effects would be expected to show up in an experiment of a given design.

Lehmer's tables,[12] referred to above, give directly the value of ϕ required for a given power, or, what amounts to the same thing, for a given probability of error of the second kind. The table for $k = 2$ corresponds to the two-tailed t-test.

12.19 Sequential Tests of Hypotheses. Suppose that under a hypothesis H_0 the frequency function for a variable x is $f_0(x)$ and that under an alternative hypothesis H_1 it is $f_1(x)$. If $x_1, x_2, \cdots x_n$ are the observed values of x in a sample of n, the probability of this sample under H_0 is

(12.65) $\quad p_0 = f_0(x_1) f_0(x_2) \cdots f_0(x_n)$

Under H_1 the probability is

(12.66) $$p_1 = f_1(x_1) f_1(x_2) \cdots f_1(x_n)$$

The ratio of these probabilities p_1/p_0 may be taken as a measure of our belief in H_1 rather than in H_0. We may agree to accept H_1 if $p_1/p_0 \geq A$ and to accept H_0 if $p_1/p_0 \leq B$, where A and B are reasonable limits, arbitrarily assigned. Writing $L_1 = \log p_1$, etc., and $Z_n = L_1 - L_0$, we can express these alternatives as follows:

Accept H_1 if $Z_n \geq a$;
Accept H_0 if $Z_n \leq b$.

Clearly, as far as the second alternative is concerned, this is the same principle as that used by Neyman and Pearson in defining a region of acceptance for H_0 (see Example 13 in § 12.16).

However if $b < Z_n < a$, neither of the alternatives can be accepted and the choice must remain in doubt. In the sequential probability-ratio test, the criterion of the size of Z_n is applied *as the sample is accumulated*, an item at a time, sampling being continued and Z_n recalculated until finally either H_0 or H_1 is accepted. Instead of being fixed, the sample size n is now a stochastic variable. The chief practical merit of sequential testing is that in ordinary situations a considerably smaller sample size is required *on the average* to achieve the same degree of confidence in accepting H_0 (or H_1) than is required with the customary test procedure. In routine testing it is not always convenient to take the sample in this piecemeal fashion, one item at a time, between tests, but where the method is applicable it is decidedly economical.

It may happen, of course, that the test will go on for a long time before a decision is reached. Sooner or later, however, either H_0 or H_1 must be accepted. The probability that $b < Z_n < a$ for *all* n is zero. This was shown by A. Wald in an important paper [14] which laid down the basic ideas of sequential testing.

Now the probability α of error of the first kind is the probability of rejecting H_0 when H_0 is true. If β is the probability of error of the second kind, $1 - \beta$ is the probability of rejecting H_0 when H_1 is true. Hence $(1 - \beta)/\alpha$ is the ratio of the probabilities of H_1 and H_0 for a sample which leads to the rejection of H_0. That is, $(1 - \beta)/\alpha = p_1/p_0 \geq A$, since it is only when $p_1/p_0 \geq A$ that H_0 is rejected. Similarly $\beta/(1 - \alpha) \leq B$.

For practical purposes (at least when the sample size is greater than 20) these inequalities can be replaced by equations, since as a rule one more observation will make little difference to Z_n. When the bound a or b is finally overstepped it will not be by very much. Wald has given limits to the error involved in this assumption.

We, therefore, in practice choose $A = (1 - \beta)/\alpha$ and $B = \beta/(1 - \alpha)$ where α and β are the errors of the two kinds that we are prepared to tolerate.

12.20 Expected Number of Observations in a Sequential Probability-Ratio Test.

Let n be the smallest integer for which either $Z_n \geq a$ or $Z_n \leq b$. We require to find $E_0(n)$ and $E_1(n)$, the expected values of n on the two hypotheses H_0 and H_1 respectively.

If H_0 is true, the probability of accepting H_0 is $1 - \alpha$ and the probability of accepting H_1 is α. The second case corresponds approximately to $Z_n = a \, (= \log A)$ and the first to $Z_n = b (= \log B)$. The expected value of Z_n is, therefore,

$$(12.67) \qquad E_0(Z_n) = \alpha a + (1 - \alpha) b$$

Now $Z_n = \log(p_1/p_0) = \sum_{i=1}^{n} z_i$, where $z_i = \log f_1(x_i) - \log f_0(x_i)$. Since the z_i are independent random variables with the same distribution and the number n is also a random variable,

$$E_0(Z_n) = E_0(n) E_0(z)$$

so that

$$(12.68) \qquad E_0(n) = \frac{\alpha a + (1 - \alpha) b}{E_0(z)}$$

Similarly, if H_1 is true, the probabilities of accepting H_0 and H_1 are β and $1 - \beta$ respectively. Hence

$$(12.69) \qquad E_1(Z_n) = (1 - \beta) a + \beta b$$

and

$$(12.70) \qquad E_1(n) = \frac{(1 - \beta) a + \beta b}{E_1(z)}$$

If the distribution of the variate x is known, $E_0(z)$ and $E_1(z)$ can be calculated. Thus if x is normally distributed with variance σ^2 about a mean which is either μ_0 or μ_1, we can take H_0 as the hypothesis $\mu = \mu_0$ and H_1 as the hypothesis $\mu = \mu_1$. Then

$$f_0(x_i) = \frac{1}{\sigma \sqrt{2\pi}} e^{-(x_i - \mu_0)^2 / 2\sigma^2}$$

$$f_1(x_i) = \frac{1}{\sigma \sqrt{2\pi}} e^{-(x_i - \mu_1)^2 / 2\sigma^2}$$

and

$$z_i \sigma^2 = x_i (\mu_1 - \mu_0) - \tfrac{1}{2}(\mu_1^2 - \mu_0^2)$$

The expectation of z_i on hypothesis H_0 is

$$E_0(z_i) = \int \cdots \int z_i f_0(x_1) \cdots f_0(x_n) \, dx_1 \cdots dx_n$$
$$= - (\mu_1 - \mu_0)^2 / 2\sigma^2$$

and similarly $E_1(z_i) = (\mu_1 - \mu_0)^2 / 2\sigma^2$. Hence, from (12.68) and (12.70),

(12.71) $$E_0(n) = \frac{C_0 \sigma^2}{(\mu_1 - \mu_0)^2}, \quad E_1(n) = \frac{C_1 \sigma^2}{(\mu_1 - \mu_0)^2}$$

where C_0 and C_1 depend only on α and β. It therefore appears, as is intuitively obvious, that the smaller the difference between μ_0 and μ_1, the more observations will be required to discriminate between them at a fixed level of significance.

It is of interest to compare the values in (12.71) with the fixed size of sample N necessary to discriminate between μ_0 and μ_1 by the ordinary test procedure with the same size of errors. This procedure consists in accepting H_0 if $\bar{x} \leq \lambda$ and accepting H_1 if $\bar{x} > \lambda$, λ being a suitably chosen constant. On the hypothesis H_0, $\bar{x}$ is normally distributed about μ_0 with variance σ^2/N and the probability of accepting H_1 is therefore

$$\alpha = (2\pi)^{-1/2} \int_{t_\alpha}^{\infty} e^{-t^2/2} dt = 1 - \Phi(t_\alpha)$$

where $t_\alpha = N^{1/2}(\lambda - \mu_0)/\sigma$.

Similarly the probability of an error of the second kind is $\beta = \Phi(t_\beta)$ where $t_\beta = N^{1/2}(\lambda - \mu_1)/\sigma$.

Hence

(12.72) $$N = \left(\frac{t_\alpha - t_\beta}{\mu_1 - \mu_0}\right)^2 \sigma^2$$

From (12.71) and (12.72) we see that the ratios $E_0(n)/N$ and $E_1(n)/N$ are independent of μ_1, μ_0 and σ^2, and so may be calculated for any assigned α and β. If, for example, $\alpha = \beta = 0.05$, we find that $t_\alpha = -t_\beta = 1.645$, and $E_0(n)/N = E_1(n)/N = 0.49$. There is, in this case, an expected saving of about 50% in the number of observations required.

Although, as stated above, the sequential process must ultimately terminate in a decision one way or the other, it may not be practicable to continue testing beyond a sample size of, say, n'. If the issue is still undecided at this stage, we can formulate a reasonable rule as follows:

Accept H_0 if $Z_{n'} \leq 0$;
Accept H_1 if $Z_{n'} > 0$.

The probabilities of the two kinds of error, say $\alpha(n')$ and $\beta(n')$, are somewhat different from α and β in this *truncated test*. It may be shown[14] that

$$\alpha(n') \leq \alpha + \Phi(\nu_2) - \Phi(\nu_1)$$

where

$$\nu_2 = \frac{a - n'E_0(z)}{\sqrt{n'\sigma_0(z)}}, \quad \nu_1 = -\frac{n'E_0(z)}{\sqrt{n'\sigma_0(z)}}$$

with a similar expression for $\beta(n')$. On the assumption of a normal population, $E_0(z) = -(\mu_1 - \mu_0)^2/2\sigma^2$ and $\sigma_0(z) = (\mu_1 - \mu_0)^2/\sigma^2$. If α and β are chosen as 0.05 each, if N in (12.72) is taken as 100, and if $n' = 200$, we find $\alpha(n') = \beta(n') \le 0.058$. Hence in a sequential test designed to discriminate with the same degree of accuracy as a fixed-sample test of size 100, we do not seriously increase the risk of error by stopping at 200 items, even though the test is still indecisive. The chance of our having to continue so far is, of course, quite small.

12.21 Test of a Hypothesis Against a One-sided Alternative. Let H_0 be the simple hypothesis that a parameter θ is equal to θ_0, and let the alternative one-sided hypothesis H_1 be that $\theta > \theta_0$.

The probability of error of the first kind may be arbitrarily chosen as α, but the probability of error of the second kind depends on the true value of θ. We can, however, take a value of $\theta_1 > \theta_0$ and construct a sequential test for H_0, against the single alternative hypothesis that $\theta = \theta_1$, with an assigned probability β of error of the second kind. If this test is such that the error of the second kind is less than (or equal to) β when $\theta > \theta_1$ (so that the power curve rises as θ increases beyond θ_1), the test may be used for H_0 against any alternative hypothesis $\theta > \theta_0$. Although the chance of error of the second kind may be high when θ is near θ_0 this error will not matter very much. It will merely mean accepting for θ a close approximation θ_0.

In most important practical cases the probability of error of the second kind does decrease as $\theta - \theta_0$ increases. Since, for such cases, it is also true that the probability of error of the first kind is equal to or less than α whenever $\theta \le \theta_0$, the same test can be used for the composite hypothesis $\theta \le \theta_0$ as against the alternative hypothesis $\theta > \theta_0$.

12.22 The Sequential Test for a Binomial Distribution. One important example is provided by the simple classification of manufactured test objects into two classes, say "defective" and "satisfactory." Let us suppose that a lot will be accepted if the proportion of defectives $p \le p'$ but will be rejected if $p > p'$. We fix arbitrarily two values, $\pi_0 < p'$ and $\pi_1 > p'$, such that the consequences of rejecting the lot will be serious if the true value of p is less than π_0 and such that the consequences of accepting the lot will also be serious if $p > \pi_1$. (The consequences of unjustly rejecting a good lot are, of course, trouble and expense to the manufacturer. The consequences of unjustly accepting a bad lot will be felt by the customer who buys the lot, but will ultimately injure the manufacturer's reputation.) We decide also on the risks α and β we are prepared to run of committing these serious errors, and then are able to construct a sequential test.

Since the distribution of the number of defectives d_n in the first n units inspected is binomial, the probabilities of the observed sample on the hypotheses $p = \pi_1$ and $p = \pi_0$ are

$$p_1 = \pi_1^{d_n}(1 - \pi_1)^{n-d_n}$$

and

$$p_0 = \pi_0^{d_n}(1 - \pi_0)^{n-d_n}$$

whence

(12.73) $$Z_n = d_n \log\left(\frac{\pi_1}{\pi_0}\right) + (n - d_n) \log\left(\frac{1 - \pi_1}{1 - \pi_0}\right)$$

The lot is rejected if $Z_n \geq a$ and accepted if $Z_n \leq b$, where $a = \log[(1-\beta)/\alpha]$ and $b = \log[\beta/(1-\alpha)]$. If neither is true, the test is continued. This test is equivalent to setting up acceptance numbers A_n and rejection numbers R_n for each value of n, and continuing testing as long as $A_n < d_n < R_n$. The numbers A_n and R_n are given by substituting for Z_n in (12.73). They are

(12.74)
$$A_n = \frac{b - n \log \frac{1 - \pi_1}{1 - \pi_0}}{\log \frac{\pi_1}{\pi_0} - \log \frac{1 - \pi_1}{1 - \pi_0}}$$

$$R_n = \frac{a - n \log \frac{1 - \pi_1}{1 - \pi_0}}{\log \frac{\pi_1}{\pi_0} - \log \frac{1 - \pi_1}{1 - \pi_0}}$$

Since A_n and R_n depend linearly on n, they define a sloping band of constant width in the $n - d_n$ plane. See Figure 44.

The figure is drawn for $\alpha = \beta = 0.05$, $\pi_1 = 0.03$, $\pi_0 = 0.001$. The lines defining the band are

$$A_n = -0.858 + 0.00859n$$
$$R_n = 0.858 + 0.00859n$$

The lot cannot, therefore, be accepted until 100 random samples have shown no defectives. If 1 defective appears in the first 17, or if 2 appear in the first 132, the lot is rejected, and so on.

Let L_p be the probability of accepting the lot for any given p. The curve of L_p against p is called the *operating characteristic curve* (OC for short) of the test. Since the acceptance of the lot when p is large is an error of the second kind, the OC curve is in effect a power curve for the test, $1 - L_p$ corresponding to the power. L_p decreases as p increases, from 1 when $p = 0$ to 0 when $p = 1$. If $p = \pi_0$, $L_p = 1 - \alpha$, and if $p = \pi_1$, $L_p = \beta$. Wald has shown that if π_0 and π_1 are not too far apart (so that the expected value and the variance of z are small) then L_p is approximately given by

(12.75) $$L_p = \frac{A^h - 1}{A^h - B^h}$$

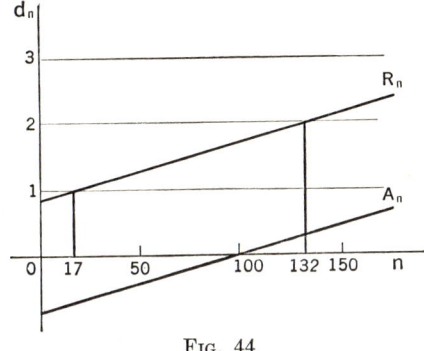

FIG. 44

where h is the non-zero root of the equation

$$(12.76) \qquad p\left(\frac{\pi_1}{\pi_0}\right)^h + (1-p)\left(\frac{1-\pi_1}{1-\pi_0}\right)^h = 1$$

By choosing various values of h, substituting in (12.75) to get L_p and solving (12.76) for p, the OC curve can be constructed. The probability of accepting a lot with a given proportion of defectives can then be read off.

The expected number of observations required to reach a decision can be calculated in terms of L_p and p. It is given approximately by

$$(12.77) \qquad E_p(n) = \frac{bL_p + a(1-L_p)}{p \log \frac{\pi_1}{\pi_0} + (1-p) \log \frac{1-\pi_1}{1-\pi_0}}$$

With the data assumed in Figure 44, this number is 53 for $p = 0.02$ and 36 for $p = 0.03$.

12.23 Tolerance Limits for a Parent Population. Instead of fixing confidence limits for a parameter of a parent population, it is sometimes convenient to estimate the limits between which a specified *proportion of the population* may be expected, with a specified degree of confidence, to lie. Such limits are called *tolerance limits*.

We may, for instance, wish to know what size of sample to take in order to be confident (with confidence coefficient $1 - \alpha$) that a fraction at least β of the population will have a value of x lying within the sample range.

Assuming that the random variable x is continuous with frequency function $f(x)$, we have for the joint probability of the smallest sample value x_1 and the largest value x_N, as in § 7.19,

$$dP = N(N-1)\left[\int_{x_1}^{x_N} f(x)\, dx\right]^{N-2} f(x_1)f(x_N)\, dx_1\, dx_N$$

Let

$$v = \int_{x_1}^{x_N} f(x)\, dx, \qquad u = \int_{-\infty}^{x_1} f(x)\, dx$$

Then v is the proportion of the *population* lying between x_1 and x_N, that is, within the sample range.

By differentiating under the integral sign, we see that

$$J\left(\frac{u, v}{x_1, x_N}\right) = \begin{vmatrix} f(x_1) & 0 \\ -f(x_1) & f(x_N) \end{vmatrix} = f(x_1)f(x_N)$$

Hence $du\, dv = f(x_1)f(x_N)\, dx_1\, dx_N$ so that the joint probability for u and v is $dP = N(N-1)v^{N-2}\, du\, dv$. The probability for v is given by integrating over u. Now $0 \leq u \leq 1 - v$, so that the range of integration for u is from 0 to $1 - v$. The frequency function for v is, therefore,

$$(12.78) \qquad f(v) = N(N-1)v^{N-2}(1-v)\, dv, \qquad 0 \leq v \leq 1$$

Sec. 23   Tolerance Limits for a Parent Population

The probability that $v \geq \beta$ is, then,

$$\int_\beta^1 f(v)\, dv = 1 - \alpha$$

since $1 - \alpha$ is our assumed confidence coefficient, so that

(12.79) $\qquad N\beta^{N-1} - (N-1)\beta^N = \alpha$

from which N can be obtained. Thus, for $\alpha = 0.05$ and $\beta = 0.99$ we find $N = 473$. The probability is 0.95 that at least 99% of a parent population (continuously distributed) will lie between the least and greatest values found in a sample of 473. These limits are independent of the form of the parent distribution.

A somewhat more difficult problem arises when we wish to take account of the fact that the frequency function for the parent population depends on a parameter θ. This problem has been discussed by S. S. Wilks.[15] If $f(x,\theta)$ is the known frequency function for the parent population, then for any given δ between 0 and 1, we can determine λ_1 and λ_2 as functions of δ and θ so that

(12.80) $\qquad \displaystyle\int_{-\infty}^{\lambda_1} f(x,\theta)\, dx = \int_{\lambda_2}^{\infty} f(x,\theta)\, dx = \tfrac{1}{2}(1 - \delta)$

If $\hat\theta$ is the maximum likelihood estimate of θ from a sample of N and if

(12.81) $\qquad v = \displaystyle\int_{\hat\lambda_1}^{\hat\lambda_2} f(x,\theta)\, dx$

where $\hat\lambda_1 = \lambda_1(\hat\theta, \delta)$ and similarly for $\hat\lambda_2$, then v is the proportion of the parent population lying between $\hat\lambda_1$ and $\hat\lambda_2$. Since $\hat\theta$ tends in the stochastic sense to θ as N increases, v tends stochastically to the value δ.

Now let β be a number between 0 and δ. If the distribution of v is independent of θ, then, for N sufficiently large, the probability that $v \geq \beta$ will be greater than $1 - \alpha$, for any given α between 0 and 1, whatever the value of θ. Usually β and $1 - \alpha$ will both be near 1, and there will be a smallest value of N for which this probability is practically equal to $1 - \alpha$. The values of $\hat\lambda_1$ and $\hat\lambda_2$, calculated for a sample of this size, are called *$100\beta\%$ parameter-free tolerance limits* at the significance level α.

Example 15. A sample of 20 is drawn from a normal population of mean μ and variance σ^2. It is required to establish tolerance limits for x.

The parameters μ and σ^2 are unknown but may be estimated from the sample mean and variance. If $\bar x$ and s^2 are the sample mean and the variance, it is natural to take the tolerance limits as $\bar x \pm ks$, where k is a constant. k is determined by the condition that if

(12.82) $\qquad v = \dfrac{1}{\sigma\sqrt{2\pi}} \displaystyle\int_{\bar x - ks}^{\bar x + ks} e^{-\frac{1}{2}(x-\mu)^2/\sigma^2}\, dx$

then the probability that $v \geq \beta$ has a specified value $1 - \alpha$. The exact distribution of v is very complicated. The expectation of v can be found, using the joint distribution of $\bar x$ and s worked out in § 7.6, namely,

(12.83) $$f(\bar{x}, s) = \frac{(N/2\pi\sigma^2)^{1/2} 2(N/2\sigma^2)^{(N-1)/2}}{\Gamma[(N-1)/2]} e^{-\frac{N(\bar{x}-\mu)^2}{2\sigma^2}} s^{N-2} e^{-Ns^2/2\sigma^2}$$

We have that

(12.84) $$E(v) = \int_{-\infty}^{\infty} \int_{0}^{\infty} v f(\bar{x}, s) \, ds \, d\bar{x}$$

where v is given by (12.82). The integral may be simplified by means of suitable changes of variable, and may be expressed as

(12.85) $$E(v) = \frac{1}{(N-1)^{1/2} B\left(\frac{1}{2}, \frac{N-1}{2}\right)} \int_{-t'}^{t'} \frac{dt}{\left(1 + \frac{t^2}{N-1}\right)^{N/2}}$$

where $t' = k[(N-1)/(N+1)]^{1/2}$. Since the integrand in (12.85) is the frequency function of Student's t, $E(v)$ is equal to $1 - P$, where P is the probability in Fisher's table for a given t'. The tolerance limits which include *on the average* 95% of the values of x are given by $t' = 2.093$ for $N = 20$ (19 degrees of freedom) so that $k = (\frac{21}{19})^{1/2} t' = 2.200$. The limits are, therefore, $\bar{x} \pm 2.200 s$.

This, however, does not establish the extent of sampling fluctuation of these limits. The variance of v for large samples is given by

(12.86) $$\sigma_v^2 = t'^2 e^{-t'^2}/(\pi N)$$

as far as terms of order $1/N$.

As an approximation to the distribution of v we can try fitting a Pearson Type I function,

(12.87) $$f(v) = v^{a-1}(1-v)^{b-1}/B(a, b)$$

determining a and b by equating the mean and variance of this distribution to $1 - P$ and σ_v^2 respectively. The values of a and b so found are

(12.88) $$a = P(1-P)^2/\sigma_v^2 - (1-P)$$
$$b = P^2(1-P)/\sigma_v^2 - P$$

The probability that $v \geq \beta$ can then be read from Pearson's table of the Incomplete Beta function. The distribution is so skew, however, that the value of a may well turn out beyond the range of the table, and recourse must then be had to calculation of the integral by quadrature.

In the example above, if $P = 0.05$ and $t' = 2.093$, we find that $\sigma_v^2 = 0.000873$, $a = 50.76$, $b = 2.67$. Since the range of v is from 0 to 1 and its expectation is 0.95, it is evident that the distribution is very strongly skewed, with a long tail to the left. The tables go as far as $a = 50$, for $b = 2.5$ and $b = 3.0$. A rough interpolation and extrapolation gives a value of $\beta = 0.893$ corresponding to $\alpha = 0.05$. The limits calculated, namely, $\bar{x} \pm 2.200 s$, are, therefore, 89% parameter-free tolerance limits at the significance level 0.05.

Extensive tables of tolerance limits prepared by A. H. Bowker for a normal distribution are given in Chapter II of *Techniques of Statistical Analysis*, by Eisenhart, Hastay and Wallis (McGraw-Hill, 1947). These tables give the factors k for selected values of γ and β such that the probability is γ that at least a proportion β of the distribution will be included between $\bar{x} \pm ks$. All sample sizes from 2 to 200 and others at intervals between 200 and 1000 are included. For $N = 20$, $\gamma = 0.95$, and $\beta = 0.90$, the value of k is 2.286. The 90% tolerance limits with confidence coefficient 0.95 are, therefore, $\bar{x} \pm 2.286 s$.

Problems

1. Prove that the simultaneous maximum likelihood estimates of the five parameters $\mu_1, \mu_2, \sigma_1, \sigma_2$, and ρ of a bivariate normal distribution with frequency function

$$f(x,y) = \frac{1}{2\pi\sigma_1\sigma_2(1-\rho^2)^{1/2}} \exp\left\{-\frac{1}{2(1-\rho^2)}\left[\left(\frac{x-\mu_1}{\sigma_1}\right)^2 - \frac{2\rho(x-\mu_1)(y-\mu_2)}{\sigma_1\sigma_2} + \left(\frac{y-\mu_2}{\sigma_2}\right)^2\right]\right\}$$

are the sample means, the sample variances and the sample covariance respectively.

2. Obtain the maximum likelihood estimates of the parameter σ for fixed μ and λ and of the parameter λ for fixed μ and σ, for the Type III curve of equation (12.25). (Use the likelihood function given in (12.26).)

3. Find the efficiencies of the moment estimates corresponding to the estimates obtained in Problem 2.

4. Prove that the maximum likelihood estimate of the mean of a parent population of Poisson Type (with parameter μ) is equal to the sample mean $\bar{x}$ and that the variance of this estimate is $\bar{x}/N$.

5. Using a table of random sampling numbers, write down 40 pairs of two-digit numbers. Regard any pair, say 78, 16, as being an independent sample of x_1 and x_2 from a rectangular distribution on the range 0 to θ, as in Example 9, § 12.10. Calculate for each sample the two sets of confidence limits (a) $\frac{2}{3}(x_1 + x_2)$ and $2(x_1 + x_2)$ and (b) L and $2L$. Verify that for both (a) and (b) about 3/4 of the confidence intervals include the true value $\theta = 100$.

6. Suppose that in a certain population the probability that an individual is "defective" is either 0.1 or 0.3, but cannot have any other value, and that we wish to test the hypothesis $H_0(\pi = 0.1)$ against the alternative hypothesis $H_1(\pi = 0.3)$. If d_n is the number of defectives in a sample of n, and if we agree to accept H_0 if $d_n < k$ and to accept H_1 otherwise, show that in order to have the risks of error of the first and second kind about 0.02 and 0.03 respectively, we should take $n = 55$ and $k = 10$.

7. Construct a sequential acceptance-and-rejection chart, similar to that in Figure 44, for the situation described in Problem 6. Take $p_0 = 0.1$ and $p_1 = 0.3$.

8. Perform an imaginary sampling experiment from the population of Problems 6 and 7 by reading a set of one-digit random numbers and regarding each number as a sample item. For hypothesis H_0 take 0 as indicating a "defective," for hypothesis H_1 take 0, 1 and 2 as defectives. In 20 trials on each hypothesis count the number of samples necessary to reach a decision, using the chart constructed in Problem 7.

Calculate the approximate expected value of this number on each hypothesis and compare with the average number found in these trials.

9. Assuming that the proportion of defectives can vary in the population from 0 to 1, but that the acceptance limits are $p_0 = 0.1$ and $p_1 = 0.3$, construct the operating characteristic curve of the binomial sequential test with $\alpha = 0.02$, $\beta = 0.03$.

References

1. See, e.g., H. Cramér, *Mathematical Methods of Statistics*, p. 489.

2. R. A. Fisher, "The Mathematical Foundations of Theoretical Statistics," *Phil. Trans. Roy. Soc.*, A, **222**, 1922, pp. 309–368.

3. Tables of the Digamma and Trigamma functions, $\frac{d}{d\lambda}\log\Gamma(\lambda)$ and $\frac{d^2}{d\lambda^2}\log\Gamma(\lambda)$, are to be found in H. T. Davis, *Tables of the Higher Mathematical Functions*, Vols. 1 and 2. The tables in K. Pearson's *Tracts for Computers*, No. 1, prepared by Miss E. Pairman, give $\frac{d}{d\lambda}\log\Gamma(1+\lambda)$ and $\frac{d^2}{d\lambda^2}\log\Gamma(1+\lambda)$.

4. R. A. Fisher, "The Conditions Under Which χ^2 Measures the Discrepancy between

Observation and Hypothesis," *Jour. Roy. Stat. Soc.*, **87**, 1924, pp. 442–450. See also *Statistical Methods for Research Workers*, 10th Edition, § 57.

5. See M. G. Kendall, *Advanced Theory of Statistics*, Vol. II, pp. 10–11.

6. J. Neyman and E. S. Pearson, "The Problem of the Most Efficient Tests of Statistical Hypotheses," *Phil. Trans. Roy. Soc.*, A, **231**, 1933, pp. 289–337.

See also A. Wald, *The Principles of Statistical Inference*, Notre Dame Mathematical Lectures No. 1, 1942.

7. J. Neyman, "Statistical Estimation," *Phil. Trans. Roy. Soc.*, A, **236**, 1937, pp. 333–380.

8. See, for example, the following papers by R. A. Fisher:

"Inverse Probability," *Proc. Camb. Phil. Soc.*, **26**, 1930, p. 528.

"The Concepts of Inverse Probability and of Fiducial Probability Referring to Unknown Parameters," *Proc. Roy. Soc.*, A, **139**, 1933, p. 343.

"The Fiducial Argument in Statistical Inference," *Ann. Eugenics Lond.*, **6**, 1935, p. 391.

"Uncertain Inference," *Proc. Roy. Soc.*, B, **122**, 1936, p. 1.

9. A. Wald, "Asymptotically Most Powerful Tests of Statistical Hypotheses," *Ann. Math. Stat.*, **12**, 1941, pp. 1–19.

A. Wald, "Some Examples of Asymptotically Most Powerful Tests," *Ann. Math. Stat.*, **12**, 1941, pp. 396–408.

10. G. B. Dantzig, "On the Non-existence of Tests of Student's Hypothesis Having Power Functions Independent of σ," *Ann. Math. Stat.*, **11**, 1940, pp. 186–192.

11. J. Neyman and B. Tokarska, "Errors of the Second Kind in Testing Student's Hypothesis," *J. Amer. Stat. Assoc.*, **31**, 1936, pp. 318–326.

12. E. Lehmer, "Inverse Tables of Probabilities of Errors of the Second Kind," *Ann. Math. Stat.*, **15**, 1944, pp. 388–398.

13. P. C. Tang, "The Power Function of the Analysis of Variance Tests with Tables and Illustrations of Their Use," *Stat. Res. Mem.*, **2**, 1938, pp. 126–157.

14. A. Wald, "Sequential Tests of Statistical Hypotheses," *Ann. Math. Stat.*, **16**, 1945, pp. 117–186.

The essential parts of the theory are presented in Wald's book, *Sequential Analysis*, 1947.

15. S. S. Wilks, "Statistical Prediction with Special Reference to the Problem of Tolerance Limits," *Ann. Math. Stat.*, **13**, 1942, pp. 400–409. See also the same author's "Determination of Sample Size for Setting Tolerance Limits," *Ann. Math. Stat.*, **12**, 1941, pp. 94–95.

16. N. L. Johnson and B. L. Welch, "Applications of the Non-central *t*-Distribution," *Biometrika*, **31**, 1939, pp. 362–389.

17. R. A. Fisher, "The Logic of Inductive Inference," *J. Roy. Stat. Soc.*, **98**, 1935, pp. 39–54, (*Contributions to Mathematical Statistics*, 1950, **26.** 46), where the result is proved for a normal distribution of T and for large samples. The inequality was proved much more generally by H. Cramér and by C. R. Rao, independently. For this reason, many prefer to call it the Cramér-Rao inequality. Our proof follows that of Cramér.

Additional Reference. For an excellent practical discussion of the chi-square test, see W. G. Cochran, "The Chi-square Test of Goodness to Fit," *Ann. Math. Stat.*, **23**, 1952, pp. 315–345.

APPENDIX

TABLE I. ORDINATES AND AREAS OF THE NORMAL CURVE, $\phi(t) = \dfrac{1}{\sqrt{2\pi}} e^{-t^2/2}$

t	$\phi(t)$	$\int_0^t \phi(t)dt$	t	$\phi(t)$	$\int_0^t \phi(t)dt$	t	$\phi(t)$	$\int_0^t \phi(t)dt$
.00	.39894	.00000	.45	.36053	.17364	.90	.26609	.31594
.01	.39892	.00399	.46	.35889	.17724	.91	.26369	.31859
.02	.39886	.00798	.47	.35723	.18082	.92	.26129	.32121
.03	.39876	.01197	.48	.35553	.18439	.93	.25888	.32381
.04	.39862	.01595	.49	.35381	.18793	.94	.25647	.32639
.05	.39844	.01994	.50	.35207	.19146	.95	.25406	.32894
.06	.39822	.02392	.51	.35029	.19497	.96	.25164	.33147
.07	.39797	.02790	.52	.34849	.19847	.97	.24923	.33398
.08	.39767	.03188	.53	.34667	.20194	.98	.24681	.33646
.09	.39733	.03586	.54	.34482	.20540	.99	.24439	.33891
.10	.39695	.03983	.55	.34294	.20884	1.00	.24197	.34134
.11	.39654	.04380	.56	.34105	.21226	1.01	.23955	.34375
.12	.39608	.04776	.57	.33912	.21566	1.02	.23713	.34614
.13	.39559	.05172	.58	.33718	.21904	1.03	.23471	.34850
.14	.39505	.05567	.59	.33521	.22240	1.04	.23230	.35083
.15	.39448	.05962	.60	.33322	.22575	1.05	.22988	.35314
.16	.39387	.06356	.61	.33121	.22907	1.06	.22747	.35543
.17	.39322	.06749	.62	.32918	.23237	1.07	.22506	.35769
.18	.39253	.07142	.63	.32713	.23565	1.08	.22265	.35993
.19	.39181	.07535	.64	.32506	.23891	1.09	.22025	.36214
.20	.39104	.07926	.65	.32297	.24215	1.10	.21785	.36433
.21	.39024	.08317	.66	.32086	.24537	1.11	.21546	.36650
.22	.38940	.08706	.67	.31874	.24857	1.12	.21307	.36864
.23	.38853	.09095	.68	.31659	.25175	1.13	.21069	.37076
.24	.38762	.09483	.69	.31443	.25490	1.14	.20831	.37286
.25	.38667	.09871	.70	.31225	.25804	1.15	.20594	.37493
.26	.38568	.10257	.71	.31006	.26115	1.16	.20357	.37698
.27	.38466	.10642	.72	.30785	.26424	1.17	.20121	.37900
.28	.38361	.11026	.73	.30563	.26730	1.18	.19886	.38100
.29	.38251	.11409	.74	.30339	.27035	1.19	.19652	.38298
.30	.38139	.11791	.75	.30114	.27337	1.20	.19419	.38493
.31	.38023	.12172	.76	.29887	.27637	1.21	.19186	.38686
.32	.37903	.12552	.77	.29659	.27935	1.22	.18954	.38877
.33	.37780	.12930	.78	.29431	.28230	1.23	.18724	.39065
.34	.37654	.13307	.79	.29200	.28524	1.24	.18494	.39251
.35	.37524	.13683	.80	.28969	.28814	1.25	.18265	.39435
.36	.37391	.14058	.81	.28737	.29103	1.26	.18037	.39617
.37	.37255	.14431	.82	.28504	.29389	1.27	.17810	.39796
.38	.37115	.14803	.83	.28269	.29673	1.28	.17585	.39973
.39	.36973	.15173	.84	.28034	.29955	1.29	.17360	.40147
.40	.36827	.15542	.85	.27798	.30234	1.30	.17137	.40320
.41	.36678	.15910	.86	.27562	.30511	1.31	.16915	.40490
.42	.36526	.16276	.87	.27324	.30785	1.32	.16694	.40658
.43	.36371	.16640	.88	.27086	.31057	1.33	.16474	.40824
.44	.36213	.17003	.89	.26848	.31327	1.34	.16256	.40988

TABLE I. ORDINATES AND AREAS OF THE NORMAL CURVE, $\phi(t) = \dfrac{1}{\sqrt{2\pi}} e^{-t^2/2}$

t	$\phi(t)$	$\int_0^t \phi(t)dt$	t	$\phi(t)$	$\int_0^t \phi(t)dt$	t	$\phi(t)$	$\int_0^t \phi(t)dt$
1.35	.16038	.41149	1.80	.07895	.46407	2.25	.03174	.48778
1.36	.15822	.41309	1.81	.07754	.46485	2.26	.03103	.48809
1.37	.15608	.41466	1.82	.07614	.46562	2.27	.03034	.48840
1.38	.15395	.41621	1.83	.07477	.46638	2.28	.02965	.48870
1.39	.15183	.41774	1.84	.07341	.46712	2.29	.02898	.48899
1.40	.14973	.41924	1.85	.07206	.46784	2.30	.02833	.48928
1.41	.14764	.42073	1.86	.07074	.46856	2.31	.02768	.48956
1.42	.14556	.42220	1.87	.06943	.46926	2.32	.02705	.48983
1.43	.14350	.42364	1.88	.06814	.46995	2.33	.02643	.49010
1.44	.14146	.42507	1.89	.06687	.47062	2.34	.02582	.49036
1.45	.13943	.42647	1.90	.06562	.47128	2.35	.02522	.49061
1.46	.13742	.42786	1.91	.06439	.47193	2.36	.02463	.49086
1.47	.13542	.42922	1.92	.06316	.47257	2.37	.02406	.49111
1.48	.13344	.43056	1.93	.06195	.47320	2.38	.02349	.49134
1.49	.13147	.43189	1.94	.06077	.47381	2.39	.02294	.49158
1.50	.12952	.43319	1.95	.05959	.47441	2.40	.02239	.49180
1.51	.12758	.43448	1.96	.05844	.47500	2.41	.02186	.49202
1.52	.12566	.43574	1.97	.05730	.47558	2.42	.02134	.49224
1.53	.12376	.43699	1.98	.05618	.47615	2.43	.02083	.49245
1.54	.12188	.43822	1.99	.05508	.47670	2.44	.02033	.49266
1.55	.12001	.43943	2.00	.05399	.47725	2.45	.01984	.49286
1.56	.11816	.44062	2.01	.02592	.47778	2.46	.01936	.49305
1.57	.11632	.44179	2.02	.05186	.47831	2.47	.01889	.49324
1.58	.11450	.44295	2.03	.05082	.47882	2.48	.01842	.49343
1.59	.11270	.44408	2.04	.04980	.47932	2.49	.01797	.49361
1.60	.11092	.44520	2.05	.04879	.47982	2.50	.01753	.49379
1.61	.10915	.44630	2.06	.04780	.48030	2.51	.01709	.49396
1.62	.10741	.44738	2.07	.04682	.48077	2.52	.01667	.49413
1.63	.10567	.44845	2.08	.04586	.48124	2.53	.01625	.49430
1.64	.10396	.44950	2.09	.04491	.48169	2.54	.01585	.49446
1.65	.10226	.45053	2.10	.04398	.48214	2.55	.01545	.49461
1.66	.10059	.45154	2.11	.04307	.48257	2.56	.01506	.49477
1.67	.09893	.45254	2.12	.04217	.48300	2.57	.01468	.49492
1.68	.09728	.45352	2.13	.04128	.48341	2.58	.01431	.49506
1.69	.09566	.45449	2.14	.04041	.48382	2.59	.01394	.49520
1.70	.09405	.45543	2.15	.03955	.48422	2.60	.01358	.49534
1.71	.09246	.45637	2.16	.03871	.48461	2.61	.01323	.49547
1.72	.09089	.45728	2.17	.03788	.48500	2.62	.01289	.49560
1.73	.08933	.45818	2.18	.03706	.48537	2.63	.01256	.49573
1.74	.08780	.45907	2.19	.03626	.48574	2.64	.01223	.49585
1.75	.08628	.45994	2.20	.03547	.48610	2.65	.01191	.49598
1.76	.08478	.46080	2.21	.03470	.48645	2.66	.01160	.49609
1.77	.08329	.46164	2.22	.03394	.48679	2.67	.01130	.49621
1.78	.08183	.46246	2.23	.03319	.48713	2.68	.01100	.49632
1.79	.08038	.46327	2.24	.03246	.48745	2.69	.01071	.49643

TABLE I. ORDINATES AND AREAS OF THE NORMAL CURVE, $\phi(t) = \dfrac{1}{\sqrt{2\pi}} e^{-t^2/2}$

t	$\phi(t)$	$\int_0^t \phi(t)dt$	t	$\phi(t)$	$\int_0^t \phi(t)dt$	t	$\phi(t)$	$\int_0^t \phi(t)dt$
2.70	.01042	.49653	3.15	.00279	.49918	3.60	.00061	.49984
2.71	.01014	.49664	3.16	.00271	.49921	3.61	.00059	.49985
2.72	.00987	.49674	3.17	.00262	.49924	3.62	.00057	.49985
2.73	.00961	.49683	3.18	.00254	.49926	3.63	.00055	.49986
2.74	.00935	.49693	3.19	.00246	.49929	3.64	.00053	.49986
2.75	.00909	.49702	3.20	.00238	.49931	3.65	.00051	.49987
2.76	.00885	.49711	3.21	.00231	.49934	3.66	.00049	.49987
2.77	.00861	.49720	3.22	.00224	.49936	3.67	.00047	.49988
2.78	.00837	.49728	3.23	.00216	.49938	3.68	.00046	.49988
2.79	.00814	.49736	3.24	.00210	.49940	3.69	.00044	.49989
2.80	.00792	.49744	3.25	.00203	.49942	3.70	.00042	.49989
2.81	.00770	.49752	3.26	.00196	.49944	3.71	.00041	.49990
2.82	.00748	.49760	3.27	.00190	.49946	3.72	.00039	.49990
2.83	.00727	.49767	3.28	.00184	.49948	3.73	.00038	.49990
2.84	.00707	.49774	3.29	.00178	.49950	3.74	.00037	.49991
2.85	.00687	.49781	3.30	.00172	.49952	3.75	.00035	.49991
2.86	.00668	.49788	3.31	.00167	.49953	3.76	.00034	.49992
2.87	.00649	.49795	3.32	.00161	.49955	3.77	.00033	.49992
2.88	.00631	.49801	3.33	.00156	.49957	3.78	.00031	.49992
2.89	.00613	.49807	3.34	.00151	.49958	3.79	.00030	.49992
2.90	.00595	.49813	3.35	.00146	.49960	3.80	.00029	.49993
2.91	.00578	.49819	3.36	.00141	.49961	3.81	.00028	.49993
2.92	.00562	.49825	3.37	.00136	.49962	3.82	.00027	.49993
2.93	.00545	.49831	3.38	.00132	.49964	3.83	.00026	.49994
2.94	.00530	.49836	3.39	.00127	.49965	3.84	.00025	.49994
2.95	.00514	.49841	3.40	.00123	.49966	3.85	.00024	.49994
2.96	.00499	.49846	3.41	.00119	.49968	3.86	.00023	.49994
2.97	.00485	.49851	3.42	.00115	.49969	3.87	.00022	.49995
2.98	.00471	.49856	3.43	.00111	.49970	3.88	.00021	.49995
2.99	.00457	.49861	3.44	.00107	.49971	3.89	.00021	.49995
3.00	.00443	.49865	3.45	.00104	.49972	3.90	.00020	.49995
3.01	.00430	.49869	3.46	.00100	.49973	3.91	.00019	.49995
3.02	.00417	.49874	3.47	.00097	.49974	3.92	.00018	.49996
3.03	.00405	.49878	3.48	.00094	.49975	3.93	.00018	.49996
3.04	.00393	.49882	3.49	.00090	.49976	3.94	.00017	.49996
3.05	.00381	.49886	3.50	.00087	.49977	3.95	.00016	.49996
3.06	.00370	.49889	3.51	.00084	.49978	3.96	.00016	.49996
3.07	.00358	.49893	3.52	.00081	.49978	3.97	.00015	.49996
3.08	.00348	.49897	3.53	.00079	.49979	3.98	.00014	.49997
3.09	.00337	.49900	3.54	.00076	.49980	3.99	.00014	.49997
3.10	.00327	.49903	3.55	.00073	.49981			
3.11	.00317	.49906	3.56	.00071	.49981			
3.12	.00307	.49910	3.57	.00068	.49982			
3.13	.00298	.49913	3.58	.00066	.49983			
3.14	.00288	.49916	3.59	.00063	.49983			

TABLE II.* 5% (Roman Type) and 1% (Bold Face Type) Points for the Distribution of F

n_2	1	2	3	4	5	6	7	8	9	10	11	12	14	16	20	24	30	40	50	75	100	200	500	∞	n_2
1	161 4,052	200 4,999	216 5,403	225 5,625	230 5,764	234 5,859	237 5,928	239 5,981	241 6,022	242 6,056	243 6,082	244 6,106	245 6,142	246 6,169	248 6,208	249 6,234	250 6,258	251 6,286	252 6,302	253 6,323	253 6,334	254 6,352	254 6,361	254 6,366	1
2	18.51 98.49	19.00 99.01	19.16 99.17	19.25 99.25	19.30 99.30	19.33 99.33	19.36 99.34	19.37 99.36	19.38 99.38	19.39 99.40	19.40 99.41	19.41 99.42	19.42 99.43	19.43 99.44	19.44 99.45	19.45 99.46	19.46 99.47	19.47 99.48	19.47 99.48	19.48 99.49	19.49 99.49	19.49 99.49	19.50 99.50	19.50 99.50	2
3	10.13 34.12	9.55 30.81	9.28 29.46	9.12 28.71	9.01 28.24	8.94 27.91	8.88 27.67	8.84 27.49	8.81 27.34	8.78 27.23	8.76 27.13	8.74 27.05	8.71 26.92	8.69 26.83	8.66 26.69	8.64 26.60	8.62 26.50	8.60 26.41	8.58 26.35	8.57 26.27	8.56 26.23	8.54 26.18	8.54 26.14	8.53 26.12	3
4	7.71 21.20	6.94 18.00	6.59 16.69	6.39 15.98	6.26 15.52	6.16 15.21	6.09 14.98	6.04 14.80	6.00 14.66	5.96 14.54	5.93 14.45	5.91 14.37	5.87 14.24	5.84 14.15	5.80 14.02	5.77 13.93	5.74 13.83	5.71 13.74	5.70 13.69	5.68 13.61	5.66 13.57	5.65 13.52	5.64 13.48	5.63 13.46	4
5	6.61 16.26	5.79 13.27	5.41 12.06	5.19 11.39	5.05 10.97	4.95 10.67	4.88 10.45	4.82 10.27	4.78 10.15	4.74 10.05	4.70 9.96	4.68 9.89	4.64 9.77	4.60 9.68	4.56 9.55	4.53 9.47	4.50 9.38	4.46 9.29	4.44 9.24	4.42 9.17	4.40 9.13	4.38 9.07	4.37 9.04	4.36 9.02	5
6	5.99 13.74	5.14 10.92	4.76 9.78	4.53 9.15	4.39 8.75	4.28 8.47	4.21 8.26	4.15 8.10	4.10 7.98	4.06 7.87	4.03 7.79	4.00 7.72	3.96 7.60	3.92 7.52	3.87 7.39	3.84 7.31	3.81 7.23	3.77 7.14	3.75 7.09	3.72 7.02	3.71 6.99	3.69 6.94	3.68 6.90	3.67 6.88	6
7	5.59 12.25	4.74 9.55	4.35 8.45	4.12 7.85	3.97 7.46	3.87 7.19	3.79 7.00	3.73 6.84	3.68 6.71	3.63 6.62	3.60 6.54	3.57 6.47	3.52 6.35	3.49 6.27	3.44 6.15	3.41 6.07	3.38 5.98	3.34 5.90	3.32 5.85	3.29 5.78	3.28 5.75	3.25 5.70	3.24 5.67	3.23 5.65	7
8	5.32 11.26	4.46 8.65	4.07 7.59	3.84 7.01	3.69 6.63	3.58 6.37	3.50 6.19	3.44 6.03	3.39 5.91	3.34 5.82	3.31 5.74	3.28 5.67	3.23 5.56	3.20 5.48	3.15 5.36	3.12 5.28	3.08 5.20	3.05 5.11	3.03 5.06	3.00 5.00	2.98 4.96	2.96 4.91	2.94 4.88	2.93 4.86	8
9	5.12 10.56	4.26 8.02	3.86 6.99	3.63 6.42	3.48 6.06	3.37 5.80	3.29 5.62	3.23 5.47	3.18 5.35	3.13 5.26	3.10 5.18	3.07 5.11	3.02 5.00	2.98 4.92	2.93 4.80	2.90 4.73	2.86 4.64	2.82 4.56	2.80 4.51	2.77 4.45	2.76 4.41	2.73 4.36	2.72 4.33	2.71 4.31	9
10	4.96 10.04	4.10 7.56	3.71 6.55	3.48 5.99	3.33 5.64	3.22 5.39	3.14 5.21	3.07 5.06	3.02 4.95	2.97 4.85	2.94 4.78	2.91 4.71	2.86 4.60	2.82 4.52	2.77 4.41	2.74 4.33	2.70 4.25	2.67 4.17	2.64 4.12	2.61 4.05	2.59 4.01	2.56 3.96	2.55 3.93	2.54 3.91	10
11	4.84 9.65	3.98 7.20	3.59 6.22	3.36 5.67	3.20 5.32	3.09 5.07	3.01 4.88	2.95 4.74	2.90 4.63	2.86 4.54	2.82 4.46	2.79 4.40	2.74 4.29	2.70 4.21	2.65 4.10	2.61 4.02	2.57 3.94	2.53 3.86	2.50 3.80	2.47 3.74	2.45 3.70	2.42 3.66	2.41 3.62	2.40 3.60	11
12	4.75 9.33	3.88 6.93	3.49 5.95	3.26 5.41	3.11 5.06	3.00 4.82	2.92 4.65	2.85 4.50	2.80 4.39	2.76 4.30	2.72 4.22	2.69 4.16	2.64 4.05	2.60 3.98	2.54 3.86	2.50 3.78	2.46 3.70	2.42 3.61	2.40 3.56	2.36 3.49	2.35 3.46	2.32 3.41	2.31 3.38	2.30 3.36	12
13	4.67 9.07	3.80 6.70	3.41 5.74	3.18 5.20	3.02 4.86	2.92 4.62	2.84 4.44	2.77 4.30	2.72 4.19	2.67 4.10	2.63 4.02	2.60 3.96	2.55 3.85	2.51 3.78	2.46 3.67	2.42 3.59	2.38 3.51	2.34 3.42	2.32 3.37	2.28 3.30	2.26 3.27	2.24 3.21	2.22 3.18	2.21 3.16	13

n_1 degrees of freedom (for greater mean square)

* Reproduced from *Statistical Methods* by G. W. Snedecor by permission of the author and the publisher, Collegiate Press, Inc., Ames, Iowa.

410

TABLE II. 5% (Roman Type) and 1% (Bold Face Type) Points for the Distribution of F

n_2	1	2	3	4	5	6	7	8	9	10	11	12	14	16	20	24	30	40	50	75	100	200	500	∞	n_2
14	4.60 **8.86**	3.74 **6.51**	3.34 **5.56**	3.11 **5.03**	2.96 **4.69**	2.85 **4.46**	2.77 **4.28**	2.70 **4.14**	2.65 **4.03**	2.60 **3.94**	2.56 **3.86**	2.53 **3.80**	2.48 **3.70**	2.44 **3.62**	2.39 **3.51**	2.35 **3.43**	2.31 **3.34**	2.27 **3.26**	2.24 **3.21**	2.21 **3.14**	2.19 **3.11**	2.16 **3.06**	2.14 **3.02**	2.13 **3.00**	14
15	4.54 **8.68**	3.68 **6.36**	3.29 **5.42**	3.06 **4.89**	2.90 **4.56**	2.79 **4.32**	2.70 **4.14**	2.64 **4.00**	2.59 **3.89**	2.55 **3.80**	2.51 **3.73**	2.48 **3.67**	2.43 **3.56**	2.39 **3.48**	2.33 **3.36**	2.29 **3.29**	2.25 **3.20**	2.21 **3.12**	2.18 **3.07**	2.15 **3.00**	2.12 **2.97**	2.10 **2.92**	2.08 **2.89**	2.07 **2.87**	15
16	4.49 **8.53**	3.63 **6.23**	3.24 **5.29**	3.01 **4.77**	2.85 **4.44**	2.74 **4.20**	2.66 **4.03**	2.59 **3.89**	2.54 **3.78**	2.49 **3.69**	2.45 **3.61**	2.42 **3.55**	2.37 **3.45**	2.33 **3.37**	2.28 **3.25**	2.24 **3.18**	2.20 **3.10**	2.16 **3.01**	2.13 **2.96**	2.09 **2.89**	2.07 **2.86**	2.04 **2.80**	2.02 **2.77**	2.01 **2.75**	16
17	4.45 **8.40**	3.59 **6.11**	3.20 **5.18**	2.96 **4.67**	2.81 **4.34**	2.70 **4.10**	2.62 **3.93**	2.55 **3.79**	2.50 **3.68**	2.45 **3.59**	2.41 **3.52**	2.38 **3.45**	2.33 **3.35**	2.29 **3.27**	2.23 **3.16**	2.19 **3.08**	2.15 **3.00**	2.11 **2.92**	2.08 **2.86**	2.04 **2.79**	2.02 **2.76**	1.99 **2.70**	1.97 **2.67**	1.96 **2.65**	17
18	4.41 **8.28**	3.55 **6.01**	3.16 **5.09**	2.93 **4.58**	2.77 **4.25**	2.66 **4.01**	2.58 **3.85**	2.51 **3.71**	2.46 **3.60**	2.41 **3.51**	2.37 **3.44**	2.34 **3.37**	2.29 **3.27**	2.25 **3.19**	2.19 **3.07**	2.15 **3.00**	2.11 **2.91**	2.07 **2.83**	2.04 **2.78**	2.00 **2.71**	1.98 **2.68**	1.95 **2.62**	1.93 **2.59**	1.92 **2.57**	18
19	4.38 **8.18**	3.52 **5.93**	3.13 **5.01**	2.90 **4.50**	2.74 **4.17**	2.63 **3.94**	2.55 **3.77**	2.48 **3.63**	2.43 **3.52**	2.38 **3.43**	2.34 **3.36**	2.31 **3.30**	2.26 **3.19**	2.21 **3.12**	2.15 **3.00**	2.11 **2.92**	2.07 **2.84**	2.02 **2.76**	2.00 **2.70**	1.96 **2.63**	1.94 **2.60**	1.91 **2.54**	1.90 **2.51**	1.88 **2.49**	19
20	4.35 **8.10**	3.49 **5.85**	3.10 **4.94**	2.87 **4.43**	2.71 **4.10**	2.60 **3.87**	2.52 **3.71**	2.45 **3.56**	2.40 **3.45**	2.35 **3.37**	2.31 **3.30**	2.28 **3.23**	2.23 **3.13**	2.18 **3.05**	2.12 **2.94**	2.08 **2.86**	2.04 **2.77**	1.99 **2.69**	1.96 **2.63**	1.92 **2.56**	1.90 **2.53**	1.87 **2.47**	1.85 **2.44**	1.84 **2.42**	20
21	4.32 **8.02**	3.47 **5.78**	3.07 **4.87**	2.84 **4.37**	2.68 **4.04**	2.57 **3.81**	2.49 **3.65**	2.42 **3.51**	2.37 **3.40**	2.32 **3.31**	2.28 **3.24**	2.25 **3.17**	2.20 **3.07**	2.15 **2.99**	2.09 **2.88**	2.05 **2.80**	2.00 **2.72**	1.96 **2.63**	1.93 **2.58**	1.89 **2.51**	1.87 **2.47**	1.84 **2.42**	1.82 **2.38**	1.81 **2.36**	21
22	4.30 **7.94**	3.44 **5.72**	3.05 **4.82**	2.82 **4.31**	2.66 **3.99**	2.55 **3.76**	2.47 **3.59**	2.40 **3.45**	2.35 **3.35**	2.30 **3.26**	2.26 **3.18**	2.23 **3.12**	2.18 **3.02**	2.13 **2.94**	2.07 **2.83**	2.03 **2.75**	1.98 **2.67**	1.93 **2.58**	1.91 **2.53**	1.87 **2.46**	1.84 **2.42**	1.81 **2.37**	1.80 **2.33**	1.78 **2.31**	22
23	4.28 **7.88**	3.42 **5.66**	3.03 **4.76**	2.80 **4.26**	2.64 **3.94**	2.53 **3.71**	2.45 **3.54**	2.38 **3.41**	2.32 **3.30**	2.28 **3.21**	2.24 **3.14**	2.20 **3.07**	2.14 **2.97**	2.10 **2.89**	2.04 **2.78**	2.00 **2.70**	1.96 **2.62**	1.91 **2.53**	1.88 **2.48**	1.84 **2.41**	1.82 **2.37**	1.79 **2.32**	1.77 **2.28**	1.76 **2.26**	23
24	4.26 **7.82**	3.40 **5.61**	3.01 **4.72**	2.78 **4.22**	2.62 **3.90**	2.51 **3.67**	2.43 **3.50**	2.36 **3.36**	2.30 **3.25**	2.26 **3.17**	2.22 **3.09**	2.18 **3.03**	2.13 **2.93**	2.09 **2.85**	2.02 **2.74**	1.98 **2.66**	1.94 **2.58**	1.89 **2.49**	1.86 **2.44**	1.82 **2.36**	1.80 **2.33**	1.76 **2.27**	1.74 **2.23**	1.73 **2.21**	24
25	4.24 **7.77**	3.38 **5.57**	2.99 **4.68**	2.76 **4.18**	2.60 **3.86**	2.49 **3.63**	2.41 **3.46**	2.34 **3.32**	2.28 **3.21**	2.24 **3.13**	2.20 **3.05**	2.16 **2.99**	2.11 **2.89**	2.06 **2.81**	2.00 **2.70**	1.96 **2.62**	1.92 **2.54**	1.87 **2.45**	1.84 **2.40**	1.80 **2.32**	1.77 **2.29**	1.74 **2.23**	1.72 **2.19**	1.71 **2.17**	25
26	4.22 **7.72**	3.37 **5.53**	2.98 **4.64**	2.74 **4.14**	2.59 **3.82**	2.47 **3.59**	2.39 **3.42**	2.32 **3.29**	2.27 **3.17**	2.22 **3.09**	2.18 **3.02**	2.15 **2.96**	2.10 **2.86**	2.05 **2.77**	1.99 **2.66**	1.95 **2.58**	1.90 **2.50**	1.85 **2.41**	1.82 **2.36**	1.78 **2.28**	1.76 **2.25**	1.72 **2.19**	1.70 **2.15**	1.69 **2.13**	26

n_1 degrees of freedom (for greater mean square)

TABLE II. 5% (ROMAN TYPE) AND 1% (BOLD FACE TYPE) POINTS FOR THE DISTRIBUTION OF F

n_1 degrees of freedom (for greater mean square)

n_2	1	2	3	4	5	6	7	8	9	10	11	12	14	16	20	24	30	40	50	75	100	200	500	∞	n_2
27	4.21 **7.68**	3.35 **5.49**	2.96 **4.60**	2.73 **4.11**	2.57 **3.79**	2.46 **3.56**	2.37 **3.39**	2.30 **3.26**	2.25 **3.14**	2.20 **3.06**	2.16 **2.98**	2.13 **2.93**	2.08 **2.83**	2.03 **2.74**	1.97 **2.63**	1.93 **2.55**	1.88 **2.47**	1.84 **2.38**	1.80 **2.33**	1.76 **2.25**	1.74 **2.21**	1.71 **2.16**	1.68 **2.12**	1.67 **2.10**	27
28	4.20 **7.64**	3.34 **5.45**	2.95 **4.57**	2.71 **4.07**	2.56 **3.76**	2.44 **3.53**	2.36 **3.36**	2.29 **3.23**	2.24 **3.11**	2.19 **3.03**	2.15 **2.95**	2.12 **2.90**	2.06 **2.80**	2.02 **2.71**	1.96 **2.60**	1.91 **2.52**	1.87 **2.44**	1.81 **2.35**	1.78 **2.30**	1.75 **2.22**	1.72 **2.18**	1.69 **2.13**	1.67 **2.09**	1.65 **2.06**	28
29	4.18 **7.60**	3.33 **5.42**	2.93 **4.54**	2.70 **4.04**	2.54 **3.73**	2.43 **3.50**	2.35 **3.33**	2.28 **3.20**	2.22 **3.08**	2.18 **3.00**	2.14 **2.92**	2.10 **2.87**	2.05 **2.77**	2.00 **2.68**	1.94 **2.57**	1.90 **2.49**	1.85 **2.41**	1.80 **2.32**	1.77 **2.27**	1.73 **2.19**	1.71 **2.15**	1.68 **2.10**	1.65 **2.06**	1.64 **2.03**	29
30	4.17 **7.56**	3.32 **5.39**	2.92 **4.51**	2.69 **4.02**	2.53 **3.70**	2.42 **3.47**	2.34 **3.30**	2.27 **3.17**	2.21 **3.06**	2.16 **2.98**	2.12 **2.90**	2.09 **2.84**	2.04 **2.74**	1.99 **2.66**	1.93 **2.55**	1.89 **2.47**	1.84 **2.38**	1.79 **2.29**	1.76 **2.24**	1.72 **2.16**	1.69 **2.13**	1.66 **2.07**	1.64 **2.03**	1.62 **2.01**	30
32	4.15 **7.50**	3.30 **5.34**	2.90 **4.46**	2.67 **3.97**	2.51 **3.66**	2.40 **3.42**	2.32 **3.25**	2.25 **3.12**	2.19 **3.01**	2.14 **2.94**	2.10 **2.86**	2.07 **2.80**	2.02 **2.70**	1.97 **2.62**	1.91 **2.51**	1.86 **2.42**	1.82 **2.34**	1.76 **2.25**	1.74 **2.20**	1.69 **2.12**	1.67 **2.08**	1.64 **2.02**	1.61 **1.98**	1.59 **1.96**	32
34	4.13 **7.44**	3.28 **5.29**	2.88 **4.42**	2.65 **3.93**	2.49 **3.61**	2.38 **3.38**	2.30 **3.21**	2.23 **3.08**	2.17 **2.97**	2.12 **2.89**	2.08 **2.82**	2.05 **2.76**	2.00 **2.66**	1.95 **2.58**	1.89 **2.47**	1.84 **2.38**	1.80 **2.30**	1.74 **2.21**	1.71 **2.15**	1.67 **2.08**	1.64 **2.04**	1.61 **1.98**	1.59 **1.94**	1.57 **1.91**	34
36	4.11 **7.39**	3.26 **5.25**	2.86 **4.38**	2.63 **3.89**	2.48 **3.58**	2.36 **3.35**	2.28 **3.18**	2.21 **3.04**	2.15 **2.94**	2.10 **2.86**	2.06 **2.78**	2.03 **2.72**	1.98 **2.62**	1.93 **2.54**	1.87 **2.43**	1.82 **2.35**	1.78 **2.26**	1.72 **2.17**	1.69 **2.12**	1.65 **2.04**	1.62 **2.00**	1.59 **1.94**	1.56 **1.90**	1.55 **1.87**	36
38	4.10 **7.35**	3.25 **5.21**	2.85 **4.34**	2.62 **3.86**	2.46 **3.54**	2.35 **3.32**	2.26 **3.15**	2.19 **3.02**	2.14 **2.91**	2.09 **2.82**	2.05 **2.75**	2.02 **2.69**	1.96 **2.59**	1.92 **2.51**	1.85 **2.40**	1.80 **2.32**	1.76 **2.22**	1.71 **2.14**	1.67 **2.08**	1.63 **2.00**	1.60 **1.97**	1.57 **1.90**	1.54 **1.86**	1.53 **1.84**	38
40	4.08 **7.31**	3.23 **5.18**	2.84 **4.31**	2.61 **3.83**	2.45 **3.51**	2.34 **3.29**	2.25 **3.12**	2.18 **2.99**	2.12 **2.88**	2.07 **2.80**	2.04 **2.73**	2.00 **2.66**	1.95 **2.56**	1.90 **2.49**	1.84 **2.37**	1.79 **2.29**	1.74 **2.20**	1.69 **2.11**	1.66 **2.05**	1.61 **1.97**	1.59 **1.94**	1.55 **1.88**	1.53 **1.84**	1.51 **1.81**	40
42	4.07 **7.27**	3.22 **5.15**	2.83 **4.29**	2.59 **3.80**	2.44 **3.49**	2.32 **3.26**	2.24 **3.10**	2.17 **2.96**	2.11 **2.86**	2.06 **2.77**	2.02 **2.70**	1.99 **2.64**	1.94 **2.54**	1.89 **2.46**	1.82 **2.35**	1.78 **2.26**	1.73 **2.17**	1.68 **2.08**	1.64 **2.02**	1.60 **1.94**	1.57 **1.91**	1.54 **1.85**	1.51 **1.80**	1.49 **1.78**	42
44	4.06 **7.24**	3.21 **5.12**	2.82 **4.26**	2.58 **3.78**	2.43 **3.46**	2.31 **3.24**	2.23 **3.07**	2.16 **2.94**	2.10 **2.84**	2.05 **2.75**	2.01 **2.68**	1.98 **2.62**	1.92 **2.52**	1.88 **2.44**	1.81 **2.32**	1.76 **2.24**	1.72 **2.15**	1.66 **2.06**	1.63 **2.00**	1.58 **1.92**	1.56 **1.88**	1.52 **1.82**	1.50 **1.78**	1.48 **1.75**	44
46	4.05 **7.21**	3.20 **5.10**	2.81 **4.24**	2.57 **3.76**	2.42 **3.44**	2.30 **3.22**	2.22 **3.05**	2.14 **2.92**	2.09 **2.82**	2.04 **2.73**	2.00 **2.66**	1.97 **2.60**	1.91 **2.50**	1.87 **2.42**	1.80 **2.30**	1.75 **2.22**	1.71 **2.13**	1.65 **2.04**	1.62 **1.98**	1.57 **1.90**	1.54 **1.86**	1.51 **1.80**	1.48 **1.76**	1.46 **1.72**	46
48	4.04 **7.19**	3.19 **5.08**	2.80 **4.22**	2.56 **3.74**	2.41 **3.42**	2.30 **3.20**	2.21 **3.04**	2.14 **2.90**	2.08 **2.80**	2.03 **2.71**	1.99 **2.64**	1.96 **2.58**	1.90 **2.48**	1.86 **2.40**	1.79 **2.28**	1.74 **2.20**	1.70 **2.11**	1.64 **2.02**	1.61 **1.96**	1.56 **1.88**	1.53 **1.84**	1.50 **1.78**	1.47 **1.73**	1.45 **1.70**	48

412

TABLE II. 5% (Roman Type) and 1% (Bold Face Type) Points for the Distribution of F

n_1 degrees of freedom (for greater mean square)

n_2	1	2	3	4	5	6	7	8	9	10	11	12	14	16	20	24	30	40	50	75	100	200	500	∞	n_2
50	4.03 7.17	3.18 5.06	2.79 4.20	2.56 3.72	2.40 3.41	2.29 3.18	2.20 3.02	2.13 2.88	2.07 2.78	2.02 2.70	1.98 2.62	1.95 2.56	1.90 2.46	1.85 2.39	1.78 2.26	1.74 2.18	1.69 2.10	1.63 2.00	1.60 1.94	1.55 1.86	1.52 1.82	1.48 1.76	1.46 1.71	1.44 1.68	50
55	4.02 7.12	3.17 5.01	2.78 4.16	2.54 3.68	2.38 3.37	2.27 3.15	2.18 2.98	2.11 2.85	2.05 2.75	2.00 2.66	1.97 2.59	1.93 2.53	1.88 2.43	1.83 2.35	1.76 2.23	1.72 2.15	1.67 2.06	1.61 1.96	1.58 1.90	1.52 1.82	1.50 1.78	1.46 1.71	1.43 1.66	1.41 1.64	55
60	4.00 7.08	3.15 4.98	2.76 4.13	2.52 3.65	2.37 3.34	2.25 3.12	2.17 2.95	2.10 2.82	2.04 2.72	1.99 2.63	1.95 2.56	1.92 2.50	1.86 2.40	1.81 2.32	1.75 2.20	1.70 2.12	1.65 2.03	1.59 1.93	1.56 1.87	1.50 1.79	1.48 1.74	1.44 1.68	1.41 1.63	1.39 1.60	60
65	3.99 7.04	3.14 4.95	2.75 4.10	2.51 3.62	2.36 3.31	2.24 3.09	2.15 2.93	2.08 2.79	2.02 2.70	1.98 2.61	1.94 2.54	1.90 2.47	1.85 2.37	1.80 2.30	1.73 2.18	1.68 2.09	1.63 2.00	1.57 1.90	1.54 1.84	1.49 1.76	1.46 1.71	1.42 1.64	1.39 1.60	1.37 1.56	65
70	3.98 7.01	3.13 4.92	2.74 4.08	2.50 3.60	2.35 3.29	2.23 3.07	2.14 2.91	2.07 2.77	2.01 2.67	1.97 2.59	1.93 2.51	1.89 2.45	1.84 2.35	1.79 2.28	1.72 2.15	1.67 2.07	1.62 1.98	1.56 1.88	1.53 1.82	1.47 1.74	1.45 1.69	1.40 1.62	1.37 1.56	1.35 1.53	70
80	3.96 6.96	3.11 4.88	2.72 4.04	2.48 3.56	2.33 3.25	2.21 3.04	2.12 2.87	2.05 2.74	1.99 2.64	1.95 2.55	1.91 2.48	1.88 2.41	1.82 2.32	1.77 2.24	1.70 2.11	1.65 2.03	1.60 1.94	1.54 1.84	1.51 1.78	1.45 1.70	1.42 1.65	1.38 1.57	1.35 1.52	1.32 1.49	80
100	3.94 6.90	3.09 4.82	2.70 3.98	2.46 3.51	2.30 3.20	2.19 2.99	2.10 2.82	2.03 2.69	1.97 2.59	1.92 2.51	1.88 2.43	1.85 2.36	1.79 2.26	1.75 2.19	1.68 2.06	1.63 1.98	1.57 1.89	1.51 1.79	1.48 1.73	1.42 1.64	1.39 1.59	1.34 1.51	1.30 1.46	1.28 1.43	100
125	3.92 6.84	3.07 4.78	2.68 3.94	2.44 3.47	2.29 3.17	2.17 2.95	2.08 2.79	2.01 2.65	1.95 2.56	1.90 2.47	1.86 2.40	1.83 2.33	1.77 2.23	1.72 2.15	1.65 2.03	1.60 1.94	1.55 1.85	1.49 1.75	1.45 1.68	1.39 1.59	1.36 1.54	1.31 1.46	1.27 1.40	1.25 1.37	125
150	3.91 6.81	3.06 4.75	2.67 3.91	2.43 3.44	2.27 3.14	2.16 2.92	2.07 2.76	2.00 2.62	1.94 2.53	1.89 2.44	1.85 2.37	1.82 2.30	1.76 2.20	1.71 2.12	1.64 2.00	1.59 1.91	1.54 1.83	1.47 1.72	1.44 1.66	1.37 1.56	1.34 1.51	1.29 1.43	1.25 1.37	1.22 1.33	150
200	3.89 6.76	3.04 4.71	2.65 3.88	2.41 3.41	2.26 3.11	2.14 2.90	2.05 2.73	1.98 2.60	1.92 2.50	1.87 2.41	1.83 2.34	1.80 2.28	1.74 2.17	1.69 2.09	1.62 1.97	1.57 1.88	1.52 1.79	1.45 1.69	1.42 1.62	1.35 1.53	1.32 1.48	1.26 1.39	1.22 1.33	1.19 1.28	200
400	3.86 6.70	3.02 4.66	2.62 3.83	2.39 3.36	2.23 3.06	2.12 2.85	2.03 2.69	1.96 2.55	1.90 2.46	1.85 2.37	1.81 2.29	1.78 2.23	1.72 2.12	1.67 2.04	1.60 1.92	1.54 1.84	1.49 1.74	1.42 1.64	1.38 1.57	1.32 1.47	1.28 1.42	1.22 1.32	1.16 1.24	1.13 1.19	400
1000	3.85 6.66	3.00 4.62	2.61 3.80	2.38 3.34	2.22 3.04	2.10 2.82	2.02 2.66	1.95 2.53	1.89 2.43	1.84 2.34	1.80 2.26	1.76 2.20	1.70 2.09	1.65 2.01	1.58 1.89	1.53 1.81	1.47 1.71	1.41 1.61	1.36 1.54	1.30 1.44	1.26 1.38	1.19 1.28	1.13 1.19	1.08 1.11	1000
∞	3.84 6.64	2.99 4.60	2.60 3.78	2.37 3.32	2.21 3.02	2.09 2.80	2.01 2.64	1.94 2.51	1.88 2.41	1.83 2.32	1.79 2.24	1.75 2.18	1.69 2.07	1.64 1.99	1.57 1.87	1.52 1.79	1.46 1.69	1.40 1.59	1.35 1.52	1.28 1.41	1.24 1.36	1.17 1.25	1.11 1.15	1.00 1.00	∞

TABLE III. VALUES OF χ^2 CORRESPONDING TO GIVEN PROBABILITIES *

Degrees of freedom n'	Probability of a deviation greater than χ^2						
	.01	.02	.05	.10	.20	.30	.50
1	6.635	5.412	3.841	2.706	1.642	1.074	.455
2	9.210	7.824	5.991	4.605	3.219	2.408	1.386
3	11.341	9.837	7.815	6.251	4.642	3.665	2.366
4	13.277	11.668	9.488	7.779	5.989	4.878	3.357
5	15.086	13.388	11.070	9.236	7.289	6.064	4.351
6	16.812	15.033	12.592	10.645	8.558	7.231	5.348
7	18.475	16.622	14.067	12.017	9.803	8.383	6.346
8	20.090	18.168	15.507	13.362	11.030	9.524	7.344
9	21.666	19.679	16.919	14.684	12.242	10.656	8.343
10	23.209	21.161	18.307	15.987	13.442	11.781	9.342
11	24.725	22.618	19.675	17.275	14.631	12.899	10.341
12	26.217	24.054	21.026	18.549	15.812	14.011	11.340
13	27.688	25.472	22.362	19.812	16.985	15.119	12.340
14	29.141	26.873	23.685	21.064	18.151	16.222	13.339
15	30.578	28.259	24.996	22.307	19.311	17.322	14.339
16	32.000	29.633	26.296	23.542	20.465	18.418	15.338
17	33.409	30.995	27.587	24.769	21.615	19.511	16.338
18	34.805	32.346	28.869	25.989	22.760	20.601	17.338
19	36.191	33.687	30.144	27.204	23.900	21.689	18.338
20	37.566	35.020	31.410	28.412	25.038	22.775	19.337
21	38.932	36.343	32.671	29.615	26.171	23.858	20.337
22	40.289	37.659	33.924	30.813	27.301	24.939	21.337
23	41.638	38.968	35.172	32.007	28.429	26.018	22.337
24	42.980	40.270	36.415	33.196	29.553	27.096	23.337
25	44.314	41.566	37.652	34.382	30.675	28.172	24.337
26	45.642	42.856	38.885	35.563	31.795	29.246	25.336
27	46.963	44.140	40.113	36.741	32.912	30.319	26.336
28	48.278	45.419	41.337	37.916	34.027	31.391	27.336
29	49.588	46.693	42.557	39.087	35.139	32.461	28.336
30	50.892	47.962	43.773	40.256	36.250	33.530	29.336

For larger values of n', the quantity $(2\chi^2)^{1/2} - (2n' - 1)^{1/2}$ may be used as a normal deviate with unit standard deviation.

* This table is reproduced from "Statistical Methods for Research Workers," with the generous permission of the author, Professor R. A. Fisher, and the publishers, Messrs. Oliver and Boyd.

Table III. Values of χ^2 Corresponding to Given Probabilities (cont.)

Degrees of freedom n'	\multicolumn{6}{c}{Probability of a deviation greater than χ^2}
	.70	.80	.90	.95	.98	.99
1	.148	.0642	.0158	.00393	.000628	.000157
2	.713	.446	.211	.103	.0404	.0201
3	1.424	1.005	.584	.352	.185	.115
4	2.195	1.649	1.064	.711	.429	.297
5	3.000	2.343	1.610	1.145	.752	.554
6	3.828	3.070	2.204	1.635	1.134	.872
7	4.671	3.822	2.833	2.167	1.564	1.239
8	5.527	4.594	3.490	2.733	2.032	1.646
9	6.393	5.380	4.168	3.325	2.532	2.088
10	7.267	6.179	4.865	3.940	3.059	2.558
11	8.148	6.989	5.578	4.575	3.609	3.053
12	9.034	7.807	6.304	5.226	4.178	3.571
13	9.926	8.634	7.042	5.892	4.765	4.107
14	10.821	9.467	7.790	6.571	5.368	4.660
15	11.721	10.307	8.547	7.261	5.985	5.229
16	12.624	11.152	9.312	7.962	6.614	5.812
17	13.531	12.002	10.085	8.672	7.255	6.408
18	14.440	12.857	10.865	9.390	7.906	7.015
19	15.352	13.716	11.651	10.117	8.567	7.633
20	16.266	14.578	12.443	10.851	9.237	8.260
21	17.182	15.445	13.240	11.591	9.915	8.897
22	18.101	16.314	14.041	12.338	10.600	9.542
23	19.021	17.187	14.848	13.091	11.293	10.196
24	19.943	18.062	15.659	13.848	11.992	10.856
25	20.867	18.940	16.473	14.611	12.697	11.524
26	21.792	19.820	17.292	15.379	13.409	12.198
27	22.719	20.703	18.114	16.151	14.125	12.879
28	23.647	21.588	18.939	16.928	14.847	13.565
29	24.577	22.475	19.768	17.708	15.574	14.256
30	25.508	23.364	20.599	18.493	16.306	14.953

For larger values of n', the quantity $(2\chi^2)^{1/2} - (2n' - 1)^{1/2}$ may be used as a normal deviate with unit standard deviation.

TABLE IV. VALUES OF t CORRESPONDING TO GIVEN PROBABILITIES *

Degrees of freedom n	Probability of a deviation greater than t					
	.005	.01	.025	.05	.1	.15
1	63.657	31.821	12.706	6.314	3.078	1.963
2	9.925	6.965	4.303	2.920	1.886	1.386
3	5.841	4.541	3.182	2.353	1.638	1.250
4	4.604	3.747	2.776	2.132	1.533	1.190
5	4.032	3.365	2.571	2.015	1.476	1.156
6	3.707	3.143	2.447	1.943	1.440	1.134
7	3.499	2.998	2.365	1.895	1.415	1.119
8	3.355	2.896	2.306	1.860	1.397	1.108
9	3.250	2.821	2.262	1.833	1.383	1.100
10	3.169	2.764	2.228	1.812	1.372	1.093
11	3.106	2.718	2.201	1.796	1.363	1.088
12	3.055	2.681	2.179	1.782	1.356	1.083
13	3.012	2.650	2.160	1.771	1.350	1.079
14	2.977	2.624	2.145	1.761	1.345	1.076
15	2.947	2.602	2.131	1.753	1.341	1.074
16	2.921	2.583	2.120	1.746	1.337	1.071
17	2.898	2.567	2.110	1.740	1.333	1.069
18	2.878	2.552	2.101	1.734	1.330	1.067
19	2.861	2.539	2.093	1.729	1.328	1.066
20	2.845	2.528	2.086	1.725	1.325	1.064
21	2.831	2.518	2.080	1.721	1.323	1.063
22	2.819	2.508	2.074	1.717	1.321	1.061
23	2.807	2.500	2.069	1.714	1.319	1.060
24	2.797	2.492	2.064	1.711	1.318	1.059
25	2.787	2.485	2.060	1.708	1.316	1.058
26	2.779	2.479	2.056	1.706	1.315	1.058
27	2.771	2.473	2.052	1.703	1.314	1.057
28	2.763	2.467	2.048	1.701	1.313	1.056
29	2.756	2.462	2.045	1.699	1.311	1.055
30	2.750	2.457	2.042	1.697	1.310	1.055
∞	2.576	2.326	1.960	1.645	1.282	1.036

The probability of a deviation *numerically* greater than t is twice the probability given at the head of the table.

* This table is reproduced from "Statistical Methods for Research Workers," with the generous permission of the author, Professor R. A. Fisher, and the publishers, Messrs. Oliver and Boyd.

TABLE IV. VALUES OF t CORRESPONDING TO GIVEN PROBABILITIES (*cont.*)

Degrees of freedom n'	Probability of a deviation greater than t					
	.2	.25	.3	.35	.4	.45
1	1.376	1.000	.727	.510	.325	.158
2	1.061	.816	.617	.445	.289	.142
3	.978	.765	.584	.424	.277	.137
4	.941	.741	.569	.414	.271	.134
5	.920	.727	.559	.408	.267	.132
6	.906	.718	.553	.404	.265	.131
7	.896	.711	.549	.402	.263	.130
8	.889	.706	.546	.399	.262	.130
9	.883	.703	.543	.398	.261	.129
10	.879	.700	.542	.397	.260	.129
11	.876	.697	.540	.396	.260	.129
12	.873	.695	.539	.395	.259	.128
13	.870	.694	.538	.394	.259	.128
14	.868	.692	.537	.393	.258	.128
15	.866	.691	.536	.393	.258	.128
16	.865	.690	.535	.392	.258	.128
17	.863	.689	.534	.392	.257	.128
18	.862	.688	.534	.392	.257	.127
19	.861	.688	.533	.391	.257	.127
20	.860	.687	.533	.391	.257	.127
21	.859	.686	.532	.391	.257	.127
22	.858	.686	.532	.390	.256	.127
23	.858	.685	.532	.390	.256	.127
24	.857	.685	.531	.390	.256	.127
25	.856	.684	.531	.390	.256	.127
26	.856	.684	.531	.390	.256	.127
27	.855	.684	.531	.389	.256	.127
28	.855	.683	.530	.389	.256	.127
29	.854	.683	.530	.389	.256	.127
30	.854	.683	.530	.389	.256	.127
∞	.842	.674	.524	.385	.253	.126

The probability of a deviation *numerically* greater than t is twice the probability given at the head of the table.

INDEX

Acceptance, region of, 388
Addition theorem (probabilities), 8
Additivity (analysis of variance), 247, 251
Adjoint, of matrix, 296
Aitken, A. C., 83, 295, 307, 322
Allan, F. E., 365
Analysis of covariance, 274
Analysis of variance, 238, Chap. IX
   assumptions, 249–252
   in regression, 325
   one-way classification, 238, 260
   power of test, 395
   three-way classification, 241, 262
   two-way classification, 246, 262
Anderson, R. L., 329, 365
Angular transformation, 253
Association (between attributes), 227
Asymptotic series, 59
Asymptotically normal distribution, 132, 133
   most powerful tests, 391
Attributes, sampling of, 38
   association of, 227

Banachiewicz, T., 322
Barnard, G. A., 230, 233, 237
Bartlett, M. S., 179, 198, 253, 256, 287
Bayes, T., 15, 385
   assumption, 15, 17
   rule (theorem), 14, 15, 17, 18, 21, 129, 130, 258
   rule for future events, 18
Behrens-Fisher test, 257, 259, 264, 385
Bernoulli, J., 22
   distribution (*see* Binomial distribution)
   numbers, 81, 82
   theorem, 41, 85
Bertrand, J., 14, 53
Bessel, F. W., correction, 161
   formula, 186
   function, 363
Beta function, 61, 62
   incomplete, 64, 224
   tables, 64, 66, 324

Beta variate, 95, 96, 101, 104, 184
Beta prime variate, 96, 97, 101
Bienaymé-Tchebycheff inequality, 84, 85, 371
   sharper form, 86
Bilinear form, 294
Binomial distribution, 22, Chap. II
   charts, 148, 159
   confidence limits, 147, 149
   graphical representation, 23
   mode, 32
   moment generating function, 73
   moments, 29, 30
   normal approximation, 33, 34
   special case of multinomial, 113
   sum of binomial variates, 79
   tables of, 23, 148
   transformation of, 252
Binomial theorem, 6, 7
Birge, R. T., 321, 322
Bivariate normal distribution, 92
Bliss, C. I., 118, 126
Blocks, 242
   complete, 278, 281
   incomplete, 281, 282
   randomized, 278
Bose, R. C., 278, 288, 362, 366
Bowker, A. H., 404
Brandt, A. E., 229
Bross, I. J., 288
Buffon, G. L. (Comte de), 14, 123

Camp, B. H., 51, 52, 159, 236
   method for tetrachoric r, 207, 236
Carver, H. C., 143, 144, 159
Cauchy distribution, 28, 72, 73, 91, 101
Central limit theorem, 41, 88, 89, 108
   Liapounoff condition, 90
   Lindeberg condition, 89
   with dependent variables, 90
Chance (*see* Probability), 13, 84
Characteristic function, 73, 88, 93
   derivatives, 88
   limit of sequence of, 75
   uniqueness theorem for, 76
Chebyshev, *see* Tchebycheff

Index

Chi square distribution, 98, 99, 100
  approximations, 99, 126
  Cochran's theorem, 100
  contingency tables, 228, 229, 235
  criterion of goodness of fit, 109, 118, 377
  cumulants, 98
  effect of pooling, 118
  Fisher's theorem, 100
  limiting distribution, 114, 116, 378
  minimum, 378
  moments, 98
  non-central, 362, 396
  relation to variance, 167
  relation to z, 181
  tables of, 117, 188
  test of hypotheses, 117
Church, A. E. R., 159
Clopper, C. J., 148, 159
Cochran, W. G., 100, 118, 126, 250, 260, 278, 287, 288, 406
  theorem, 100
Collective, 4, 32
Combination (of probabilities), 233
Combinations, 5
Comparative trial (2×2 table), 232
Components of variance, 260, 263
Condition equations, 318, 319
Confidence belt, 130, 135
  coefficient, 132, 382
Confidence interval, 130, 132, 381–387
  asymptotically shortest, 391
  geometrical picture, 383
  most selective, 382
  shortest, 382, 385
  unbiased, 382
Confidence limits, 132, 134, 382
  binomial distribution, 147, 149, 193, 194
  correlation coefficient, 220, 223
  difference of means, 186
  difference of parameters, 149
  F-distribution, 183
  mean, 134, 184, 384
  Poisson distribution, 150, 193
  regression constants, 209, 314
  regression estimate, 211
  standard deviation, 188
  variance, 188, 263
  variance ratio, 216
  x, given y, 212

Confidence regions, 391
Conformable matrices, 291, 292
Confounding (in design), 282
  partial, 286
Consistent statistic, 370, 371
Contingency, tables, 227, 229
  coefficient of mean square, 228
  exact distribution for 2×2 tables, 230
Convergence, in probability, 4, 85
  mathematical, 3
  of improper integrals, 56
  stochastic, 4, 26, 85
Convolution, 70, 90
Correction for continuity, 230
  for inefficient estimate, 380
Correlation, between errors, 251
  intra-class, 282
  multiple, 339, 345, 358
  normal, 202
  partial, 350
  rank, 224–227
  serial, 151, 157, 354
  tetrachoric, 205
  total, 340
Correlation coefficient, 69, 92
  average from samples, 223
  between observed and estimated x, 345
  between statistics, 379
  bias, 223
  confidence limits, 220, 223
  distribution when $\rho = 0$, 215
  distribution when $\rho \neq 0$, 217
  distribution-free test, 223
  estimate of, 221
  multiple, 348
  partial, 350, 353
  partial with k variates, 353
Correlation ratio, 323, 324, 395
Correlation surface, 202
Correlograms, 354
Cost of sampling, 159
Covariance, 68
  analysis of, 274–278
  in linear regression, 309
  matrix of, 310
  of two linear functions, 126
Cowden, D. J., 332, 364, 365
Cox, G. M., 260, 278, 287
Craig, A. T., 30, 54, 129, 162, 197

Index

Craig, C. C., 107, 126
Cramer, G. (Cramer's rule), 297, 298
Cramér, H., 5, 21, 75, 76, 93, 118, 119, 126, 405, 406
Credibility, 5
Croxton, F. E., and Cowden, D. J., 188, 198, 287
Cumulants, 77
    additive property, 78
    estimates by k-statistics, 109, 110
Cumulant generating function, 77
Cumulative frequency function (see Distribution function)
Curtiss, J. H., 93, 287
Curve fitting, 108
    chi square test, 118
    efficiency, 109
    by maximum likelihood, 376
    by moments, 109, 376
    polynomials, 326
Czuber, E., 197

Dantzig, G. B., 393, 406
David, F. N., 220, 223, 236
Davis, H. T., 336, 366, 405
Decimal points (matrix calculation), 304, 305
Degrees of freedom, 98, 162, 167
    in analysis of variance, 263
Delta process (for standard errors), 141, 197
De Lury, D. B., 320, 329, 366
Deming, W. E., and Birge, R. T., 174, 197
De Moivre, A. (Laplace theorem), 36, 39, 40
Density (probability), 13
Design of experiments, 278
Determinants, 83, 295
    alien cofactors, 295
    cofactors, 295
    development of, 295
    functional (see Jacobian)
    minors, 295
    multiplication of, 296
Diagonal principal, 293
Dice experiments, 42
Dichotomy, 22, 205
    double, 233
Differentiation under integral sign, 56, 368, 402

Digamma function, 376, 405
Discrete variable, 24, 69
Discriminant, perfect, 355, 359
    observed, 360
    theoretical, 358
Discriminant function, 355–361
Distance between means, 356
    generalized 362
Distribution, asymptotically normal, 132
    bivariate normal, 92
    joint, 67, 69, 70, 167
    marginal, 68
    singular, 92
Distribution-free test, 223, 250
Distribution function, 24, 42, 69, 111
    for ungrouped data, 112
Dixon, W. J., 159
Doob, J. L., 21
Doolittle, M. H., 298
Duncan, D. B., 322
Dwyer, P. S., 298, 322

Edgeworth, F. Y., 108
Efficient estimation, 109, 119
    statistic, 371, 379
Eisenhart, C., 287, 404
Elderton, W. P., 126
Elimination, systematic, 269, 298, 306
Equations, condition, 318
    linear, 316
    normal, 207, 290, 317
    observation, 316
    of constraint, 318
Error function, 43
    law (see Normal distribution)
Errors, conditional, 273
    correlation between, 251
    experimental, 210, 243
    of first kind, 118, 232, 387, 389
    of second kind, 387, 389, 394, 399, 400
Estimate, standard error of, 201, 208, 209, 211
Estimates best, 171, 367
    efficient, 109
    inefficient (correction of), 380
    least squares, 172
    maximum likelihood, 172, 221, 261, 311
    maximum probability, 172

Index

minimum variance, 290
modal, 172
most-efficient, 109, 119, 371, 373, 379
of x, given y, 336
regular, 368
unbiased, 110, 171, 173, 221, 261, 290, 311, 367
Estimation, Chap. XII
interval, 129
of components of variance, 260
of treatment effects, 265
point, 129
Events, compound, 7, 8
exclusive, 8
independent, 10, 11
simple, 7, 8
Excess (*see* Kurtosis)
Expectation, 25, 26, 70, 79
theorems, 71, 72
Experimental design, 278
Exponential regression, 332
modified, 332, 334
Extreme values, distribution of, 190

Factorial, 5, 22, 23
function, 56
moments, 91
moment generating function, 91
Stirling approximation to, 49, 59
F-distribution, 181–184
significance levels of, 184
Feller, W., 21, 32, 54, 90, 93
Fermat, P. de, 13
Fiducial inference, 260, 264, 385
limits, 258, 259
probability, 258n, 386
Fieller, E. C., 366
Finite parent population, 142, 149, 159
Fisher, R. A. (references), 21, 93, 159, 198, 236, 237, 287, 288, 322, 366, 405, 406
analysis of variance, 158
approximation to χ^2, 99
Bayes' theorem, 15, 17
chi-square, 100, 117
combination of probabilities, 233
correlation coefficient, 217, 219, 220
cumulants, 77
definition of statistic, 127
efficiency of estimates, 376
exact test, 231

fiducial inference, 260, 264, 385
g-statistics, 190
harmonic components, 336
inequality on variance, 367, 370
intra-class correlation, 283
kurtosis, 27, 190
levels of significance, 40, 118, 136
multiple correlation, 350
normal law, 43
null hypothesis, 136
regression, 315
skewness, 27, 190
t-distribution, 175, 178
theorem, 100
variance, 165, 167
variance ratio, 182
z-distribution, 180
z'-transformation, 221, 253
Fisher and Yates (tables), 43, 111, 159, 176, 182, 193, 215, 236, 237, 259
Latin squares, 280
orthogonal polynomials, 329
random numbers, 152
Forsyth, A. R., 159
Fortuyn, A. B. D., 237
Fourier transform, 76, 93
Freedom, degrees of, 98, 162, 167, 263
Frequency function, 23, 67, 215
surface, 173
test, 154
Fry, T. C., 44, 45, 46, 119
Function, Beta, 61, 64, 66
characteristic, 72, 88, 93
cumulative frequency, 24, 42, 69, 111
factorial, 56
frequency, 23, 67
Gamma, 56, 62, 64, 117
hypergeometric, 49, 219, 350
linear, 93
moment generating, 72, 93
odd or even, 55
orthogonal, 209
Functional determinant (*see* Jacobian)

Gaddum, J. H., 123
Games, theory of, 32
Gamma function, 56, 62, 64, 117
variate, 94, 95, 101, 376
Gap test of randomness, 154
Gauss, C. F., 161, 298

Index

Gaussian distribution (*see* Normal distribution)
Geary, R. C., 170, 197
Generalized T-test, 362
Glover, J. W. (tables), 23, 42, 59, 108, 332, 365
Goldstine, H. H., 322
Gompertz curve, 364
Goodness of fit, 109, 377
Gosset, W. S. (*see* Student), 160, 197
Goulden, C. H., 281, 287, 288
Gowen, J. G., 267
Graeco-Latin square, 280
Gram-Charlier, A series, 108
  system of curves, 101, 107
Grouping (*see* Sheppard's corrections)
Griffith, B. A., 366
g-statistics, 110, 190, 197

Harmonic curve, 334
Hartley, H. O., 193, 198, 256, 287
Hastay, M. W., 404
Helmert, F. R., 165, 174, 197
Hermite polynomials, 107
Hilferty, M. M., 99, 126
Homogeneity of variance, 254
Homoscedastic, 204
Hotelling, Harold, correlation ratio, 324, 365
  credibility, 5
  generalized T-test, 362, 366
  matrix calculation, 308, 322
  nuisance parameters, 264
  rank correlation, 225, 237
Householder, A. S., 322
Houseman, E. E., 329, 365
Hypergeometric distribution, 48, 49, 230
Hypergeometric function, 49, 219, 350
  confluent, 324, 396
Hypothesis, alternative, 245
  composite, 388, 392
  null, 135, 136, 245, 325
  sequential test, 400
  simple, 388
  test of, 117, 118, 387

Independence, 10, 11, 68, 69, 70
  and zero covariance, 239, 313
  of mean and variance, 170
  of residuals, 312
  trial (2 × 2 table), 230

Inefficient estimate, correction, 380
Inference, statistical, 388, Chap. XII
  (*see also* Estimates, Hypothesis)
Inflection, in curvilinear regression, 337
Information, 372, 375
Integral, convergence of, 56
  definite, 55
  improper, 55
  Stieltjes, 24, 53, 69
Interaction, 243, 269
Interval estimation, 129 (*see* Confidence limits)
Intra-class correlation, 282
Inverse (of matrix), 296, 297, 301, 304
Irwin, J. O., 159
Iteration method, 308

Jackson, D., 198, 354, 366
Jacobian, 58, 83, 165
Jeans, Sir James, 1, 53
Jeffreys, H., 4, 21
Johnson, N. L., 393, 406
Johnson, P., 287

Kaplansky, I., 53
Kelley, T. L. (tables), 43
Keeping, E. S., 197, 366
Kendall, M. G., 81, 93, 159, 237, 239, 287, 336, 382, 406
  random numbers, 152, 153, 159
  rank correlation, 226
Kenney, J. F., 93, 178, 198
Kerrich, J. E., 51
Keynes, J. M., 4, 21
Knopp, K., 66, 93
Kolmogoroff, A., 5, 21, 87
Kosambi, D. D., 197
Kronecker delta, 295
k-statistics, 109, 189, 190
Kurtosis, 27, 53, 103, 104

Lagrange multipliers, 319, 392
Laplace, P. S., 2, 17
  distribution, 91
  theorem, 36, 39, 40
Large numbers, strong law of, 86
  weak law of, 85
Largest value, distribution of, 191
Latin square, 279
Least squares estimate, 172, 290, 342
  method, 207, Chap. X, 323, 341, 356

Lee, A., 206
Lehmer, E., 393, 395, 396, 406
Level of significance, 40, 117, 136, 183
Lexis, W., scheme, 47
  ratio, 48
Liapounoff, A., 90
Likelihood, 213, 290, 372, 392
  maximum, 93, 109, 146, 213, 255, 290, 375–381
Limit, mathematical, 3
  stochastic, 4
  (*see also* Confidence, Fiducial, Tolerance)
Lindeberg, J. W., 89
Linear equations, 316
  transformations, 82, 294, 350, 354
Linear functions, covariance, 126
  cumulant generating function, 78
  distribution of, 79
  of predictand, 291
  variance of, 93
Linear regression (*see* Regression)
Logarithmic probability paper, 122, 125
  transformation, 122, 123, 253
  regression, 210
Logistic curve, 364
Log-normal distribution, 122, 123
Lukacs, E., 197

Madow, W. G. and L. H., 156, 159
Mahalanobis, P. C., 362, 366
Mainland, D. (tables), 194, 198, 231, 237
Marginal distributions, 68, 199, 202
  totals, 228
Massey, F. J., 159
Matrix addition, 291
  adjoint, 296
  algebra, 83, 291, Chap. X
  approximation to inverse, 308
  conformable, 291, 292
  diagonal, 293
  division, 297
  inverse, 296, 301, 304
  multiplication, 291, 292
  non-symmetric, 307
  norm, 308
  null, 291
  of linear transformation, 294
  of variance-covariance, 310

orthogonal, 297
rank, 296
scalar, 293
singular, 296
skew-symmetric, 293
square, 291
symmetric, 292
transpose, 292, 297
triangular, 298, 306
unit, 293
Maximum (curvilinear regression), 337
  probability, 172
Maximum likelihood, 93, 109, 146, 213, 290, 371–381
  curve-fitting by, 376
  estimates, 172, 261, 311, 312
Mean, 26, 79, 112
  confidence limits, 134, 184
  difference of, 178
  distribution, 137
  standard error, 133
Mean square (analysis of variance), 240–244
  (regression), 216
Median, efficiency of, 371
Mendel, G. (Abbé), 123
Méré, Chevalier de, 13
Merrington, M., 176, 182, 256, 287
Metron, 175, 180, 197
Miner, J. R., 352, 366
Mises, R. von, 4, 21
Missing plot technique, 271, **273**
Modal estimate, 172
  value, 172
Mode, 32, 101, 103
Model, mathematical, 239, 243, 260
Molina, E. C. (tables), 44, 45, 54
Moment generating function, 72, 93
  change of scale, 75
  factorial, 91
Moments, 26
  binomial, 29
  factorial, 91
  of Pearson system, **103**
  product, 68
  standard errors, 140
Morgenstern, O., 33
Most-efficient estimates, 119
Multinomial distribution, 112
  cumulant generating function, 115
  moment generating function, 114

Multiple correlation, 339, 345–350, 358
Multiple regression, 289
  omission of variates, 301, 315
Multiplication theorem (probabilities), 10
Multiplicative effects, 251

Nayer, P. P. N., 256, 287
Neumann, J. von, 33, 322
Neyman, J., 159, 287, 406
  confidence intervals, 130, 260, 381–387
  L_1-criterion, 256
  power of t-test, 393, 396
Non-central distributions, chi square, 362, 396
  F, 324
  t, 393, 394
Non-normality, 179, 250
Non-parametric inference, 367
Non-uniformity of variance, 252
Normal correlation surface, 202
Normal distribution (law, curve), Chap. II
  abridged table, 39
  approximation to binomial, 33, 34
  cumulants, 78
  derivatives, 107, 108
  distribution function, 42, 111
  fitting by moments, 109
  limit of Poisson distribution, 80
  moment generating function, 74
  tables, 42, 43
Normal equations, 207, 289, 290, 317, 334, 348
  numerical solution, 298
Normal variates (and Gamma variate), 95
Normality, asymptotic, 132
  test of, 111
Nuisance parameter, 264, 391
Null hypothesis, 135, 136, 245, 325
Numbers, random, 152, 153

Observation equations, 316
Olds, E. G., 197
Operating characteristic curve, 401
Optimum sampling, 155
Order (of terms), 88, 115
Orthogonal data, 265
  functions, 209
  matrix, 297

polynomials, 327
rows of matrix, 307
transformation, 82, 84, 115, 217, 260, 297, 350

Pabst, M. R., 225, 237
Paired variates, 186, 187
Pairman, E., 405
Parameters, 122, 127, 133
  estimation of, 109, 117
Partial correlation, 350
  regression, 289, 351
Pascal, B., 13
Pearl, R., 365, 366
Pearson, E. S., 130, 159, 191, 197, 230, 231, 233, 237, 250, 287
  confidence intervals, 130, 260, 381–387
  L_1-criterion, 256
  notation for covariance, 274
  2×2 tables, 231
Pearson, K., 126
  chi-square, 114
  curves, 101, 102, 110
  goodness of fit, 114
  kurtosis, 27
  method of moments, 109
  multinomial distribution, 112
  skewness, 27
  tables (Beta and Gamma Functions), 64, 66, 324
  tables, part I, 23, 43, 44, 104, 117, 188
  tables, part II, 104, 190–192, 236, 365
  tetrachoric r, 206
  type O, 102, 106
  type I, 96, 102, 104
  type II, 216
  type III, 35, 94, 102, 104–106, 121, 125, 197, 376
  type VI, 96, 102, 105
  type VII, 106
  types IX to XII, 126
Permutations, 5
Petersburg problem, 32
Peirce, B. O. (tables), 43
Periodogram, 335
Periods, reality of, 335
Pitman, E. J. G., 217, 223, 236, 237, 239, 250, 251, 288
Poisson distribution, 43, 44, 46
  chart of, 150
  confidence limits, 150, 193

426 Index

cumulants, 78
moment generating function, 74, 75
moments, 46
normal limit, 80
transformation, 253
Poisson exponential limit (*see* Poisson distribution)
  scheme, 47
  variates, 80
Point estimation, 129 (*see* Estimates)
Poker test of randomness, 154
Polynomials, fitting of, 326
  orthogonal, 327
Pooling (of small classes), 118, 119, 124
Population, 127, 129
  finite, 142, 159 (ref. 7)
Power curve, 389, 401
  of analysis of variance test, 395
  of test, 388
  of t-test, 393
Precision, 318
Probabilities, combination of, 233
Probability, Chap. I
  addition theorem, 8
  a posteriori, 14, 129
  a priori, 14, 15, 130
  axiomatic, 5, 10, 11
  classical, 2
  conditional, 8, 11
  continuous, 13
  frequency definition, 3
  integral (*see* Normal curve), 43
  multiplication theorem, 10
  notation for, 8
Probability density function, 13, 24
  conditional, 199
  cumulative (*see* Distribution function)
Probability function (tables), 43
Probability paper, 111, 122
Probable error, 129, 134
Probits, 43, 111, 112, 122, 125
Product moment, 68
Proportion (of successes), 30, 145
  difference of, 146, 147
Proportional sampling, 156
  sub class numbers, 271

Quadratic form, 294
  function, 337
Quality control, 193, 367

Random order, 153
  sample, 127, 151, 152
  sampling numbers, 152
  variable, 84, 214
Randomization (experimental), 251, 278
Randomized blocks, 278
Randomness, 4, 84
  tests for, 153, 154
Range, distribution of, 190
Rank (of matrix), 296
Rank correlation, 224
  Kendall's method, 226
Rao, C. R., 406
Rectangular distribution, 75, 91, 92, 192, 234
Regression, Chap. VIII, Chap. X
  coefficients, 200, 209, 211, 309, 314
  cubic, 329
  curve, 199, 203, 207, 327, 329, 332, 336, 337
  exponential, 332
  geometrical, 339
  linear, 199, 274, 346
  multiple, 289
  of log y, 210
  of means, 275
  parabolic, 327
  partial, 289
  plane, 340, 344
  surface, 340, 343
  test of linearity, 324
  variance, 310, 344
  weighted, 333
  with both variates subject to error, 213
Residuals, 310, 313, 348
  sum of squares of, 311, 323, 349
Reversal rule (inversion), 297
  (transposition), 293
Richardson, C. H., 51
Ricker, W. E., 159
Rider, P. R., 181, 198
Rietz, H. L., 40, 127, 159, 179, 197, 198
Robinson, G., 366
Robbins, H., 93
Romanovsky, V., 30, 171, 197
Roy, S. N., 362, 366

Salvosa, L. R., 106, 121, 125

Index

Sample, purposive, 151
  random, 127, 151, 152
  self-weighting, 156
  size, 133, 145
  space, 167, 383
  stratified, 154
  systematic, 151, 156, 329
Sampling, Chap. VI, Chap. VII
  cost of, 157
  experimental, 137
  fluctuations, 127
  from finite population, 142, 149, 159
  numbers, 152
  of attributes, 38
  optimum, 155
  proportional, 156
  sequential, 396–401
  systematic, 156, 329
Satterthwaite, F. E., 322
Sawkins, D. T., 217, 236
Scalar, 291
  matrix, 293
Schwarz inequality, 369
Seath, D. M., 359
Seidel, P. L., 330–334, 366
  weighted process, 334
Semi-invariants (see Cumulants)
Sequential sampling, 396
  binomial, 400
  O. C. curve, 401
  probability-ratio test, 397
  truncated, 399
Serial correlation, 151, 157
Series, asymptotic, 59
  power, 55
Sheppard's corrections, 80, 109, 121
Shewhart, W. A., 2, 144, 159
Shohat, J., 24, 53
Significance, level of, 40, 117, 136, 183, 245
  tests of, 128, 135, 178, 182, 184, 215, 276, 357, 363
Significant figures, 301
Signs, runs of, 119, 125
Singular matrix, 296
Skewness, 27, 101
  Pearson curves, 103, 104
Skew-symmetric matrices, 293
Smith, B. Babington, 152, 153, 159
Snedecor, G. W., 182, 184, 187, 198, 237, 253, 267, 277, 287, 333, 365

F-distribution, 181
Soper, H. E., 220, 237
Spearman, C., 224, 237
Split plot design, 280
Square-root method, 298
  transformation, 253
Squariance, 239
Standard deviation, 27
  best estimate, 171
  distribution, 170
  standard error of, 171
Standard error, 110, 132
  g-statistics, 190
  k-statistics, 189
  kurtosis, 141
  mean, 133
  moments, 140–142
  proportions, 145, 146
  skewness, 141
  standard deviation, 171
  variance, 163
Standard error of estimate, 201, 208, 209, 211, 344
Standardized variable, 27
Statistic, 122, 127, 133
  asymptotically most-efficient, 373
  asymptotically normal, 373
  consistent, 370
  efficient, 371, 379
  estimate of parameter, 109, 117
  most-efficient, 371, 373, 379
  studentized, 178, 362, 384
  sufficient, 371, 373, 384, 385
Step function, 25
Stieltjes integral, 23, 24, 53, 69
Stirling's approximation, 49, 59, 113, 176
Stochastic convergence, 4, 26, 85, 370
  variable, 84
Stratified sampling, 154
Strong law of large numbers, 86, 87
Student (W. S. Gosset), 160, 197
  distribution of variance, 165
  power of t-test, 393
  rank correlation, 225
  t-distribution, 101, 175, 179, 180, 181, 336, 337, 358, 384, 393
  z-distribution, 174
Studentized statistic, 178, 362, 384
Sukhatme, P. V., 258, 259, 287

428 Index

Sum of squares, distribution of, 100
  (analysis of variance), 239
  (regression), 216
  of residuals, 311
Symmetric matrices, 292
Systematic sampling, 151, 156, 329

Table (2 × 2), 205, 227, 230
  (2 × n), 229
Tang, P. C., 324, 366, 395, 396, 406
Taylor's theorem, 252
Tchebycheff, P. L., 84, 86, 371
t-distribution (*see* Student)
Test of significance, 128, 135
  asymptotically most powerful, 391
  distribution-free, 223, 250
  most powerful, 390
  one-sided alternative, 400
  one-tailed, 184
  power of, 388
  sequential, 397, 400
  unbiased, 390
  uniformly most powerful, 391
Tetrachoric correlation, 205
Thiele, T. N., 77, 93
Thompson, A. J., 152
Thompson, C. M., 117, 126, 182, 184, 188, 256, 287
Ties (rank correlation), 226
Tippett, L. H. C., 152, 159, 190, 191, 192, 198
Todhunter, I., 21
Tokarska, B., 393, 396, 406
Tolerance limits, 402
  parameter-free, 403
  sampling fluctuation of, 404
  tables of, 404
Transformation,
  angular, 253
  Fisher's, 221, 253
  identical, 294
  linear, 294, 350, 354
  logarithmic, 253
  orthogonal, 82, 83, 84, 116, 217, 260, 297, 350
  square-root, 253
  to stabilize variance, 252
Transpose (matrix), 292
Treatments (analysis of variance), 158, 265
Trend line, 208 (*see* Regression)

Triangular distribution, 91
  matrix, 298, 306
Trigamma function, 376, 405

Unbiased estimate, 110, 171, 261
Unequal numbers (analysis of variance), 265
Universe (*see* Population)
Uspensky, J. V., 10, 36, 38, 40, 44, 45, 54

Variable (*see* Variate)
Variance, 27, 68, 72, 110, 161
  analysis of (*see* Analysis of Variance)
  components of, 260
  definition, 161
  distribution of, 165–170
  estimate from k samples, 162
  expected value, 160
  Fisher's inequality, 367, 370
  homogeneity of, 254
  minimum, 155, 221, 290
  non-uniformity, 252
  of g-statistics, 190
  of harmonic components, 335
  of k-statistics, 189
  of linear functions, 93, 126
  of regression coefficients, 309
  of strata, 154
  of t-distribution, 176
  proportional to y^2, 210
  standard error of, 163
Variance ratio (*see* F-distribution), 180, 182
  confidence limits, 216, 235
Variate, 25, 84
  correlated, 93
  dropped from regression, 301, 315
  paired, 186
  uncorrelated, 69
Varieties (analysis of variance), 241
Vector, column, 294
  row, 294

Wald, A., 397, 406
Walker, Sir Gilbert, 335, 366
Walker, H., 163
Wallis, W. A., 404
Wallis's formula, 61, 63
Watson, G. N., 363
Weak law of large numbers, 85

Index

Weatherburn, C. E., 94, 126
Weights, of observations, 318
Welch, B. L., 250, 251, 288, 393, 406
Whittaker, E. T., 363, 366
Wilks, S. S., 148, 161, 197, 403, 406
Wilson, E. B. (approximation to χ^2), 99, 126
Wolf, R., 42

Woo, T. L., 228, 237, 234, 365

Yates, F.. 230
Yule, G. U., and Kendall, M. G., 117, 118, 197, 364

z-**distribution** (Fisher), 180, 181
 (Student), 174, 181
z'-transformation (Fisher), 221, 223